THE PENGUIN DICTIONARY OF

PHYSICS

EDITOR: VALERIE H. PITT
LAURENCE URDANG ASSOCIATES LTD

PENGUIN BOOKS

Penguin Books Ltd, Harmondsworth, Middlesex, England
Penguin Books, 625 Madison Avenue, New York, New York 10022, U.S.A.
Penguin Books Australia Ltd, Ringwood, Victoria, Australia
Penguin Books Canada Ltd, 2801 John Street, Markham, Ontario, Canada L3R 1B4
Penguin Books (N.Z.) Ltd, 182–190 Wairau Road, Auckland 10, New Zealand

An abridgement of Longman's *A New Dictionary of Physics* (first published 1975, edited by H. J. Gray and Alan Isaacs) in which the contributors included:

> John Daintith, Ph.D., B.Sc.
> Valerie Pitt, M.Phil., B.Sc.
> Carol Young, B.Sc.
> John Young, B.Sc.
> Stephen Dresner, B.Sc.
> Paul Collins, Ph.D., B.Sc.
> John Illingworth, M.Sc., B.Sc.

with some entries from the original edition (*Dictionary of Physics*, first published 1958) by:

Professor Allan Ferguson, S. G. Starling, Professor J. A. Crowther, Professor W. Wilson, Professor Kathleen Lonsdale, Dr E. G. Richardson, Dr C. Dodd, W. Swaine, C. J. G. Austin, W. Ashworth, and J. R. Barker.

—

This abridgement first published 1977
Reprinted 1978 (twice), 1979, 1980, 1982, 1983

—

—

Made and printed in Great Britain by
Richard Clay (The Chaucer Press) Ltd,
Bungay, Suffolk
Set in Monotype Times

CONTENTS AND TABLES

PREFACE

THIS dictionary is an abridged version of the recently revised and published *New Dictionary of Physics* (Longman, 1975). Both books were prepared by members of the scientific staff of Laurence Urdang Associates Ltd. Entries in the Longman's dictionary that have been omitted from this dictionary include all biographies and entries concerned with experimental determinations of constants. Other entries have been shortened and updated where necessary and some additions have been made.

Although this dictionary is primarily concerned with the terminology of contemporary physics, words with a physical basis that are used in other scientific fields, such as physical chemistry, computing, astronomy, geophysics, medical physics, engineering subjects, and music, have also been included. SI units are used throughout.

The dictionary should thus prove useful to students and teachers of physics and related subjects, to doctors, and to scientists, technologists, and technicians in research and industry. It contains many long entries in which a word of major importance is defined and discussed together with closely associated words. Shorter definitions supplement the longer entries.

The editor thanks Mr H. J. Gray and Dr Alan Isaacs, editors of the *New Dictionary of Physics*, and also the contributors to the Longman's dictionary, in particular Dr John Daintith, for entries that have passed into the *Penguin Dictionary of Physics*. With the exception of some of the longer electronic entries, which have been shortened by the original authors (Carol and John Young), the abridgements have been made by the editor without consulting the original contributors. Any changes of emphasis or style are therefore the responsibility of the editor.

VALERIE H. PITT, 1976

NOTES

An asterisk indicates a cross reference.

An entry having an initial capital letter is either a proper name or a trade name

Syn. is an abbreviation for 'synonymous with'.

All other abbreviations will be found in the Tables of SI units (page 422) and the Table of Symbols (pages 426–8).

A

Å (or Å.U. or A.U.). Symbol for ångstrom.

ab-. A prefix which, when attached to the name of a practical electrical unit, denotes the corresponding unit in the *CGS system of electromagnetic units. This system of units is no longer employed.

Abbe condenser. A simple two lens *condenser that has good light-gathering ability, the *numerical aperture being 1·25. It is therefore extensively used in general microscopy. Aberrations are not well corrected. A modified Abbe condenser called a *variable-focus condenser* is used to obtain a greater illuminated field area. The lower lens can be adjusted to bring light to a focus between the lenses producing a parallel beam.

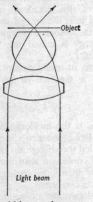

Abbe condenser

Abbe criterion. *See* resolving power.

Abbe number. *Syn.* constringence. The reciprocal of dispersive power. *See* dispersion.

aberration. (1) Of a lens or mirror. Any of a number of image defects revealed as blurring or distortion. The theory of *centred optical systems holds good for rays passing close to the axis. For larger angles, it is no longer accurate to replace the sine of the angle by the angle itself (as is done in the simple theory), the point, line and plane correspondence between object and image no longer holds good, and certain defects in the image or aberrations occur.

By expanding the sine series to two or more terms, $\sin \theta = \theta - \theta^3/3! + \theta^5/5! - \ldots$, the deviations of the path of a ray from that predicted by the simple theory can be expressed in terms of five sums called the *Seidel sums* or the *Seidel terms*. The presence of one or more of these terms can be linked with certain recognizable defects in the image, i.e. those called *spherical aberration, *coma, *astigmatism, *curvature of field, and *distortion. In addition, if light of more than one colour is involved, false colour effects may be introduced in the image, a defect which is known as *chromatic aberration. Of these six defects only spherical and chromatic aberrations are found in the images of axial points. The other four aberrations occur only when extra-axial points are involved.

(2) Of light. The seasonal small displacement of stars, attributable to the effect of the orbital motion of the Earth round the Sun on the direction of arrival of the light.

(3) A defect in the image produced by an *electron lens system.

ablation. The removal of material from the surface of a body by decomposition or vaporization. It can result from friction with the atoms or molecules of the atmosphere.

absolute expansion. *See* coefficient of expansion.

9

absolute humidity. *See* humidity.

absolute magnitude. *See* magnitude.

absolute permittivity. *See* permittivity.

absolute temperature. *See* thermodynamic temperature.

absolute unit. If a quantity y is uniquely defined in terms of quantities $x_1, x_2, \ldots$ by

$$y = f(x_1, x_2, \ldots),$$

the unit U_y of y can be obtained from the units U_{x_1}, U_{x_2} of x_1, x_2 from the equation

$$U_y \propto f(U_{x_1}, U_{x_2}, \ldots).$$

In any given system an absolute unit is one for which the constant of proportionality is unity. All units of the *SI system are absolute.

absolute zero. The lowest temperature theoretically possible; the temperature at which the thermal energy of random motion of the particles of a system in thermal equilibrium is zero. It is, therefore, the zero of *thermodynamic temperature: $0 \text{ K} = -273 \cdot 15°\text{C} = -459 \cdot 67°\text{F}$.

absorbance. *See* internal transmission density.

absorbed dose. *See* dose.

absorptance. *Syn.* absorption factor. Symbol: α. A measure of the ability of a body or substance to absorb radiation as expressed by the ratio of the absorbed *radiant or *luminous flux to the incident radiant or luminous flux. For radiant heat the absorptance of a body, measured against a vacuum, depends on the thermodynamic temperature T of the body receiving the radiation and on the wavelength. The absorptance at a fixed frequency of radiation is called the

spectral absorptance. *See also* internal absorptance.

absorption. (1) Of electromagnetic radiation. When radiation passes from one medium to another three processes can occur: *reflection, *transmission, or absorption. Absorption is the transformation of the energy of the radiation into a different form. The nature of this process depends on the frequency of the radiation and on the substance involved. For example, infrared radiation may be converted directly to heat by exciting the vibrations of atoms or molecules, visible radiation may cause electronic transitions, and X-rays and ultraviolet radiation may cause ionization of the material (*see* photoelectric effect; photoionization). The extent to which this process occurs is given by the absorptance of the specimen or medium. *See also* linear attenuation coefficient; linear absorption coefficient.

(2) Of sound. When energy in the form of a sound wave passes from any one medium to another a portion of the energy of the incident radiation is absorbed into the second medium. The ratio of the absorbed energy to the incident energy is called the *absorption coefficient.

The loss in sound energy as it passes through a medium is given by the equation:

$$E = E_0 \, e^{-\mu\alpha x},$$

where E_0 is the incident energy, E the energy after a distance x, and $\mu\alpha$ a constant called the absorption coefficient or, to avoid confusion with the absorption coefficient mentioned earlier, the *linear absorption coefficient.

The absorption of sound energy is caused principally by viscous forces opposing the relative motion of the particles as the sound passes (involving transformation of mechanical energy into heat) and by heat being conducted from the compressed particles to the rarefied ones. This results in an increase of *entropy. Heat radiated from compressions to rarefactions also causes some energy dissipation at low frequencies.

The effects of viscosity and heat conduction are summed up in the *Stokes-Kirchhoff equation*:

$$\mu_\alpha = \frac{4\pi^2}{v\rho}\left(\frac{4}{3}\eta + \frac{(c_p - c_v)}{c_p c_v}\lambda\right)f^2,$$

where v is the velocity of sound, ρ the density of gas, η its viscosity, c_p and c_v its principal specific heat capacities, λ its thermal conductivity, and f the frequency of the sound.

Absorption of sound by gases is basically due to viscosity, the conduction and radiation effects becoming more important for waves of larger amplitude. Water vapour content (humidity) also affects the absorption, μ_α taking a maximum value at about 15 % relative humidity.

absorption bands (and lines). *See* absorption spectrum.

absorption coefficient. (1) Of electromagnetic radiation. *See* linear absorption coefficient. (2) Of sound. Symbol: α. The ratio of the absorbed sound energy at a boundary to the incident sound energy. Its value depends on the material and on the frequency of the sound.

absorption edge (discontinuity or limit). An abrupt discontinuity in the graph relating the *linear absorption coefficient of X-rays in a given substance with the wavelength of the radiation. At certain wavelengths the absorption shows a sudden decrease in value. This occurs when the energy quantum of the radiation becomes smaller than the work required to eject an electron from one or other of the energy levels in the absorbing atom, and the radiation thus ceases to be absorbed in that level. Thus, radiation of wavelength greater than the K

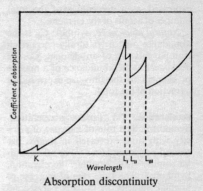

Absorption discontinuity

absorption edge cannot eject electrons from the K level of the absorbing substance.

absorption factor. *See* absorptance.

absorption spectrum. When light from a high temperature source producing a continuous emission spectrum is passed through a medium into a spectroscope, the spectrum reveals dark regions where absorption has taken place (*continuous*, *line*, and *band* types). In general, the medium absorbs those wavelengths which it would emit if its temperature were raised high enough. The absorbed radiation excites atoms from the *ground state to an *excited state. Solids and liquids show broad continuous absorption spectra, gases give more discontinuous types (line and band). *See* spectrum.

absorptivity. (1) A measure of the ability of a substance to absorb radiation, as expressed by the *internal absorptance of a layer of substance when the path of the radiation is of unit length and the boundaries of the material have no influence. (2) Symbol: a_λ. Former term for *absorptance.

abundance. Symbol: C. The number of atoms of a given isotope in a mixture of the isotopes of an element; usually

11

expressed as a percentage of the total number of atoms of the element.

Natural abundance, symbol: C_0, is the abundance in a naturally occurring isotopic mixture of an element. *Cosmic abundance* is the abundance of a nuclide or element in the universe expressed as a fraction of the total.

acceleration. (1) Linear acceleration. Symbol: *a*. The rate of increase of velocity with time expressed in metres per second per second ($m\,s^{-2}$) or other similar units. (2) Angular acceleration. Symbol: α. The time rate of increase of angular velocity in radians per second per second ($rad\,s^{-2}$) or other similar units.

acceleration of free fall. *See* free fall.

accelerator. A machine for increasing the kinetic energy of charged particles or ions, such as protons or electrons, by accelerating them in an electric field. A magnetic field is used to maintain the particles in the desired direction. The particles can either travel in a straight or circular path. *See* linear accelerator; betatron; cyclotron; synchroton; synchrocyclotron; Van de Graaff generator. *See also* focusing; intersecting storage ring.

accelerometer. Any device used to measure acceleration. An *integrating accelerometer* is capable of performing one integration to obtain the velocity and a subsequent integration to obtain the distance travelled.

acceptor. (1) The *impedance of a circuit comprising *inductance and *capacitance in *series has a minimum value at one particular frequency (the frequency to which the circuit is tuned – *see* tuned circuit). Such a circuit is an acceptor for that frequency. In practice, the effective resistance of such a circuit cannot be made zero and hence the impedance at

the frequency to which the circuit is tuned cannot be zero either. *See also* rejector. (2) *See* semiconductor.

access time. The mean time interval between demanding a particular piece of information from a computer *storage device and obtaining it.

accommodation. The ability of the eye to alter its focal length and to produce clear images of objects at different distances. *See* near point.

accumulator. A device for the reversible interchange of electrical and chemical energy. The common 'lead' accumulator consists in principle of two plates coated with lead sulphate immersed in aqueous sulphuric acid. If connected to a suitable d.c. supply, current is sent through the cell, and the anode is converted to lead peroxide and the cathode reduced to metallic lead. If the two plates are then connected through an external circuit, the chemical action is reversed and current flows round the external circuit from the brown peroxide plate to the grey lead plate. The action may be summarized in the equation:

$$\underset{(+\text{ plate})}{PbO_2} + \underset{(-\text{ plate})}{Pb} + 2H_2SO_4 \underset{\text{charge}}{\overset{\text{discharge}}{\rightleftharpoons}} 2PbSO_4 + 2H_2O$$

See also Edison accumulator.

achromat. *See* achromatic lens.

achromatic colours. Colours having no hue or saturation but only lightness. White, greys, and black are examples.

achromatic condenser. A *condenser corrected for chromatic and spherical *aberrations, usually by having four elements, two of which are an *achromatic lens. It has a *numerical aperture of 1·4. It is used in microscopes when high magnification is required. *See also* Abbe condenser.

achromatic lens. *Syn.* achromat. A combination of two lenses using, if necessary, different kinds of glass, designed to remove the major part of *chromatic aberration. The elementary theory assumes two lenses of powers P_1 and P_2 placed in contact (with total power $P = P_1 + P_2$) made of glasses of *dispersive powers ω_1 and ω_2 so that the condition for achromatism ($\omega_1 P_1 + \omega_2 P_2 = 0$) is satisfied. To produce an achromatic converging lens, e.g. for telescope or photographic objectives, the dispersive power of the higher power convergent lens must be less than that of the divergent lens of the combination. It is thus possible to bring two colours, say red and blue, to the same focus. There will still be some residual colour effects known as a *secondary spectrum. See also* apochromatic lens.

achromatic prism. A combination of two or more prisms which produces the same deviation of two or more colours so that objects viewed through them will not appear coloured (*see* chromatic aberration). As with thin lenses, 'narrow angle' prisms are placed in contact in opposition, so that the *dispersive powers of the two glasses are inversely proportional to their angles of *deviation.

achromatism. The removal of *chromatic aberration, or chromatic differences of magnification, or both, arising from dispersion of light. Owing to irrationality of dispersion the correction is attempted for two colours in the first approximation, and for three colours in higher corrections.

aclinic line. *Syn.* magnetic equator. A curve drawn in such a manner that all places on the curve have zero magnetic dip. *See* isoclinal.

acoustic absorption coefficient. *See* sound absorption coefficient.

acoustic capacitance. The imaginary component of acoustic *impedance due to the stiffness or elasticity (k) of the medium; it is equal to S^2/k where S is the area in vibration.

acoustic delay line. *See* delay line.

acoustic filters. Just as in the case of electrical filters lines of acoustic *impedances can be made by proper adjustment to transmit high frequencies only (high-pass filter) or low frequencies only (low-pass filter) or any given band of frequency (band-pass filter).

If any simple harmonic motion is impressed on equal impedances Z_1 connected in a conduit and separated by branches containing other equal impedances Z_2, it will not pass through unless the ratio Z_1/Z_2 for the frequency of this SHM lies between certain values; i.e. all other frequencies which do not satisfy this condition will be rapidly attenuated and only those covering this range will get through.

acoustic grating. A series of objects, such as rods of equal size, placed in a row a fixed distance apart constitute an acoustic grating having similar properties to an optical *diffraction grating. When a sound wave is incident upon an acoustic grating, secondary waves are set up which reinforce each other or cancel out according to whether or not they are in phase. The result for a sinusoidal sound wave is a series of maxima and minima spaced round the grating. When the incident sound is normal to the grating the condition for a maximum diffracted sound at an angle θ to the normal is: $\sin \theta = m\lambda/e$, where λ is the wavelength of the sound, e is the width of a rod plus the space between it and the next and m is an integer. e must be greater than λ for a diffraction pattern to be formed and this condition necessitates very large gratings for low frequency sounds.

acoustic impedance. *See* impedance.

acoustic inertance. The imaginary component of *impedance, due solely to inertia. It corresponds to inductance in electric circuits. In the case of a mass (m) of gas in a conduit of cross section S, the inertance (L) is equal to m/S^2.

acoustic mass, stiffness. *See* reactance (acoustic).

acoustics. The science concerned with the production, properties, and propagation of sound waves.

acoustoelectronics. The study and use of devices in which electrical signals are converted into acoustic waves by *transducers and the acoustic signals are propagated through a solid medium. Since sound travels more slowly than electrons, acoustic *delay lines are much lighter and more compact than purely electronic devices of comparable performance.

actinic. Of radiation, such as light or ultraviolet radiation. Able to produce a chemical change in exposed materials.

actinium series. *See* radioactive series.

actinometer. (1) An instrument used to measure intensity of radiation. Actinometers usually depend on determining the extent to which a screen fluoresces or the extent to which a substance is decomposed by the radiation. (2) An instrument designed to measure the intensity of solar radiation; they are now usually called *pyrheliometers.

action. (1) The product of a component of momentum, p_i, and the change in the corresponding positional coordinate, q_i; or more precisely the integral $\int p_i dq_i \dots$ (2) Twice the time integral of the kinetic energy of a system, measured from an arbitrary zero time. *See* least action principle.

activation analysis. A sensitive analytical technique in which the sample is first activated by bombardment with high-energy particles, usually neutrons, or gamma rays, and the subsequent decay of radioactive nuclei is then used to characterize the atoms present. For example stable sodium nuclei can be activated by neutron capture:

$$^{23}\text{Na} + n \rightarrow {}^{24}\text{Na} + \gamma.$$

The ^{24}Na nuclei decay to give γ-rays, electrons, and neutrinos:

$$^{24}\text{Na} \rightarrow {}^{24}\text{Mg} + \gamma + e^- + \bar{\nu}.$$

The electrons have a characteristic energy spread and the γ-rays a single energy of 1·38 MeV. Sodium can thus be detected by the presence of lines at this energy in the *gamma-ray spectrum of the irradiated material.

The technique can be used for a large number of elements. If the intensity of γ-ray emission is compared with that from a similarly treated standard, a quantitative analysis can be made.

activation cross section. *See* cross section.

active aerial. *See* directive aerial.

active component. An electronic component such as a *transistor or *thermionic valve, that can be used to introduce *gain into a circuit. *Compare* passive component.

active current (or voltage). *Syn.* power component; in-phase component. The component of an alternating current (or voltage) that is in phase with the voltage (or current), the current and voltage being regarded as vector quantities.

activity. (1) Symbol A. The number of atoms of a radioactive substance that disintegrate per unit time ($-dN/dt$). It is measured in *curies. (2) *See* optical activity.

additive process. A process by which almost any colour can be produced or reproduced by mixing together lights of three colours, called *additive primary colours*, usually red, green, and blue, the proportions of which determine the colour obtained; white light is obtained from approximately equal proportions of red, green, and blue light; yellow from a mixture of red and green light. *Colour television uses an additive process for final colour production. See also* chromaticity. *Compare* subtractive process.

adiabatic demagnetization. A process used for the production of temperatures near absolute zero. A paramagnetic salt is placed between the poles of an electromagnet and the field switched on, the resulting heat being removed by a helium bath. The substance is then isolated thermally and on switching off the field the substance is demagnetized adiabatically and cools.

adiabatic process. A process in which no heat enters or leaves a system. An adiabatic expansion results in cooling of a gas whereas an adiabatic compression has the opposite effect. If an *ideal gas undergoes an adiabatic change in volume the pressure (*p*) is related to the volume (*V*) by the equation: $pV^\gamma = K$, where K is a constant and γ is the ratio of the *heat capacities C_p/C_v of the gas. Any reversible adiabatic change (*see* reversible change) is *isentropic*, i.e. during the change the entropy of the system remains constant. *Compare* isothermal process.

admittance. Symbol: Y. The reciprocal of *impedance; it is related to *conductance (G) and *susceptance (B) by:

$$Y^2 = G^2 + B^2.$$

adsorption. The formation of a layer of foreign substance (*adsorbate*) on an impermeable surface.

advanced gas-cooled reactor (AGR). *See* gas-cooled reactor.

advection. A process of transfer of atmospheric properties by horizontal motion in the atmosphere, such as the movement of cold air from polar regions. Advection is concerned with large scale motions in the atmosphere; vertical locally induced motions are *convection processes. In oceanography, advection is the flow of sea water as a current.

aeoleotropic. *See* anisotropic.

aerial. *Syn.* antenna. That part of a radio system from which energy is radiated into (*transmitting aerial*) or received from (*receiving aerial*) space. An aerial with its *feeders and all its supports is known as an *aerial system*. The most important types of aerial are the *dipole aerial and *directive aerial.

aerial array. *Syn.* beam aerial. An arrangement of radiating or receiving elements so spaced and connected that directional effects are produced. With suitable design, very great directivity can be obtained and also, as a consequence, large *aerial gain. An array of elements along a horizontal line which has marked directivity in the horizontal plane in a direction at right angles to the line of the array is referred to as a *broadside array*. One that has directivity in the horizontal plane along the line of the array is called an *end-fire array* (or *staggered aerial*). Arrays are commonly designed for directivity in both horizontal and vertical planes. The horizontal directivity is influenced by the number of aerial elements that are arranged horizontally, whereas the vertical directivity depends upon the number of elements which are stacked in tiers (or stacks), one vertically above the other.

aerial gain. The ratio of the signal power produced at the receiver input by the aerial, to that which would be produced

15

by a standard comparison aerial under similar conditions (i.e. similar receiving conditions and the same transmitted power). If the type of standard comparison aerial is not specified, a *half-wave dipole is implied.

aerial resistance. The resistance that takes into account the energy consumed by an aerial system as a result of radiation and losses (e.g. I^2R losses in aerial wires, dielectric losses, earth losses, etc.). It is equal to the power supplied to the aerial divided by the square of the current at the aerial supply point.

aerial system. *See* aerial.

aerodynamics. The study of the motion of gases (particularly air) and the motion and control of solid bodies in air.

aerofoil. A body for which, when in relative motion with a fluid, the resistance to motion (drag) is many times less than the force perpendicular to motion (lift). The flight of aircraft depends on the use of aerofoils for wing and tail structure. The essential features of the aerofoil are the rounded leading edge A and the sharp

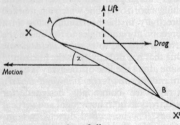

Aerofoil

trailing edge B (*see* diagram). The projection of the section on to the common tangent XX' is called the *chord*; the angle α is the angle of incidence or attack.

Due to viscosity, the layers of fluid passing over the upper and lower surfaces of the aerofoil arrive at the trailing

edge with different velocities. This leads to the production of an eddy or vortex at the trailing edge accompanied by a counter-circulation around the aerofoil. This circulation is essential for the production of the lift force.

aerometer. *See* hydrometer.

aerophysics. The physics of the earth's atmosphere, especially as it interacts with bodies travelling at high speeds or high altitudes.

afterglow. *See* persistence.

afterheat. The heat generated in a nuclear reactor after it has been shut down. This is caused by radioactive substances that form in the fuel elements.

age equation or theory. *See* Fermi age theory.

age of the earth. *See* dating.

age of the universe. A time of between 10×10^9 and 20×10^9 years as determined by the *Hubble constant. This value is clearly uncertain and depends on current theories of *cosmology. *See also* expanding universe.

agonic line. A curve drawn in such a manner that all places on the curve have zero magnetic *declination. *See* isogonal.

air. Normal dry air has the following composition by volume:

Nitrogen	78·08%
Oxygen	20·94%
Argon	0·9325%
Carbon dioxide	0·03%
Neon	0·0018%
Helium	0·0005%
Krypton	0·0001%
Xenon	0·000 009%
Radon	6×10^{-18}%

For dry air:
Specific heat capacity at
    constant volume $718\ \mathrm{J\,kg^{-1}\,K^{-1}}$

Specific heat capacity at
constant pressure   1006 J kg^{-1} K^{-1}
Ratio of specific heat
capacities   1·403
Boiling point (at atmos-
pheric pressure) $-$193° C to
$-$185° C
depending on
age.

Liquid air is produced by strong cooling under high pressure (*see* liquefaction of gases). It has a pale blue colour due to the presence of liquid oxygen.

air equivalent. A measure of the efficiency of an absorber of nuclear radiation, expressed as the thickness of a layer of air at standard temperature and pressure that causes the same amount of absorption or the same energy loss.

air pumps. Air-exhausting pumps are used for withdrawing air or other gases from a closed chamber. Many of them are based upon the ordinary piston principle; others, e.g. the *filter pump, use a jet of mercury or water to trap and remove air from the vessel to be exhausted.

Airy disc. The diffraction pattern that constitutes the image of a distant point-object given by a telescope. The larger the aperture of the telescope, the smaller is the disc. *See* diffraction of light.

albedo. (1) The fraction of incident light diffusely reflected from a surface. Typical values: fresh clean snow 0·8 to 0·9; fields and woods 0·02 to 0·15; mean for the whole earth 0·4; moon 0·073. (2) The probability that a neutron entering into a region through a surface will return through that surface.

allobar. A mixture of the isotopes of an element in proportions that differ from the natural isotopic composition.

allochromy. The emission of electromagnetic radiation from atoms, molecules, etc., induced by incident radiation of a different wavelength, as in *fluorescence or the *Raman effect.

allotropy. The existence of a solid, liquid, or gaseous substance in two or more forms (*allotropes*) that differ in physical rather than chemical properties.

allowed band. *See* energy bands.

alloy. A material, other than a pure element, that exhibits characteristic metallic properties. At least one major constituent must be a metal.

Steels are alloys of iron with carbon, often with other elements deliberately added; there is a wide range of alloy-steels used for special purposes, e.g. rustless chromium steels and high permeability silicon steels.

Brass has copper and zinc as its major constituents. Most grades are about 5% denser than steel with a lower strength and melting point.

Bronze has copper and tin as its major constituents.

Amalgams are alloys involving the metal mercury.

alloyed junction. A semiconductor junction, used in *transistors, that is formed from a wafer of semiconductor which forms the *base region. Metal contacts are bonded on to the wafer and the structure is heated. The metal contacts alloy with the semiconductor to form the *emitter and *collector regions: now rarely used except for the manufacture of germanium transistors.

Alnico. A series of proprietary permanent magnet alloys of 18 % Ni, 10 % Al, 12 % Co, 6 % Cu, 54 % Fe.

alpha decay. A radioactive disintegration process whereby a parent nucleus decays spontaneously into an *alpha particle and a daughter nucleus. The *mean life of the parent nucleus varies from 10^{-7} seconds to 10^{10} years. On classical theory the maximum height of the *potential barrier between the α-particle (atomic number Z_a) and the daughter nucleus (Z) is given by

$$V_R = \frac{Z_a Z e^2}{R}.$$

R is the radius of the nucleus. If a particle is inside a potential well with an energy $E_0 < V_R$, then the α-particle will be unable to escape. *Wave mechanics is necessary to explain the movement of α-particles through the barrier, in terms of the *tunnel effect. The mean life, τ, of the parent depends on E_0, the energy available for reaction in a particular nucleus, and can be expressed approximately as:

$$\frac{1}{\tau} = 10^{21} \exp\left[\frac{-4(V_R - E_0)^{\frac{3}{2}}}{E_0}\right].$$

For $Z = 80$, V_R is 25 MeV. If $E_0 = 4$ MeV, $\tau = 3 \times 10^{12}$ years; if $E_0 = 8$ MeV, $\tau = 10^{-6}$ s.

alpha particle (α-particle). The nucleus of a helium (^{4}He) atom, carrying a positive charge of $2e$. Its *proton number and *neutron number are both 2, a *magic number, so that it is a very stable particle. It has a relative atomic mass of 4·002 60.

alpha rays (α-rays). A stream of *alpha particles which are ejected from many radioactive substances with speeds (of the order of $1·6 \times 10^6$ metres per second) characteristic of the emitting substance. They have a penetrating power of a few cm in air but can be stopped by a thin piece of paper, the maximum range varying as the cube of the velocity. They produce intense *ionization along their track and can be detected by a *spark counter, *Geiger counter, *bubble chamber, by their effect on a photographic plate, by the scintillations they produce on a fluorescent screen, etc.

alphatron. An ionization-type vacuum gauge in which a small quantity of radium provides a constant source of

alpha rays as the ionizing source. The number of ions formed in the gauge depends directly on the number of gas molecules with which this constant radiation can collide. The positive ions formed are collected by a grid and cause a current flow which is amplified and measured.

alternating current (a.c.). An electric current that periodically reverses its direction in the circuit, with a *frequency, f, independent of the constants of the circuit. In its simplest form, the instantaneous current I varies with the time t in accordance with the relation $I = I_0 \sin (2\pi ft)$, where I_0 is the peak value of the current.

alternator. *See* synchronous alternating-current generator.

altimeter. An aneroid *barometer measuring the decrease in atmospheric pressure with height above ground and calibrated to read the height directly.

altitude. (1) The vertical distance above sea level. (2) One of a pair of coordinates, the other being *azimuth, giving the position of a star. *See* celestial sphere.

amalgam. *See* alloy.

ambient. (1) Surrounding, encompassing; e.g. ambient temperature is the temperature of an immediate locality. (2) Freely moving, circulating; e.g. ambient air.

Amici prism. *See* direct vision prism.

ammeter. An instrument for measuring electric current. The most common types are (*a*) the *moving coil*, (*b*) the *moving iron*, and (*c*) the *thermoammeter*. In (*a*), the current passes through a coil, pivoted with its plane parallel to the lines of a radial magnetic field produced by a permanent horseshoe magnet. The rotation is controlled by hair springs, and the deflection is directly proportional to the current. This is the most accurate type of ammeter, but only measures direct current. It can be adapted for alternating current measurement by embodying a metal rectifier in the circuit. In (b), the current passing through a fixed coil magnetizes two specially shaped pieces of soft iron, the mutual repulsion of which when magnetized causes the rotation of a pointer over a scale. Since the effect depends on the square of the current, the instrument can be used both for a.c. and d.c. measurements. It is less accurate than (a) and the scale is non-uniform. The control may be either by gravity or by a spring. In (c), the current passes through a thin resistance wire (usually in a vacuum) which, in consequence, becomes heated. The rise in temperature is measured by a thermojunction soldered to the wire and connected to a sensitive moving coil instrument. It is particularly useful for measuring high-frequency currents.

ammonia clock. *See* clocks.

amount of substance. Symbol: n. This dimensionally independent physical quantity is not the same as *mass. It is proportional to the number of specified particles of a substance, the specified particle being an atom, molecule, ion, radical, electron, photon, etc., or any specified group of any of these particles. The constant of proportionality is the same for all substances and is known as the *Avogadro constant (or number). It is measured in *moles.

ampere. Symbol: A. The *SI unit of electric current, defined as that constant current which, if maintained in two straight parallel conductors of infinite length, of negligible circular cross section, and placed one metre apart in a vacuum, would produce between these conductors a force equal to 2×10^{-7} newton per metre of length. This unit, at one time called the absolute ampere,

replaced the *international ampere* (A_{int}) in 1948. The latter was defined as the constant current that, when flowing through a solution of silver nitrate in water, deposits silver at a rate of 0·001 118 grammes per second. 1 A_{int} = 0·999 850 A.

ampere balance. An instrument for determining the size of the ampere by balancing the force between two current-carrying conductors against the force of a mass in a gravitational field. *See* current balance.

ampere-hour. The quantity of electricity conveyed across any cross section of a conductor when an unvarying current of one ampere flows in the conductor for one hour. The term is employed in stating the capacity of accumulators. One ampere-hour = 3600 coulombs.

Ampère–Laplace theorem. A theorem stating that the magnetic field strength due to the current in a conductor can be given in the form:

$$dB = \frac{\mu_0}{4\pi} \frac{I \sin \theta}{r^2} \, dl$$

where dB is the elemental magnetic flux density at a point distance r from an elemental length dl of conductor carrying a current I; θ is the angle between the direction of I and the radius vector r; μ_0 is the *magnetic constant, i.e. $4\pi \times 10^{-7}$ henry per metre. For an infinitely long straight conductor $B = \mu_0 I/2\pi r$. *See also* Ampère's theorem.

Ampère's rule. A rule giving the relation between the direction of an electric current and that of its associated magnetic field. If you imagine yourself to be swimming in the wire in the direction of the current and facing a magnetic needle, then the *north* pole of the needle is deflected towards your *left* hand.

Ampère's theorem. Along any closed path round N conductors of elemental

19

length d*l*, each of which carries a current *I*,

$$\oint B dl = \mu_0 NI,$$

where $B = \mu_0 I/2\pi r$ and μ_0 is the *magnetic constant.

ampere-turn. Symbol: A or A t. The *magnetomotive force produced when a current of one ampere flows through one turn of a coil.

amplidyne. A special form of *metadyne generator designed so that the power required by the controlling field winding is reduced to an extremely small value. It has an important use as an automatic regulator (voltage or speed) since it can control the excitation of a large generator or motor while requiring only very small control power (commonly less than 1 watt).

amplification factor. The limiting value of the ratio of a small change in anode voltage of an electron tube to the change in grid voltage which would restore the anode current to the value it had before the anode voltage change.

$$\mu = -\left[\frac{\delta V_A}{\delta V_G}\right]_{IA \text{ const.}}$$

amplifier. Symbol: —▷— A device for reproducing an electrical input at an increased intensity. If an increased e.m.f. is produced operating into a high impedance, the device is a *voltage amplifier*, and if the output provides an appreciable current flow into a relatively low impedance the device is a *power amplifier*. The most commonly used amplifiers operate by *transistors or *thermionic valves. *See also* classes A, AB, B, C, D amplifiers.

amplitude. The *peak value of an alternating quantity in either the positive or negative direction. This term is applied particularly to the case of a sinusoidal vibration.

amplitude distortion. *See* distortion (electrical, sound).

amplitude fading. *See* fading.

amplitude modulation (a.m.). A type of *modulation in which the amplitude of the *carrier wave is varied above and below its unmodulated value by an amount that is proportional to the amplitude of the modulating signal and at a frequency equal to that of the modu-

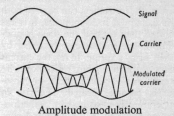

Amplitude modulation

lating signal. An amplitude-modulated wave in which the modulating signal is sinusoidal may be represented by: $e = [A + B \sin pt] \sin \omega t$, where A = amplitude of the unmodulated carrier wave, B = peak amplitude variation of the composite, $\omega = 2\pi \times$ frequency of carrier wave, $p = 2\pi \times$ frequency of modulating signal. The modulation factor, $m = B/A$, gives $e = [1 + m \sin pt] A \sin \omega t$. *Compare* frequency modulation.

a.m.u. Abbreviation for atomic mass unit.

analog circuit. *See* linear circuit.

analog computer. *See* computer.

analog digital converter. *Syn.* digitizer. A device for converting a continuously varying signal, normally voltage or frequency, into a series of numbers on a medium suitable for use by a digital *computer.

analogous pole. The end of a pyroelectric crystal that becomes positively charged with rising temperature. *Compare* antilogous pole.

analyser. A device (crystal, conglomerate of crystals, or glass plate or *Nicol prism of a *polariscope, *saccharimeter, etc.) by which the direction of polarization of a beam of light can be detected; usually the light has been passed through a *polarizer before arriving at the analyser.

anamorphic lens. An optical system of cylindrical lenses or of prisms in which image formation occurs on different scales in the horizontal and vertical directions, producing an image squeezed in one plane. It is used in wide-screen cinematography for compressing images on to the film, the image geometry being restored in a subsequent projection using another such system.

anaphoresis. *See* electrophoresis.

anastigmat. A photographic objective in which correction of *spherical aberration, *coma, *astigmatism, *curvature of image, and *chromatic aberration, are attempted for large apertures and wide fields, involving the use of three- and four-lens cemented or uncemented objectives.

AND circuit. *See* logic circuit.

Anderson bridge. A *bridge for comparing an inductance with a capacitance (*see* diagram). R_4 and X are adjusted until the bridge is balanced, as shown by the indicating instrument, I (a microphone, etc.). Then $R_2R_3 = R_1R_4$ and $L = C[R_2R_3 + (R_3 + R_4)X]$.

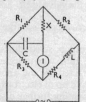
Anderson bridge

anechoic chamber. *See* dead room.

anelasticity. A property of a solid in which stress and strain are not uniquely related in the pre-plastic range.

anemograph. A recording *anemometer.

anemometer. A device for measuring the velocity of a fluid, specifically, of the air. They are of three types: (1) those that depend for their measurement on the difference of pressure between two points in the flow, such as the *venturi tube and the *Pitot tube; (2) those that use the cooling experienced by a heated body exposed to the fluid (*see* hot-wire anemometer); (3) those that use the momentum of the fluid to drive a small windmill, set of cups, or waterscrew facing the direction of flow.

aneroid. Not containing a liquid, e.g. aneroid *barometer; aneroid manometer.

angle of friction. The angle whose tangent is the coefficient of *friction. In measuring the coefficient of friction a body is placed on a plane and the latter tilted until the body will just slide down when gently tapped. The angle of the plane to the horizontal is then the angle of friction.

ångstrom. Symbol Å. A length unit of 10^{-10} m (0.1 nm), used in spectroscopy. The use of this unit is discouraged.

Ångstrom pyrheliometer. *See* pyrheliometer.

angular acceleration. *See* acceleration.

angular dispersion. *See* dispersion.

angular displacement. The angle through which a point, line, or body is rotated, in a specified direction and about a specified axis.

21

angular frequency. Symbol: ω. The frequency of a periodic quantity expressed as the product of the frequency in hertz and the factor 2π.

angular impulse. The time integral of the torque applied to a system, usually for a short time. It is equal to the change in *angular momentum which it would cause on a free mass acting about a principal axis.

angular momentum. *Syn.* moment of momentum about an axis. Symbol: L. The product of *moment of inertia and *angular velocity ($I\omega$). Angular momentum is a vector quantity. It is conserved in an isolated system. *See also* atomic orbital.

angular velocity. Symbol: ω. The rate at which a body rotates about an axis, expressed in radians per second. It is a vector quantity equal to the linear velocity divided by the radius.

anharmonic motion. The motion of a body subjected to a restoring force that is not directly proportional to the displacement from a fixed point in the line of motion.

anhysteretic. The magnetic state of a specimen when, in a constant magnetic field H, it has been subjected to an alternating field progressively reduced from a value greater than H to zero.

anion. An ion that carries a negative charge and in electrolysis moves towards the *anode.

anisotropic. *Syn.* aeleotropic. Not *isotropic.

anisotropy. The variation of physical properties with direction.

annihilation. The conversion of a particle and its corresponding *antiparticle into radiation (called *annihilation radiation*)

on collision. The annihilation radiation has an energy equivalent to the mass of the two colliding particles in accordance with the law of *conservation of mass and energy. For example, when an *electron and *positron collide the annihilation radiation consists of two *photons of gamma radiation each of 0·511 MeV. *See also* pair production.

annular effect. The phenomenon in fluid motion analogous to the *skin effect in alternating electric currents. With steady direct flow at low velocity in a tube, the velocity falls steadily from the centre towards the walls (*see* Poiseuille flow), but when the motion is alternating, as it is, for instance, when sound waves are being propagated in the tube, the mean alternating velocity rises from the centre towards the walls and finally falls within a thin laminar *boundary layer to zero at the wall itself. This is known as a periodic boundary layer. Its thickness increases as the square root of the frequency of the alternation. Similar conditions hold if the alternating flow overlays a direct flow in the tube.

anode. The positive electrode of an electrolytic cell, discharge tube, valve or solid-state rectifier. It is the electrode by which electrons leave a system.

anode drop (or fall). The finite difference of potential, of the order of 20 volts, between the anode in a *gas-discharge tube and a point in the gas close to the anode.

anode load. The total impedance in the anode circuit of a *thermionic valve external to the valve itself.

anode rays. *See* gas-discharge tube.

anode saturation. A condition arising in a valve or tube when electrons are no longer attracted by the anode. This is due to a build up of electrons around the anode preventing further discharge. *See also* space charge.

anomalous dispersion. Rapid changes of refractive index with wavelength when the wavelength lies in the neighbourhood of absorption bands of the material. On the longer wavelength side of the absorption band the refractive index is high, and on the shorter wavelength side, low. Normal *dispersion is such that shorter wavelengths are associated with higher refractive index.

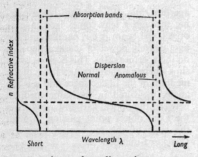

Anomalous dispersion

anomalous viscosity. In colloids, and in fact all fluids which consist of two or more phases at the same time, the coefficient of *viscosity is not a constant but is a function of the rate at which the fluid is sheared as well as of the relative concentration of the phases; these fluids are said to be *non-Newtonian*.

anomaly. An angular distance describing the position of an orbiting body such as a planet. There are three types of anomaly: *true* and *eccentric anomaly* (*see* diagram) and *mean anomaly*. A planet's velocity is not constant but is greater at perihelion than at aphelion. The mean

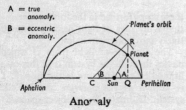

Anomaly

anomaly is the angle between the perihelion, the sun, and a fictitious planet having the same period as the real planet but moving with a constant velocity.

antenna. *See* aerial.

anticathode. A metal block in an X-ray tube upon which the electrons are focused, and from which the X-radiation is thus emitted. It either forms the anode of the tube or is connected to it.

anticoincidence circuit. A circuit with two input terminals, designed to produce an output pulse if only one input terminal receives a pulse within a specified time interval.

antiferromagnetism. The property of certain materials that have a low positive magnetic *susceptibility (as in *paramagnetism) and exhibit a temperature dependence similar to that encountered in *ferromagnetism. The susceptibility increases with increasing temperature up to a certain point, called the *Néel temperature*, and then falls with increasing temperature according to the *Curie–Weiss law. The material thus becomes paramagnetic above the Néel temperature, which is analogous to the *Curie point in the transition from ferromagnetism to paramagnetism.

Antiferromagnetism is a property of certain inorganic compounds such as MnO, FeO, and MnS. It results from interactions between neighbouring atoms leading to an antiparallel arrangement of adjacent magnetic dipole moments.

antilogous pole. That end of a pyroelectric crystal that becomes negatively charged with rising temperature. *Compare* analogous pole.

antimatter. Matter composed entirely of *antiparticles. The existence of antimatter in the universe has not been detected.

antinodal points. *Syn.* negative nodal points. The pair of conjugate points of a thick lens or *centred optical system for which the convergence ratio is −1.

antinode. The position of maximum disturbance in a *standing wave system; the converse of *node.

antiparallel. Parallel but pointing in opposite directions.

antiparticle. To each elementary particle, except for the photon and $\pi°$, there exists another particle having charge (Q), *baryon number (B), *strangeness (S), and *isospin quantum number (I_3) of equal magnitude but opposite sign. These particles are called antiparticles. The photon and $\pi°$ are their own antiparticles. The antiparticle corresponding to a particle a is usually denoted ā. *See also* annihilation.

antiprincipal points. *Syn.* negative principal points. The pair of conjugate points of a thick lens or *centred optical system for which the *lateral magnification is −1. Corresponding principal and antiprincipal points are equally spaced from the appropriate focus.

antiresonance. The condition in which a vibrating system responds with minimum amplitude to an alternating driving force, by virtue of the inertia and elastic constants of the system.

aperiodic. (1) Non-periodic (*see* period). Applied to a system (e.g. an electric circuit, instrument, etc.) that is adequately *damped. (2) Without frequency discrimination. Applied to a circuit designed for use at a frequency (or over a range of frequencies) sufficiently far removed from any of its natural or *resonant frequencies for its characteristics to be substantially independent of frequency within the required limits.

aperture. Part of a lens or mirror through which light is allowed to pass.

aperture angle. The semi-angle subtended by the entrance pupil of an instrument at the object. *See* numerical aperture.

aperture distortion. Loss of definition in a *television image due to the finite size of the scanning spot or aperture. Thus, it is impossible to reproduce any details in the original object that are finer than the area represented by the aperture.

aperture ratio. When a light beam passing through a lens comes from a near object, the beam is not parallel and the light-passing power of the lens depends on the aperture ratio. This is given by $2n \sin a$ where n is the refractive index of the medium in the image space and a is the angle, measured in the same medium between the optical axis and a ray from the axial object point passing through the edge of the mechanical aperture. *Compare* f-number.

apertures and stops in optical systems. Light passing through an optical system will be limited by the *apertures of the various lenses or other components of the system. The mounts holding the components must therefore be considered as stops.

Consider an optical system containing the two stops (or lens apertures) S and T (Fig. *a*). Let S′ and T′ be the images of

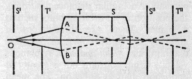

a Stops in optical system

these stops formed in the 'object space' – that is by rays of light passing through the system from right to left.

The amount of light from O which passes through the system is in this case limited by the aperture in the stop T. T is known as the *aperture stop* of the system. Its image in the object space, T′

is called the *entrance pupil*. T″, the image of the aperture stop in the image space (rays passing from left to right), is called the *exit pupil*.

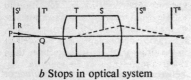

b Stops in optical system

Now consider light coming from the extra-axial point P (Fig. *b*). The ray PQ which passes through the centre of the entrance pupil is called the *principal ray*. The field of view in the plane of S′ will be limited by the diameter of the aperture in S, and no light from points further from the axis than the point R will pass through the system. The actual stop S which limits the field of view in this way is known as the *field stop*. Its image in the object space, S′, is the *entrance port* or *entrance window*. Its image in the image space, S″, is the *exit port* or *exit window*. The *field of view* is measured by the angle subtended by the entrance window at the centre of the entrance pupil.

aperture synthesis. A procedure for obtaining full-size aperture results using a series of *radio telescopes of small aperture. The large aperture is divided into units equal in size to the actual small-aperture aerials, which are moved into every combination of position and orientation. The information gained enables a map to be constructed that extends over a large area of the sky.

aphelion. *See* perihelion.

Apjohn's formula. A formula for calculating the pressure of water vapour in the air using readings of a *wet and dry bulb hygrometer: $P_w - P = 0.000\ 75\ H(t - t_w) \times [1 - 0.008(t - t_w)]$. P_w is the saturated vapour pressure at the temperature t_w of the wet bulb, P is the actual pressure at temperature t, and H is the barometric pressure.

aplanatic. Of optical surfaces and points. Having or producing an image that is free from *spherical aberration and *coma for all rays.

apochromatic lens. A lens with a high degree of correction of *chromatic aberration. The residual secondary spectrum of a lens achromatized for two colours is further reduced by using lens combinations with three or more different kinds of glass with appropriate partial dispersions: used in microscope objectives and special photographic lenses.

apocynthion. The time or the point at which a spacecraft launched from the earth into lunar orbit is furthest from the surface of the moon. *Compare* pericynthion.

apogee. *See* perihelion.

apolune. The time or the point at which a spacecraft launched from the moon into lunar orbit is furthest from the surface of the moon. *Compare* perilune.

apostilb. A unit of *luminance defined as the luminance of a uniformly diffusing surface that emits 1 *lumen per square metre. It is equivalent to a luminance of $1/\pi$ *candela per square metre or 10^{-4} *lambert.

apparent expansion. *See* coefficient of expansion.

apparent magnitude. *See* magnitude.

appearance potential. The potential through which an electron must fall in order to produce a given ion from its parent atom or molecule. It is thus the minimum energy required to cause the ionization: $A + e \rightarrow A^+ + 2e$. If the appearance potential is measured in volts for a particular ion it is numerically equal to the *ionization potential of the parent atom or molecule.

Appleton layer. *See* ionosphere.

apsis (*plural*: apsides). *Syn.* apse. Either of the two extreme points on the major axis of the orbit of a planet or comet, i.e. the *perihelion or aphelion.

arc. A luminous electrical gas discharge characterized by high current density and low potential gradient. The intense ionization necessary to maintain the large current is provided mainly by the evaporation of the electrodes, which are raised to incandescence by the discharge. *See* conduction in gases; gas-discharge tube.

Archimedes' principle. A body floating in a fluid displaces a weight of fluid equal to its own weight. *See* buoyancy.

arcing contacts. Auxiliary contacts in any type of *circuit-breaker switch, designed to close before and open after the main contacts thereby protecting the latter from damage by an *arc.

arcing ring. A metal ring fitted to an insulator to prevent damage to the latter by a power arc.

arc lamp. A type of lamp that utilizes the brilliant light accompanying an electric arc. The major portion of the light comes from the incandescent crater formed at the positive electrode.

areal velocity. The area swept out in unit time by the radius vector to a point describing a plane curve. *See* Kepler's laws (2).

Argand diagram. A representation of complex numbers with reference to perpendicular axes: the horizontal axis of real quantities and the perpendicular axis of imaginary quantities. The complex quantity $x + iy$, where $i = \sqrt{(-1)}$, is represented by the line OP (or the point P). The length of OP is the *modulus* of the complex quantity $z = x + iy$ and is thus $r = \sqrt{(x^2 + y^2)}$ while the angle

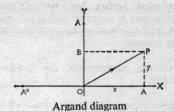

Argand diagram

between OX and OP is the *amplitude* or *argument* θ of z and it can be shown that z may alternatively be written as $re^{i\theta} = r\cos\theta + ir\sin\theta = x + iy$.

armature. (1) *Syn.* rotor. The rotating part in an electric *motor or *generator. (2) Any moving part in a piece of electrical equipment in which a voltage is induced by a magnetic field or which closes a magnetic circuit, e.g. the moving contact in an electromagnetic relay. (3) *See* keeper.

artificial horizon. Device employed when finding the altitude of a heavenly body, if no natural horizon is visible. A telescope directed to a star and then turned to view the light reflected in the surface of a pool of mercury must be rotated through twice the angular altitude.

artificial line. An electrical *network comprising resistance, inductance, and capacitance elements, designed to behave in exactly the same way at any particular frequency as an actual *transmission line as far as the terminals are concerned.

artificial radioisotopes. *See* radioactivity.

asdic. An acronym for *a*llied *s*ubmarine *d*etection *i*nvestigation *c*ommittee. *See* sonar.

aspherical lens or mirror. A lens or mirror whose surface is part of a parabola, ellipse, hyperbola, etc., rather than part of a sphere, thus reducing optical aberration, especially *spherical aberration, to a minimum. A *bispherical lens* has a spherical surface but with different curvatures in the centre and at the edge. It has the same advantages as an aspherical element.

Assmann psychrometer. *See* psychrometer.

astatic system. A system of magnets so arranged that there is no resultant directive force or couple on the system when placed in a uniform magnetic field. The simplest form consists of a pair of equal

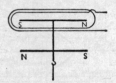

Astatic galvanometer

and parallel magnets mounted on the same axis, with their polarities in opposite directions. If a current-bearing coil encircles one of the magnets, its field affects mainly the magnet so encircled. This is the principle of the *astatic galvanometer.*

astigmatic lenses. Planocylindrical, sphero-cylindrical, and sphero-toric lenses (*see* toric lenses) used to correct *astigmatism of the eye.

astigmatism. With a simple lens it is found that a point object off the axis gives rise to two images each in the form of a line. The tangential fan of rays O A B is brought to a focus at T′, while the so-called sagittal fan O C D is focused at S′. If the object were a wheel centred on the axis the spokes would be seen at S′ and the rim at T′. This defect is called astigmatism. It can also occur with normal incidence, due to meridian differences of curvature. A similar effect is found in the images of extra-axial points formed by spherical mirrors.

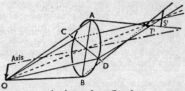

Astigmatism (lens)

Astigmatism in the eye is caused either by curvature differences of the cornea or to a lesser extent because the crystalline lens is somewhat tilted. *See* toric lens.

astrometry. *See* astronomy.

astronomical telescope. (1) *Syn.* Kepler telescope. *See* refracting telescope. (2) A *telescope designed for astronomical use.

astronomical unit (A.U.). A unit of length used in astronomy. It is the mean distance between the centre of the earth and the centre of the sun and is equal to 149·6 million km or about 92·9 million miles.

astronomy. The study of the universe and its contents. The main branches of the subject are: *astrometry*, positional measurements of the stars and planets on the *celestial sphere; *celestial mechanics*, relative motions of systems of bodies associated by *gravitational fields; *astrophysics*, the internal structure of planets and stars and their consequent external features and positions on the *Hertzsprung–Russell diagram. *See also* radio astronomy; cosmology.

astrophysics. *See* astronomy.

asynchronous motor. An a.c. motor whose actual speed bears no fixed relation to the supply frequency and varies with the load. An *induction motor is a typical example.

atmometer. An instrument for measuring the rate of evaporation of water into the atmosphere.

atmosphere. (1) The *air. (2) Any gaseous medium. (3) A unit of pressure equal to 760 mmHg or 101 325 N m^{-2}. It is approximately equal to 1 kg cm^{-2}. Atmospheric pressure fluctuates about this value. *See also* atmospheric layers.

atmospheric absorption. *See* atmospheric windows.

atmospheric electricity. The general electrical properties of the atmosphere, both under normal conditions and at the time of electric discharge (i.e. a lightning flash).

The following data characterize the properties of the atmosphere at, or just above, sea level. They are mean fine-weather values:

direction of field	downward
potential gradient	130 volts per metre
total conductivity	3 × 10^{-4} siemens per metre
small ion mobility	1·4 × 10^{-4} (m s^{-1})/ (V m^{-1})
air-earth current density	2 × 10^{-14} ampere per metre^2

An average lightning flash has a potential of about 4 × 10^9 volts. It provides a charge of 15 coulombs, and possesses about 2 × 10^{10} joules of energy. The average upward current is rather less than one ampere.

atmospheric layers. The gaseous layers into which the earth's atmosphere can be divided according to the change in physical properties, especially temperature. The altitude figures given in the diagram are approximate, as they vary over the earth's surface, and also show seasonal and diurnal changes. There are five main layers – the *troposphere*, *stratosphere*, *mesosphere*, *thermosphere* (or *chemosphere*), and *exosphere*. The troposphere is the most turbulent layer, cloud precipitation and other meteorological phenomena occurring here. The relatively high temperature at the upper boundary of the stratosphere (*stratopause*) is due to

absorption of ultraviolet radiation by ozone. The greatest ozone concentration marks the upper limit of the *ozone layer*. The *ionosphere extends from the stratosphere into the exosphere.

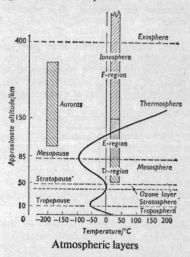

Atmospheric layers

atmospheric pressure. *See* atmosphere.

atmospherics. Electromagnetic radiation produced by natural causes, such as lightning, and the disturbing effects which such radiation produces in a radio receiver.

atmospheric windows. The gaps in atmospheric absorption that allow *electromagnetic radiations of certain wavelengths to penetrate the earth's atmosphere from space.

(i) *optical window.* This allows through the whole visible spectrum (approx. 760–400 nm) and ultraviolet wavelengths down to about 200 nm. Radiation of wavelengths less than 200 nm is absorbed by ozone in the stratosphere.

(ii) *infrared window.* This allows through wavelengths of 8–11 μm, corresponding to the region in which there is no absorption of infrared radiation by water vapour in the atmosphere.

(iii) *radio window*. This allows through short wave radio waves of wavelengths 8 mm–20 m. *See* radio astronomy.

atom. The smallest particle of an element that can take part in a chemical reaction. The atom was originally thought by Dalton to be indivisible. The discovery of the electron and the experiments of Geiger and Marsden on the scattering of alpha-particles by thin metal foils led Rutherford to propose a model in which nearly all the mass of the atom is concentrated at its centre in a region of positive charge, the *nucleus, with a radius of about 10^{-14} to 10^{-15} metres. The remainder of the atom (radius $\sim 10^{-10}$ m) is almost empty except for one or more electrons orbiting the central positive charge. The positive charge of the nucleus is Ze, where Z is the number of electrons and is called the *atomic number.

In 1913 Bohr perfected the Rutherford theory of the atom by an early use of *quantum theory. An electron moving in a circle around the nucleus can be held in orbit by a balance between the electrostatic force of attraction to the nucleus and the centrifugal force due to its motion. It would be subjected to a central acceleration and according to classical electromagnetic theory it should radiate energy and thus spiral into the nucleus. Bohr resolved this difficulty by assuming that the classical principles of electromagnetic theory only apply to macroscopic systems and cannot be applied on the atomic scale. The electron in a hydrogen atom, for example, is assumed to occupy one of a number of fixed orbits: when in a particular orbit it does not radiate energy – energy is only emitted when the electron jumps from one orbit to another. The characteristic of these orbits (or *shells*) is that the angular momentum of the electron (mvr) is equal to $n(h/2\pi)$, where h is the *Planck constant and n is an integer (1, 2, 3, etc.). It can be shown that the radii of the orbits is given by:

$$r = \frac{n^2 \varepsilon_0 h^2}{\pi m e^2 Z},$$

where m is the mass of the electron, e its charge, ε_0 the *electric constant, and n the *principal quantum number* (*see* atomic orbital). The smallest orbit, for which $n = 1$, is the orbit of lowest energy; for hydrogen ($Z = 1$) it has a radius (a_0) of 5.29×10^{-11} metres. The energy of the electron in its allowed orbits is the sum of its kinetic energy and its potential energy in the field of the nucleus. It is given by $E = -me^4/8h^2\varepsilon_0^2 n^2$. Thus the electron can occupy the first orbit with energy $-me^4/8h^2\varepsilon_0^2$ or a second orbit in which the energy is $-me^4/8h\varepsilon_0^2 2^2$, etc. These are *stationary states of the hydrogen atom; usually the atom will be in its *ground state in which the electron is in the lowest energy orbit, i.e. $n = 1$. Bohr's theory was highly successful in explaining the frequencies of lines in the *hydrogen spectrum.

A refinement to this theory was introduced by Sommerfeld who suggested that electrons moved round the nucleus in ellipses which, because of the variation of mass with velocity (*see* relativity), precess about the nucleus with constant angular velocity (*see* precession). Each electron was given two *quantum numbers; the ratio of the principal quantum number n and the *azimuthal quantum number* k determining the eccentricity of the ellipse (when $n = k$ the orbit is a circle). Modern quantum theory replaces k by l (*see* atomic orbital). Sommerfeld's theory was successful in explaining fine structure in some spectral lines. The theory was further refined by the introduction of two additional quantum numbers to account for other spectra.

Modern *quantum theory has replaced the fixed planetary orbits of Bohr by something that appears more insubstantial. It suggests that there is no significance to be attached to the exact position of a nucleus or its orbiting electrons when they have definite energies (*see* uncertainty principle). Instead the probability that a particle will be in a certain position is expressed by the magnitude of the square of its *wavefunction. This form of treatment, known as *wave mechanics, permits explanations of more complicated atomic phenomena and at the same time incorporates all the explanations of the older theories. *See also* nucleus.

atom bomb. *See* nuclear weapons.

atomic clock. *See* clocks.

atomic heat. The former name for the *molar heat capacity of an element. *See* Dulong and Petit's law.

atomic mass unit (unified). *Syn.* dalton. Abbreviation: a.m.u. Symbol: u. A unit mass equal to $\frac{1}{12}$ of the mass of an atom of carbon-12. It is equal to $1\cdot6605 \times 10^{-27}$ kg or approximately 931 MeV.

atomic number. *Syn.* proton number. Symbol: Z. The number of protons in the nucleus of an atom or the number of electrons revolving around the nucleus. It determines the chemical properties of an element and its position in the *periodic table. All the isotopes of an element have the same atomic number although different isotopes have different *mass numbers.

atomic orbital. An allowed *wave function of an electron in an atom obtained by a solution of *Schrödinger's wave equation. In a hydrogen atom, for example, the electron moves in the electrostatic field of the nucleus and its potential energy is $-e^2/r$, where e is the electron's charge and r its distance from the nucleus. A precise orbit cannot be considered as in Bohr's theory of the *atom but the behaviour of the electron is described by its wave function, Ψ, which is a mathematical function of its position with respect to the nucleus. The significance of the wave function is that

its modulus squared, $|\Psi|^2$, is proportional to the probability of finding the electron at a particular point. It can be shown that the electron can only have certain allowed wave functions (eigenfunctions). Each of these corresponds to a probability distribution in space given by the manner in which $|\Psi|^2$ varies with position. They also have an associated value of the energy E. These allowed wave functions, or orbitals, are characterized by three quantum numbers similar to those characterizing the allowed orbits in the earlier quantum theory of the atom:

n, the *principal quantum number*, can have values of 1, 2, 3 etc. The orbital with $n = 1$ has the lowest energy. The states of the electron with $n = 1, 2, 3$, etc., are called shells and designated the K, L, M shells, etc.

l, the *azimuthal quantum number*, which for a given value of n can have values of $0, 1, 2, \ldots (n-1)$. Thus when $n = 1$, l can only have the value 0. An electron in the L shell of an atom with $n = 2$ can occupy two 'sub-shells' of different energy corresponding to $l = 0$ and $l = 1$.

Orbitals with $l = 0, 1, 2,$ and 3 are called $s, p, d,$ and f orbitals respectively. The significance of the l quantum number is that it gives the angular momentum of the electron. The orbital angular momentum of an electron is given by $\sqrt{l(l + 1)}(h/2\pi)$.

m, the *magnetic quantum number*, which for a given value of l can have values $-l, -(l - 1), \ldots, 0, \ldots (l - 1)$, l. Thus for a p orbital for which $l = 1$, there are in fact three different orbitals with $m = -1, 0,$ and 1. These orbitals, with the same values of n and l but different m values, have the same energy. The significance of this quantum number is that it indicates the number of different states that would be produced if the atom were subjected to an external magnetic field (*see* Larmor precession).

According to wave theory the electron may be at any distance from the nucleus but in fact there is only a reasonable chance of it being within a distance of $\sim 5 \times 10^{-9}$ metres. Indeed the maximum probability occurs when $r = a_0$ where a_0 is the radius of the first Bohr orbit (*see* atom). It is customary to represent an orbital by a surface enclosing a volume within which there is an arbitrarily decided probability (say 95%) of finding the electron. Although *s* orbitals are spherical ($l = 0$), orbitals with $l > 0$ have an angular dependence.

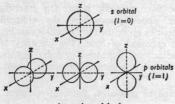

Atomic orbitals

Finally, the electron in an atom can have a fourth quantum number, M_s, characterizing its direction of *spin. The four quantum numbers lead to an explanation of the *periodic table. *See also* Pauli exclusion principle.

atomic pile. Former name for *nuclear reactor.

atomic stopping power. *See* stopping power.

atomic unit of energy. (1) *Syn.* hartree. The potential energy of an electron in the first orbit in Bohr's theory of the hydrogen *atom. It is given by e^2/a_0, where e is the electron's charge and a_0 the atomic unit of length. It is equal to 27·190 electronvolts or $4·850 \times 10^{-18}$ joule.
(2) *Syn.* rydberg. The atomic unit of energy is sometimes defined as one half of this value. This is the ionization potential of the hydrogen atom.

atomic unit of length. Symbol: a_0. The radius of the first orbit in Bohr's theory of the hydrogen *atom. It is equal to $5·29 \times 10^{-9}$ metre.

atomic unit of mass. A unit of mass equal to the rest mass of the electron, $9·1084 \pm 0·003 \times 10^{-31}$ kg. *Compare* atomic mass unit.

atomic volume. The volume in the solid state of one mole of an element. Thus, atomic volume = atomic weight ÷ density of the solid.

atomic weight. *Syn.* relative atomic mass. Symbol: A_r. The average weight of the atoms of a given specimen of an element expressed in unified *atomic mass units.

attenuation. The reduction of a radiation quantity, such as intensity, particle flux density, or energy flux density, upon the passage of the radiation through matter. It may result from any type of interaction with the matter, such as absorption, scattering, etc. In an electric circuit it is the reduction in current, voltage, or power along a path of energy flow. *See* linear attenuation coefficient; attenuation constant.

attenuation coefficient. *See* linear attenuation coefficient.

attenuation constant. Symbol: α. For a plane progressive wave at a given frequency. The rate of exponential decrease in amplitude of voltage, current, or field-component in the direction of propagation of the wave. For example, $I_2 = I_1 e^{-\alpha d}$ where I_2 and I_1 are the currents at two points (I_1 being nearer the source of the wave) a distance d apart. α is usually expressed in *nepers or decibels. *See* propagation coefficient.

attenuation distortion. *See* distortion (electrical).

attenuation equalizer. An electrical *network designed to provide compensation for attenuation *distortion in a specific band of frequencies.

attenuator. An electrical *network or *transducer specifically designed to

31

attenuate a wave without distortion. The amount of attenuation may be fixed or variable. A fixed attenuator is also called a *pad*. They are usually calibrated in decibels.

atto-. Symbol: a. The prefix 10^{-18}, e.g. 1 am = 10^{-18} metres.

attracted disc electrometer. A type of absolute electrometer in which a circular metal disc A is held parallel to a larger metal disc B, by an extensible spring. The force per unit area on A, when a potential difference V is maintained between A and B, is equal to $V^2/8\pi d^2$, where d is the distance between the discs. A *guard ring ensures the uniformity of the field over the area of the attracted disc A.

audio frequency. Any frequency to which a normal ear can respond; it extends from about 20 to 20 000 hertz. In communication systems satisfactory intelligibility of speech (i.e. of commercial quality) can be obtained if frequencies lying between about 300 and 3400 hertz are reproduced, and any frequency within this range is described as a *voice frequency*.

Auger effect. *Syn.* Auger ionization. The spontaneous ejection of an electron (*Auger electron*) by an excited positive ion to form a doubly charged ion: i.e. $A \xrightarrow{-e} A^{+*} \rightarrow A^{2+} + e^-$, where A^{+*} represents an excited state of a singly charged ion and A^{2+} a doubly charged ion that may or may not be in its ground state. The first step may result from an internal process such as gamma-ray emission from the nucleus with subsequent absorption of this photon in the electron shells of the atom. Alternatively, it may be induced by an external stimulus, such as bombardment by electrons or photons. *Compare* autoionization.

Auger shower. *Syn.* extensive shower. A *shower of elementary particles produced by a primary *cosmic ray entering the atmosphere. They extend over large areas (about 1000 square metres) and contain a total energy of about 10^{15} electronvolts ($1·6 \times 10^{-4}$ joule).

aurora. An intermittent electrical discharge occurring in the rarefied *upper atmosphere. Charged particles in the *solar wind become trapped in the earth's magnetic field and move in helical paths along the lines of force between the two magnetic poles. On entering the upper atmosphere the charged particles excite the air molecules causing an emission of light. The intensity of the aurora is greatest in polar regions although it is seen in temperate zones.

autodyne oscillator. *See* beat reception.

autoemission. *Syn.* autoelectronic emission. *See* cold cathode; field emission.

autoionization. A form of ionization involving two steps, first the excitation of an atom (or molecule) into a state with an energy above its *ionization potential and secondly de-excitation from this state to give a positive ion with a lower energy and an ejected electron. The process is similar to the *Auger effect with the difference that the initial vacancy in an electron shell is caused by transfer of an electron from one orbital to another empty orbital. In the Auger effect the vacancy is formed by complete removal of the electron to give an ion. Autoionization results in a singly charged positive ion A^+: $A \rightarrow A^* \rightarrow A^+ + e$, where A^* is an excited atom. The electron ejected has a characteristic energy equal to the difference between the energy of the excited atom and that of the ion.

automatic frequency control (a.f.c.). A method of automatically maintaining the frequency of any source of alternating voltage within specified limits.

automatic gain control (a.g.c.). A method of automatically holding the output volume constant in a radio receiver, despite variations in the input signal.

autoradiograph. If a thin specimen of metal, biological tissue, etc., is labelled with a *radioisotope and placed in contact with a photographic plate for a suitable exposure time an image is produced by the action of the radiation emitted. On developing the film, called an autoradiograph, the distribution of the radioisotope in the specimen can be seen.

autotransductor. A transductor in which the same windings are used for the main and control currents.

autotransformer. A *transformer with a single winding, tapped at intervals, instead of two or more independent windings. The voltage drop across each tapped section is related to the total applied voltage in the same proportion as the number of turns of the section is related to the total number of turns of the winding.

avalanche. A cumulative ionization process, such as that occurring in a *Geiger counter, when a single particle or photon ionizes several gas molecules. Each electron and ion formed is accelerated in a strong electric field and gains sufficient energy to ionize other molecules and produce more electrons and ions. These in turn cause further ionization and the initial event leads to a large *shower of charged particles.

avalanche breakdown. A breakdown in a *semiconductor diode caused by the cumulative multiplication of free charge carriers under the action of a strong electric field. Some free carriers gain enough energy to liberate new hole-electron pairs by collision.

average life or lifetime. *See* mean life.

Avogadro constant. *Syn.* Avogadro's number. Symbol: L or N_A. The number of molecules contained in one mole of any substance. *Amount of substance is proportional to the number of specified entities of that substance, the Avogadro constant being the proportionality factor. It is the same for all substances and its value is $6 \cdot 022\ 169 \times 10^{23}$ mol^{-1}. *See also* Loschmidt's number.

Avogadro's hypothesis. Equal volumes of all gases measured at the same temperature and pressure contain the same number of molecules, i.e. the volume occupied at a given temperature and pressure by a mole of a gas is the same for all gases ($22 \cdot 4 \times 10^{-3}$ m^3 at S.T.P.). *See* ideal gas.

axial ratio. The relative lengths of the three edges of the *unit cell of a crystal lattice, taking that of the b axis as unity.

axis (of a lens). For *spherical lenses, a straight line perpendicular to each face and joining the centres of the two surfaces. For *cylindrical and spherocylindrical lenses, a line (on the surface) parallel to the geometrical axis of the cylinder surface. *See also* optical (or optic) axis.

azimuth. Position as measured by an angle round some fixed point or pole. *See* celestial sphere.

azimuthal quantum number. *See* atom; atomic orbital.

B

Babinet compensator. Two narrow angle wedges of quartz with parallel refracting edges and hypotenuse faces adjacent, cut with their optic axes perpendicular and parallel to the refracting edges. As one prism opposes the effect of the other with respect to ordinary and extraordinary components, although outwardly a parallel slab, the effect across the plate will be one of variable thickness. If the prisms slide over one another maintaining parallel edges, the effect of a variable thickness at one point may be obtained. Linearly or elliptically polarized light of different path differences can be produced as required.

back electromotive force. An e.m.f. that opposes the normal flow of current in an electric circuit.

back focal length. The distance from the last surface of a system to the second principal focus.

background noise. *Syn.* random noise. *See* noise.

background radiation. (1) The low intensity radiation resulting from the bombardment of the earth by *cosmic rays and from the presence of naturally occurring *radioisotopes (such as ^{40}K, ^{14}C) in rocks, soil, air, building materials, etc. (2) *See* cosmic background radiation.

back heating. *See* magnetron.

backing pump. *See* pumps, vacuum.

backing store. A large capacity computer *storage device such as a *disk, *magnetic tape, or *drum. *Compare* memory.

back layer photocell. *See* rectifier photocell.

back scatter. The scattering process by which radiation emerges from the same surface of a material as that through which it enters. The term also applies to the radiation undergoing such a process.

backward-wave oscillator. *See* travelling-wave tube.

baffle. A partition used with a sound radiator to increase the path difference between sound originating from the front and back of the radiator. It is most commonly used to improve the frequency response of a loudspeaker.

balance. An instrument whose primary function is to compare two masses. The balance with the widest usage is the equal-armed balance. If P and Q are two slightly different masses, placed one in each pan of the balance whose arms are a cm long, and the balance comes to rest with the arms making a small angle θ with the horizontal then

$$\tan \theta = \frac{(P - Q)a}{(P + Q + 2w)h + Wk},$$

where w is the weight of a scale pan, and W is the weight of the balance beam, h is the height of the central knife-edge above the line joining the outer knife-edges, and k is the distance of the centre of gravity of the beam below the central knife-edge. Tan $\theta/(P - Q)$ is a measure of the sensitivity of the balance for a load P.

Other forms of balance are (1) the *decimal balance*, which has arms in the ratio 10:1 and thus avoids the necessity for using heavy weights; (2) the *spring balance* which consists essentially of a helical spring with its axis vertical. It may be used either by extending the spring or by compressing it as in the familiar use of household scales; (3) the *torsion balance*, which consists essentially of a vertical straight torsion wire, the

34

upper point of which is fixed while the lower carries a horizontal beam; (4) the *hydrostatic balance*. The equal-armed balance may be used as a hydrostatic balance by placing a wooden bridge across, but not touching, one of the balance pans and hanging a piece of the substance whose relative *density is required from a hook at the top of the pan support and weighing this first in air and second in a beaker of water standing on the bridge. *See also* microbalance.

balanced amplifier. A push–pull amplifier. *See* push–pull operation.

ballast resistor. A resistor constructed from a material having a high *temperature coefficient of resistance in such a way that, over a range of voltage, the current is substantially constant. It is connected in series with a circuit to stabilize the current in the latter by absorbing small changes in the applied voltage. The most common types are the *barretter and the *thermistor.

ballistic. Of an instrument. Designed to measure an impact or sudden rush of energy.

ballistic galvanometer. A galvanometer adapted to measure the quantity of electricity, Q, flowing through the instrument during the passage of a transient current, where $Q = \int_0^\infty I \, \mathrm{d}t$. The period of the moving part of the galvanometer must be long compared with the duration of the current; the electromagnetic impulse due to the passage of the transient can then be deduced from the ballistic 'throw,' θ. For a suspended-magnet galvanometer $Q \propto \sin \frac{1}{2}\theta$: for a moving coil instrument $Q \propto \theta$.

Balmer series. *See* hydrogen spectrum.

band. (1) In communications, a range of frequencies within specified limits used for a definite purpose. (2) In computers, a group of tracks on a magnetic *drum

used for storing information. (3) A closely spaced group of energy levels in atoms. *See* energy bands. (4) *See* spectrum.

band-pass filter. *See* filter.

band pressure level. The *sound pressure level of a sound within a specified band of sound frequency.

band spectrum. *Syn.* molecular spectrum. *See* spectrum.

bandwidth. (1) In a communication system. The band of frequencies, in the transmitted signal, taken up by the modulating signal on each side of the frequency of the carrier signal. (2) In an amplifier. The band of frequencies over which the *power amplification falls within specified limits of the maximum value (usually one half).

bar. A CGS unit of pressure equal to 10^5 N m^{-2} (pascal). The millibar (symbol: mb) is a commonly used unit of pressure in meteorology. 1000 millibars is sometimes regarded by meteorologists as the *standard atmosphere, although this should be 1013·25 mb. The bar has in the past also been defined as 1 dyne per centimetre squared, but this is now called the *barye.

Barkhausen effect. The magnetization of a ferromagnetic substance does not increase or decrease steadily with steady increase or decrease of the magnetizing field but proceeds in a series of minute jumps. The effect gives support to the domain theory of *ferromagnetism.

Barlow lens. A planoconcave lens placed between the *objective and *eyepiece in a *telescope to increase magnification.

barn. Symbol: b. A unit of nuclear *cross section. 1 barn = 10^{-28} metre.

Barnett effect. A long iron cylinder

35

rotating at high speed about its longitudinal axis develops a slight magnetization proportional to the angular speed of rotation. This magnetization is due to the effect of the rotation on the electronic orbits in the atoms of the iron and on the electrons themselves, which have their own intrinsic *spin. *Compare* Einstein and de Haas effect.

barograph. A recording *barometer. The common type consists of an aneroid barometer operating a pen that traces a line on a sheet of graph paper mounted on a slowly revolving drum.

barometer. An instrument for measuring atmospheric pressure. (1) *Mercury barometers*. These consist of a glass tube about 80 cm long, closed at one end. The tube is filled with mercury and then placed, open end downward, in a reservoir of mercury. As the atmospheric pressure changes the level of the mercury changes and, to a lesser degree, so does the level in the reservoir. The pressure is measured by the difference *h* between the levels (*see* pressure). The space at the top of the tube is known as a *Torricellian vacuum*.

In *Fortin's barometer*, the scale for measuring the height is fixed and the level of the mercury in the reservoir is adjusted (by moving the flexible bottom of the reservoir) to be at the zero of the scale. The difference in height can then be read directly. There are also instruments in which the scale is moved so that its zero coincides with the lower mercury level.

(2) The *aneroid barometer* consists basically of an evacuated flat cylindrical closed metal box with corrugated elastic faces which are kept from collapsing together by a spring. As the external pressure varies, the distance between the faces alters and a pointer is operated. Such an instrument is calibrated by comparison with a mercury barometer. It is also used as an *altimeter.

barometric formula. A formula indicating the variation of pressure with height for the gas in the earth's atmosphere assuming that the temperature does not vary with height:

$$p = p_0\, e^{-mgx/RT},$$

where p is the pressure at a height x, m the mass of a molecule, g the acceleration of *free fall and p_0 the pressure when $x = 0$. This formula is derived from the *hydrostatic equation*, which shows that the rate of fall of atmospheric pressure with height is proportional to the density ρ:

$$\frac{dp}{dx} = -g\rho.$$

barostat. A constant pressure device or pressure regulator, especially one that compensates for changes of atmospheric pressure.

barrel distortion. *See* distortion (optical).

barretter. A device used for stabilizing voltage, consisting of a sensitive metallic resistor whose resistance increases with temperature. The resistor is usually enclosed in a glass bulb, e.g. an iron wire in an atmosphere of hydrogen. When used in series with a circuit the voltage drop is kept constant over a range of variations in current. *See also* ballast resistor.

barrier-layer photocell. *See* rectifier photocell.

Bartlett force. *See* exchange force.

barycentre. *See* centre of mass.

barye. A former CGS unit of pressure. 1 barye = 0·1 pascal.

baryon. A collective name for *nucleons and other *fermions that decay into nucleons by the emission of *mesons. All baryons have a mass equal to or greater than that of the proton. Baryons, like mesons, take part in *strong inter-actions. A *quantum number, called the *baryon number* (*B*), may be defined such that baryons have baryon number *B* = 1, antibaryons *B* = −1, and all other particles *B* = 0. The total baryon number is conserved in all particle interactions. Baryons are thought to be composed of three tightly bound quarks, anti-baryons of three anti-quarks. *See* Table 8, page 425.

base. The region in a junction *transistor separating the emitter and collector, to which the *base electrode* is attached.

base units. *See* SI units; coherent units.

Bateman equations. A set of equations that describe the decay of a chain of radioactive nuclides. If only the parent nuclide is initially present and there are N_1^0 atoms, then the number of atoms of the *n*th nuclide after a time *t* is given by the equation:

$$N_n(t) = \sum_1^n \frac{\lambda_1\lambda_2 \dots \lambda_{n-1} N_1^0 e^{-\lambda_n t}}{(\lambda_1 - \lambda_n)(\lambda_2 - \lambda_n) \dots (\lambda_{n-1} - \lambda_n)}$$

where λ_n is the decay constant and N_n the number of atoms of the *n*th nuclide.

battery. Two or more accumulators, primary cells, or condensers, electrically connected and used as a single unit.

beam aerial. *See* aerial array.

beam coupling. The production in a circuit of an alternating current between two electrodes, when a density modu-lated electron beam is passed.

beam current. The current consisting of the beam of electrons arriving at the screen of a *cathode-ray tube.

beat-frequency oscillator. An apparatus for generating electrical oscillations, the frequency of which can usually be varied over a range of audio frequencies or

*video frequencies. It incorporates two radio-frequency oscillators one of which has a fixed frequency while the other has a frequency that can be varied at will. The output is obtained by the beating (*see* beat reception) of the two radio-frequency oscillations. The output volt-age remains substantially constant at all output frequencies within the range covered.

beat oscillator. *See* beat reception.

beat reception. *Syn.* heterodyne recep-tion. A method of radio reception in which beating is employed. The *beats (usually at an audio frequency) are pro-duced by combining the received radio-frequency oscillations with radio-fre-quency oscillations generated in the receiver by a separate oscillator (called a *beat oscillator*) and applying the com-bined oscillations to a detector. They are then applied, usually after amplification, to a loudspeaker or similar device to render them audible.

It is possible to design the beat oscilla-tor so that it simultaneously performs the functions of the detector and ampli-fier and in this form it is called an *auto-dyne oscillator*. *Compare* superhetero-dyne receiver.

beats. If two tones very nearly equal in frequency are sounded simultaneously, fluctuations in sound intensity known as beats are observed. The phenomenon may be compared with that of *inter-ference. At certain equal time intervals the wavetrains are in phase and reinforce each other; at intermediate periods they are in opposite phase and tend to neutra-lize each other. Combining the two tones of frequencies *m* and *n* a tone of fre-quency (*m* + *n*)/2 is observed whose amplitude varies from 2*A* to 0 (*A* being the amplitude of each of the primary tones) at a *beat frequency* of (*m* − *n*). If (*m* − *n*) exceeds 20 per second the beats merge into a tone called a difference tone.

The electrical counterpart of beats is used in *beat reception.

Beaufort scale. A numerical scale used in meteorology in which successive values of wind velocities are assigned numbers ranging from 0 (calm) to 12 (hurricane) thus indicating wind forces. Numbers 13–17 are often added to indicate specific hurricane speeds.

Beckmann thermometer. A *mercury in glass thermometer used for the accurate determination of small temperature changes. The bulb is much larger than that of an ordinary thermometer and the scale behind the capillary tube, which is about 30 cm long, is divided into hundredths of a degree and covers only about 5° or 6° C. The temperature change to be measured can take place about any mean temperature in the range, say, 0° C to 100° C, by varying the amount of mercury present in the lower bulb. This is made possible by running in more mercury from a small reservoir bulb at the top of the capillary, or conversely by running some mercury from the lower bulb into the reservoir where it plays no further part in the production of the thermometer reading. The variable amount of mercury present in the bulb means that the scale graduations will only exactly represent true centigrade degrees at the setting for which the scale has been calibrated.

Becquerel effect. The e.m.f. produced by illuminating the surface of one electrode in an electrolytic cell.

Becquerel rays. The *alpha, *beta, and *gamma rays spontaneously emitted by uranium compounds.

Beer-Lambert law. The proportion of light absorbed by a dilute liquid medium varies exponentially with the product of the path length of the light in the medium, the molar concentration, and the molecular extinction coefficient.

Beilby layer. An amorphous layer about 5 nm thick produced by polishing a surface; the ordinary crystalline material is present below this layer. It has been found that this surface layer is produced by sliding friction generating sufficient heat to melt the surface. A substance can thus be polished by one of higher melting point.

bel. Symbol: B. A logarithmic unit used particularly in telecommunications for comparing two amounts of power. Two amounts of power, P_2 and P_1, are said to differ by N bels when $N = \log_{10}(P_2/P_1)$.

If P_1 is the power input of an electrical network and P_2 the corresponding power output, the above expression gives the gain of the network in bels. Note that if $P_2 < P_1$, N is negative, i.e. the gain is negative, or is in fact a loss. A more commonly used unit is the *decibel* (symbol: dB) which is one tenth of a bel. Thus: $N = 10 \log_{10}(P_2/P_1)$ dB. One decibel represents an increase in intensity of 26 % which is about the smallest change which the ear can detect. The decibel is not a measure of loudness since the sensitivity of the ear to changes of intensity varies with frequency.

If the two powers are dissipated in impedances which have equal resistance R then, since

$$P_2 = |I_2|^2 R \text{ and } P_1 = |I_1|^2 R,$$
$$N = \log_{10} \left|\frac{I_2}{I_1}\right|^2 = 2 \log_{10} \left|\frac{I_2}{I_1}\right| \text{ bels.}$$

See neper.

bending moment. The algebraic sum of the moments, about any cross section of a beam, of all the forces acting on the beam on one side of this section. It is immaterial which side of the section is considered if the beam is in equilibrium.

Benedick's effect. An e.m.f. produced in a closed circuit, composed of one metal only, under asymmetrical temperature distribution. The effect is not present if the metal is spectroscopically pure and free from internal strain.

Bernouilli's theorem. In the steady motion of a fluid acted on by external forces which possess a gravitational *potential (V) then

$$\int \frac{dp}{\rho} + \frac{1}{2} v^2 + V = C,$$

where p and ρ are the pressure and density of the fluid; v is the velocity of the fluid along a stream line; and C is a constant, depending on the particular stream line chosen, called *Bernouilli's constant*. The equation is a mathematical statement of the principle of conservation of energy and may be expressed in a generalized form

$$\int \frac{dp}{\rho} - \frac{\partial \varphi}{\partial t} \pm \frac{1}{2} v^2 \pm V = A,$$

where φ is the velocity potential and A is a function of the time (t). For steady motion this reduces to the original equation.

Berthelot's equation of state. The equation

$$\left(p + \frac{a}{Tv^2}\right)(v - b) = RT.$$

This gives better experimental agreement than Van der Waal's equation at moderate pressures, but fails at the critical point. An empirical modification:

$$pv = RT\left[1 + \frac{9}{128}\frac{T_c}{p_c}\frac{p}{T}\left(1 - \frac{6T_c^2}{T^2}\right)\right]$$

is useful when correcting temperatures on a gas scale to those on the thermodynamic scale and is used when experimental results on the compressibility of the gas are not available.

Bessel functions. A power series in x which are solutions of a linear differential equation of the form

$$x^2 \frac{d^2y}{dx^2} + x \frac{dy}{dx} + (x^2 - n^2)y = 0.$$

They have many applications in physics, for example in problems of heat conduction, etc. There are various kinds of Bessel functions, the most important being denoted by $J_n(x)$, the Bessel function of order n.

beta current gain factor. Symbol: β. The short-circuit current amplification factor of a *transistor with common-emitter connection. It is given by:

$$\beta = \left(\frac{\partial i_C}{\partial i_B}\right)_{V_{CE}\ constant}$$

where i_C is the collector current and i_B is the base current. β is always greater than unity and in practice takes values up to 500.

beta decay. The spontaneous transformation of a nucleus into one of its neighbouring *isobars accompanied by the ejection of an electron or positron. The nucleus produced always has the same *mass number as the initial nucleus but differs in *atomic number by one. If an electron is emitted the number of nuclear protons increases by one, if a positron is emitted it decreases by one. Electron emission results from decay of neutrons to give protons, electrons and antineutrinos: $n \rightarrow p + e^- + \bar{\nu}$. The ^{14}C nucleus, for example, decays to give a nitrogen nucleus: $^{14}C \rightarrow ^{14}N + e^- + \bar{\nu}$. Positron emission results from decay of protons to give neutrons, positrons, and *neutrinos: $p \rightarrow n + e^+ + \nu$. Unlike neutrons, free protons are stable and do not decay unless energy is supplied to induce this change. In some complex nuclei this energy can be obtained from the *binding energy of the neutron produced when this exceeds that of the original proton. This occurs in the process:

$$^{11}_{6}C \rightarrow ^{11}_{5}B + e^+ + \nu,$$

where the difference in energy between the ^{11}C and ^{11}B nuclei is more than enough to compensate for the proton decay. It is found that electrons and positrons ejected in beta decay always have a distribution of energies and not a single energy equal to the energy released. The 'missing energy' is carried away by the neutrino ν or antineutrino ν̄. The total energy carried by the electron and antineutrino or by the positron and neutrino is constant for a particular decay and thus the neutrino enables energy to be conserved. The neutrinos also enable *angular momentum to be conserved. Beta decay is a *weak interaction. *See also* radioactivity.

beta particle (β-particle). An energetic *electron or *positron emitted by the nucleus of a *radioisotope during *beta decay.

beta rays (β-rays). A stream of *beta particles with a wide range of energies that are emitted by the nuclei of certain *radioisotopes (*see* beta decay). They are a type of *ionizing radiation and can penetrate a very thin metal foil. Their penetrating power is greater than that of *alpha rays.

beta-ray spectroscopy. *See* electron spectroscopy.

betatron. A cyclic *accelerator for producing high energy electrons by means of magnetic induction rather than by the usual accelerating electric field. If an electron is describing a circular orbit of radius *r* in the magnetic field between the poles of an electromagnet, an increase in the magnetic flux through the orbit produces an acceleration of the electron. If the field at the circumference of the orbit is equal to half the average field inside the orbit, the radius *r* is unaltered, i.e. the particle continues in the same path. This is achieved by shaping the pole pieces. In the betatron the magnet is excited by alternating current, and the electrons are injected into the field when the current is beginning to rise from zero. They are deflected out of the field just before the current reaches its peak value,

having completed several hundred thousand revolutions. The angular velocity ω of a particle moving in a fixed orbit, in which the magnetic field strength is H, is given by $\omega = eH/m$, where m is the particle mass. To maintain a constant angular frequency and orbit, H is increased by the same factor as m increases (due to the relativistic velocity of the particle). The functioning of the machine is therefore not affected by the relativistic mass increase. Energies up to 300 MeV have been produced.

betatron synchrotron. *See* synchrotron.

bevatron. The *proton synchrotron at Berkeley, US, that accelerates protons to 6 GeV.

B/H loop. *See* hysteresis loop.

bias. *Syn.* bias voltage. A voltage applied to an electronic device to determine the portion of the *characteristic of the device at which it operates.

biaxial crystal. A crystal having two directions along which the polarized components of a ray of light will be transmitted with the same velocity.

bichromate cell. *See* dichromate cell.

biconcave lens. A lens with both surfaces concave. A *biconvex* lens has both surfaces convex.

bifilar electrometer. An electrostatic voltmeter in which two conducting quartz fibres stretched by a small weight or by spring tension are separated by being attracted in opposite directions towards two plate electrodes. The separation is measured by microscope.

bifilar suspension. A type of suspension used in electrical instruments in which the moving part is suspended on two parallel threads, wires, or strips.

bifilar winding. A method of winding a resistance wire to form non-inductive resistors, in which the wire is doubled back on itself and wound double from the looped end.

Bifilar winding

big-bang or superdense theory. A theory in *cosmology postulating that at some time about 10×10^9 years ago all the matter of the universe was packed into a superdense small agglomeration, subsequently being hurled in all directions at enormous speeds by a cataclysmic explosion. *See* expanding universe; cosmic background radiation. *Compare* steady-state theory.

Billet split lens. A lens cut in two, so that the optical centres of the semi-lenses are slightly displaced laterally; in consequence, two real images of a slit are formed and in the overlapping region in front of these (coherent) images *interference takes place.

bimetallic strip. Two metals having different coefficients of expansion rivetted together: an increase in temperature of the strip causes the strip to bend, due to unequal expansion of the components. One end is rigidly fixed and movement of the other end can serve to open or close an electric circuit of a temperature control device, or to move the pointer-type thermometer.

bimorph cell. A device for converting electrical signals into mechanical motion using the *piezoelectric effect. It consists of two piezoelectric crystals (Such as Rochelle salt) cut and joined together so that an applied voltage causes one to expand and the other to contract. The composite crystal thus bends as a result of the voltage across it. The converse effect of generation of an electric voltage by bending the cell is also used. Bimorph

cells are used in record player pickups and loudspeakers.

binary notation. A method of expressing numbers by two digits, 0 and 1, rather than the ten digits used in decimal notation.

Decimal	Binary	Decimal	Binary
0	0	5	101
1	1	6	110
2	10	7	111
3	11	8	1000
4	100	9	1001

Since only two symbols are used they can be represented by either of two alternatives, for example the presence or absence of a pulse in an electronic circuit; binary notation is used in computing. *See also* bit.

binary star. A system of two stars that revolve around a common centre of gravity.

binding energy. Symbol: E_B. The mass of a nucleus is slightly less than the mass of its constituent protons and neutrons. By Einstein's law of the *conservation of mass and energy ($E = mc^2$), this mass difference (the mass defect) is equivalent to the energy released when the nucleons bind together. This energy is the binding

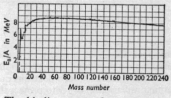

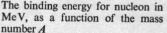

The binding energy for nucleon in MeV, as a function of the mass number A

energy. A nucleus must be supplied with its binding energy before it will undergo *fission (except in the case of radioactive decay). The graph of binding energy per nucleon, E_B/A, against *mass number, A,

41

shows that as A increases E_B/A increases rapidly up to a mass number of 50-60 (iron, nickel, etc.) and then decreases slowly. There are therefore two ways in which energy can be released from a nucleus, both of which entail a rearrangement of nuclei occurring in the lower half of the curve to form nuclei in the upper, higher-energy part of the curve. Fission is the splitting of heavy atoms, such as uranium, into lighter atoms, accompanied by an enormous release of energy. Fusion of light nuclei, such as deuterium and tritium, releases an even greater quantity of energy.

binomial distribution. In a trial that can only have one of two results (say success or failure), the binomial distribution of probabilities, P_r, for obtaining r successes in n independent trials is given by

$$P_r = \frac{n!}{r!(n-r)!} p^r q^{n-r},$$

where p is the probability of success in any one of the trials, and q is that of failure ($p = 1 - q$).

binomial expansion. If $|x| < 1$, the expression $(1 + x)^n$, where n may be any positive or negative number and not necessarily an integer, is equal to

$$1 + nx + \frac{n(n-1)x^2}{2} + \frac{n(n-1)(n-2)x^3}{3 \cdot 2}$$
$$+ \frac{n(n-1)(n-2)(n-3)x^4}{4 \cdot 3 \cdot 2} + \dots$$

biological shield. A massive structure surrounding the *core of a nuclear reactor, provided to absorb neutrons and gamma radiation in order to protect the operating personnel. Such shields are commonly of concrete.

biophysics. Physics applied to biology.

Biot and Savart's law. The magnetic field due to current flowing in a long straight conductor is directly proportional to the current and inversely proportional to the distance of the point of observation from the conductor. The law is derivable from the *Ampère–Laplace theorem.

Biot–Fourier equation. An equation for the conduction of heat through a solid: $\partial Q/\partial t = (\lambda/c\rho)\nabla^2 T$. $\partial Q/\partial t$ is the rate of flow of heat, λ the *thermal conductivity, c the *specific heat capacity, ρ the density, and $\nabla^2 T$ the temperature gradient. For heat flow in one dimension $\nabla^2 T$ becomes dT/dx.

Biot's law. The degree of rotation of the plane of *polarization of light propagated through an optically active medium is inversely proportional (approximately) to the square of the wavelength of the light and proportional to the path length in the medium and to the concentration if the medium is a liquid.

bipolar electrode. A metal plate in an electrolytic cell through which the current, or part of it, passes, but which is not connected either to the anode or the cathode of the cell. Since the current passes through the plate one face serves as a subsidiary cathode, the other as an anode.

bipolar integrated circuit. See integrated circuit.

bipolar transistor. A *transistor in which both electrons and holes play an essential part, e.g. a junction *transistor.

biprism. A prism with a very obtuse angle acting as two narrow angle prisms placed base to base thereby splitting a beam into two parts with a small angle between the parts. A doubled image (small separation) of a single object can be formed.

birefringence. See double refraction.

bispherical lens. See aspherical lens or mirror.

bistable. *Syn.* bistable multivibrator. A type of circuit having two stable states. *See* flip-flop.

bit. A contraction of *bi*nary digi*t*, used in computer technology to mean: (1) Either of the digits 0 or 1 as used in *binary notation. (2) A unit of information coded as a physical state of a two-valued system. Examples include:

electric current	on or off
magnetization	north or south
light	present or absent

Bitter patterns. Patterns demonstrating the presence of *domains in ferromagnetic crystals. They can be observed by coating the polished surface of the material with a colloidal suspension of ferromagnetic particles. The particles tend to gather at the domain boundaries where there is a strong magnetic field. The technique can also be used for detecting cracks and imperfections in ferromagnetic material.

black body. *Syn.* full radiator. A body or receptacle that absorbs all the radiation incident upon it; i.e. a body that has both an *absorptivity and *emissivity of 1 and that has no reflecting power. The radiation from a heated black body is called *black body radiation. While a black body is in fact only a theoretical ideal, it is in practice most nearly realized by the use of a small slit or hole in the wall of a *uniform temperature enclosure.

black body radiation. The thermal radiation from a *black body at a given temperature, having a spectral distribution of energy of the form shown in the diagram. Each curve has a definite maximum that shifts towards the region of shorter wavelengths as the temperature rises. The intensity of radiation of any given wavelength increases steadily as the temperature rises.

Many theoretical and empirical attempts were made to find a general formula to represent the black body spectrum. Thermodynamic reasoning does not give a complete answer, though it does predict two characteristic features of the radiation, namely that for curves at different temperatures the value of $\lambda_{max} T =$ constant. This statement is known as the *Wien displacement law*. The second deduction is that the heights of corresponding ordinates vary directly as T^5. These two rules permit the construction of complete curves for all temperatures once any one is accurately known, but no further deductions can be made without making assumptions that are independent of any purely thermodynamic foundation. Wien deduced a formula (*Wien's formula*)

$$M_{e,\lambda} = c_1 \lambda^{-5} \exp(-c_2/\lambda T),$$

where $M_{e,\lambda}$ is the *radiant exitance for wavelength λ and c_1 and c_2 are constants. The formula is successful for short wavelengths, but it gives values somewhat too low for long wavelengths.

Rayleigh and Jeans applied the principle of equipartition of energy to a system of electromagnetic vibrations of different frequencies and gave

$$E_\lambda = CT\lambda^{-4}$$

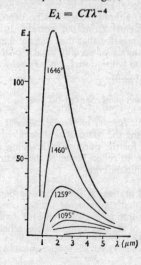

which is in agreement with experiment only for long wavelengths. Planck gave, by reasoning which formed the starting point of the quantum theory,

$$M_{e,\lambda} = \frac{C\lambda^{-5}}{(e^{hc/\lambda kT} - 1)},$$

in which C is equal to $2\pi hc^2$ and k and h are the Boltzmann and Planck constants. This formula, *Planck's formula*, agrees with experiment for all wavelengths. The total amount of energy of all wavelengths emitted by a black body is given by *Stefan's law, namely $M_e = \sigma T^4$ where σ is Stefan's constant.

black body temperature. The temperature of a body as measured by a (radiation) *pyrometer. It is usually appreciably less than the true temperature, T, of the body. For a temperature T_0 observed by a *total radiation pyrometer, $T_0^4 = \varepsilon T^4$ where ε is the emissivity of the source.

black hole. *Syn.* collapsar. An astronomical body with so high a gravitational field that the relativistic curving of space around it causes gravitational self-closure, i.e. a region is formed from which neither particles nor photons can escape, although they can be captured permanently from the outside. It has been suggested that they are the unseen companions of certain binary systems. *See also* white dwarf; pulsar; Schwarzschild radius.

black-out point. *See* cut-off bias.

blanket. A layer of *fertile material surrounding the *core of a nuclear reactor either for the purpose of breeding new fuel or to reflect some of the neutrons back into the core.

blazed grating. A diffraction grating so ruled that the reflected light is concentrated into a few, or even into a single order of the spectrum. *See also* echelette grating.

blink microscope. An instrument used to detect small differences in the *luminosity or position of stars between two photographs of the same part of the sky. The photographs are viewed alternately in rapid succession using a mechanical device.

Bloch's functions. The solutions of *Schrödinger's wave equation for an electron moving in a potential that varies periodically with distance. They have the form $\psi = u_k re^{ik.r}$, where u is a function depending on k, the wave vector, and k varies periodically with distance r; k has the same period as the potential and the lattice. Bloch's functions are used in the mathematical formulation of the band theory of solids (*see* energy bands).

Bloch wall. The transition layer, of finite thickness, between adjacent ferromagnetic *domains magnetized in different directions. It allows the spin directions to change slowly from one orientation to another, rather than abruptly.

blocking layer photocell. *See* rectifier photocell.

blocking oscillator. A type of oscillator in which, after completion of (usually) one cycle of oscillation, blocking (i.e. cessation of oscillation) takes place for a period of time determined by the circuit constants. The whole process is then repeated indefinitely. It has applications as a pulse generator or as a time-base generator and is fundamentally a special type of *squegging oscillator.

Blondel–Rey law. The apparent brilliance, B, of a light source, flashing at a frequency less than 5 hertz, is given by: $B = B_0 t/(t + a)$ where t is the duration of the flash, B_0 is the actual brilliance, and a is a constant. *Compare* Talbot's law.

blooming of lenses. The process of depositing a transparent film (about one quarter wavelength) of lower refractive index on the surface of a lens of higher index, whereby, through destructive interference, surface reflection is eliminated.

body-centred. The form of crystal structure in which the atoms occupy the centre of the lattice as well as the vertices.

body force. *See* force.

Bohr atom. *See* atom.

Bohr–Breit–Wigner theory. The theory that a *nuclear reaction occurs in two stages. In the first the colliding particle is captured by the nucleus to produce a new highly excited compound nucleus. In the second this compound nucleus emits one or more particles or gamma-ray photons to form a different nucleus.

Bohr magneton. *See* magneton.

boiling point. The temperature of a liquid at which visible evaporation occurs throughout the bulk of the liquid, and at which the vapour pressure of the liquid equals the external atmospheric pressure. It is the temperature at which liquid and vapour can exist together in equilibrium at a given pressure. *See also* Clausius–Clapeyron equation.

boiling-water reactor (BWR). A type of thermal *nuclear reactor in which water is used both as coolant and moderator, being allowed to boil by direct contact with the fuel elements.

bolometer. An instrument for the detection of radiant heat by means of the change of resistance of platinum strips when heated. For total radiation measurements the surface bolometer is used, while for measuring the distribution of energy in the spectrum of a *black body a linear bolometer is used. The surface bolometer consists of very thin (10^{-3} mm), blackened strips of platinum arranged in series on an insulating former to give a resistance of about 60 ohms. Two similar strips are used, in adjacent arms of a *Wheatstone bridge, one being exposed to the radiation and the other shielded. The change in resistance of the exposed strip is estimated from the deflection of the galvanometer in the bridge circuit: a temperature change of 10^{-7} °C can be observed. The linear bolometer consists of a single narrow very thin strip of platinum suitably mounted.

Boltzmann constant. Symbol: k. A constant equal to R/L, where R is the *universal gas constant and L is the *Avogadro constant. It has the value $1 \cdot 380\ 622 \times 10^{-23}$ J K^{-1}.

Boltzmann entropy hypothesis. *See* entropy.

Boltzmann's formula. A formula showing the number of particles (N) having an energy (E) in a system of particles in thermal equilibrium. It has the form $N = N_0\,e^{-E/kT}$, where N_0 is the number of particles having the lowest energy, k the Boltzmann constant, and T the thermodynamic temperature.

If the particles can only have certain fixed energies, such as the energy levels of *atoms, then the formula gives the number of particles (N_1) in a state at an energy (E_1) above the *ground state energy. In certain cases several distinct states may have the same energy and the formula then becomes:

$$N_1 = g_1 N_0\,e^{-E_1/kT},$$

where g_1 is the *statistical weight of the level of energy E_1, i.e. the number of states having energy E_1. The distribution of energies obtained by the formula is called a *Boltzmann distribution*.

bomb calorimeter. A device used for measuring the heat evolved by the combustion of a fuel.

bond energy. The energy required to break a chemical bond between two

45

atoms in a molecule. The bond energy depends on the type of atoms and on the nature of the molecule.

bonding pad. Metal pads usually arranged around the edge of a semiconductor *chip on which wires may be bonded to make electrical connection to the component(s) or circuit(s) on the chip.

booster. (1) A generator connected in series with an electric circuit to enable the voltage acting in the circuit to be increased (positive booster) or decreased (negative booster). Positive boosters are commonly used to compensate for the voltage drop which occurs in *feeders. A *booster transformer* is a *transformer having its secondary winding connected in series with the main circuit to perform the functions of a booster. (2) In broadcasting, a repeater station that receives the signal transmitted from a main station, amplifies it, and then retransmits it, sometimes with a change in frequency.

bootstrap theory (From the phrase, 'pulling oneself up by the bootstraps'). A theory that leads to or is concerned with the self-consistency of a more enveloping theory. The fact that all *hadrons can take part in *strong interactions either as initial and final particles or as the exchanged particle responsible for the interaction 'force' provides self-consistency constraints on the *scattering amplitudes describing such reactions. Theories which attempt to satisfy these constraints are known as bootstrap theories.

A *bootstrap device* or *circuit* can operate independently and self-sufficiently: an example is an electronic amplifier that uses its output voltage to bias its input.

boron chamber. An *ionization chamber lined with boron or boron compounds or filled with boron trifluoride gas.

boron counter. A radiation counter that uses a nuclear reaction with boron-10 for the detection of slow neutrons.

Bose–Einstein statistics and distribution law. *See* quantum statistics.

boson. Any *elementary particle having integral *spin. Bosons obey Bose–Einstein statistics (*see* quantum statistics). All particles are either bosons or *fermions: photons and *mesons are bosons.

Bouguer's law. *See* linear absorption coefficient.

boundary layer. If a fluid of low viscosity (air, water) has a relative motion with respect to solid boundaries, then at a large distance from the boundaries the frictional factors are negligible with regard to the inertia factors while near the boundaries the frictional factors are appreciable.

The fluid may be divided into two parts: first, a thin layer of fluid close to the solid boundaries in which the viscosity of the fluid is of major importance – this layer is called the boundary layer; secondly, the portion of the fluid that remains outside this boundary layer within which the fluid may be considered as non-viscid. It can be shown that the thickness of the boundary layer is directly proportional to $\sqrt{v}$ where v is the *kinematic viscosity and that the normal pressure on the solid boundary is unaltered by the presence of the boundary layer.

Bourdon tube (and gauge). A curved tube of oval cross section with the longer diameter of the oval perpendicular to the plane in which the tube is curved. If the volume of the tube is made to increase (by an excess pressure inside), the oval cross section becomes more nearly circular and the tube tends to straighten out. It is used (*a*) in a *thermograph. The tube is closed at both ends and completely filled with a liquid. The liquid expands more than the tube material with increase in temperature and causes the tube to straighten out. One end of the tube is fixed and the other, connected to a tracing point, draws a graph of temperature against time on a slowly moving surface. (*b*) In a *pressure gauge. The tube is closed at one end and the pressure applied at the other. One end of the tube is fixed and the other operates a pointer which indicates the pressure on a calibrated dial. A series of these gauges can be used from vacuum to several hundred atmospheres.

Boyle's law. If a given mass of gas is compressed at constant temperature, the product of the pressure and volume remains constant. The law is found to be only approximately true for real gases, being exactly fulfilled only at very low pressures. An *ideal gas by definition obeys Boyle's law exactly.

Boyle temperature. In order to represent the behaviour of a real gas it is necessary to use an *equation of state of the form

$$pv = A + Bp + Cp^2 + Dp^3 + Ep^4,$$

where A, B, C, D, E, etc. are the virial coefficients.

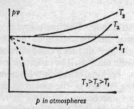

Boyle temperature

Of these B is the most important, and for all gases it varies with temperature in a similar way. At low temperatures B has large negative values. As the temperature is increased, the value of B increases through zero to positive values. The temperature for which B is zero is known as the Boyle temperature.

The coefficients C, D, E, etc., are all small compared with B, and are significant only at very high pressures. Consequently at the Boyle temperature the gas

obeys *Boyle's law almost exactly. Thus, in the diagram the *isothermal at the Boyle temperature, T_3, when plotting (pv) against p is approximately horizontal.

Boys' radiomicrometer. A thermocouple and moving coil galvanometer combined to make a sensitive detector of radiant energy. A single antimony–bismuth junction is connected directly to a moving coil. Usually a small blackened platinum disc is fixed to the junction as a collector for radiation.

Brackett series. *See* hydrogen spectrum.

Bragg's law. If a parallel beam of *X-rays, wavelength λ, strikes a set of crystal planes it is reflected from the different planes, *interference occurring between X-rays reflected from adjacent planes.

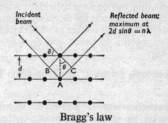

Bragg's law

Bragg's law states that constructive interference takes place when the difference in pathlength, BAC, is equal to an integral number of wavelengths: $2d \sin \theta = n\lambda$ where n is an integer. The angle θ is called the *Bragg angle* and a bright spot will be obtained on an interference pattern at this angle. A dark spot will be obtained if $2d \sin \theta = m\lambda$, where m is half-integral. The structure of a crystal can be determined from a set of interference patterns found at various angles from the different crystal faces.

branch and branch point. Of an electrical network. *See* network.

branching. The occurrence of competing

decay processes (*branches*) in the *disintegration of a particular radioisotope. The ratio of the number of disintegrating nuclei that follow a particular branch of a decay process to the total number of disintegrating nuclei of a radioisotope is the *branching fraction*.

brass. *See* alloy.

Bravais lattice. An indefinitely repetitive arrangement of points in space that fulfils the condition that the environment of each point is identical to that of every other point. There are fourteen such arrangements. *See* crystal systems.

breakdown. (1) A sudden disruptive electrical discharge through an insulator or between the electrodes of a vacuum or gas-filled valve. (2) A sudden transition from high dynamic resistance in a semiconductor device to substantially lower dynamic resistance, for increasing magnitude of bias. The voltage at which breakdown occurs is called the *breakdown voltage*.

breakdown potential. *See* conduction in gases.

breaking-current. Of a *switch, *circuit-breaker or similar apparatus. Current that is broken on one pole (*see* number of poles) at the instant when the contacts separate. The following terms are applicable when the current is alternating: (i) Symmetrical breaking-current: the *root-mean-square value of only the a.c. component of the breaking-current. (ii) Asymmetrical breaking-current: the r.m.s. value of the total breaking-current including both the a.c. and d.c. components. The d.c. component is a transient which appears under fault conditions.

breeder reactor. A *nuclear reactor in which more fissile material is produced than is consumed. It is a *converter reactor in which the *conversion factor is greater than one. *See also* fast breeder reactor.

breeding. A process of nuclear transformation in which the *conversion factor is greater than one.

breeding ratio. The ratio of the number of fissionable atoms produced in a *breeder reactor to the number of fissionable atoms of the same kind that are destroyed. It is the *conversion factor when this exceeds one. The breeding ratio minus one is sometimes called the *breeding gain*.

Breit–Wigner formula. An equation giving the absorption *cross section, σ, of a particular nuclear reaction when the intermediate excited nucleus can decay in any of several ways. The cross section is a function of the energy, E, of the bombarding particle and when E is close to the energy E_c of the *compound nucleus,

$$\sigma = \frac{\sigma_0}{1 + (E - E_c)^2/(\Gamma/2)^2}$$

where σ_0 is the resonance *cross section and Γ is the width of the excited *energy level.

bremsstrahlung. Electromagnetic radiation produced by the rapid deceleration of an electron during a close approach to an atomic nucleus. The radiative loss due to this 'braking effect' increases rapidly with the energy of the electron, and for energies exceeding 150 MeV is responsible for most of the absorption of the electron's energy. The energy lost at each encounter is radiated as a single photon. Bremsstrahlung radiation forms an important constituent of *cosmic rays and is the continuous radiation that occurs in the production of *X-rays by electron bombardment. *See also* synchrotron radiation.

Brewster angle. *See* polarizing angle.

Brewster's law. *See* plane polarized light; polarizing angle.

Brewster window. A reflecting surface used in certain gas *lasers to reduce reflection losses that would arise from using external mirrors. The surfaces are set at the Brewster angle to the incident light. *See* polarizing angle.

bridge. A circuit made up of electrical elements (e.g. resistances, inductances, capacitors, rectifiers, etc.) arranged in the form of a quadrilateral. Two opposite corners of the quadrilateral are made the input and the other pair the output of the circuit. (*See* bridge rectifier.) Bridges are most commonly used in a variety of measuring instruments in which the output is connected to a current detector and the circuit adjusted until the bridge is balanced and no current is detected. In this way an unknown resistance, capacitance, or inductance can be compared with known standards.

bridge rectifier. A *full-wave rectifier consisting of a *bridge with a rectifier in each arm.

Bridge rectifier

Bridgman effect. The absorption or liberation of heat arising from a nonuniform current distribution which occurs when an electric current passes through an *anisotropic crystal.

Brillouin function. Symbol: B_J. The magnetization of a paramagnetic substance can be expressed by the equation: $M = NgJ\mu_BB_J(x)$, where N is the number of atoms per unit volume, g the *Landé factor, J is the magnetic moment *quantum number, and μ_B the Bohr *magneton. x is given by the expression $gJ\mu_BH/kT$, where H is the magnetic field

strength and T the thermodynamic temperature. The Brillouin function is expressed by the equation:

$$B_J = \frac{2J+1}{2J} \coth\left[\frac{(2J+1)x}{2J}\right] - \frac{1}{2J}\coth\frac{x}{2J}.$$

Brillouin zone. If *Schrödinger's equations for electronic energies are solved with a periodic function $u(k)$ to give the energies of an electron in a solid, the solutions fall into permitted bands (*see* energy bands). If the solutions are plotted in the *reciprocal lattice of the crystal being considered, the zones enclosing the solutions for $k = 1, 2, \ldots n$, are called Brillouin zones.

Brinell test. *See* hardness.

British thermal unit (btu). The amount of heat required to raise the temperature of 1 lb of water by 1° F. The International Tables btu equals 1055·06 J or 251·997 calories.

broadside array. *See* aerial array.

Broca galvanometer. An instrument having an *astatic system formed by two magnets, capable of movement, each with a *consequent pole in the middle. The coil of many turns of wire carrying the current encloses the consequent poles.

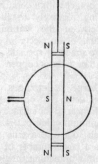

Broca galvanometer

The arrangement combines a large magnetic moment with a small moment of inertia, and thus gives a high sensitivity with a reasonably small period.

Bronson resistance. An *ionization chamber enclosing a constant source of ionization, usually a layer of uranium oxide. If the potential difference between the electrodes is small compared with that required for saturation, the ionization current is approximately proportional to the applied p.d., and the system acts as a high resistance. The resistance can be increased by decreasing the activity of the source employed.

bronze. *See* alloy.

Brownian movement. The unceasing and irregular motion of small particles about 1 μm in diameter, such as pollen grains, when held in suspension in a liquid. It is a visible demonstration of molecular bombardment by the molecules of the liquid. (*See* kinetic theory.) The smaller the suspended particles the more noticeable the motion. It can also be observed in particles of smoke.

Brownian motion sets a theoretical imit to the sensitivity of a chemical balance at 10^{-9} g and similarly sets a limit to galvanometer measurements of currents at 10^{-22} A.

brush. A conductor that serves to provide electrical contact with a conducting surface moving relatively to the brush, usually between the stationary and moving parts of an electrical machine. Brushes are made of specially prepared carbon with or without copper.

brush discharge. A luminous discharge from a conductor that occurs when the electric field near to the surface exceeds a certain minimum value but is not sufficiently high to cause a true spark. It appears as a large number of intermittent luminous branching threads, penetrating some distance into the gas surrounding the conductor, the distance being greater for an anode than for a cathode at the same potential. A non-uniform field is essential for the effect.

bubble chamber. An instrument in which the tracks of an ionizing particle are made visible as a row of tiny bubbles in rounding the conductor, the distance the liquid inside a large chamber. The liquid, usually hydrogen, helium, or deuterium, is maintained under pressure so that it can be heated without boiling to a temperature slightly above its normal boiling point. Immediately before the passage of a particle, the pressure is reduced, and the liquid would normally boil after about 50 milliseconds. However, the release of energy resulting from ionization of atoms along the track of the moving particle causes rapid localized boiling along this path. After about 1 ms, the bubbles are big enough to photograph and a record is obtained of the particle's track and that of any decay or reaction products. The pressure in the chamber is then increased again to prevent the bulk of the liquid from boiling.

bucket-brigade device. *See* charge-transfer device.

buckling. A constant that is a measure of the curvature of the *neutron flux distribution inside a nuclear reactor.

buffer. An isolating circuit used to minimize reaction between two circuits. Usually it has a high input *impedance and low output impedance. An *emitter follower is an example.

bulk lifetime. The average time interval between the generation and recombination of *minority carriers in the bulk material of a *semiconductor.

bulk modulus. *See* modulus of elasticity.

bumping. In the absence of nuclei, bubbles do not form until the temperature of a liquid is above the boiling point so that when formed the vapour pressure inside the bubbles greatly exceeds the applied pressure. The consequent rapid expansion of the bubbles causes violent motion (bumping) of the containing vessel. Small pieces of porous pot placed in the liquid, by providing nuclei, prevent this occurring.

bunching. *See* velocity modulation.

Bunsen burner. A gas burner in which a regulated amount of air mixes with the gas stream at the bottom of the tube of the burner, the flame being at the top. The air is drawn in by the suction effect of the fine gas jet, a consequence of *Bernouilli's theorem.

Bunsen cell. A primary cell, much used before the introduction of accumulators. The negative pole is an amalgamated zinc rod immersed in dilute sulphuric acid in a porous pot. The positive pole is a plate of hard gas carbon immersed in strong nitric acid, which serves as the depolarizer. The e.m.f. is about 1·9 volt.

Bunsen ice calorimeter. A calorimeter for measuring the specific heat capacity of a solid or liquid of which only a small quantity is available.

buoyancy. Archimedes' principle states that if a body is wholly or partly immersed in a fluid, it experiences an upward force equal to the weight of the fluid which would fill the space occupied by the immersed part of the body. This force, the buoyancy, acts through the centre of gravity of that fluid which would replace the immersed part of the body and this point is the *centre of buoyancy* of the body. The plane in which the liquid surface intersects the stationary floating body is the *plane of flotation*. For the body to be in equilibrium (*a*) the upthrust must be equal to the weight of the body, (*b*) the centre of gravity of the body and the centre of buoyancy must be in the same vertical line.

burden. The load connected across the secondary terminals of an instrument transformer under specified conditions, usually expressed in *volt-amperes.

burn-up. The significant reduction in the quantity of one or more *nuclides arising from neutron absorption in a *nuclear reactor. The term can be applied to fuel or other materials.

busbar. *Syn.* bus, busline. Generally, any conductor of low *impedance or high current-carrying capability relative to other connections in a system. It is usually used to connect many like points in a system, as when an earth bus is used.

bypass capacitor. A *capacitor connected in a circuit in order to provide a path of comparatively low *impedance for alternating current. The frequency of the a.c. passed depends on the magnitude of the capacitance. Such a capacitor effectively short-circuits the a.c. components and is commonly used in parallel with a resistor either to supply d.c. voltage to a point in the circuit, or to separate out a desired a.c. component.

byte. In computer technology: (1) A sequence of *bits processed as a unit. (2) A subdivision of a *word. (3) The storage space allocated to one character.

C

cadmium cell. *See* Weston standard cell.

cadmium ratio. Symbol: R_{Cd}. The ratio of the neutron-induced radioactivity in a sample to the radioactivity induced under identical conditions when the sample is covered with cadmium, which has a high capture cross section for thermal neutrons. For large values of the ratio, it is therefore a measure of the ratio of *thermal to *fast neutrons.

cadmium sulphide cell. A compact photoconductive cell (*see* photoconductivity) consisting of a layer of cadmium sulphide sandwiched between two electrodes. The high electrical resistance of the CdS drops when light falls on the cell. A current flowing through the cell will vary according to the amount of incident light. A battery is required to provide the current. The cell is used in *exposure meters and cameras. It has a much higher sensitivity than the *selenium cell.

caesium clock. *See* clocks.

calculus of variations. A mathematical method for solving those physical problems that can be stated in the form that a certain definite integral shall have a stationary value for small changes of the functions in the integrand and of the limits of integration. Such problems include: (1) determination of conditions of equilibrium from the *least energy principle; (2) determination of the path of a ray of light from *Fermat's principle of stationary time; (3) solution of dynamical problems by means of *Hamilton's principle.

calender year. *See* time.

calibration. Determination of the absolute values of the arbitrary indications of an instrument.

Callendar's compensated air thermometer. A *constant pressure gas thermometer in which the error due to the gas in the connecting tube and the manometer being at a different temperature from

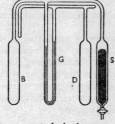

Compensated air thermometer

that in the bulb of the thermometer is eliminated. The pressure of the air in the thermometer bulb B is kept equal to that of the air in the bulb D by altering the amount of mercury in the reservoir S until the levels of the sulphuric acid in the manometer G are equal. The bulb D carries a tube equal in size and in close proximity to the tube connecting B to S. If D and S are immersed in melting ice then the thermodynamic temperature of the bulb B is given by $T = T_0[b/(d - s)]$ where b, d, and s are the volumes of air in B, D, and S respectively.

calomel electrode. A *half-cell consisting of a mercury electrode in contact with a solution of potassium chloride saturated with calomel (mercurous chloride, Hg_2Cl_2). It is used as a reference electrode in physical chemistry.

caloric theory. The theory of the nature of heat widely held up to 1800, according to which heat was an imponderable, self-repellant fluid, caloric. It was unable to account for the production of an unlimited supply of heat by friction and was abandoned when Joule showed that heat was a form of energy.

calorie. A unit of heat energy no longer employed in scientific calculations. Formerly defined as the quantity of heat required to raise the temperature of one gramme of water from 14·5° C to 15·5° C at standard pressure: now defined as 4·1868 joules.

calorific value. The amount of heat liberated by the complete combustion of unit mass of a fuel, the water formed being assumed to condense to the liquid state. The determination is carried out in a *bomb calorimeter and the value is usually expressed in J kg^{-1} or similar units.

calorimeter. Any vessel or apparatus in which quantitative thermal measurements may be made. The simplest form, used for the *method of mixtures, consists of a copper can containing water and resting on insulating feet inside a water jacket at a definite temperature. Through an insulating lid, used to prevent evaporation, passes a thermometer to record the temperature changes of the water in the copper can, together with a stirrer.

calorimetry. The study of the measurement of quantities of heat. It is used to determine *specific heat capacities, *specific latent heats, *calorific values of fuels, and heats of combustion, reaction, and solution.

calutron. An electromagnetic separator of isotopes, based on the principle of the *mass spectrometer. It has been used to separate the fissile radioisotope uranium-235 from uranium-238.

camera lucida. A microscope accessory for attachment at the eyepiece end, whereby an image is projected in the plane of drawing paper, permitting the simultaneous view of a hand-manipulated pencil to draw the outline.

camera tube. Most camera tubes used in *television cameras are either *image*

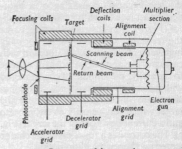

a Image orthicon tube

orthicon or *vidicon tubes* or improvements on these basic types.

In the image orthicon tube (Fig. *a*), an image is produced on a *photocathode, which emits electrons in proportion to the intensity of the incident light. These electrons are focused onto the target area causing it to emit *secondary electrons. The secondary electrons are drained off to a power supply leaving a positive static charge pattern corresponding to the original light image. A low-velocity electron beam is used to scan the target; the positive charges are neutralized by electrons taken from the beam, which becomes density modulated in proportion to the original video information.

The *vidicon tube* is smaller, simpler, and cheaper than the image orthicon and is widely used for outside broadcasts. A light image is formed on the photoconductive target area of the tube. This may be considered as a large number of

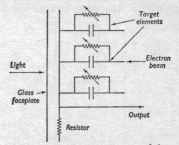
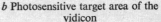

b Photosensitive target area of the vidicon

discrete elements consisting of a light-dependent resistor with a parallel capacitor (Fig. *b*). If light strikes the target area the resistance drops below its normally high value. Charge may be stored in each capacitor by applying a positive voltage to the array; the amount of charge stored will depend on the resistance. The capacitors are discharged by scanning the target with a low-velocity electron beam and a current flows out of the target (Fig. *c*). The current is a function of the charge stored and hence the illumination.

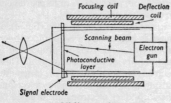

c Vidicon tube

The *Plumbicon* is a development of the vidicon, the photoconductive layer being replaced by a *semiconductor. The target elements are essentially semiconductor current sources controlled by light illumination. Such tubes have very low dark current and good sensitivity and light transfer characteristics. *See also* colour television.

Campbell's bridge. A *bridge for comparing a mutual inductance with a capacitance. The usual arrangement is

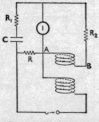

Campbell's bridge

illustrated in the diagram. I is an indicating instrument, such as a microphone or *oscilloscope, L the self inductance of the coil between A and B, and M the mutual inductance of the pair of coils. The resistances are varied until the bridge is balanced, when:

$$\frac{L}{M} = \frac{R + R_1}{R} \text{ and } \frac{M}{C} = RR_2.$$

Canada balsam. A viscous transparent resin used as a cement for optical elements, prisms, and lenses; refractive index: 1·55.

candela. Symbol: cd. The *SI unit of *luminous intensity, defined as the luminous intensity, in the perpendicular direction, of a surface of 1/600 000 square metre of a *black body at the temperature of freezing platinum under a pressure of 101 325 newtons per metre squared. This unit is sometimes called the *new candle*.

candle. *See* international candle.

candle power. Former name for *luminous intensity.

canonical distribution. A term used in *statistical mechanics, expressed by

$$f = A \exp \left(-\text{energy}/\Theta\right)$$
$$\mathrm{d}p_1 \ldots \mathrm{d}p_n \, \mathrm{d}q_1 \ldots \mathrm{d}q_n,$$

in which f means the fraction of the systems in an assemblage (molecules in a gas for example) whose momenta lie between $p_1 \ldots p_n$ and $p_1 + \mathrm{d}p_1 \ldots p_n + \mathrm{d}p_n$ and whose associated coordinates lie between $q_1 \ldots q_n$ and $q_1 + \mathrm{d}q_1 \ldots q_n + \mathrm{d}q_n$. A is a constant and Θ is the modulus of the distribution. The modulus, Θ, can be identified with kT, the product of the *Boltzmann constant and the thermodynamic temperature. Maxwell's law of *distribution of velocities among the molecules in a gas is a limiting case of a canonical distribution.

canonical ensemble. *See* statistical mechanics.

canonical equations. Equations of classical mechanics as expressed in the form of *Hamilton's equations, namely

$$\mathrm{d}p_i/\mathrm{d}t = -\partial H/\partial q_i;\ \mathrm{d}q_i/\mathrm{d}t = \partial H/\partial p_i,$$

p_i and q_i being respectively the momenta and associated coordinates, while H is the energy of the system expressed as a function of p_i, q_i and time.

capacitance. Symbol: C. The property of an isolated *conductor, or set of conductors and *insulators, to store electric charge. If a charge Q is placed on an isolated conductor, the voltage is increased by an amount V. The capacitance of the conductor is defined as Q/V; for a given conductor it is independent of Q and depends on the size and shape of the conductor. Two conductors together form a *capacitor and the capacitance C is defined as the ratio of charge on either conductor to the potential difference between them. The unit of capacitance is the *farad. *See also* mutual capacitance.

capacitive coupling. *See* coupling.

capacitive reactance. *See* reactance.

capacitive tuning. *See* tuned circuit.

capacitor. An arrangement of one or more pairs of conductors separated by insulators between which an electric field can be produced. The conductors are arranged so as to produce an appreciable *capacitance, sometimes of a specified value. The conductors are called electrodes or plates, and the insulator is called the *dielectric. The dielectric may be solid, liquid, or gaseous.

Symbols:

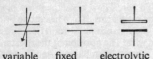

variable   fixed   electrolytic

capacitor microphone. A type of microphone consisting essentially of a diaphragm forming one plate of a capacitor, the other plate being fixed. Movement of the diaphragm caused by sound pressure variations alters the capacitance of the capacitor. The narrow air gap is usually

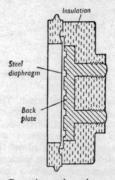

Capacitor microphone

sealed from the outside air. The microphone is connected in series with a high resistance across a steady potential difference of about 300 v. Changes in capacitance thus produce corresponding changes of potential difference across the capacitor. The microphone has no background noise and is a high quality instrument with a good frequency response. Its output, however, is low and it has directional effects.

capillarity. A term to describe the effects of *surface tension. the most prominent of these effects being the rise or fall of liquids in vertical capillary tubes. The elevation of a liquid in a capillary tube is given by *Juvin's rule.

capillary electrometer. An electrolytic cell, one electrode of which is a pool of mercury A, while the other is the meniscus B of a thread of mercury in a capillary tube, CD. If a potential difference is applied to the electrodes, a small charging current flows through the cell, producing *polarization at the meniscus

B. (The polarization at A is negligible on account of its much greater area.) The electric field due to this polarization alters the *surface tension of the mercury and the meniscus, therefore, moves to a

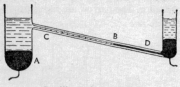

Capillary electrometer

new position of equilibrium. The apparatus is very sensitive, but cannot be used to measure potential differences greater than 0·9 volt. The movement of the mercury is not strictly proportional to the applied p.d., and the electrometer is most conveniently used as a null instrument.

capture. Any process by which an atom, ion, molecule, or nucleus acquires an additional particle. *Radiative capture* involves the emission by a nucleus of *capture gamma rays* immediately following a capture, by a nucleus, of one of its orbital electrons. The process is $p + e \rightarrow n + \nu$, the neutrino ($\nu$) being emitted. Usually the K-shell electron is captured in this process (*K-capture*) although other shells are sometimes involved.

The capture of an electron into an orbit of an atom, molecule, or ion is called electron attachment.

Carathéodory's principle. A theorem in thermodynamics that can be used to derive the second law, without making reference to thermodynamic cycles. It states that it is impossible to reach every state in the neighbourhood of any arbitrary initial state by means of adiabatic processes only.

carbon cycle. A cycle of six *nuclear reactions resulting in the formation of

one helium nucleus from four hydrogen nuclei:

$$^1_1H + ^{12}_6C \rightarrow ^{13}_7N$$
$$^{13}_7N \rightarrow ^{13}_6C + ^0_1e$$
$$^1_1H + ^{13}_6C \rightarrow ^{14}_7N$$
$$^1_1H + ^{14}_7N \rightarrow ^{15}_8O$$
$$^{15}_8O \rightarrow ^{15}_7N + ^0_1e$$
$$^1_1H + ^{15}_7N \rightarrow ^{12}_6C + ^4_2He$$

The carbon-12 is reformed at the end of the cycle and therefore acts as a catalyst. This cycle is believed to be the source of energy in some stars. *See* thermonuclear reaction.

carbon-14 dating. *See* dating.

carbon microphone. A device making use of the variation of electrical resistance of carbon with the applied pressure. When two surfaces of carbon blocks are touching, their total area of contact is made up of a large number of very small areas. The number of these contact points increases with the sound pressure applied to the two surfaces and so the electrical resistance is reduced.

Cardew voltmeter. *See* hot-wire ammeter.

cardinal points. *See* centred optical systems.

cardioid condenser. An aplanatic microscope condenser for dark ground illumination, using reflection first at a spherical surface and then at a cardioid (heart-shaped) surface; the latter is sometimes replaced by a spherical surface since only a small portion is used at any time.

Carey–Foster bridge. A modification of the *Wheatstone bridge designed to measure the difference in resistance between two nearly equal resistances in terms of the resistance per cm of the bridge wire. Two resistances are placed in the ratio arms of a Wheatstone bridge and the balance point found on a resistance wire. The position of the resistances are then interchanged and a new balance point found; the distance between the points on the resistance wire is proportional to the difference between the resistances. If the resistance wire has been precalibrated the difference in length is equal to the difference between the resistances.

Carnot–Clausius equation. For a reversible closed cycle (*see* reversible change), the total change in the *entropy of the system, dq/T, is zero; dq is the quantity of heat taken in by the system during an infinitesimal reversible change of state and T is the absolute temperature of the system during this change.

Carnot cycle. A reversible cycle in which the working substance is compressed

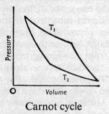

Carnot cycle

adiabatically from T_2 to T_1, expands at T_1 isothermally, then expands adiabatically from T_1 to T_2 and finally is compressed isothermally at T_2. This brings the pressure, volume and temperature back to their initial values. It represents the cycle of the ideal heat engine. *See* thermodynamics.

Carnot's theorem. No engine can be more efficient than a reversible engine working between the same temperatures. Hence all reversible engines working between the same temperatures are equally efficient, the efficiency being independent of the nature of the working substance, depending only on these temperatures. *See* thermodynamics.

carrier. (1) An electron or *hole that can move through a metal or *semiconduc-

tor. Carriers enable charge to be transported through a solid and are responsible for conductivity. *See also* majority carrier; minority carrier. (2) A substance used to provide a bulk quantity of material containing traces of *radioisotopes for use in physical and chemical operations. (3) A carrier wave.

carrier wave. The wave, usually of radio frequency, whose characteristics are modified in the process of *modulation. The carrier wave is modulated in accordance with a characteristic of another wave or signal, called the *modulating wave*, usually of audio frequency. The resultant signal is the *modulated wave*.

Cartesian sign convention. *See* optics sign conventions.

cascade. (1) A number of *capacitors are said to be connected in cascade (or in series) if the outer plate of the first capacitor is connected to the inner plate of the next, and so on. All the plates are insulated except the last. The *capacitance of the compound capacitor is given by

$$1/C = 1/C_1 + 1/C_2 + \ldots$$

The charges on all the capacitors are equal. (2) A chain of electronic circuits or elements connected in series, so that the output of one is the input of the next.

cascade liquefaction. A method of liquefaction in which a gas, such as methyl chloride, with a high critical temperature is liquefied by increase of pressure, and evaporation of this liquid cools a second gas, such as ethylene, below its critical temperature so that it too may be liquefied by increase of pressure. The liquid ethylene evaporates under reduced pressure at about $-160°C$ in the jacket 3 (*see* diagram), in which oxygen is cooled and liquefied under pressure, being collected in the Dewar vessel D. Neither hydrogen nor helium can be liquefied by this method since

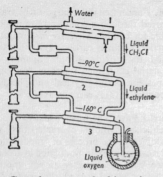

Cascade process of refrigeration

their critical temperatures (33° K and 5·2° K) cannot be reached in this way.

cascade shower. *See* cosmic rays.

Cassegrainian or Cassegrain telescope. *See* reflecting telescope.

catadioptric system. A reflective optical system involving mirrors, etc. *Compare* dioptric system.

cataphoresis. *See* electrophoresis.

catching diode. *Syn.* clamping diode. A semiconductor *diode used at some point in a circuit to prevent the voltage going above or falling below a specific value. A diode will start to conduct at a well-defined forward voltage, typically 0·7 V, and will therefore prevent the voltage applied in the forward direction from rising above this value. Two diodes may be used together to keep the voltage within specified limits.

cathetometer. A device for measuring vertical heights consisting of a vertical scale along which a horizontally mounted telescope or microscope may be moved.

cathode. The negative electrode of an electrolytic cell, discharge tube, or valve. It is the electrode by which elec-

trons enter a system. *See also* thermionic cathode.

cathode follower. A radio circuit in which the load is in the cathode circuit of a valve instead of, as is usual, in the anode circuit. The cathode follower cannot act as a voltage amplifier but can be used as a current amplifier over a wide frequency range. The output voltage remains in phase with the input voltage; the input impedance is very high but the output impedance very low.

cathode-ray oscilloscope (CRO). An instrument that enables a variety of electrical signals to be examined visually. Any variable that can be converted into an electrical signal can be studied. The signal of interest is fed, after amplification, on to one set of deflection plates of a *cathode-ray tube, usually the vertical deflection plates. The beam is moved horizontally across the screen by the voltage from a sweep generator (usually called a *time-base generator) incorporated in the oscilloscope. The resultant trace seen on the screen is a composite of the two voltages, and suitable choice of sweep speed in the horizontal direction allows easy visualization of the input signal. The simplest type of time base is a constantly variable sweep generator producing a *sawtooth waveform, so that the trace moves slowly and uniformly across the screen, then returns almost instantaneously to the starting point. A more sophisticated type of sweep-trigger circuit may be employed when the sweep is initiated by an external trigger pulse (often the presented signal), so that each sweep is started in synchronism with the trigger pulse.

Extra facilities usually found on a modern CRO include a delayed trigger, access to the X-deflection plates allowing an external time base or other modulating signal to be used, and often facilities for beam intensity modulation.

cathode rays. *See* gas-discharge tube.

cathode-ray tube (CRT). A funnel-shaped electronic tube that permits the visual observation of electrical signals. A CRT always includes an *electron gun for producing a beam of electrons, a grid to control the intensity of the electron beam and thus the brightness of the display, and a luminescent screen to convert the electron beam into visible light. *Focusing of the beam of electrons and the deflection of the beam according to the electrical signal of interest may be done either electrostatically or electromagnetically, or by a combination of both methods. In general, electrostatic deflection is employed when high frequency waves are to be displayed, as in most *cathode-ray oscilloscopes, and electromagnetic deflection is employed when high-velocity electron beams are required to give a bright display, as in *television or *radar receivers.

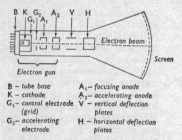

B – tube base
K – cathode
G_1 – control electrode (grid)
G_2 – accelerating electrode

A_1 – focusing anode
A_2 – accelerating anode
V – vertical deflection plates
H – horizontal deflection plates

a Electrostatic focusing and deflection

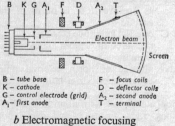

B – tube base
K – cathode
G – control electrode (grid)
A_1 – first anode

F – focus coils
D – deflector coils
A_2 – second anode
T – terminal

b Electromagnetic focusing and deflection

cation. An ion that having lost one or more electrons has a net positive charge and thus moves towards the cathode of an electrolytic cell.

catoptric power. Of a mirror. *See* power.

Cauchy dispersion formula. A formula for the dispersion of light of the form: $n = A + (B/\lambda^2) + (C/\lambda^4)$, where n is the refractive index, λ the wavelength, and A, B, and C are constants. It gives a reasonable agreement with experiment for many substances over limited regions of the spectrum. Sometimes only the first two terms are necessary.

causality. The principle that every effect is a consequence of an antecedent cause or causes. For causality to be true it is not necessary for an effect to be predictable as the antecedent causes may be too numerous, too complicated, or too interrelated for analysis.

According to the *uncertainty principle, however, events on the sub-atomic scale are neither predictable nor can they be shown to obey causal laws. If both the position and momentum of an electron, say, cannot be established precisely, consecutive observations of what may be thought of as the same electron may in fact be observation of two different electrons. Therefore individual particles cannot be identified. In *quantum theory the classical certainty of causality is replaced by probabilities that specific particles exist in specific positions and take part in specific events.

caustic curve (and surface). Rays in a meridian plane from an object after reflection or refraction at spherical surfaces

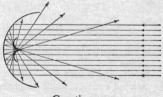

Caustic curve

59

in general do not focus at one point. Consecutive rays, moving away from the axis, intersect at points lying on a curved line (the caustic), possessing an apex or cusp lying at a paraxial focus. Reflected and refracted rays are tangential to the caustic.

cavity resonator. *Syn.* resonant cavity; rhumbatron. When suitably excited by external means, the space contained within a closed or substantially closed conducting surface will maintain an oscillating electromagnetic field, and the complete device, a cavity resonator, displays marked electrical resonance effects. It has several resonant frequencies which are determined by its dimensions: used in place of the more conventional types of resonant circuits at frequencies exceeding about 300 megahertz.

celestial mechanics. *See* astronomy.

celestial sphere. A sphere of infinite radius, with its centre at the centre of the earth E, that rotates once in 24 hours of sidereal *time: used for positional astronomy.

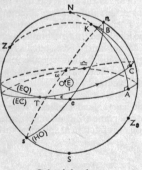

Celestial sphere

N   north celestial pole: point of projection of earth's north pole
S   south celestial pole
EQ   celestial equator: circle of projection of earth's equator

EC   ecliptic: circle of projection of apparent path of the sun around the earth; the sun moves anticlockwise as viewed from N
♈   first point of Aries: point of intersection of equator and ecliptic, where sun ascends north of equator; occurs at vernal equinox
♎   first point of Libra; occurs at autumnal equinox
ε obliquity of ecliptic: $23.4°$
O   observer on earth
Z   zenith: point of projection of O
Z_0 nadir
HO   horizon: great circle having Z, Z_0 as poles
n   north point (of horizon): point of intersection of ZN extended and horizon
s   south point
K   celestial object
BK   altitude (a) of K
nB   azimuth (k) of K: measured in degrees east of the north point
AK   declination (δ) of K: regarded as positive if K is north of the equator
♈A   right ascension (a) of K: measured in hours and minutes (24 hours $= 360°$) anticlockwise from ♈
ZNn   meridian for observer at 0: when K lies on meridian it is said to transit and to have an *hour angle* H of zero; H increases after transit, and is equal to the difference between local sidereal time and the right ascension of the body
CK   celestial latitude (β) of K: regarded as positive if K is north of the ecliptic
♈C   celestial longitude (λ) of K: measured in degrees anticlockwise from ♈
nN   altitude of north celestial pole, equal to terrestrial latitude of observer

For almost all astronomical observations, right ascension and declination coordinates are employed.

cell. (1) A pair of plates in an electrolyte from which electricity is derived by chemical action; a unit of a battery. A *primary cell* is one in which the current is produced directly from chemical action by the solution of one of the plates. Current can be drawn at once from a primary cell as soon as it is made. A *secondary cell* has to be 'charged' by passing a current through it in the reverse direction to its discharge, the chemical actions in the cell being reversible (*see* accumulator). The potential difference between the poles of a cell in a closed circuit depends on its internal resistance, and on the external resistance through which it is maintaining a current. The p.d. (u) between the terminals of a cell is given by $u = ER/(r + R)$, where E is the e.m.f. on open circuit, r is the internal resistance, and R the external resistance. *See* polarization. (2) *See* unit cell.

cell constant. The area of the electrodes in an electrolytic *cell divided by the distance between them.

Celsius scale. The official name (since 1948) of the centigrade temperature scale with the ice-point as $0°$ and the boiling point as $100°$. The degree Celsius (symbol: $°C$) is $1/100$ of this temperature interval and is equal in magnitude to the kelvin; on the International Practical Scale of Temperature (1968), temperatures are expressed in both kelvin and degrees Celsius.

cent. The interval equal to $1/1200$ of the interval of two frequencies having the ratio $2:1$, viz. the octave.

centi-. Symbol: c. The prefix meaning 10^{-2}, e.g. $1 \text{ cm} = 10^{-2}$ metre.

centigrade scale. *See* Celsius scale.

centrad. A small angle unit, one hundredth of a radian, used to specify angles of deviation of narrow angle prisms. *See* prism dioptre.

central force. A force on a moving body that is always directed towards a fixed point or towards a point moving according to known laws. The body is then in a *central orbit*.

central processing unit. *See* CPU.

centred optical systems. A system consisting of a number of spherical refracting or reflecting surfaces having their centres on a common axis. Gauss elucidated the properties of such systems in terms of certain constants – the *Gaussian points* or *constants*. Maxwell considered a perfect system in which there was complete point, line, and plane correspondence between object and image. Such correspondence is found in practice provided the rays forming the image are restricted to those passing near the axis of the system.

A ray AB (Fig. *a*) entering the (converging) system parallel to the axis will in general cross the axis after emergence at some point F' (the *second focal point*). Similarly the ray CD, at the same height

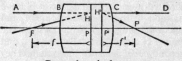

a Centred optical system

above the axis as AB, will have passed into the system after crossing the axis at some point such as F (the *first focal point*). The two incident rays shown fix an object point H for which the corresponding image point must be H'. The plane HP drawn through H perpendicular to the axis is the *first principal plane*. The plane H'P' similarly drawn through H' is the *second principal plane*. The principal planes thus have the properties of being *conjugate (object and image planes), and of yielding unit magnification (since HP = H'P'). P and P' are the first and second *principal points*.

The *first focal length* of the system, f,

is defined as the distance from the first principal point to the first focal point. The *second focal length*, f', is the distance P'F'. If there is the same medium on both sides of the system the two focal lengths are equal. If the media on the object and image side have different refractive indices n and n', then the relation between the numerical values of the focal lengths is that $n/f = n'/f'$.

Provided object distances are measured from the first principal plane and image distances from the second, the results of simple thin lens theory can be applied to any centred optical system. In a thin lens the principal planes coincide in the plane of the lens.

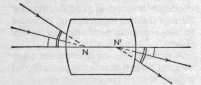

b Nodal points of centred optical system

In Fig. *b*, the rays entering the system directed towards the axial point N leave as though from the axial point N' and make the same angle with the axis. The points N and N' are called the first and second *nodal points* of the system. They are conjugate points of unit angular magnification. With the same medium on both sides of the system the principal points coincide with the nodal points.

The three pairs of points – focal, principal, and nodal – are called the *cardinal points* of the system. If the positions of the cardinal points of a system are known, the position, nature, and size of the image of any object can be calculated without reference to details of the system.

centre of area. *See* centroid.

centre of buoyancy. *See* buoyancy.

centre of curvature. *See* curvature.

centre of figure. *Syn.* centre of volume. *See* centroid.

centre of gravity. (1) Of a body in a uniform gravitational field (e.g. a body small compared with the earth in the earth's gravitational field). The force on the body (its weight) is the resultant of the forces on the individual particles. As these forces are all parallel, their resultant passes through a particular point fixed with respect to, but not necessarily on, the body. This point is the centre of gravity and it coincides with the *centre of mass of the body. (2) Of a body in a non-uniform gravitational field. The forces on the particles of the body (no longer a system of parallel forces) are reducible, in general, to a single force and a couple. This single force does not, in general, pass through a single point fixed with respect to the body, as the body is turned in the field. If the matter in the body is distributed with spherical symmetry, the couple reduces to zero and the force always passes through the centre of mass; only such a body has a centre of gravity in a non-uniform field, and is said to be *centrobaric* or *barycentric*.

centre of inertia. *See* centre of mass.

centre of mass. *Syn.* centroid; barycentre; centre of inertia. A point such that if any plane passes through it, the sum of the products of the masses of the constituent particles by their perpendicular distances from the plane (the sum of the *mass moments*) is zero. In common usage, centre of mass and *centre of gravity are synonymous since when the latter exists it coincides with the former.

centre of pressure. The point on a plane surface, immersed in a fluid, at which the resultant pressure on the surface may be taken to act. If the surface is horizontal the centre of pressure coincides with the *centre of gravity; otherwise it is below the centre of gravity but gets nearer to it as the liquid depth increases. (It is defined with respect to a plane area because the system of forces on a curved area is not always reducible to a single force.) *See* buoyancy.

centrifugal force. *See* force.

centrifugal moment. The total moment of the centrifugal forces of all the particles of a rotating body about any line.

centrifugation potentials. An electric field generated in a colloidal solution when centrifuged. The disperse phase is generally heavier than the continuous phase and moves away from the rotational axis though retaining its charge. The smaller counter-ions remain behind. This gives rise to a p.d. between points in the solution at different distances from the axis. It can be used as a means of determining the *zeta-potential in colloidal solutions.

centrifuge. A rapidly rotating bar or flywheel on a vertical axle from the rim of which a series of tubes are suspended so that their lower closed ends are free to tilt upwards and outwards. At high speed the centrifugal force outwards is far greater than gravity, and suspensions put in the tubes settle out much more quickly than in the ordinary way. It is also used for measuring sizes, shapes, and weights of particles. *See also* ultra-centrifuge.

centripetal force. *See* force.

centrobaric. *See* centre of gravity.

centroid. (1) *See* centre of mass. (2) *Syn.* centre of area. Of a surface. The centre of mass of a thin uniform sheet of matter with the same shape as the surface. (3) *Syn.* centre of figure. Of a volume. The centre of mass of a uniform solid with the same shape as the volume.

centrosymmetry. Symmetry with respect to a point. Crystals that are centrosym-

metrical have their faces arranged in parallel pairs which are alike or enantiomorphous in surface characteristics.

Cerenkov radiation. The bluish light emitted by a beam of high-energy charged particles passing through a transparent medium at a speed, v, that is greater than the velocity of light c' in that medium. The light is emitted at angles, θ, to the direction of motion of the particles, thus forming a conical wave front of angle 2θ, where $\cos \theta = c'/v$; $c' = c/n$, where n is the refractive index of the medium. The angle θ can be used to measure the energy of the particles. The radiation represents the excess energy resulting from the difference in velocity of the particle and the velocity of its associated electric and magnetic fields which cannot exceed the velocity of light in the medium. Cerenkov radiation is analogous to the shock wave produced by a *sonic boom.

CGS system of units. A system of units based on the centimetre as unit of length, the gramme as unit of mass, and the second as unit of time. Although strictly applicable to mechanical measurements only, the system was extended to cover thermal measurements by the addition of the inconsistently defined *calorie. In extending the system further to enable electrical measurements to be carried out, it was recognized that a further fundamental quantity needed definition. This idea gave rise to two alternatives: (a) the CGS-electromagnetic units, which are based on the *permeability of free space having unit size; (b) the CGS-electrostatic units, which are based on the *permittivity of free space having unit size. Because, as Maxwell proved, the product of the permeability and permittivity of free space is c^{-2}, where c is the velocity of electromagnetic radiation, systems (a) and (b) are mutually exclusive.

The *Gaussian* (or symmetric) *system of units* uses units from system (a) to measure magnetic quantities and those from system (b) to measure electric quantities. In consequence, some equations of electromagnetic relationships contain *c* explicitly. All versions of the CGS system have now been superseded by *SI units. *See* conversion tables (Table 1) on pages 421–2.

chain reaction. A series of nuclear transformations initiated by a single nuclear fission. For example, the fission of a ^{235}U nucleus is accompanied by the emission of one, two, or three neutrons, each of which is capable of causing further fission of ^{235}U nuclei.

When each transformation causes an average of one further transformation the reaction is said to be *critical*. If the average number of further transformations is less than one, the reaction is *subcritical*; if it exceeds one, it is *supercritical*. *See also* critical mass.

channel. (1) In communications, a specified band of frequencies, or a particular path, used in the transmission and reception of electric signals. (2) In a *field-effect transistor the region between *source and *drain, whose conductivity is modulated by the voltage applied to the *gate.

characteristic. A relation between two magnitudes that characterizes the behaviour of any device or apparatus. The relations are usually plotted in the form of a graph (*characteristic curve*) and are most frequently used for *valves and *transistors.

The most usual characteristics are: (1) the *static characteristics* showing, for example, *collector current against *base voltage, with all other voltages kept constant, (2) the *dynamic characteristics* showing the current from one electrode against the voltage of another under dynamic conditions, such as (a) a specified load impedance or (b) a sinusoidal voltage superimposed on the initial constant supply voltage.

characteristic equations. *See* equations of state.

characteristic function. One of a set of functions satisfying a particular equation with specified boundary conditions. The corresponding values of some parameter associated with these solutions are known as *characteristic values*.

In *wave mechanics, characteristic functions are *well-behaved* (i.e. physically possible) solutions of *Schrödinger's wave equation for an atomic particle, and the corresponding values of the energy of the particle are the characteristic values. If there is more than one solution of the differential equation corresponding to a particular characteristic value, the system is said to be *degenerate*.

Characteristic functions and values occur in *matrix mechanics also. In quantum mechanics particularly, characteristic values and functions are often called *eigenvalues* and *eigenfunctions*.

characteristic temperatures. *See* Debye theory of specific heat capacities.

characteristic value. *See* characteristic function.

characteristic X-radiation. The characteristic spectrum of an element may be mapped by making it the target in an X-ray tube. *See* X-rays; X-ray spectrum.

charge. Symbol: Q. A property of some *elementary particles that causes them to exert forces on one another. The natural unit of negative charge is that possessed by the electron and the proton has an equal amount of positive charge. The use of the terms negative and positive are purely conventional and are used to differentiate the types of forces that charged particles exert on each other. Like charges repel and unlike charges attract each other. The force is thought to result from the exchange of photons between the charged particles. The charge of a body or region arises as a result of an excess or defect of electrons with respect to protons. Charge is the integral of electric current with time and is measured in coulombs. The electron has a charge of $1.602\ 192 \times 10^{-19}$. *See also* electromagnetic interaction.

charge conjugation parity. *Syn.* C-parity. Symbol: *C*. A quantum number associated with those elementary particles (such as π^0 and η) that have zero charge, baryon number, and strangeness. It is conserved in *strong and *electromagnetic interactions. In simple terms, it shows whether the *wave function describing the particle is unchanged ($C = +1$) or changes sign ($C = -1$) when the particle is replaced by its *antiparticle.

charge-coupled device. *See* charge-transfer device.

charge density. (1) *Volume charge density*. Symbol: ρ. The electric charge per unit volume of a medium or body. It is measured in coulombs per metre cubed. (2) *Surface charge density*. Symbol: σ. The electric charge per unit area of a surface. It is measured in coulombs per metre squared.

charge independence. *See* nuclear force.

charge-transfer device. A *semiconductor device in which discrete packets of charge are transferred from one location to the next. Such devices can be used for the short-term storage of charge in a particular location. Several types of charge-transfer device exist: (1) *Bucket-brigade devices*. These consist of a number of capacitors linked by a series of switches (usually *bipolar or *field-effect (MOS) transistors. As each switch is closed, charge is transferred from one capacitor to the next. They are frequently used as *delay lines in both digital and analog systems. (2) *Charge-coupled devices* (CCD). Charge-coupled devices consist of arrays of MOS

capacitors (i.e. MOSFETs without source or drain diffusions) (Fig. a).

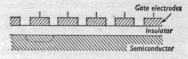

a Charge-coupled device

If a suitable potential is applied to the gate electrode a depletion region will be formed in the semiconductor beneath the gate. Minority carriers injected into the system will enter the depletion region and be held at the surface of the semiconductor until they recombine. If the adjacent capacitor has a more depleted region than the first, and the physical separation is sufficiently small, the charge stored will be transferred to the second. Packets of charge may be transferred along a line of capacitors by suitably adjusting the gate potentials. CCDs are used in imaging systems by exposing the array to a light image. The capacitors become charged according to the light intensity distribution. This charge pattern may then be shifted out to provide a video signal.

(3) *Surface-charge transistor* (SCT). A modification of the charge-coupled device. An extra electrode (the transfer gate) is provided between each storage location, overlapping the storage electrodes (source/receiver electrodes). When a suitable potential is applied to it, this electrode provides a transfer path between the storage locations. A single SCT is shown in Fig. *b*.

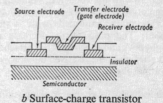

b Surface-charge transistor

Charles's law. The volume of a fixed mass of any gas increases for each degree rise in temperature by a constant fraction of the volume at 0° C, the pressure being constant throughout.

The law is not strictly valid for actual gases, but for the *permanent gases (which cannot be liquefied at room temperature by application of pressure) the fraction is close to 1/273. *See* ideal gas.

charm. *See* psi particle.

chemical energy. Energy stored in the chemical bonds of a substance. It is converted into another form when a chemical reaction occurs. For example when a substance burns chemical energy is converted into heat. In an electric cell, chemical energy is converted into electric energy.

chemical hygrometer. A *hygrometer in which water flowing from the aspirator D causes a known volume of air to be drawn through E, any moisture con-

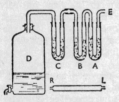

Chemical hygrometer

tained in the air being removed in the drying tubes A, B, and C. The process is repeated with the tube R L, containing water, attached at E. Air passing through R L becomes saturated with water vapour. The ratio of the increase in weight of A and B before R L is attached and after gives the relative *humidity of the atmosphere.

chemical shift. A change in the position of a spectrum peak resulting from a small change in energy level caused by a chemical effect.

chemiluminescence. *See* luminescence.

chemosphere. *See* atmospheric layers.

chief ray. The central or representative ray of a pencil from an object point on or off the axis, to the centre of the entrance pupil.

Child's law. Under space-charge-limited conditions, where the voltage drop V across an electronic tube is less than that which would give the maximum electron emission possible, the current density, j, follows the law

$$j \propto V^{3/2}/s^2$$

for flat surfaces, where s is the cathode-to-anode distance in cm and j is in A/cm^2.

chi-meson (χ^0). A *boson *resonance of mass 958 MeV/c^2. Also denoted η' ('eta-dash'). It has zero *isospin and *charge, negative *parity and positive *G-parity. The *spin is probably zero.

chip. An extremely small piece of *semiconductor containing a component (transistor, resistor, etc.) or an *integrated circuit.

Chladni's plates. Flat plates used to investigate vibrations in solids. Clamped at one point (a *node) a plate is vibrated, as by bowing, at another point. This causes fine sand, sprinkled on the surface, to collect along the nodal lines. A great variety of patterns (*Chladni's figures*) can be obtained by clamping and exciting the plate at different positions.

choke. (1) An *inductor that presents a relatively high impedance to alternating current. It is often used in audio-frequency and radio-frequency circuits to impede the audio-frequency or radio-frequency signals, or to smooth the output of a rectifying circuit. (2) A groove cut into the metal surface of a *waveguide, approximately one-quarter of a wavelength deep, to prevent the escape of microwave energy.

chroma. The attribute of a visual sensation by which the amount of pure colour can be judged, irrespective of the amount of white or grey present.

chromatic aberration. *Syn.* chromatism. Since the refractive index of a refracting medium depends on the wavelength (*see* dispersion), the focal length of a lens varies according to the colour of the incident light. The image of a point source of white light is therefore blurred and appears coloured: tinged with a

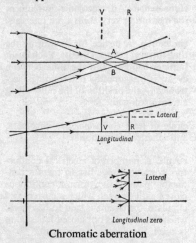

Chromatic aberration

surround of blue or violet at the focus for red, and with red at the blue focus. At an intermediate position a white circle AB occurs – the *circle of least confusion.* For standards of comparison, the colours corresponding with the C (red) and F (blue-green) lines of hydrogen are chosen. The distance between the foci for these colours is the *longitudinal chromatic aberration.* The reciprocals of the principal focal lengths are the powers; the difference of these powers is commonly referred to as the *chromatic aberration.* For a thin lens, the last-mentioned chromatic aberration is ωP, where ω is the dispersive power of the glass and P is the power of the lens for yellow

(sodium D) light. The sizes of the images for different colours will be different; the difference in size is called the *lateral chromatic aberration* for the object considered. When chromatic aberrations have been corrected for two colours (*see* achromatic lens), owing to irrationality of dispersion there is a residual chromatic aberration referred to as the *secondary spectrum. See also* apochromatic lens.

chromaticity. An objective description of the *colour quality* of a visual stimulus, such as a coloured light or a surface, irrespective of its *luminance (*see* colour system). Chromaticity and luminance completely specify a colour stimulus. The colour quality is defined in terms of its *chromaticity coordinates.* These three coordinates, x, y, z, are equal to the ratio of each of the *tristimulus values* of a light to their sum. The tristimulus values, X, Y, Z, are the amounts of the three reference or matching stimuli required to match exactly the light under consideration in a given trichromatic system. Hence

$$x = \frac{X}{X + Y + Z} \text{ (redness)}$$

$$y = \frac{Y}{X + Y + Z} \text{ (greenness)}$$

$$z = \frac{Z}{X + Y + Z} \text{ (blueness)}$$

Thus all colour can be reduced to a common function since $x + y + z = 1$. When x, y, and z all approximately equal $\frac{1}{3}$, the colour is almost white.

A *chromaticity diagram* is obtained when x is plotted against y, the graph being horseshoe-shaped and the locus of all monochromatic colours (*see* diagram). The straight line joining the ends is the locus of pure purple, i.e. combinations of the extreme red and blue monochromatic colours. All colours lie within these loci. White lies at the point,

C (the white point), having coordinates $x = y = \frac{1}{3}$. Any colour lies on the line joining a spectral colour (on the horseshoe) to C. The wavelength of the spectral colour used is the *dominant wavelength* for the colour under consideration. The position of this colour on the line depends on the proportions of the spectral colour and white required to obtain the colour. The *excitation purity* of the colour is the ratio of the distances of the colour and the spectral colour from the white spot. The dominant wavelength is roughly equivalent to hue (*see* colour), and excitation purity to

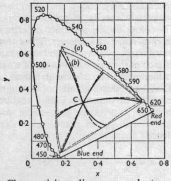

Chromaticity diagram and two colour triangles.

saturation. One or more *colour triangles* can be drawn on the chromaticity diagram. They represent the entire range of chromaticities that can be obtained from a combination, by a *subtractive process of three dyes of the *primary colours cyan (blue-green), magenta (red-blue), and yellow. Triangle (a) shows the colours obtained by a combination of the three dyes above; triangle (b) is obtained by mixing the three dyes and a white dye.

chromatic resolving power. *See* resolving power.

chromatic scale. *See* musical scale.

chromatism. *See* chromatic aberration.

chromatography. Any of various methods for the chemical analysis of liquid or gaseous mixtures.

chrominance signal. *See* colour television.

chronon. A hypothetical particle of time; the time taken for a photon to traverse the diameter of an electron. It is approximately equal to 10^{-24} seconds.

chronoscope. An electronic instrument for measuring very short time intervals.

chronotron. A device for measuring the time interval between events. Each event initiates a pulse, and the time between events is measured by determining, electronically, the position of the pulse along a transmission line.

circle of least confusion. *See* chromatic and spherical aberration.

circuit. A number of electrical conductors connected together to form a conducting path. If they form a continuous closed path through which a current can circulate, the circuit is said to be *closed*; when the circuit is not closed it is said to be *open*. *See also* magnetic circuit.

circuital. *See* curl.

circuit-breaker. A device for making and breaking an electric circuit under normal or under fault conditions. *See* contactor; switch; tripping device.

circular polarized light. *See* polarization.

civil year. *See* time.

cladding. The process of bonding one metal to another to prevent corrosion of one of the metals. It is used in *nuclear reactors to prevent corrosion of a *fuel element by the *coolant and the escape of fission products.

clamping diode. *See* catching diode.

Clark cell. A voltaic cell, formerly adopted as a standard of e.m.f. It consists of a mercury electrode surrounded by a paste of mercury sulphate, the negative electrode being a rod of pure zinc in a saturated solution of zinc sulphate. Its e.m.f. was defined as 1·4345 volts at 15° C. It has now been superseded by the *Weston standard cell.

class A amplifier. An amplifier operated under such conditions that the output current flows over the whole of the input cycle. The output wave shape is essentially a replica of the input wave shape. It has low distortion and low efficiency.

class AB amplifier. An amplifier operated so that, in general, the output current flows for more than half but less than the whole of the input cycle. It tends to operate as *class A for low input signal levels and *class B at high input signal levels.

class B amplifier. An amplifier operated to produce a half-wave rectified output, i.e. the output current is cut-off at zero input signal. In order to duplicate the input waveform successfully two transistors (or valves) are required, each conducting for one half of the input cycle. It has high efficiency but suffers from crossover distortion.

class C amplifier. An amplifier in which output current flows for less than half of the input cycle. The output waveform is not a replica of the input waveform for all amplitudes. It is more efficient than other types, but introduces more distortion.

class D amplifier. An amplifier operating by means of pulse-width modulation. (*See* pulse modulation.) The input signal is used to modulate a square wave with respect to its *mark space ratio. The modulated square wave then operates

*push–pull switches so that one switch operates when the input is high, and the other when the input is low. The resultant current in the output load is proportional to the mark–space ratio and hence the input signal. Class D amplifiers are theoretically highly efficient, but to avoid distortion the switches must be operated faster than is generally practicable.

classical physics. The long established part of physics, excluding *relativity and *quantum theory.

Clausius–Clapeyron equation. The equation:

$$\frac{\mathrm{d}p}{\mathrm{d}T} = \frac{L}{T(v_2 - v_1)},$$

where v_1 and v_2 are the specific volumes of the substance in two different physical states, L is the specific latent heat for the change from one of these states to the other. It gives the variation of boiling point or freezing point with applied pressure.

Clausius's equation. The equation:

$$c_2 - c_1 = T\frac{\mathrm{d}}{\mathrm{d}T}\left(\frac{L}{T}\right),$$

where c_1 and c_2 are the specific heat capacities of the liquid and vapour respectively and L is the specific latent heat of vaporization at the thermodynamic temperature T.

Clausius's equation of state. *See* equations of state.

Clausius's virial law. The mean kinetic energy of a system is equal to its virial equation. It is a general theorem which can be used to obtain, for example, the *equation of state for a solid.

clinical thermometer. A mercury in glass thermometer used for the accurate determination of the temperature of the human body and graduated from 95° to 110° F (or 35° to 43° C). The mercury in the thin-walled bulb B expands past the constriction S into the capillary tube. On removing the thermometer from the

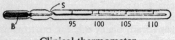

Clinical thermometer

patient the mercury beyond S cannot recede into the bulb because of the constriction.

clock frequency. The master frequency delivered by an electronic device, called a *clock*, at fixed intervals to synchronize operations in a *computer, and to monitor and measure properties of the circuits involved.

clock pulses. The regular pulses delivered to the elements in a *logic circuit to effect logical operations.

clocks. The earliest clocks were based on processes that take place at a constant rate. More sophisticated devices use periodic processes of constant frequency.
(1) *Pendulum clock*. The pendulum clock employs Galileo's discovery that the period of a pendulum is a function only of its length and not its mass or initial displacement: accurate to about 0·01 seconds per day.
(2) *Crystal clock*. For precise scientific measurements a higher degree of accuracy is obtained from the crystal clock in which a quartz crystal is made to oscillate at about 100 000 hertz by *electrostriction: accurate to about 0·001 seconds per day.
(3) *Atomic clock*. Even greater accuracy can be obtained from atomic clocks in which the periodic process is a molecular or atomic event associated with a particular spectral line. When energy is supplied to an ammonia molecule it can exist in a vibrationally excited state in which the nitrogen atom passes through the plane of the hydrogen atoms to an equivalent position on the opposite side.

This oscillation has a frequency of 23 870 hertz and ammonia therefore strongly absorbs radiation of this frequency. This is the basis of the *ammonia clock*. A quartz oscillator can supply energy to ammonia gas at this frequency. When the oscillator supply varies from this value the energy is no longer absorbed and is used in a feedback circuit to correct the oscillator.
(4) *Caesium clock*. A device in which the frequency is defined by the energy difference between two different states of the caesium nucleus in a magnetic field (*see* *nuclear magnetic resonance). A beam of caesium atoms is split by a non-uniform magnetic field into distinct components. Atoms in the lower energy state are directed into a cavity and fed with radio-frequency radiation at a frequency of 9 192 631 770 hertz, which corresponds to the energy difference between the two states. Some caesium atoms are raised to the higher energy state by absorption of this radiation and the mixture of caesium atoms is analysed by a further magnetic field. A signal from the atom detector is fed back to the r-f oscillator supply to prevent it from drifting from the resonant frequency. In this way the supply is locked to the spectral line frequency and the accuracy is better than one part in 10^{13}. The caesium clock is used in the international (SI unit) definition of the *second.
See also synchronous clock; clock frequency.

closed circuit. *See* circuit.

closed circuit television. A television system in which all the parts (camera, control system, and receiver) are physically linked by cables and there are no aerials or open circuits.

close-packed structure. A crystalline arrangement in which similar atoms, supposed spherical, are packed as economically of space as is possible. The two common arrangements are the *face-centred cubic and hexagonal close-packed structures (see crystal systems), but combinations of these also occur. The essential condition is that each atom shall be symmetrically surrounded by twelve others.

cloud chamber. *Syn.* Wilson cloud chamber. An apparatus for making visible the tracks of ionizing particles. It consists of a gas-filled chamber containing a saturated vapour, which can be made supersaturated by the sudden cooling produced in an adiabatic expansion. The excess moisture is deposited in drops on the trail of ions left behind by the passage of a particle. Adiabatic expansion can be produced by having a well-fitting movable piston as the base of the chamber; alternatively, the piston may be replaced by a rubber diaphragm. *See* diffusion cloud chamber.

cloud-ion chamber. An instrument combining the functions of an ionization chamber (utilizing free electron collection) and the Wilson *cloud chamber, in the same gas volume. Isoamyl alcohol and argon mixture can be used to satisfy the necessary conditions for the gas.

coaxial cable. *Syn.* coax. A cable that consists of a central wire surrounded by an insulator with an outer coaxial conducting cylinder. The outer conductor is often earthed. Coaxial cables do not produce external fields and are not affected by them. They are used for transmission of high-frequency signals.

Cockcroft–Walton generator or accelerator. A high voltage direct-current *accelerator especially for the acceleration of protons. The d.c. voltage is produced from a circuit of rectifiers and capacitances to which a low a.c. voltage is applied.

Coddington lens. A powerful magnifying glass; in effect, a complete sphere with a central stop.

coefficient of contraction. The ratio of the area of the *vena contracta of a jet of fluid to the area of the orifice through which it is discharging; values lie between 0·5 and 1.

coefficient of coupling. The ratio between the actual mutual inductance between two coils and the maximum possible.

coefficient of expansion. (1) For a solid, the expression $\Delta X / X \times 1/t$, where t is the rise in temperature producing an increase ΔX in the magnitude of the quantity X. The unit is $(°C)^{-1}$. If X is the length of the solid the coefficient of *linear expansion* is obtained; if X is the area of the surface the coefficient of *superficial expansion* is obtained; and if X is the volume the coefficient of *cubic expansion* is obtained. In general

$$X_t = X_0(1 + \alpha t)$$

where X_0 is the original value of the quantity and α the appropriate coefficient of expansion. Since the coefficients are small the coefficient of superficial expansion may be taken as twice and the coefficient of cubic expansion as three times the coefficient of linear expansion.

(2) For a liquid, there are two coefficients of cubic expansion. The coefficient of *apparent expansion* is the coefficient calculated from $\Delta V / V \times 1/t$ without account being taken of the expansion of the containing vessel. The coefficient of *real* or *absolute expansion* is the coefficient obtained when allowance is made for the expansion of the containing vessel, and is equal to the sum of the coefficient of apparent expansion and the coefficient of cubic expansion of the material of the containing vessel.

(3) For a gas, the expansion is considerable. The coefficient of increase of volume of a gas at constant pressure is the ratio of the change in volume per degree change in temperature to the volume at 0° C, the pressure remaining constant. The coefficient of increase of pressure of a gas at constant volume is

the ratio of the change in pressure per degree change in temperature to the pressure at $0°$ C, the volume remaining constant. (*See* Charles's law.) For an ideal gas both these coefficients (a) are equal to $0.003\,660\,8$ per $°$C so that $V = V_0$ $(1 + at)$ which means that the volume V would become zero at a temperature of $-1/a$ or $-273.15°$ C. This temperature is the absolute zero of *thermodynamic temperature.

coefficient of friction. *See* friction.

coefficient of restitution. If two spheres collide directly, the relative velocity after impact is in a constant ratio to the relative velocity before impact, and in the opposite direction. If the bodies collide obliquely, the same result holds for the relative velocity components along the line of centres at the instant of collision. This constant ratio, which depends on the materials of the spheres and is unity for perfectly elastic bodies and zero for completely inelastic ones, is called the coefficient of restitution. It becomes slightly dependent on the relative velocity if this is very high.

coefficient of viscosity. *See* viscosity.

coercive force. The reversed magnetic field required to reduce the *magnetic flux density in a substance from its remanent value to zero. It is represented by OC on the *hysteresis loop.

coercivity. The value of the coercive force for a substance that has been initially magnetized to saturation.

coherent. Of or relating to waves that are in *phase both temporally and spatially. Most practical radiation sources are not coherent over an appreciable length of time since *wave trains of limited length are emitted at random intervals. The *laser is a source of coherent radiation.

coherent units. A system of units, such as *SI units, in which the quotient or pro-duct of any two units gives the unit of the resultant physical quantity. The *base units* of a coherent system are an arbitrarily defined set of physical quantities: all the other units in the system are derived from the base units by defining relationships and are called *derived units*.

coincidence circuit. A circuit with two input terminals that is designed to produce an output pulse only when both input terminals receive a pulse within a specified time interval.

cold cathode. The cathode of an electronic tube which is caused to emit electrons by having a sufficiently high voltage gradient, i.e. by *autoemission*, instead of being operated at a high temperature.

cold emission. *See* field emission.

cold trap. A tube, cooled with liquid air or dry-ice (frozen carbon dioxide) in acetone, that will condense vapour passing into it.

collapsar. *See* black hole.

collector. The electrode in a *transistor through which *carriers leave the inter-electrode region.

collector ring. *See* slip ring.

collimator. (1) A system that produces a beam of parallel light or other radiation. It is used in *spectrometers, *telescopes, etc. (2) *Syn.* finder. A small fixed telescope attached to a larger one in order to set the line of sight of the large instrument.

collision. In *kinetic theory a collision describes the mutual action of molecules, atoms, etc., when they encounter one another. A collision is thought of as being either elastic or inelastic. (1) *Elastic collision*. One in which the total kinetic energy of translation is unchanged after the collision, none being translated into other forms. In nuclear physics, an elastic collision is one in which the incoming particle is scattered without exciting or breaking up the encountered nucleus. (2) *Inelastic collision.* This may be one of two kinds: (i) one particle loses kinetic energy while a second gains kinetic, excitation, or ionization energy; (ii) one particle loses excitation or ionization energy only, while the second gains kinetic, excitation, or ionization energy as before.

collision density. The total number of a specified type of collision occurring per unit time per unit volume of material.

colorimetry. The science that aims at specifying and reproducing colours as a result of measurement. Colorimeters are of three types: (*a*) colour album or filter samples for comparison – essentially empirical; (*b*) monochromatic colorimeters which match colours with a mixture of monochromatic and white lights; (*c*) trichromatic colorimeters in which a match is effected by a mixture of three colours.

colour. (1) The sensation normally experienced when light of sufficient intensity and with a relative distribution of energy across its spectrum different from that of white light (e.g., normal daylight) strikes the retina of the eye. Besides possessing *luminosity*, colours are regarded as possessing the attributes of *hue* and *saturation*. Saturation is the degree to which a colour departs from white and approaches a pure spectral colour. Hue is determined by the frequency of vibration of light waves – a pure continuous spectrum shows a continuous variation of saturated hues. When a hue is diluted with white light (desaturated, impure), the colour is classed as a *tint*. The *shade* of a colour refers to its *luminosity*.

The hues of the spectrum are broadly grouped in the following list (wavelengths in nanometres): red (740–620),

orange (620–585), yellow (585–575), green (575–500), blue (500–445), indigo (445–425), violet (425–390). When suitably presented, the eye can discriminate between hues in the middle part of the spectrum with wavelength differences from 1–3 nm. Approximately 130 steps of just detectable hue difference across the spectrum are possible. As a hue is diluted with white about 20 tints are possible.

By mixing colours, other colours emerge and a sharp distinction must be drawn between combining coloured lights, the mixing of pigments, and the transmission of light by colour filters. Mixing coloured lights is an *additive process. The other two are *subtractive processes. When lights of different colours illuminate a white screen viewed by eye, or if they produce overlapping illumination on the retina of the eye, the ensuing sensation has another colour whose hue and saturation depend on the relative proportions of the mixing colours (Newton) and its luminosity is the sum of the separate luminosities (Abney). By using lights of three *primary colours in various proportions it is possible in general to produce any other colour. *See* chromaticity; surface colour; colour system. (2) *See* psi particle.

colour blindness. *See* colour vision.

colour equation. An algebraic equation that expresses the results of an additive mixture (*see* additive process) of three *primary colours in terms of another colour or white. *See also* colour system; chromaticity.

colour mixture. *See* additive process; subtractive process.

colour picture tube. A type of *cathode-ray tube designed to produce the coloured image in *colour television. Varying the intensity of excitation of three different phosphors which produce the three primary colours red, green, and

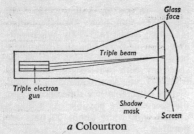

a Colourtron

blue, will reproduce the original colours of the image by an *additive process.

The conventional colour picture tube consists of three electron guns tilted slightly so that the electron beams intersect just in front of the screen. Each beam has a focusing system and is directed towards a different colour phosphor. A mask prevents excitation of adjacent phosphor. One main type of tube (e.g. the *colourtron*) has triangular arrangements of both guns and phosphor dots (Figs. *a*, *b*). The other main type has the

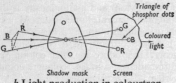
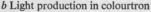

b Light production in colourtron

guns arranged in line horizontally, a grille of vertical wires and the phosphors being arranged as vertical stripes on the screen.

A modern development, the *Trinitron*, has a single electron gun with three cathodes aligned horizontally, an aperture grille, and vertically striped phosphors. The cathodes are tilted so that the electron beams intersect twice (Fig. *c*).

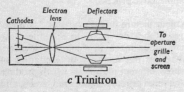

c Trinitron

This allows a single electron lens system to be used for all three beams. The system is much smaller and lighter and has a greater effective diameter of the lens system than conventional tubes, hence producing sharper focusing.

colour quality. *See* chromaticity.

colour system. The representation of a colour in terms of a specific set of co-ordinates. For objective colour systems, dominant wavelength, excitation purity, and luminance (*see* chromaticity) are frequently used. For subjective colour systems, the coordinates are usually luminosity *L*, saturation or chroma *S*, and hue *H*. If these form a system of cylindrical coordinates, the colour is found inside a roughly elliptical solid.

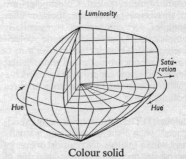

Colour solid

colour television. Television, based on an additive colour process, in which a composite signal is produced from the three video outputs from *camera tubes, each of which is sensitive to red, blue, or green light. A colour decoder in the receiver extracts the video information for each colour and a coloured image is produced (*see* colour picture tube).

The composite signal is broadcast in two parts to achieve compatibility with black-and-white (monochrome) receivers. The *luminance signal* contains brightness information and produces a black-and-white image. The *chrominance signal* contains the colour information and is transmitted as a subcarrier of suitable frequency.

colour temperature. Of a non-black body. The temperature of a *black body that has approximately the same energy distribution as occurs in the spectrum of the body. *See also* selective radiation.

colour triangle. *See* chromaticity.

colourtron. *See* colour picture tube.

colour vision. The human eye contains two sorts of light-sensitive cells – *rods* and *cones*. The rods respond only to visible wavelengths of low intensity, but the response does not vary with wavelength. The cones respond to the higher intensity of daylight and as the response varies with wavelength, individual colours can be recognized. Colour vision can be explained by the *trichromatic theory* which assumes that there are three separate systems of cones sensitive to either red, green, or blue light. Incident light will therefore stimulate one or more of these systems to an extent depending on its colour (*see* additive process). *Colour blindness* can be explained by the absence of one or more sets of cones.

column of air. The vibrations of air columns are the sources of sound in the organ as well as in the different types of wind instruments. The simplest case is the air in a hollow cylindrical pipe, the ends of which may be open or closed. For simplicity, the motion in the tube is assumed uniform, i.e. the viscosity of the medium inside the tube is neglected so that only plane waves need be considered. The diameter of the tube should therefore be sufficiently great yet small with respect to the length, l, of the pipe and with the wavelength of the sound. The walls of the pipe are assumed to be rigid.

Under these conditions, when a cylindrical air column is set into resonant vibration by some means, *standing waves are set up due to *progressive and

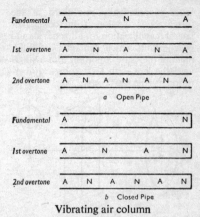

a Open Pipe

b Closed Pipe

Vibrating air column

retrogressive waves. In the open pipe (both ends open, Fig. *a*), there must be a displacement antinode A at each end and therefore in the fundamental mode of vibration a *node N in the middle. The frequency of the fundamental is $c/2l$, where c is the velocity of sound in the medium inside the pipe. The frequencies of the different modes are in the ratio $1:2:3:\ldots$, thus representing a full harmonic series of wavelengths.

For a closed pipe (one end closed and the other open, Fig. *b*), there must always be a node at the closed end and an antinode at the open end. In the fundamental mode the frequency is $c/4l$. In general, the frequencies bear the ratios $1:3:5:\ldots$, representing the odd harmonic series of wavelengths. *See also* end correction.

coma. An aberration of a mirror or lens in which the image of a point lying off the axis presents a comet-shaped appearance. While the rays from the central zone Z_A (*see* diagram), focus to a point A, the zones Z_B and Z_M form annular rings B and M of progressively varying diameter and centration. The overlap of these circles produces the comatic patch AM, which is called the *tangential coma*; the radius of M is the *sagittal coma*: the latter is practically one third of the former. For freedom from coma, the lateral magnification for all zones should be constant, which demands the fulfilment of the *sine condition. For a single lens, the lens with least spherical aberration has the least coma.

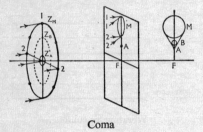

Coma

combination tones. If two tones of frequencies f_1, f_2 are sounded together very loudly, at least two other rather faint tones, of frequencies $(f_1 + f_2)$ and $|f_1 - f_2|$ (the absolute value), may be heard. The first is a *summation tone* and the second a *difference tone*; collectively they are known as combination or *resultant tones*. Other audible combination tones are: $2f_1$, $3f_1$, $2f_2$, $3f_2$, $|f_1 - 2f_2|$, and $|f_2 - 2f_1|$. *Compare* beats.

common base connection. A method of operating a *transistor in which the *base (usually earthed) is common to the input and output circuits, the *emitter is the input terminal and the *collector is the output terminal.

common collector connection. A method of operating a *transistor in which the *collector (usually earthed) is common to both input and output circuits, the *base is the input terminal, and the *emitter is the output terminal.

common emitter connection. A method of operating a *transistor in which the *emitter (usually earthed) is common to both input and output circuits, the *base is the input terminal, and the *collector the output terminal.

common impedance coupling. *See* coupling.

communications satellite. *See* satellite.

commutator. (1) A device for reversing the direction of the current in an electric circuit or in some part of a circuit. (2) A device employed in electrical machines to connect in turn each of the sections of an armature winding with an external electric circuit. It may be used as a simple current-reverser or to convert a.c. into d.c. (or vice versa).

compandor. *See* volume compressors (and expanders).

comparator. (1) A device for measuring the difference in length between two line standards or for measuring horizontal distances by comparison with a standard scale. (2) A circuit, such as a differential amplifier, that compares two signals and produces an output that is a function of the result of the comparison.

compass. A magnet freely pivoted horizontally so that it can set itself along the lines of force of the earth's magnetic field. It usually carries a scale divided into degrees and marked with the cardinal points, or these may be printed on a circular card to which the magnet, or system of magnets, is fixed. *See also* gyrocompass.

compensated pendulum. A pendulum so constructed that the distance between the support and the centre of gravity of the bob is independent of temperature so that the time period does not vary with temperature.

compensating eyepiece. An eyepiece in a microscope or telescope that corrects the chromatic differences of magnification of the objective.

compiler. A computer *program taking a high level programming language as its input and converting it to a set of machine instructions.

complementarity. The principle that a system, such as an electron, can be described either in terms of particles or in terms of wave motion (*see* de Broglie equation). According to Bohr these views are complementary. An experiment that demonstrates the particle-like nature of electrons will not also show their wave-like nature, and vice versa.

complementary colours. Two pure spectral colours which when mixed produce white light. There is no complementary spectral colour to green.

Colour	$\lambda/10^{-9}$ m	Comple-mentary	$\lambda/10^{-9}$ m
Red	656	Green-Blue	492
Orange	607	Blue	489
Golden Yellow	585	Blue	485
Yellow	567	Indigo Blue	464
Green Yellow	563	Violet	433

complementary transistors. A pair of transistors of opposite type, i.e. n–p–n and p–n–p bipolar junction *transistors. Complementary MOS *field-effect transistors (COSMOS or C/MOS) are used for very low dissipation logic circuits. The basic *inverter is shown in the illustration.

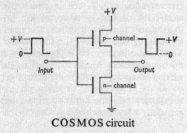

COSMOS circuit

compole. An auxiliary magnetic pole mounted midway between the main poles of an electrical machine having a com-mutator, to produce an auxiliary magnetic flux in the region occupied by the conductors of the coils undergoing commutation. As a result of this, an e.m.f. is induced in these coils which, with correct design, neutralizes the e.m.f. of self-induction and gives rise to sparkless or 'black' commutation. A compole is excited by a winding which carries the load current of the machine.

compound microscope. *See* microscope.

compound nucleus. The highly excited nucleus, of short lifetime, formed immediately after a nuclear collision.

compound pendulum. *See* pendulum.

compound-wound machine. A d.c. machine in which the *field magnets are provided with both series and shunt excitation windings. The series windings carry the load current of the machine and if the series field assists the shunt field, the machine is said to be *cumulatively compound-wound*; if the series field opposes the shunt field, the machine is said to be *differentially compound-wound*.

compressibility. Symbol: κ. The reciprocal of the bulk modulus; it is the ratio of volume strain to pressure change (stress), $(1/v)(\delta v/\delta p)$, at constant temperature. The compressibility of solids is small; liquids are usually considered incompressible; gases are highly compressible fluids.

compression. As longitudinal waves of sound traverse an elastic medium, the particles of the medium start vibrating in the direction of wave propagation, about their normal position. As a result local changes of density occur due to the relative juxtaposition of neighbouring particles. Compressions occur at points of maximum density and *rarefactions* at points of minimum density. A continuous variation of pressure in the medium results as the wave passes.

77

compressor. *See* volume compressors.

Compton effect. An increase in wavelength that occurs when radiation is scattered by free electrons. The change is $\Delta\lambda = (2h/mc)\sin^2 \frac{1}{2}\varphi$ (*Compton equation*), where φ is the angle between the direction of the incident and scattered radiation, h is the Planck constant, and m is the mass of the electron. The effect can be observed by passing X- or gamma-rays through elements of low atomic number, since the binding energies of the electrons in these elements are negligible in comparison with the quantum energy of the radiation. *See* photon.

Compton electron. An electron projected with finite velocity by collision with a photon. The photon suffers a decrease in frequency (*see* Compton effect) and hence a loss in energy equal to $(h\nu - h\nu')$, where h is the Planck constant and ν and ν' the frequencies before and after collision. This energy is transferred to the electron.

Compton recoil. When an X-ray photon is scattered by an electron at an angle φ, the electron recoils at an angle θ using some of the photon's energy and hence reducing its frequency. The incident photon has a momentum of $h\nu/c$ and the scattered photon $h\nu'/c$, while the recoiling electron has a momentum of $m\nu/\sqrt{1 - \beta^2}$, where $\beta = \nu/c$. *See* Compton effect; Compton electron.

computer. Any device for the processing of information received in a prescribed and acceptable form according to a set of instructions.

The *digital computer* manipulates large amounts of information at high speed. Its input must be discrete rather than continuous, and may consist of combinations of numbers, characters, and special symbols, written in an appropriate programming language. The information is represented internally in

*binary notation. The basic components are the *CPU in which operations are carried out on the data, the main store or *memory, in which information is held in units of *bytes or *words, each of which has a unique address, and *peripheral devices which perform input/output and permanent storage of information. A *computer system* consists of complementary *hardware and *software.

The *analog computer* accepts data as a continuously varying quantity. A problem is solved by physical analogy, usually electrical. The magnitudes of the variables in an equation are represented by voltages fed to circuit elements connected in such a way that the input voltages interact according to the same equation as the original variables. The output voltage is then proportional to the numerical solution of the problem.

The *hybrid computer* combines some of the properties of digital and analog computers. It accepts a continuously varying input which is then converted into a set of discrete values for digital processing. Digital processing is considerably faster and more sophisticated than analog processing.

concave. Curving inwards. Concave mirrors are converging in action. Concave lenses are thinner at the centre and are diverging in action.

concentration cell. A cell in which two electrodes of the same metal are immersed in solutions of different concentrations of one salt of the same metal. The solutions may be separated by a porous partition. Metal dissolves in the weaker and is deposited from the stronger solutions. The e.m.f. depends on the substances and the concentrations, but is usually a few hundredths of a volt.

concentric lens. A convexoconcave lens whose surfaces have the same centre of curvature; its central thickness is equal to the difference in the radii of curvature.

condensation (sound). The ratio of the instantaneous excess of density to the normal density at a point in a medium transmitting longitudinal sound waves: $s = \delta\rho/\rho$.

condensation pump. *See* pumps, vacuum.

condenser. (1) (light). A mirror or lens combination used in optical instruments (e.g. projectors, compound microscopes) to concentrate light from a source into a defined beam so that the light source can be focused on to an object (which may be an opaque object or a transparent slide). It is usually a planoconvex lens or a pair of planoconvex lenses with plane sides facing out. The design differs widely according to the purpose. A *Fresnel lens is often used as a condenser in a projector. The *microscope condenser* is an elaborate sub-stage lens or mirror combination, for use with higher power objectives, so that rays converge without *aberration and fill the aperture of the objective uniformly. Its *numerical aperture should not be less than that of the objective. *See also* Abbe condenser.

(2) (heat). A device for the continuous removal of heat, e.g. a stream of cold water which removes the latent heat evolved when a vapour condenses to a liquid as in distillation. In a heat engine it is the system or reservoir to which the working substance rejects that part of the heat which is not converted into work.

(3) (electric). Obsolete term for capacitor.

conductance. Symbol: G. The reciprocal of resistance, measured in siemens (d.c.). It is the real part of the *admittance Y, where $Y = G - iB$ and B is the *susceptance (a.c.).

conduction band. *See* energy bands.

conduction current. *See* current.

conduction electrons. *See* energy bands.

conduction in gases. The passage of an electric current through a gas. It is dependent on the presence of ions (*see* gaseous ions). Natural ionization caused by cosmic rays, ultraviolet light, etc., gives rise to a continuous minute current when a small electric field is maintained between two electrodes in the gas. This is due to the collection of ions of opposite sign at each electrode.

With increasing field strength, there is an initial rise in the current, and it then remains constant, until the applied potential difference is sufficiently high to allow the ions to create further ions by collision. With further increased field strength, the current strength increases regularly and rapidly until a critical p.d. known as the *breakdown potential* is reached. At this point additional phenomena suddenly occur depending on the pressure, and the distance between the electrodes. The process is known as an *electric discharge*. Around atmospheric pressure a spark passes (*spark discharge*), while at lower pressures a regular series of glowing masses of gas appear in the tube the colour of the glow depending on the gas (*see* glow discharge). With small distances between the electrodes a brilliant light is emitted (*arc discharge*). Immediately after the onset of discharge the p.d. across the discharge tube drops to a definite value (maintenance potential); the current strength remains constant. The curve relating current to applied p.d. for a given separation of electrodes in a gas at a particular pressure is known as the discharge characteristic.

In a discharge in gases at low pressures (below 10^{-2} mmHg) cathode rays (*see* gas-discharge tube) are produced. At lower pressures *X-rays are produced by the impact of the cathode rays on the anode of the discharge tube. Glow discharge is utilized in display lighting tubes using neon, mercury vapour, etc., as the gas. Spark and arc discharges are utilized in ultraviolet lamps and sources.

79

conduction of heat. The transference of heat through a body, without visible motion of any part of the body, due to a temperature gradient. The heat energy diffuses though the body by the action of molecules possessing greater kinetic energy on those possessing less. In the case of liquids and gases this is achieved by molecular collisions, whereas in the case of solid electric insulators it is dependent on the elastic binding forces between the atoms. For solid electric conductors the former mechanism applied to the free electrons in the material predominates. *See* thermal conductivity; Wiedemann–Franz law.

conductivity. (1) Symbol: κ. The reciprocal of *resistivity. It is also defined as the current density divided by the electric field strength: this definition is often more useful when considering solutions; it is then known as the *electrolytic conductivity*. Conductivity is measured in siemens per metre. (2) *See* thermal conductivity.

conductor. A substance or body that offers a relatively small resistance to the passage of an electric current. *See also* energy bands.

cone of friction. The resultant force of one flat surface on another is the resultant of the normal reaction and the frictional force. This resultant must lie in the cone whose axis is the normal to the surfaces and whose semi-apical angle has its tangent equal to the coefficient of limiting friction.

conjugate. (1) (general). Joined in a reciprocal relation, as two points, lines, quantities, or things, which are interchangeable with respect to the properties of each. (2) (light). Of foci, planes, and points. Relating to interchangeable properties of object and image. Thus, if I is the image of O, then if I is made the object, its image would be O.

conjugate impedances. Impedances that have equal resistance components, and also equal reactance components, the latter having opposite signs.

conjunction. *See* opposition.

conpernic. A magnetic alloy of nickel (50 %) and iron (50 %), used in magnetic shielding.

consequent poles. Magnetic poles in excess of the usual pair in any magnetized body.

conservation of charge. The principle that the total net charge of any system is constant.

conservation of energy. *See* conservation of mass and energy.

conservation of mass and energy. The principle that in any system the sum of the mass and the energy remains constant. It follows from the special theory of *relativity and is a general statement of two classical laws. The principle of *conservation of energy* states that the total energy in any system is constant. The principle of *conservation of mass* states that the total mass of any system is constant. These are strictly only approximations and cannot be used individually in systems that have velocities approaching that of light or in nuclear reactions. In the principle of conservation of mass and energy it is held that mass and energy are interconvertible according to the equation: $E = mc^2$. *See* Einstein's law.

conservation of momentum. (1) In any system of mutually interacting or impinging particles, the linear momentum in any fixed direction remains unaltered unless there is an external force acting in that direction. (2) Similarly, the angular momentum is constant in a system rotating about a fixed axis provided that no external torque is applied.

conservative field. A field of force in which the work done in taking a particle from one point to another is independent of the path taken between them.

consonance. A combination of two or more notes generally accepted as giving a satisfying effect in itself, i.e. irrespective of context. *Dissonance* describes any combination of notes not forming consonance.

constantan. An alloy of about 50 % copper and 50 % nickel with a comparatively high resistance and low temperature coefficient of resistance. Used extensively in electrical resistance windings and with copper, iron, silver, etc., in forming thermocouples with a comparatively large e.m.f.

constant pressure gas thermometer. A thermometer in which the volume occupied by a given mass of gas at a constant pressure is used for the measurement of the temperature of the bath in which the bulb containing the gas is immersed. A temperature of $t_p°$ C on this scale is defined as

$$t_p = \frac{V_t - V_0}{V_{100} - V_0} \times 100° \text{ C} \qquad (1)$$

where V_t, V_{100}, and V_0 are the volumes occupied by the gas at the temperature t_p, the steam point, and the ice point respectively.

The scale given by employing an actual gas in the thermometer will differ from the *ideal gas scale, due to the fact that the gas does not obey Boyle's law exactly except at infinitely low pressure. A correction must therefore be applied to the readings.

constant volume gas thermometer. A thermometer in which the pressure exerted by a constant volume of gas is used for the measurement of the temperature of the bath in which the bulb containing the gas is immersed. A

temperature of $t°$ C on this scale is defined as

$$t = \frac{p_t - p_0}{p_{100} - p_0} \times 100° \text{ C} \qquad (1)$$

where p_0, p_{100} and p_t are the pressures exerted by the gas when at the ice point, the steam point, and at the temperature t respectively. Using hydrogen or nitrogen gas in a platinum–iridium or platinum–rhodium bulb, temperatures from $-260°$ C to $1600°$ C may be standardized. There are two chief errors causing the temperature on the gas scale to differ from the *thermodynamic temperature: (1) the gas is not ideal so that the product $(p \times V)$ is equal to $(A + Bp)$ and only becomes independent of the pressure if the pressure is very small. (2) The volume of the gas is not constant and not all at the same temperature.

constrain. To limit to a predetermined position or path. If the motion of a system is subject to frictionless constraining forces (*constraints* or reactions) then these forces exist in equal and opposite pairs (Newton's 3rd law of motion) and do no net work. Such constraints include: (*a*) the reaction on a movable body in smooth contact with a fixed body; (*b*) the pair of reactions at a smooth contact; (*c*) the reaction of a body rolling on a fixed body. Constraints reduce the number of *degrees of freedom of the system. *See* virtual work principle.

constringence. *See* Abbe number.

contactor. A type of switch for making and breaking an electric circuit, designed for frequent use. Its operation is electromagnetic, electropneumatic, or mechanical.

contact potential. The difference of potential that arises when two conductors of different material are placed in contact. Thus a metal will be at a different potential from a conducting liquid in

contact resistance

which it is immersed; an electric field will exist between plates of different metals when the plates are electrically connected. The contact potential is usually of the order of a few tenths of a volt. It results from the difference between the *work functions of the two metals.

contact resistance. Resistance at the surface of contact of two conductors.

containment. (1) The process of preventing a *plasma from coming into contact with the walls of the reaction vessel in a controlled *thermonuclear reaction. The time for which ions are trapped in the plasma is called the *containment time*. (2) The prevention of the release of unacceptable quantities of radioactive material beyond a controlled zone in a nuclear reactor. (3) The containment system of a nuclear reactor.

continuity principle. For continuous motion, the increase of mass of fluid in any time interval δt within a closed surface drawn in the fluid is equal to the difference between the mass flow in and the mass flow out through the surface. This is expressed mathematically in the *equation of continuity*:

$$\frac{\partial \rho}{\partial t} + \frac{\partial (\rho u)}{\partial x} + \frac{\partial (\rho v)}{\partial y} + \frac{\partial (\rho w)}{\partial z} = 0$$

where ρ is the density of the fluid at time t and (u, v, w) are the Cartesian components of the vector velocity V at the space point (x, y, z).

continuous flow calorimeter. A type of calorimeter in which heat is supplied at a constant rate to fluid flowing at a constant rate. A steady state is eventually reached when all temperatures remain constant with time so that small temperature differences may be accurately determined without any error due to lag of the thermometers. The heat capacity of the calorimeter does not enter into the thermal equation and since all tempera-

tures are steady the external loss of heat by radiation or other means is more regular and certain.

continuous spectrum. *See* spectrum.

control electrode. Of a *valve. The electrode to which the input signal voltage is applied to produce changes in the currents of one or more of the other electrodes. It is commonly a grid (*control grid*). In connection with cathode-ray tubes it is a synonym for *modulator electrode.

control rod. One of a number of rods that can be moved up or down along its axis into the *core of a *nuclear reactor to control the rate of the *chain reaction. The rods usually contain a neutron absorber such as cadmium or boron.

convection. The process of transfer of heat in a fluid by the movement of the fluid itself. There are two distinct types of convection:

(1) *natural* (or *free*) *convection*, when the motion of the fluid is due solely to the presence of the hot body in it giving rise to temperature and hence density gradients, the fluid thus moving under the influence of gravity;

(2) *forced convection*, in which a relative motion between the hot body and the fluid is maintained by some external agency (e.g. a draught), the relative velocity being such as to make the contribution of the gravity currents negligible.

A theoretical treatment of convection is best achieved by means of dimensional analysis using mass, length, time, and temperature as primary dimensions.

For dynamically similar bodies it is shown that for natural convection

$$\left(\frac{hl}{\lambda\theta}\right) = f_1\left(\frac{l^3 g\alpha\rho^2\theta}{\eta^2}\right) f_2\left(\frac{C\eta}{\lambda\rho}\right).$$

The expression contains three dimensionless groups, namely: $(hl/\lambda\theta)$, the *Nusselt number; $(l^3 g\alpha\rho^2\theta/\eta^2)$, the *Grashof or free convection number; $(C\eta/\lambda\rho)$, the *Prandtl number. The form of the functions f_1 and f_2 must be assumed to be dependent on the shapes of the bodies, etc., involved.

In the case of forced convection the expression takes the form

$$\left(\frac{hl}{\lambda\theta}\right) = F_1\left(\frac{lv\rho}{\eta}\right)F_2\left(\frac{C\eta}{\lambda\rho}\right),$$

introducing in addition to the Nusselt and Prandtl numbers, the *Reynolds number $(lv\rho/\eta)$.

convection current. (1) (heat). A stream of fluid, warmer or colder than the surrounding fluid and in motion because of the buoyancy forces arising from the consequent differences in density.

(2) (electricity). A moving electrified body constitutes an electric convection current, and this type of current can flow without potential difference or energy change and produces no heat. It can nevertheless produce a magnetic effect.

convectron. An instrument to give electrical indication of deviation from the vertical. It is based on the fact that convection cooling of a straight, fine wire is much greater when the wire is horizontal than when vertical.

conventional current. The concept of a current that flows from positive to negative, i.e. in the opposite direction to the electron flow.

conversion. *See* converter reactor.

conversion electron. *See* internal conversion.

conversion factor. *Syn.* conversion ratio. In nuclear physics, the ratio of the number of fissile atoms produced from the fertile material in a *converter reactor to the number of fissile atoms of fuel destroyed in the process.

converter reactor. A *nuclear reactor in which *fertile material is transformed by a nuclear reaction into *fissile material. This process is known as *conversion*. A converter reactor can be used to produce electrical power. *See also* conversion factor; fast breeder reactor.

convex. Curving outwards. A convex mirror is diverging in action. A convex lens is thicker at the centre. Thin convex lenses are converging in action.

coolant. A fluid used to reduce the temperature of a system by conducting away heat produced by the system. In a *nuclear reactor the coolant transfers heat from the *core to the steam-raising plant or to an intermediate heat exchanger.

Coolidge tube. An early type of X-ray tube.

cooling curve. A temperature/time curve used for the determination of melting points (constant temperature portion).

cooling method. The determination of the specific heat capacity of a liquid by comparing the time taken for the liquid and an equal volume of water to cool in identical vessels through the same range of temperature.

Cooper pair. *See* superconductivity.

coordination lattice. A crystal lattice in which each ion bears the same relation to the neighbouring ions in all directions, so that the identity of the molecules becomes ambiguous.

copper loss. *Syn.* I^2R loss. The power loss in watts due to the flow of electric current in the windings of an electrical machine or transformer. It is equal to the product of the square of the current and the resistance of the winding.

Corbino effect. If a current is passed from the centre to the circumference of a metal disc, the surface of which is normal to a magnetic field, a current will flow round the circumference.

core. (1) Of an electromagnetic circuit. In general, it is the part of the *magnetic circuit which is situated within the winding. (2) The central part of a *nuclear reactor in which the *chain reaction takes place. In a thermal reactor it includes the fuel assembly (*see* fuel element) and the moderator, but not the reflector. (3) A small ferrite ring used in a computer *memory to store one *bit of information. The direction of magnetization of the core is sensed and read as 0 or 1. Cores are permanent magnets, and the information is not lost when the computer is shut down.

core loss. *Syn.* iron loss. The total power loss in the iron core of a magnetic circuit when subjected to cyclic changes of magnetization such as that occurring in the core of a transformer. The loss is due to magnetic *hysteresis and *eddy currents. It is usually expressed in watts at a given frequency and value of the maximum flux density.

core store. *See* memory.

core-type transformer. A *transformer in which the windings enclose the greater part of the core.

Coriolis force. *See* force.

corona. (1) An electric discharge appearing round a conductor when the potential gradient at the surface is raised above a critical value, so that a partial breakdown of the surrounding gas takes place. (2) The outermost region of the sun's atmosphere having a temperature of about one million degrees.

corpuscular theory. The theory that a luminous body was supposed to emit small elastic particles with the speed of light. They travelled in straight lines in isotropic media, were repelled on reflection, and suffered change of direction by attraction on refraction. Since this theory required a faster rate of travel in optically dense media, it was supplanted by *wave theory*. This offers a readier explanation of interference, diffraction, and polarization but fails to explain the interactions of light with matter; these can only be explained by a quasi-corpuscular theory involving packets of energy: light quanta or photons. Thus two models are required to explain the phenomenon of light, according to Bohr's principle of *complementarity. *See* quantum theory.

correcting plate. A thin lens or lens system used to correct *spherical aberration in spherical mirrors and *coma in parabolic mirrors. *See* Schmidt corrector.

correlation. A reciprocal relationship between two variables x and y. If measurements indicate in a vague way that x and y are related, statistical methods may then be applied to the results to determine whether or not this apparent connection is significant. A quantity called the *correlation coefficient* r is evaluated; $r = 0$ corresponds to no connection whatever, and $r = 1$ to perfect correlation.

correspondence principle. The principle, due to Bohr, that since the classical laws of physics are capable of describing the properties of macroscopic systems the principles of *quantum mechanics, which are applicable to microscopic systems, must give the same results when applied to large systems.

cosine law. (light) (1) *See* Lambert's law. (2) Of the intensity of illumination on an inclined surface. The intensity varies as the cosine of the angle of incidence and is independent of the nature of the surface.

cosmic background radiation. Electromagnetic radiation that permeates all space and, to date, has been detected in the radio, microwave, X-ray, and gamma-ray regions of the spectrum. The radio background (300 m – 60 cm) is the total emission of all radio sources in the universe. It confirms evidence that there are now far fewer radio galaxies and quasars than in the past, implying that the *steady-state theory of the universe is false.

The microwave background radiation (60 cm – 0·6 mm) is that of a black-body radiator at a temperature of 2·76 kelvin. It is believed to consist of photons remaining after the universe had cooled appreciably, after the big bang, and having insufficient energy to undergo interactions. It is thus considered evidence for the *big-bang theory. The microwave background has a constant strength in all directions (i.e. it is isotropic); this indicates that the universe is expanding at a uniform rate and also that different parts of the universe had the same initial temperature.

Little is known about the X-ray and γ-ray backgrounds ($<1·3$ nm). The X-ray background, like the radio background, is probably the sum of the radiation from all discrete X-ray sources.

cosmic rays. Energetic particle radiation reaching the earth from space. It consists mainly of protons with smaller amounts of heavier nuclei, up to atomic number 28 (Ni). It also contains small numbers of neutral species such as neutrinos and photons. This is known as the *primary radiation* and the particles have energies between 10^7 and 10^{19} eV.

The primary particles collide with oxygen and nitrogen nuclei in the atmosphere and these events, together with subsequent decays and interactions of the resulting particles, lead to large numbers of *elementary particles and photons constituting the *secondary radiation*. A large number of particles can be formed from one primary particle and this is known as a *shower*.

Penetrating showers are mainly *muons

formed by decay of *pions, which are formed by impact of the primary radiation with nuclei. *Neutrinos are also produced by pion decay: $\pi^+ \rightarrow \mu^+ + \nu$, $\pi^- \rightarrow \mu^- + \bar{\nu}$. Muons do not interact strongly with matter and a large proportion are detected at the earth's surface. *Soft showers* are mainly electrons and positrons. A neutral pion (π^0) decays into two very energetic gamma-ray photons with energies of about 70 MeV. These each can produce one electron and one positron in passing near the nucleus of an atom (*see* pair production). Each particle then loses energy and emits *bremsstrahlung radiation – more photons – which produce yet more electrons and positrons, and so on. Thus the original particle leads to a large number of other particles, called a *cascade shower*. *See also* Auger shower.

The intensity of cosmic radiation at sea level is about 1 particle per square centimetre per minute. This varies with latitude because charged particles are affected by the earth's magnetic field, being a minimum at the equator. Particles must have a minimum energy before they can overcome the earth's field and enter the atmosphere. There is also an *east–west effect* in that more particles approach from the west than the east, which shows that cosmic rays have a positive charge.

The origin of cosmic rays is still uncertain. Large increases in secondary radiation coincide with strong solar flares. The higher-energy cosmic rays come from outside the solar system and may be produced by *supernova explosions.

cosmogeny. The study of the origin and development of the universe or of a particular system in the universe, such as the solar system or a satellite system of a planet.

cosmology. The branch of astronomy concerned with the evolution, general structure, and nature of the universe as a whole. *See also* big-bang theory; steady-state theory.

cosmotron. The *proton synchrotron at Brookhaven, US, that accelerates protons to an energy of 3 GeV.

Cotton–Mouton effect. Some isotropic transparent solids and liquids show slight double refraction towards light when in a strong magnetic field. *See* Kerr effects; magnetic effects.

Coudé system. *See* telescope.

coulomb. Symbol: C. The *SI unit of electric *charge, defined as the charge transported in one second by an electric current of one ampere.

Coulomb field. The *electric field around a point charge.

Coulomb force. A force of attraction or repulsion resulting from the interaction of the *electric fields surrounding two charged particles. The magnitude of the force is inversely proportional to the square of the distance between the particles.

coulombmeter. An instrument in which the electrolytic action of a current is used for measurement of the quantity of electricity passing through a circuit. It is sometimes called a *voltameter*.

Coulomb scattering. The *scattering of charged particles, such as alpha particles, by nuclei as a result of the electrostatic forces between them. If the incident beam contains one alpha particle per square centimetre then the number of particles, w, per unit solid angle which suffer a deflection φ is given by:

$$w(\varphi) = \left(\frac{Z_1 Z_2 e^2 m}{p^2} \right)^2 \frac{1}{\sin^4 \varphi},$$

where $Z_1 e$ and $Z_2 e$ are the charges of the scattered and scattering particles and m and p are the mass and momentum of the scattered particle.

Coulomb's law. The mutual force F exerted by one electrostatic point charge Q_1 on another Q_2 is given by

$$F = Q_1 Q_2 / 4\pi \varepsilon d^2,$$

where d is their separation and ε is the absolute *permittivity of the medium.

Coulomb's theorem. The intensity E of an electric field near a surface possessing a surface density of charge σ is given by

$$E = \sigma / \varepsilon,$$

where ε is the absolute *permittivity of the medium.

counter. (1) Any device for detecting and counting individual particles and photons. The term is used for the detector and for the instrument itself. Most detectors work by multiplication of the number of ions or electrons formed by a single particle or photon; each ionizing event leads to a pulse of current or voltage and these are electronically counted. *See* Geiger counter, crystal counter, boron chamber, proportional counter, semiconductor counter, and scintillation counter. (2) Any electronic circuit that records and counts pulses of current or voltage. *See also* counter/frequency meter.

counter/frequency meter. An instrument containing a frequency standard, usually an *oscillator controlled by a quartz crystal, that can be used as a counter or frequency meter by counting the number of events, or cycles, in a specified time. It may also be used to measure the time between events by counting the number of standard pulses occurring during a given number of events or cycles.

couple. (1) A system composed of, or equivalent to, two equal and antiparallel forces. The *moment is equal to the product of either force by the perpendicular distance between them and is the same about any axis perpendicular to the plane of the forces. It is an axial *vector.

(2) If a magnet of moment M is inclined at an angle θ to a field of strength H, the couple acting on it is $HM\sin\theta$.

coupled systems. Two or more mechanical vibrating systems connected so that they react on one another. In such systems there is a transfer of energy from one system to another involving a change in the natural frequency of the individual systems. There are conditions, particularly at *resonance, when the energy drain from one system to another is sufficiently great for one system to be unable to maintain maximum amplitude. Most musical instruments may be considered to be coupled systems.

coupling. (1) Of two oscillating electric circuits. The means by which the circuits interact so that energy is transferred from one to the other. In Fig. *a*, the circuits are coupled by mutual inductance between their individual inductances. This is *mutual-inductance coupling*. The coupling is sometimes made by means of an impedance which is common to both circuits (Figs. *b* and *c*). This is *common impedance coupling*. The *coupling coefficient*, K, may be defined by

$$K = X_m/\sqrt{X_1 X_2},$$

where X_m is the reactance common to both circuits, X_1 and X_2 are respectively the total reactances of the two circuits, both of the same kind as X_m. Thus, in Fig. *a*:

$$K = \omega M/\sqrt{\omega L_1 \times \omega L_2} = M/\sqrt{L_1 L_2}.$$

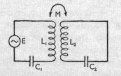

a Mutual-inductance coupling

In Fig. *b*:

$$K = \omega L_m/\sqrt{\omega(L_1 + L_m) \times \omega(L_2 + L_m)}$$

$$= L_m/\sqrt{(L_1 + L_m)(L_2 + L_m)}.$$

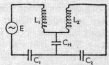

b Inductive coupling

In Fig. *c*:

c Capacitive coupling

$$K = \cfrac{\cfrac{1}{\omega C_M}}{\sqrt{\cfrac{1}{\omega}\cfrac{C_1 + C_M}{C_1 C_M} \times \cfrac{1}{\omega}\cfrac{C_2 + C_M}{C_2 C_M}}}$$

$$= \sqrt{\cfrac{C_1 C_2}{(C_1 + C_M)(C_2 + C_M)}}.$$

Sometimes the coupling is mixed, e.g. the types shown in Figs. *a* and *c* are applied simultaneously. (2) An interaction between different properties of a system or an interaction between two or more systems. There are two extreme types of coupling for atomic or nuclear particles:

In *Russell–Saunders coupling* (L–S coupling), the resultant, L, of the *orbital angular momentum of all particles interacts with the resultant, S, of the *spin of all particles. In *j–j coupling*, the total angular momenta (orbital + spin) of individual particles interact with each other.

C-parity. *See* charge parity.

CPU (central processing unit). The part of a digital *computer that takes instructions and data from the *memory and performs operations such as addition, comparison, multiplication, or storage on the data in accordance with the instructions.

cradle guard. *See* guard wires.

creep. The slow permanent deformation of a crystal or other specimen under sustained stresses.

critical. *See* chain reaction.

critical angle. Symbol: C. The angle of incidence of light proceeding from a denser medium towards a lighter one, at which grazing incidence occurs (angle of refraction $= 90°$). Light incident at a greater angle suffers total internal reflection. $\sin C = n'/n$ in which $n > n'$ where n is the refractive index of one medium and n' of the other.

critical angle refractometers. *Refractometers in which grazing incidence (*see* critical angle) is arranged between a medium whose refractive index is required and another of known index; the position of the boundary of light transmitted enables the refractive index to be calculated or to be observed directly on a scale.

critical constants. *See* critical pressure; critical temperature; critical volume.

critical damping. *See* damped.

critical isothermal. The isothermal curve relating the pressure and volume of a gas at its critical temperature.

critical mass. The minimum mass of a fissile material that will sustain a *chain reaction. *See also* nuclear weapons.

critical point. *See* critical state.

critical potential. *See* excitation energy.

critical pressure. The saturated *vapour pressure of a liquid at its critical temperature.

critical reaction. *See* chain reaction.

critical state. The state of a substance when it is at its critical temperature, pressure, and volume. Under these conditions the density of the liquid is the same as that of the vapour. The point corresponding to this state on an isotherm is the *critical point*.

critical temperature. The temperature above which a gas cannot be liquefied by increase of pressure. *See* equations of state.

critical velocity. The velocity of fluid flow at which the motion changes from *laminar to turbulent flow.

critical volume. The volume of a certain mass of substance measured at the critical pressure and temperature.

Crookes dark space. *See* gas-discharge tube.

Crookes glass. A type of spectacle glass containing cerium and other rare earths that has a low transmission of ultraviolet radiation.

Crookes tube. A low pressure discharge tube as used by Crookes for studying the properties of cathode rays.

crossed cylinder. A thin lens with cylindrical surfaces whose axes are crossed obliquely or at right angles. More particularly, a weak lens which has the effect of equal concave and convex cylinders crossed at right angles.

crossed lens. A form of spherical lens that shows minimum *spherical aberration in parallel light.

crossed Nicols. Two Nicol prisms arranged so that their vibration planes are perpendicular (*crossed*). The combination is opaque as the first Nicol polarizes the light in one plane and the second (analyser) prevents the polarized vibrations perpendicular to its own standard direction from passing on. *See* Polaroid.

crossover network. A type of filter circuit designed to pass frequencies above a specified value through one path, and frequencies below that value through another. This frequency is the *crossover frequency*, and the circuit is so designed that at this frequency the output of the two channels is equal. Such a network is widely used in high-fidelity systems to feed the bass and treble components to the appropriate speakers.

cross section. Symbol: σ. A measure of the probability of a particular collision process, stated as the effective area particles present to incident particles for that process. For example, if a beam of neutrons is passed through matter one possible reaction is neutron *capture. It is supposed that capture occurs when the neutron is some minimum distance, d, from the centre of the nucleus. For capture, the nuclei appear to present an effective cross sectional area (called the *capture cross section*) σd^2 to the incident neutrons. σ is sometimes called the *activation cross section*. Its value depends on the energy of the incident neutrons as well as the nuclei considered. In particular, when the kinetic energy of a neutron equals the energy difference between the *ground state of the nucleus and some higher state, the cross section is high and is called the *resonance cross section*.

The use of cross sections is also applied to other nuclear reactions, as well as to interactions between atoms, electrons, ions, etc. Cross section has units of m^2 and is often measured in *barns.

cryogenics. The study of the production and effects of very low temperatures. A *cryogen* is a refrigerant used for obtaining very low temperatures.

cryometer. A thermometer designed for the measurement of very low temperatures.

cryostat. A vessel that can be maintained at a specified low temperature; a low-temperature thermostat.

cryotron. A type of switch that depends on *superconductivity. It consists of a wire surrounded by a coil in a liquid helium bath. Both the wire and the coil are superconducting and a low voltage can produce a current in the wire. If a current is also passed through the coil its magnetic field alters the superconducting properties of the wire and switches off the current, thus the presence or absence of a current in the coil determines the ability of the wire to conduct.

crystal. (1) *See* crystal structure; crystal systems. (2) A piezoelectric crystal. *See* piezoelectric effect.

crystal analysis. *See* X-ray crystallography.

crystal base. The entire content of the *unit cell, whether considered as a symmetrical arrangement of atoms or as a symmetrical distribution of electron density.

crystal clock. *See* clocks.

crystal-controlled oscillator. An electromechanical oscillator employing a mechanically vibrating quartz crystal. The link between the mechanical vibrations and the electric circuits is provided by the *piezoelectric effect of the quartz crystal. It can be designed to have a very high degree of frequency stability. *See* clocks.

crystal counter. A device for detecting and counting subatomic particles that depends on their ability to increase the conductivity of a crystal. If a potential difference is applied across a crystal that is struck by a particle or photon the electron-ion pairs produced by the impact cause a transient increase in its conductivity. The pulses of current

crystal detector

resulting from successive impacts are electronically counted.

crystal detector. A *detector that depends for its action upon the rectifying properties of certain crystals when placed in contact with one another, or of a crystal in contact with a metal. It was used extensively in the earliest types of radio receiver, and more recently as a detector and mixer of centimetric waves.

crystal diffraction. The constructive and destructive interference of waves scattered by the periodic arrangement of electrons, nuclei, or field of force in a crystal to give a pattern of discrete spectra.

crystal filter. A filter that has one or more piezoelectric crystals forming resonant or antiresonant circuits in the filter.

crystal grating. The symmetrical arrangement of the atoms in a crystal in a series of parallel planes that enables the crystal to act as a three dimensional diffraction grating for X-rays.

crystallography. The science of the forms, properties, and structure of crystals, that is, of solids in which physical properties may vary regularly with direction, being the same along all parallel directions. _See also_ X-ray crystallography.

crystal microphone. A device making use of the *piezoelectric effect to convert the mechanical stress produced by sound pressure into electrical energy. Crystals of quartz or Rochelle salt cut in a certain direction show electrical charges on their faces when pressure is applied. Thus, the varying pressures caused by a sound wave striking the crystal face will produce alternating e.m.f.s across the crystal.

crystal oscillator. _See_ piezoelectric oscillator.

90

crystal parameter. The distance from the origin of the axis of a crystal to the intersection of any axis with a face, in terms of the arbitrary unit selected for measurement along that axis. _See_ rational intercepts, law of.

crystal structure. The specification both of the geometric framework (_see_ unit cell; space group) to which the crystal may be referred, and of the arrangement of atoms or electron density distribution relative to that framework.

crystal systems. The 14 *Bravais lattices and 32 *point groups can be referred to 7 systems of 3 axes: (1) _triclinic_, in which the axes need be neither equal nor mutually perpendicular; (2) _monoclinic_, in which the axes need not be equal, but one is perpendicular to the other two; (3) _orthorhombic_, in which the axes need not be equal, but they are all mutually perpendicular; (4) _tetragonal_, in which two axes must be equal, and all are mutually perpendicular; (5) _rhombohedral_, in which all axes are equal, and equally inclined to each other at an angle of less than 120°; (6) _hexagonal_, in which two axes are equal and inclined to each other at 120°, both being perpendicular to the third unique axis; (7) _cubic_, in which all axes are equal and mutually perpendicular. Sometimes (5) and (6) are amalgamated.

cubic system. _See_ crystal systems.

cumulatively compound-wound. _See_ compound-wound machine.

curie. Symbol: Ci. The unit of *activity of a radioactive substance corresponding to $3 \cdot 7 \times 10^{10}$ disintegrations per second. It is approximately equal to the activity of 1 g of radium.

Curie balance. An instrument for the measurement of the *susceptibility of feebly magnetic materials. The specimen is placed in a glass tube at the end of an arm with a balance weight, the system being suspended by a silk fibre. It is deflected by a strong permanent magnet, and the deflection is compared with that produced with distilled water or some other substance of known permeability in the tube.

Curie constant. The product of the magnetic *susceptibility per unit mass and the thermodynamic temperature; this quantity is approximately constant for many paramagnetic substances. *See* Curie's law.

Curie point or temperature. Symbol: θ_c or T_c. *See* Curie–Weiss law.

Curie scale of temperature. A temperature scale, used for the measurement of temperatures near the absolute zero, based on the assumption that a paramagnetic substance continues to obey Curie's law $\chi T = $ const. at the temperatures measured (0·07 to 1 K).

Curie's law. The principle that the susceptibility (χ) of a paramagnetic substance is universely proportional to the *thermodynamic temperature (T): $\chi = C/T$. The constant C is called the *Curie constant* and is characteristic of the material. This law is explained by assuming that each molecule has an independent *dipole moment and that the tendency of the applied field to align these molecules is opposed by the random motion due to temperature.

Curie–Weiss law. A modification of *Curie's law, followed by many paramagnetic substances (*see* paramagnetism). It has the form

$$\chi = \frac{C}{T - \theta}.$$

The law shows that the susceptibility is proportional to the excess of temperature over a fixed temperature θ, known as the *Weiss constant*, which is a temperature characteristic of the material.

For ferromagnetic solids (*see* ferromagnetism) there is a change from ferromagnetic to paramagnetic behaviour above the *Curie point* (or *temperature*) and the paramagnetic material then obeys the Curie–Weiss law above this temperature, θ_c. Below this temperature the law is not obeyed. The value θ can be thought of as a correction to Curie's law reflecting the extent to which the magnetic dipoles interact with each other. In materials exhibiting *antiferromagnetism θ corresponds to the *Néel temperature*.

curl. *Syn.* rotation. A vector quantity associated with a vector field, *F*. It is the vector product (*see* vector) $\nabla \times F$, where ∇ is the differential operator *del. Thus:

$$\operatorname{curl} F = \nabla \times F = \mathbf{i} \times \frac{\partial F}{\partial x} + \mathbf{j} \times \frac{\partial F}{\partial y} + \mathbf{k} \times \frac{\partial F}{\partial z},$$

where **i, j, k** are *unit vectors along the x-, y-, and z-axes respectively.

A field which has a curl is generally described as *rotational, vortical,* or *circuital*; if the curl is zero everywhere the field is irrotational or non-vortical. *Compare* gradient; divergence.

current. Symbol: I. The rate of flow of electricity; the unit is the *ampere. A *conduction current* is a current flowing in a conductor, the electricity being conveyed by the motion of electrons or ions through the material of the conductor. A conduction current of 1 ampere is equivalent to the flow of about 10^{18} electrons per second. *See also* displacement current.

current balance. An instrument for accurately determining a given current or, more fundamentally, the size of the *ampere by measuring the force between current-carrying conductors.

current density. Symbol: j. The ratio of the current to the cross-sectional area of the current-carrying medium. The medium may be a conductor or a beam of charged particles. The ratio may be specified either as a *mean current density* or as density at a point.

current transformer. *Syn.* series transformer. An instrument transformer in which the primary winding is connected in series with the main circuit and the secondary winding is closed through an instrument (e.g. ammeter) or other device. The ratio of primary and secondary currents is approximately the inverse of the primary to secondary turns-ratio of the transformer: used to extend the range of a.c. instruments, to isolate instruments from high-voltage circuits, and to operate protective relays in a.c. power systems.

curvature. For a spherical lens or mirror or a wavefront, the radius of the sphere on which such surfaces lie is the *radius of curvature*, r. The centre of the sphere is called the *centre of curvature*. The reciprocal of the radius of curvature is the curvature of the surface, *R*. If *r* is in metres then *R* is in *dioptres. A plane wavefront (zero curvature) incident on a lens or mirror will be changed into a spherical wavefront having a curvature of $1/f$ impressed on it, where f is the focal length of the lens or mirror. This ratio gives the *power of the lens or mirror.

curvature of field (or of image). In general, a plane object at right angles to the axis of an optical system will not give rise to a plane image. Instead, in the absence of *astigmatism, the image would lie on a paraboloidal surface known as the *Petzval surface*. This aberration is called curvature of field. The effects of astigmatism will be superimposed on those of curvature of field with the result that the tangential and sagittal focal planes T and S are displaced from the Petzval surface P. Two possible cases are indicated in the diagram.

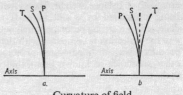

Curvature of field

In the case shown in Fig. *b*, the effects of astigmatism have been used to offset the curvature of the Petzval surface, and a flat screen placed in the position indicated by the dotted line would show a reasonably focused image. Variations of this sort are achieved in practice using optical systems with more than one lens, altering the spacing of the various component lenses, and adding suitably positioned stops.

cut-off bias. *Syn.* black-out point. (1) Of a valve. The grid bias voltage that will just reduce the anode voltage to zero. (2) Of a cathode-ray tube. The bias voltage that will just reduce the electron beam current to zero. In both cases it depends upon the voltages applied to the other electrodes and these must be specified.

cut-off frequency. Of a passive electrical or acoustical network (a non-dissipative system). A frequency, reached by varying the frequency of the applied voltage or driving force, at which the attenuation quickly changes from a small value to a much higher value.

An active electrical or acoustical network as a dissipative system has a cut-off frequency as given by a passive electrical network or a non-dissipative system having the same inductance (or inertia) and capacitance (or elastic) components. *See also* filter.

cycle. (1) An orderly set of changes regularly repeated. (2) One complete set of changes in the value of a periodic function.

cyclotron. An *accelerator in which a beam of energetic particles is produced. Charged particles describe a spiral path of many turns at right angles to a constant magnetic field, and are given an acceleration, always in the same sense, from an alternating electric field, each time they cross the gap between the two conductors (*dees*). The cyclotron depends on the fact that the time t taken by a particle of mass m and charge e to describe a semicircle in a plane at right angles to a uniform magnetic field H is $\pi m/He$, and is thus independent of the velocity. The radius r of the semicircle described by a particle increases as the velocity v increases: $v = Her/m$. As the beam approaches the circumference of the dees, an auxiliary electric field deflects the particles from the circular path and they leave through a thin window. The energy that can be obtained from such a device is limited by the relativistic increase in mass of the particle as the velocity increases, the maximum being about 25 MeV.

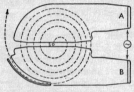

The magnetic field is perpendicular to the plane of the paper

Cyclotron

cylindrical lens (or surface). A mirror or lens may have one face a portion of the curved surface of a cylinder. Thin lenses for correcting astigmatism of the eye require one surface to be cylindrical (or *toric) and the other spherical (spherocylindrical).

cylindrical winding. A type of winding used in *transformers. The coil is helically wound and may be single-layer or multilayer. Its axial length is usually several times its diameter.

D

d'Alembert's principle. *See* force.

dalton. *See* atomic mass unit.

Dalton's law of partial pressures. The total pressure of a mixture of gases is equal to the sum of the *partial pressures that would be exerted by the gases if they were present separately in the container. *See* ideal gas.

damped. (1) Of a free oscillation. Progressively dying away due to an expenditure of energy by friction, viscosity, or other means. If the damping is such

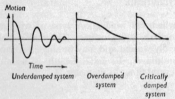

Motion

Time ——►
Underdamped system   Overdamped system   Critically damped system

that the system just fails to oscillate, the system is *critically damped* and for greater or less degrees of damping than this it is *overdamped* or *underdamped* respectively. In electrical indicating instruments, three systems of damping are in common use: air friction, fluid friction (oil), and eddy-current, and for such instruments the damping is usually designed to be slightly less than critical. The first two systems rely on viscous forces, and in all three systems, resistance is nearly proportional to velocity of motion.

(2) Of a vibration. Decreasing in amplitude with time due to the resistance of the medium to the vibration. For small amplitudes, the resistive force is approximately proportional to the velocity. The force equation for a damped simple harmonic motion is $m\ddot{x} = -kx - \mu\dot{x}$, where x is the displacement, and m, k, and μ are inertia, elastic, and resistive terms respectively. The solution of this

equation is $x = ae^{-\alpha t}\sin(\omega t - \delta)$, where the *decay* or *damping factor* $\alpha = \mu/2m$, and the frequency $n = \omega/2\pi$ where

$$\omega = \sqrt{\left(\frac{k}{m} - \frac{\mu^2}{4m^2}\right)}.$$

damping factor. (1) *Syn.* decrement. The ratio of the amplitude of any one of a series of damped oscillations to that of the following one. (2) *Syn.* decay factor. *See* damped (vibrations).

Daniell cell. A voltaic cell in which the positive pole is of copper immersed in a saturated solution of copper sulphate and the negative an amalgamated zinc rod in a solution of zinc sulphate (or more usually dilute sulphuric acid). The two solutions are separated by a porous partition. The cell has a fairly constant e.m.f. of about 1·08 volts and an internal resistance of a few ohms.

dark-field illumination. *Syn.* dark-ground illumination. *See* microscope.

dark space. The comparatively non-luminous portion of an electrical discharge through a gas. *See* gas-discharge tube.

data set. *See* file.

dating. *Syn.* radioactive dating. Any of several methods for determining the age of archaeological and fossil remains, rocks, etc., by measuring the quantity of one or two specific radioisotopes contained in a sample.

(1) *Radiocarbon dating* (or *carbon-14 dating*) is a method for determining the age of objects up to 10 000 years old containing matter that was once living, such as wood. Natural carbon consists mainly of the stable isotope ^{12}C and a small but constant proportion of ^{14}C, a

radioisotope of half-life 5730 years resulting from the bombardment of atmospheric nitrogen by neutrons produced by the action of *cosmic rays. All living organisms absorb carbon from atmospheric CO_2, but after death, absorption ceases and the once constant ratio $^{14}C/^{12}C$ decreases due to the decay of ^{14}C:

$$^{14}_{6}C \xrightarrow{\beta} {}^{14}_{7}N + \nu.$$

The ^{14}C concentration in a sample, found by using a sensitive *counter of particles, gives an estimate of the time elapsed since death of the living organism, the age being fairly accurate as far back as four thousand years.

(2) *Potassium–argon dating*. Potassium, in combination with other elements occurs widely in nature especially in rocks and soil. Natural potassium contains 0·001 18 % of the radioisotope ^{40}K which decays, with a half-life of $1·28 \times 10^9$ years, to the stable isotope of argon, ^{40}Ar. Determination of the ratio of $^{40}K/^{40}Ar$ gives an estimation of ages up to about 10^7 years.

(3) *Rubidium–strontium dating*. Natural rubidium contains 27·85 % of the radioisotope ^{87}Rb which decays with a half-life of 5×10^{11} years into the stable isotope of strontium, ^{87}Sr. Determination of the ratio $^{87}Rb/^{87}Sr$ gives an estimate of age of up to several thousand million years.

The age of the oldest (Precambrian) rocks has been estimated by radioactive dating to be about $3·5 \times 10^9$ years. The age of the earth has been estimated as $4·6 \times 10^9$ years, the discrepancy between these ages being due to the long cooling period of the newly formed earth.

daughter product. Any nuclide that originates from a given *nuclide, the *parent*, by radioactive *decay.

Davisson–Germer experiment. First experiment demonstrating the wavelike nature of particles, a nickel crystal being used to diffract a narrow beam of electrons. *See* de Broglie waves.

day. *See* time *for* sidereal and solar days.

deadbeat. Indicating an instrument that is *damped so that any oscillating motion of its moving parts dies away very rapidly.

dead room. *Syn.* anechoic chamber. A room that absorbs practically all the incident sound. It is made sound-proof by insulating the floor, walls, and ceiling from the rest of the building and by using heavy sound-proof doors. All the surfaces, including the floor, are then covered with several centimetres of highly absorbent material such as rock wool or asbestos fibre. The possibility of the formation of standing waves is further reduced by using an asymmetrical room or by placing absorbent deflectors in suitable places in the room. Most modern dead rooms employ large numbers of inward-pointing pyramids covered with an absorbing material to minimize possible reflections of sound.

dead time. In any electrical device, the time interval immediately following a stimulus during which it is insensitive to another stimulus.

de Broglie equation. A particle of mass m moving with a velocity v will under suitable experimental conditions exhibit the characteristics of a wave of wavelength λ given by the equation $\lambda = h/mv$, where h is the Planck constant. The equation is the basis of *wave mechanics.

de Broglie waves. *Syn.* matter waves; phase waves. A set of waves that represent the behaviour under appropriate conditions of a particle (e.g. its diffraction by a crystal lattice). The wavelength is given by the *de Broglie equation. They are sometimes regarded as waves of probability, since the square of their amplitude at a given point represents the probability of finding the particle at that point. *See also* Davisson–Germer experiment.

debye. A unit of dipole moment equal to 10^{-18} e.s.u. Equal and opposite charges, each equal to the electronic charge (4.80×10^{-10} e.s.u.), displaced 10^{-8} cm, produce a dipole moment of 4.80 debyes. 1 debye $= 3.335\,64 \times 10^{-30}$ coulomb metre.

Debye length. The maximum distance at which the *Coulomb field of charged particles in a *plasma can interact.

Debye–Scherrer ring. The circular diffraction ring, concentric with the undeflected beam, formed when a narrow pencil of monochromatic X-radiation is passed through a mass of finely powdered crystal.

Debye–Sears effect. If a piezoelectric crystal is placed in a liquid and vibrated at a fixed frequency it sets up acoustic waves – alternate regions of compression and rarefaction in the liquid with nodes every half wavelength. The liquid is held in a parallel-sided glass cell through which a beam of light of known wavelength is passed. The regions of compression and rarefaction in the liquid act as a *diffraction grating with a grating interval equal to the wavelength of the acoustic waves. This wavelength can be measured from the position of the diffracted light beam and the velocity of sound in the liquid can thus be obtained from the product of its frequency and wavelength.

Debye theory of specific heat capacities. Debye applied the *quantum theory to the independent vibrations of a solid considered as a continuous elastic body with an atomic structure such that the frequencies stop abruptly at a maximum frequency (v_m). The molar heat capacity at constant volume is then given by:

$$C_v = 9R \left(\frac{4}{x^3} \int_0^x \frac{\xi^3}{e^\xi - 1} d\xi - \frac{x}{e^x - 1} \right)$$

where $x = hv_m/kT$; $\xi = hv/kT$, k is the Boltzmann constant and h is the Planck constant. The Debye *characteristic temperature* θ is defined as hv_m/k, so that C_v is a function of (θ/T) which is in agreement with experimental results.

Debye T^3 law. At low temperatures the specific heat capacity is proportional to the cube of the thermodynamic temperature.

deca-. Symbol: da. The prefix meaning 10, e.g. 1 dam $= 10$ metres.

decay. (1) The transformation of a radioactive *nuclide, the parent, into its *daughter product by disintegration, resulting in the gradual exponential decrease in the *activity of the parent. *See also* alpha decay; beta decay; radioactivity. (2) The gradual decline of brightness of an excited *phosphor. (3) *See* damped.

decay constant. *Syn.* disintegration constant. Symbol: λ. The probability per unit time of the radioactive decay of an unstable nucleus. It is given by the formula $\lambda = -dN/dt \cdot 1/N$, where $-dN/dt$ is the *activity, A, of the nuclide and N the number of undecayed nuclei present at time t. The exponential decrease with time of the activity of a radionuclide in which there are N_0 nuclei at time $t = 0$ is found from the formula $N = N_0 e^{-\lambda t}$. The time required for half the original number of nuclei to decay ($N = \frac{1}{2}N_0$) is the *half-life, $T_{\frac{1}{2}}$, given by $T_{\frac{1}{2}} = 0.69315/\lambda$. The reciprocal of the decay constant is the *mean life.

deci-. Symbol: d. The prefix meaning $\frac{1}{10}$, e.g. 1 dm $= 0.1$ metre.

decibel. Symbol: dB. *See* bel.

decimal balance. *See* balance.

declination. (1) (magnetic) The angle between the magnetic meridian and the

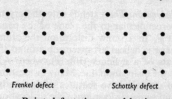

Frenkel defect   Schottky defect

a Point defects in crystal lattice

geographical meridian at a particular point. Its value depends on the position of the point on the earth's surface and at a given point changes slowly with time. (2) (astronomical) *See* celestial sphere.

declinometer. An instrument for determining the magnetic *declination. It consists essentially of an arrangement by which the angle between the magnetic axis of a compass needle and the direction of some heavenly body can be read on a horizontal circular scale.

decomposition voltage. The maximum potential difference that can be applied to the electrodes of an electrolytic cell without giving rise to a permanent current through the cell.

decoupling. The removal from a circuit or circuit element of any unwanted a.c. components, often caused by coupling between circuits, particularly those with a common power supply. Decoupling is usually achieved by using a series inductance or shunt capacitor.

decrement. *See* damping factor.

decrement gauge. *See* molecular gauge.

de-emphasis. *See* pre-emphasis.

defect. All crystalline solids consist of regular periodic arrangements of atoms or molecules. Departures from regularity are known as defects and they can be classified in two types. (1) *Point defects* are defects involving one single atom or molecule. A *Frenkel defect* is a vacant lattice site with an associated interstitial atom – i.e. an atom that is not in a normal lattice position. Such atoms are called *interstitials* and the vacant lattice site is called a *vacancy* (Fig. *a*). A *Schottky defect* is a vacant lattice point. It requires energy to create a point defect by moving an atom from its position but, since the defects introduce

disorder into a crystal, this is offset by an increase in configurational *entropy (i.e. entropy caused by disorder). Consequently all crystals above absolute zero have a certain number of such defects. The number of Schottky defects in a crystal at equilibrium is $n = N\,e^{-E/kT}$, where N is the total number of lattice sites and E the energy required to produce the defect. The number of Frenkel defects is given by $n = \sqrt{N\,N'}\,e^{-E/2kT}$, N' being the number of interstitial sites. The number of point defects rises exponentially with temperature; typically, for a metal at about 700° C, 1 in 10^5 sites are vacant. Point defects are responsible for *diffusion in solids. They can be produced in high concentrations by heating the solid to a high temperature and cooling it, by straining it, or by treatment with *ionizing radiation. (2) *Line defects* are extended departures from regularity in crystals and they are often called *dislocations*. There are two basic types, *edge dislocations* and *screw dislocations*. An edge dislocation is shown in Fig. *b*. It corresponds to an extra plane of atoms introduced in one part of the crystal. The

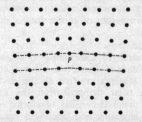

b Edge dislocation in crystal lattice

dislocation line extends into the crystal perpendicular to the plane of the paper at P. In a screw dislocation the atoms have a helical arrangement around the axis of a cylinder (Fig. *c*), where AD is the dislocation line. Many dislocations in crystals have features of both edge and screw dislocations. The dislocations in solids are responsible for plastic deformation above the *elastic limit.

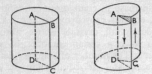

c Screw defect

They are also formed by deformation.

defect conduction. In a *semiconductor, conduction due to the presence of *holes in the valence band.

deflector coils, plates. *See* cathode-ray tube.

deformation potential. The electric potential caused by deformation of the crystal lattice of *semiconductors and conductors. *See* piezoelectric effect.

degaussing. (1) Neutralization of the magnetization of a ship by surrounding it with a system of current-carrying cables that set up an exactly equal and opposite field. (2) In colour television, the use of a system of coils to neutralize the earth's magnetic field thus preventing the formation of colour fringes on the image.

degeneracy. (1) *See* statistical weight. (2) The state of matter when it is at such a high temperature that all the electrons have been stripped from the atoms. The material consists of atomic nuclei and electrons and occurs in *neutron stars.

degenerate. *See* characteristic function; statistical weight.

degenerate semiconductor. A *semiconductor with the Fermi level located inside the valence or conduction band (*see* energy bands). The material is essentially metallic in behaviour over a wide temperature range.

degradation. (1) The decrease in the availability of energy for doing work as a result of the increase of *entropy within a closed system. *See* thermodynamics. (2) The loss of energy of a beam of particles or an isolated particle passing through matter as a result of the interaction of the particles with the matter.

degree. A unit of temperature difference. The Celsius and Fahrenheit degrees are defined as 1/100th and 1/180th respectively of the temperature difference between the ice and steam points, so that $1° C = \frac{9}{5}° F$. The unit of *thermodynamic temperature, no longer called a degree, is the *kelvin.

degrees of freedom. (1) The number of degrees of freedom of a mechanical system is equal to the number of independent variables needed to specify its state. The smallest number of co-ordinates needed to specify the state of the system is called its *generalized coordinates* and since these specify the state of the complete system, they also specify the state of any individual particle of the system. The number of degrees of freedom depends only on the possibilities of motion of the various parts of the system and not on the actual motions. For a monatomic gas the number is 3; for a diatomic gas with rigid molecules, it is 6, made up of 3 degrees of freedom of the centre of gravity to move in space, 2 degrees of freedom of the line joining the two atoms to change its direction in space and 1 for rotation about this axis. In applying the principle of *equipartition of energy the number of degrees of freedom is taken as the number of independent squared terms in the expression for the energy of a system, subject to certain reservations. (2) *Syn.* degrees of variance. *See* phase rule.

dekatron. A type of cold cathode scaling tube with usually ten cathodes arranged in a circle, and associated transfer electrodes surrounding the anode. When an impulse is received a glow discharge is transferred from one cathode to the next. The tubes may be used for switching or for visual display of counts in the decimal system.

del. *Syn.* nabla. Symbol ∇. The differential operator $i(\partial/\partial x) + j(\partial/\partial y) + k(\partial/\partial z)$, where i, j, and k are *unit vectors along the x-, y-, and z-axes respectively. The *Laplace operator is ∇^2.

delayed neutrons. Neutrons arising from nuclear *fission that are not directly formed in the fission process but are produced from excited fission products by *beta decay.

delay line. A transmission line or any other device that introduces a known delay in the transmission of a signal. An *acoustic delay line* is a device that delays a sound pulse by circulating it in a liquid or solid medium.

delay time. In general, the time taken for a pulse to traverse any device or circuit.

Delbruck scattering. The scattering of photons by the electrostatic field of an atomic nucleus. It is thought to occur for *gamma rays but the effect is small and has not been conclusively demonstrated.

delta connection. A particular example of the *mesh connection employed in *three-phase a.c. circuits in which three conductors, windings, or phases are connected in series to form a closed circuit which may be represented by a triangle ($\triangle$), the main terminals of the circuit being the junctions between the three separate circuits. *Compare* star-connection.

delta function (δ-function). *See* Dirac function.

delta radiation (δ-radiation). Secondary electrons emitted by the impact of *ionizing radiation on matter. Their energies are of the order of only 10^3 eV; they can cause further ionizations.

demagnetizing field. The magnetic field due to the free poles developed on a specimen of ferromagnetic material during the process of magnetization. The demagnetizing field (*see* diagram),

Demagnetizing field

in the medium between the free poles, opposes the applied magnetic field, H, the effective strength of which is thus reduced by an amount proportional to the existing intensity of magnetization of the specimen.

demodulation. The reverse of *modulation, i.e. the extraction or separation of the modulating signal from a modulated carrier wave. Circuits or devices used for this purpose are called demodulators or detectors.

demodulator. *See* detector.

demultiplexer. *See* multiplex operation.

denaturant. An isotope added to a *fissile material to make it unsuitable for use in nuclear weapons.

densitometer. An instrument for measuring the *transmission or *reflection density of a material. It is often used for converting the images on a photographic plate into quantitative form.

density. Symbol: ρ. (1) The mass per unit volume of a substance. In SI units it is measured in kg m^{-3}. The *relative density* (symbol d) is the density of a substance divided by the density of water: former name *specific gravity*. At the *maximum density of water, $\rho = 1000$ kg m^{-3}; therefore the relative density of any substance is one-thousandth of its density.

(2) Vapour density. The density of a gas or vapour divided by the density of hydrogen, both being at S.T.P.

(3) Density, in general, expresses the closeness of any linear, superficial, or space distribution, e.g. electron density is the number of electrons per unit volume; *see also* charge density.

(4) *See* reflection density; transmission density.

density of states curve. *See* energy bands.

depletion layer. A region in a semiconductor in which the mobile charge carrier density is not sufficient to neutralize the net fixed charge density of donors and acceptors. *See* semiconductor.

depletion mode. *See* field-effect transistor.

depolarizer. A substance used for removing the effects of *polarization in a primary cell by reacting either chemically or electrolytically with the hydrogen ions liberated at the positive pole.

depth of field. If a camera lens is focused on a particular object the image of the object will be in focus but the images of objects on either side will be slightly out of focus. The depth of field is the zone in which the image is acceptably sharp. A small aperture and short focal length produce a large depth of field.

depth of focus. The distance over which an image plane, at right angles to the lens axis, can be moved to maintain an acceptable standard of sharpness. A small aperture and short focal length produce a small depth of focus.

derived units. *See* SI units; coherent units.

Destriau effect. *See* electroluminescence.

detector. (1) *Syn.* demodulator. In communications, a circuit or apparatus used to separate the original information from the modulated *carrier wave. (2) Any device or apparatus used to detect or locate the presence of radiation, particles, etc.

deuteron. A nucleus of an atom of deuterium.

deviation. (1) *Syn.* variation. The difference between an observation and its true value. The latter has often to be replaced by its nearest known value, i.e. the mean of all the observations, in which case the difference is often called the *residual*. The *mean deviation* is the average of the deviations when all are given a positive sign. The *standard deviation* is the square root of the average of the squares of the deviations of all the observations. (*See* frequency distribution.) (2) In *frequency modulation, the amount by which the carrier frequency is changed by modulation.

deviation (angle of). The angle between the incident ray and the reflected (or refracted) or emergent ray. A ray after a single reflection is deviated ($\pi - 2i$), where i is the angle of incidence; after successive reflection at two plane mirrors the deviation is ($2\pi - 2A$) where A is the angle between the mirrors. The angle of deviation by a prism depends on the angle of incidence and the angle of the prism. *Minimum deviation* by a prism occurs when the refraction is symmetrical. The minimum deviation D appears in the equation, $n = \sin [(A + D)/2]/\sin (A/2)$ where A is the principal refracting angle of the prism and n the refractive index. For narrow angle prisms, $D = (n - 1)A$ (approximately), and over a moderate range of angle of incidence there is an approximately constant deviation.

Dewar vessel. *Syn.* vacuum or Thermos flask. A glass vessel consisting of a double-walled flask with the interspace completely evacuated to prevent gain or loss of heat by the contents of the flask through gaseous conduction and convection. Transfer of heat by radiation is reduced by silvering the inside walls.

dew point. The highest temperature a surface may have in order that dew may condense on the surface from a humid atmosphere. *See* humidity, relative.

dextrorotatory. Capable of rotating the plane of polarization of polarized light in a clockwise direction, as viewed against the direction of motion of the light. *See* optical activity.

diamagnetism. A property of substances that have a negative magnetic susceptibility so that the relative *permeability, μ_r, is less than that of a vacuum. It is caused by the motion of electrons in atoms around the nuclei. An orbiting electron produces a magnetic field in the same way as an electric current flowing in a coil of wire. If an external magnetic field is applied, the electrons change their orbits and velocities so as to produce a magnetic field that opposes the applied field, in accordance with Lenz's law.

Lines representing the flux in a uniform magnetic field become more separated when passing through the material; similarly, if a diamagnetic substance is placed in a non-uniform field it tends to move from the stronger to the weaker part of the field. If a bar of diamagnetic material is placed in a uniform magnetic field it tends to orientate itself so that the longer axis is at right angles to the flux.

Diamagnetism is a very weak effect: μ_r is only slightly less than one. It is sometimes totally masked by stronger *paramagnetism or *ferromagnetism. Copper, bismuth, and hydrogen are purely diamagnetic. The diamagnetic properties of materials are not affected by temperature.

diaphragm. An opaque screen containing a circular aperture centred and normal to the axis of an optical system; it controls the amount of light passing through the system.

diatonic scale. *See* musical scale.

dichroism. The property possessed by some crystals, such as tourmaline or Polaroid, of selectively absorbing light vibrations in one plane, while allowing the vibrations at right angles to pass through.

dichromate cell. *Syn.* bichromate cell. A primary cell in which poles of carbon and amalgamated zinc are immersed in a solution of potassium dichromate ($K_2Cr_2O_7$) in dilute sulphuric acid. A two-fluid form, in which the zinc is in dilute sulphuric acid and the carbon in an aqueous solution of dichromate, the two being separated by a porous partition, has also been used. The e.m.f. is 2·03 volts.

dielectric. A substance that is capable of sustaining an electrical stress, i.e. an insulator.

dielectric constant. *See* permittivity.

dielectric heating. The heating effect caused by rapid alternations of electrostatic charges applied across a dielectric. It is used commercially for heating of plastics, and also for special types of cooking.

dielectric hysteresis. A phenomenon, akin to magnetic hysteresis, as a result of which the *electric displacement in a dielectric depends not only on the applied electric field strength, but also on the previous electrical history of the specimen. It entails a dissipation of energy from the field when the specimen is subjected to an alternating electric flux.

dielectric loss. The total dissipation of energy that occurs in a dielectric when it is subject to an alternating electric stress.

dielectric polarization. *Syn.* electric polarization. Stress set up in a dielectric owing to the existence of an electric field, as a result of which each element of the dielectric functions as an electric dipole. It measures the increased flux present in the dielectric and is given by $(D - \varepsilon_0 E)$, where E is the applied field strength, D is the electric displacement, and ε_0 is the electric constant. *See also* displacement current.

dielectric strength. *Syn.* disruptive strength. The maximum electric field that an insulator can withstand without breakdown, under given conditions. It is usually measured in V mm^{-1}.

Diesel cycle. A *heat engine cycle in which air is the working substance and the fuel a heavy oil. From A to B the air is compressed adiabatically to a very high temperature. From B to C the burning fuel causes expansion at constant pressure, while CD is the remainder of the working stroke, being an adiabatic expansion. At D a valve opens and the pressure falls to atmospheric. A E and EA represent the exhaust and charging strokes. A separate fuel pump is necessary to inject the oil into the cylinder at high pressure.

Dieterici equation of state. *See* equations of state.

difference tone. *See* combination tones.

differential air thermometer. A simple instrument for the detection of radiant heat. Two equal closed bulbs A and B, one clear, the other blackened, contain

Differential air thermometer

air at atmospheric pressure. Radiation falling on the apparatus is more readily absorbed by the blackened bulb; the pressure inside B rises so that the liquid stands at a higher level in the left-hand connecting tube than in the right-hand tube.

differential amplifier. A type of *amplifier with two inputs, whose output is a function of the difference between the inputs.

differential galvanometer. A *galvanometer of the moving magnet type, having two separate coils through which currents can be passed in opposite directions. If the two coils are identical, the galvanometer will show no deflection when the currents in the two coils are equal.

differentially compound-wound. *See* compound-wound machine.

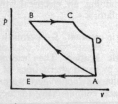

Diesel cycle

differentiator. A circuit in which the output is the differential with respect to time of the input.

diffraction analysis. The study of crystal structure by means of the diffraction of a beam of electrons, neutrons, or X-rays. *See* electron diffraction; X-ray analysis; neutron diffraction.

diffraction grating. A device for producing spectra by diffraction and for the measurement of wavelength. Commonly it consists of a large number of equidistant parallel lines (of the order 7500 per cm) ruled with a diamond point on glass, speculum metal, or an evaporated layer of aluminium (ruled gratings) or of a collodion cast taken from a ruled surface (replica grating). Diffracted light produces maxima of illumination (spectral lines) according to the equation: $d(\sin i + \sin \theta) = m\lambda$, where d is the grating interval, i.e. the distance between corresponding points of adjacent lines ($= 1/N$, in which N is the number of lines per unit distance), i the angle of incidence, θ the direction of the diffracted maximum with the normal corresponding with the *order m of the spectrum ($m = 0$ for the central image).

diffraction of light. If the shadow of an object cast on a screen by a small source of light is examined, it is found that the boundary of the shadow is not sharp. The light is not propagated strictly in straight lines. This phenomenon of diffraction, which occurs as the light passes the object, results from the wave nature of light. Banded or annular patterns, *diffraction patterns*, are produced near the edges of the shadow. Small apertures in objects produce a similar effect. Diffraction phenomena associated with a point source of light, which produces curved wavefronts, are classed as *Fresnel diffraction*. Plane wavefronts of a parallel beam of light produce *Fraunhofer diffraction*.

Certain of the effects observed in Fresnel diffraction can be explained if the wavefront falling on the obstacle is considered as a number of concentric annular zones, the distances of the peripheries of the zones from the observation point on the screen increasing by one half wavelength from zone to zone. The zones are called *Fresnel zones*. Each point on the wavefront can be considered as the source of a secondary wave and will contribute light to the observation point. Because each zone is a further half wavelength away than the next, the contributions from adjacent zones will be out of phase. Thus the total contribution can be represented as the sum of a series of terms alternatively positive and negative.

The amplitude of the light reaching the observation point from the whole unrestricted wavefront is half the amplitude that would result if all but the first Fresnel zone were blocked out. The intensity of the light will thus be one quarter of that due to the first zone alone.

If the obstacle has a circular aperture, the amount of light reaching the central point of the diffraction pattern will depend on the number of Fresnel zones that fill the aperture. If all but the first zone is blocked out by the obstacle, the intensity at the central point is four times that which would be observed if no obstacle were in place. If the first two zones are effective, the resulting intensity at the central point will be very small, since the contributions from the two zones are nearly equal but are out of phase. In this case, the diffraction pattern consists of a bright circle of light with a central dark spot. In general, if an odd number of zones is effective the centre of the pattern is bright, while an even number results in a dark central point. The general pattern consists of concentric light and dark rings.

If a circular object is used, the central Fresnel zones will be blocked out. The sum of the series of terms which represent the effective zones will still be equal to half the first term, so that this resulting amplitude at the centre of the pattern is half the amplitude due to the first effective zone. It follows that there will always be some light reaching the central point of the diffraction pattern so there is always a relatively bright spot at the centre of the shadow of a circular obstacle.

If the obstacle consists of alternately opaque and transparent annular zones, it is possible to arrange that every other Fresnel zone is effective for a particular observation point. The result will then be a high intensity of illumination at that point, since the light from the effective zones will all arrive in phase. Such an obstacle (called a *zone plate*) wil l produce at the observation point a bright 'image' of the point source and will in this sense act as a lens. It is capable of producing, by diffraction, an image of any small bright object.

In practical cases the radii of the Fresnel zones are very small. Thus diffraction effects are seen only with small obstacles or apertures and at the edges of the shadows of larger obstacles.

In considering obstacles consisting of a straight edge, a slit, or a wire, it is convenient to divide the wavefront into strips parallel to the edges of the obstacle, the distances of the edges of the strips from the observation point increasing by one half wavelength from strip to strip. The diffraction patterns can then be predicted by considering the total effects at the observation point of all the half-period strips not blocked out by the obstacle.

If the obstacle is a straight edge, then at the edge of the geometrical shadow the obstacle will block out all the strips over one half of the wavefront. Passing into the shadow there is a gradual diminution of light. Outside the shadow there are alternate bright and dark bands of decreasing contrast. In the case of a slit there will be a bright central line to the diffraction pattern if an odd number of strips of each half of the wavefront is

uncovered, and a dark line if the number is even. In general the pattern consists of an unsharp shadow of the slit crossed by dark lines. The case of the wire is rather similar to that of a circular obstacle. There is always a relatively bright line in the centre of the shadow.

In Fraunhofer diffraction, a parallel beam of light falls on the diffracting object and the effects are observed in the focal plane of a lens placed behind it. Thus in the diagram, AB represents a slit whose length is perpendicular to the plane of the paper, and on which falls a parallel beam of light. According to

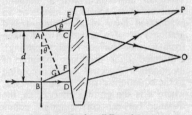

Fraunhofer diffraction

*Huygens's principle, each point in the slit must be considered as a source of secondary waves that spread out in all directions. Now the wavelets travelling straight forward along AC, BD, and so on, will arrive at the lens in phase and will produce a strong illumination at O. Secondary waves spreading out in a direction such as AE, BF, and so on will arrive at the lens with a phase difference between successive wavelets, and the effect at P will depend on whether this phase difference causes destructive *interference or not.

The resulting pattern seen in the plane OP is of alternate dark and light bands running parallel to the length of the slit. Unlike the corresponding case of Fresnel diffraction there is always a bright line at the centre of the diffraction pattern. The separation of the diffraction bands increases as the width of the slit is reduced; with a wide slit the bands are so close together that they are not readily noticeable. The separation also depends on the wavelength of the light, being greater for longer wavelengths. If white light is used, a few coloured bands are therefore produced.

In the case of a circular aperture, the diffraction pattern consists of a central bright patch (called the *Airy disc*) surrounded by alternate dark and light circular bands. Again the bands are close together if a large aperture is used but their separation increases as the diameter of the aperture used is reduced.

In the case of the slit shown in the diagram, the first dark line at P is in a direction θ such that BG is one wavelength, λ. If d is the width of the slit, then $\theta = \lambda/d$ (since θ is small). In the case of a circular aperture it can be shown that the direction of the first dark circle is given by a similar expression $\theta = 1 \cdot 22\lambda/d$.

diffraction of sound. Sound waves only cast sharp shadows when intercepted by a solid or when made to pass through a slit, if the solid or slit is of large dimension compared with the wavelength. To a certain degree however, the rays are bent or diffracted giving an interference pattern of regions of varying intensity just inside the shadow or shadows. This diffraction is more pronounced as the dimension of the solid or slit is made smaller, and in the extreme case where the dimension is less than the wavelength the sound is re-radiated from the obstacle with uniform intensity in all directions; the slit radiates only on the side away from the incident rays and thus produces hemispherical waves, but the solid radiates in all directions and therefore produces spherical waves.

The analysis of the general case is facilitated by Huygens's construction, i.e. by regarding the wavefront as consisting of an infinite number of point sources radiating spherical waves. These secondary waves interfere with each other to produce the interference patterns obtained.

The wavelength of audible sound in air varies from approximately 2 to 1000 cm depending on the frequency, and therefore, since the obstacles usually met are within this range, sound shadows are not well-defined in practice. A further contribution to the elimination of shadows is made by the presence of reflecting surfaces.

diffraction pattern. *See* diffraction of light.

diffraction spectrum. *Syn.* normal spectrum. A spectrum produced by a *diffraction grating. The angular separation of different spectral lines differs by amounts proportional to the difference in wavelength.

diffractometer. An instrument used in *diffraction analysis to measure the intensities of diffracted beams of X-rays or neutrons at different angles. An *ionization chamber or *counter is usually used and the beam to be diffracted is usually monochromatic.

diffused junction. A semiconductor junction, used in *transistors, that is formed by heating the semiconductor material in an atmosphere containing the desired impurities in gaseous form. Some atoms will be deposited on the surface of the semiconductor and diffuse inwards. The impurity profile will be well defined according to *Fick's law. Modern diffusion techniques use the *planar process of selective diffusion.

diffusion. (1) The process by which fluids and solids mix intimately with one another due to the kinetic motions of the particles (atoms, molecules, groups of molecules). Mixing occurs completely unless one set of particles is much heavier than the other, in which case dynamic equilibrium between diffusion and sedimentation under gravity occurs. Interdiffusion of solids (e.g. gold into lead) also occurs. *See* Fick's law; Graham's law. (2) The scattering of a beam of light on reflection from a rough surface or transmission through certain materials. (3) The degree to which the directions of propagation of sound waves vary over the volume of a reverberant sound field.

diffusion cloud chamber. A type of *cloud chamber in which supersaturation is achieved by diffusion of a vapour from a hot to a cold surface through an inert gas. As the vapour supply is continually replenished by diffusion, the chamber can be made almost continuously sensitive to ion tracks. There are no moving parts.

diffusion coefficient. *See* Fick's law.

diffusion current. *See* limiting current.

diffusion length. In a *semiconductor, the average distance travelled by *minority carriers between generation and recombination.

diffusion pump. *See* pumps, vacuum.

diffusion theory. A theory concerning the *diffusion of particles, especially neutrons, based on the assumption that, in a homogeneous medium, the *current density is proportional to the negative gradient of the particle flux density.

diffusivity. Symbol: α. A measure of the rate at which heat diffuses through a substance. It is equal to the thermal conductivity divided by the specific heat capacity at constant pressure and the density, i.e. $\alpha = \lambda/\rho c_p$. It is measured in $m^2 s^{-1}$.

digital circuit. Any circuit designed to respond to discrete values of input voltage and produce discrete output voltage levels. Usually only two values of voltage are recognized, as in binary *logic circuits. *Compare* linear circuit.

digital computer. *See* computer.

digital inverter. *See* inverter.

digital voltmeter. A voltmeter that displays the measured values as numbers composed of digits. The voltage to be measured is usually supplied as an analog signal, and the voltmeter samples the signal repetitively and displays the voltage sampled.

digitizer. *See* analog/digital converter.

digitron. *Syn.* Nixie tube. A type of cold cathode scaling tube in which the cathodes are shaped into the form of characters, usually the digits 0 to 9. A switching connection to one side of the power supply selects the cathode required. These tubes are widely used for display in electronic calculating machines and for visual display of fast count rates in counting equipment.

dilation. *Syn.* dilatation. A change of volume.

dilatometer. Any apparatus for studying thermal expansion.

dimensional analysis. A technique whose main uses are: (1) to test the probable correctness of an equation between physical quantities; (2) to provide a safe method of changing the units in a physical quantity; (3) to assist in recapitulating important formulae; (4) to solve partially a physical problem whose direct solution cannot be achieved by normal methods; (5) to predict the behaviour of a full scale system from the behaviour of a model; (6) to suggest relations between fundamental constants.

The basis of the technique is that the various terms in a physical equation must have identical dimensional formulae if the equation is to be true for all consistent systems of units. Mechanical quantities can be expressed in terms of powers of mass M, length L, and time T only. E.g. area $= L^2$, velocity $= LT^{-1}$, force $= MLT^{-2}$, energy $= ML^2T^{-2}$.

Electrical and magnetic quantities require current I or charge Q as an additional dimension. Since power $P = IV$, the dimensions of voltage are $ML^2T^{-3}I^{-1}$ or $ML^2T^{-2}Q^{-1}$. *See also* dynamic similarity.

dineutron. An unstable system consisting of a pair of *neutrons; it is assumed to have a transient existence in certain *nuclear reactions.

diode. Any electronic device with only two electrodes. There are several different types of diode and their applications depend on their voltage characteristics. Diodes are usually used as rectifiers. (1) *Semiconductor diodes, symbol: $-\triangleright\!\!\vdash$, consist of a single p–n junction. Current flows when forward voltage is applied to the diode (*see* diode forward voltage), and increases exponentially (*see* diagram). If voltage is applied in

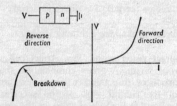

V/I curve for semiconductor diode

the reverse direction only a very small leakage current flows until the *breakdown voltage is reached. *See* p–n junction. (2) *See* thermionic valve.

diode forward voltage. *Syn.* diode drop; diode voltage. The voltage across the terminals of a semiconductor *diode when current flows in the forward direction. Because of the exponential nature of the current characteristic, the diode voltage is approximately constant over the range of currents commonly used in practical circuits. A typical value is about 0·7 V at 10 mA.

diode transistor logic (DTL). A family of integrated *logic circuits, with the inputs through *diodes and the output taken from the collector of an inverting transistor. The basic DTL gate circuit is a NAND gate. The speed of DTL logic circuits is less than *emitter-coupled logic circuits. In practice, however, the speed at which any logic circuit may be operated is determined largely by the speed of interconnections, and the slightly lower speed of DTL circuits is not a disadvantage.

diode voltage. *See* diode forward voltage.

dioptre. A unit used to express the power of a spectacle lens, viz. the reciprocal of the focal length in metres. It is also applicable to *vergence and curvature, convergence being regarded as positive.

dioptric system. A refractive optical system involving lenses, etc. *Compare* catadioptric system.

dip. *Syn.* (magnetic) inclination. The angle made with the horizontal by the direction of the earth's total magnetic field. It varies from 0° at the magnetic equator to 90° at the magnetic poles. A magnet freely suspended at its centre of gravity would set with its magnetic axis in the magnetic meridian and inclined to the horizontal at the angle of dip.

dip circle. An instrument for determining the angle of *dip. It consists essentially of a thin magnet supported so as to be free to rotate about a horizontal axis through its centre of gravity, its inclination to the horizontal being read on a vertical circle.

dipole. A system of two equal and opposite charges situated a very short distance apart. The product of either of the charges and the distance between them is the *dipole moment* (symbol: p). A small magnet constitutes a magnetic dipole.

dipole aerial. An *aerial very commonly used for frequencies below 30 MHz. It consists of a horizontally mounted conductor, of length one half wavelength of the transmitted wave. Some types have the feeders at one end, others in the centre, and the aerial may be a single conductor or a folded one.

dipole moment. *See* dipole; debye.

diproton. An unstable system consisting of a pair of *protons; it is assumed to have a transient existence in certain *nuclear reactions.

Dirac constant. Symbol: $\hbar$ (called h-bar or crossed-h). The *Planck constant divided by 2π.

Dirac function. *Syn.* δ-function. A function of x defined as being zero for all values of x other than $x = x_0$ and having the definite integral from $x = -\infty$ to $+\infty$ equal to unity. It is much used in quantum mechanics and can be used, for example, to represent an impulse in dynamics. The graph of the function is that of a single, infinitely high and infinitesimally wide peak of total area unity placed at $x = x_0$.

direct access. *Syn.* random access. A method of data organization in which any part of a computer *file may be reached without starting at the beginning and working through. *See* drum; disk.

direct-coupled amplifier. *Syn.* d.c. amplifier. An *amplifier in which the output of one stage is coupled directly to the input of the next stage or through a chain of *resistors. It is capable of amplifying *direct current.

direct current. (d.c.) An electric current that flows in one direction only and is substantially constant in magnitude.

direct-current restorer. A device to restore or impose a signal d.c. or low

frequency component to a signal after passing through a circuit that has low impedance to fast variations in current, but high impedance for d.c. or low frequency current.

directive aerial. An aerial that, as a radiator or receiver of radio waves, is more effective in some directions than in others. The directivity is often obtained by employing a *passive* (or parasitic) aerial in conjunction with an *active* aerial. The latter is connected directly to the transmitter or receiver. The former influences the directivity but, in transmission, is excited by the e.m.f. induced in it by the nearby active aerial, or, in reception, reacts with the active aerial by virtue of the mutual impedance between them. A passive aerial is called a *reflector* or a *director* according to whether it is placed respectively behind or in front of the active aerial.

director (aerial). *See* directive aerial.

direct stroke. *See* lightning stroke.

direct vision prism. *Syn.* Amici prism; roof prism. A prism combination that produces dispersion without deviation of the central part of the spectrum (yellow *D* line). It is used in the construction of the *direct vision spectroscope.*

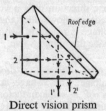

Direct vision prism

disappearing filament pyrometer. An *optical pyrometer in which an image of the hot source is focused by the telescope objective lens O onto the filament of an electric lamp L which is viewed through a red filter by the eyepiece E. The observer varies the current through the

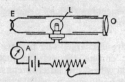

Disappearing filament pyrometer

lamp filament until the filament becomes indistinguishable against the background of the image of the source. The red filter enables the matching to be made for a small band of wavelengths.

discharge. (1) To remove or reduce an electric charge of a body. (2) The passage of an electric current or charge through a *gas-discharge tube or dielectric, usually accompanied by luminous effects. (*See* conduction in gases.) (3) The conversion of chemical energy into electrical energy in a cell.

discharge coefficient. The ratio of the actual discharge of fluid from an orifice to the discharge calculated from the velocity given by *Torricelli's law. The discharge coefficient is given by $Q/A\sqrt{2gh}$, where Q is the actual discharge through an orifice of an area A under a static head h.

discharge tube. *See* gas-discharge tube.

discomposition effect. *See* Wigner effect.

discriminator circuit. (1) An electronic circuit for changing the *frequency modulation or *phase modulation of a signal into *amplitude modulation. (2) A circuit that delivers output pulses only for input pulses of greater than a certain chosen amplitude.

disc winding. A type of winding used in transformers. It consists of a number of flat coils, each wound in the form of a disc. They are usually employed for the high-voltage windings of power transformers.

disintegration. Any process in which a nucleus emits one or more particles, such as *beta particles, *alpha particles, and *gamma rays, either spontaneously or following a collision.

disintegration constant. *See* decay constant.

disk. *Syn.* magnetic disk. A direct-access *storage device, used in computing systems, that consists of a stack of plates all of which are coated on both surfaces with magnetic iron oxide. They rotate rapidly as a single unit on a common spindle. A set of electromagnetic read-write heads can be instructed to move radially over the surfaces and retrieve or write data on concentric tracks.

dislocation. *See* defect.

dispersion. The decomposition of a beam of white light into coloured beams which spread out to produce spectra, or *chromatic aberration. More precisely, it is concerned with descriptions of the variation of refractive index (n) with wavelength (λ). With most transparent substances, n increases as λ decreases. (*See* Sellmeier's equation; Cauchy dispersion formula.) The mean dispersion is the difference of n for light of the F and C lines of hydrogen, i.e. ($n_F - n_C$). *Dispersive power* (ω) is given by the ratio ($n_F - n_C$)/($n_D - 1$). For intermediate differences, *partial* dispersions are quoted. The dispersion of a narrow angle prism refers to its chromatic aberration (ωP), where P is deviating power.

The rate at which an angle of refraction or diffraction varies with wavelength ($d\theta/d\lambda$) is also referred to as *dispersive power* or *angular dispersion*. *See also* anomalous dispersion.

dispersion of sound. At audible frequencies the *velocity of sound in a gas is given by the Laplacian equation $c = \sqrt{\gamma p/\rho}$, where γ is the ratio between the two specific heat capacities of the gas, p is the pressure, and ρ is the density.

At higher frequencies the velocity of sound in certain gases, notably CO_2, varies with frequency. Above about 200 kHz CO_2 is opaque to sound waves. This dispersion of sound is accompanied by abnormal values of absorption. According to the *relaxation theory*, at higher frequencies there is a lag in the interchange of translational and vibrational energy of the gas molecules. The oscillatory degrees of freedom therefore have no longer time in these rapid acoustic vibrations to adapt themselves completely to the adiabatic changes of temperature.

dispersive power. *See* dispersion.

displacement. (1) A change in position; the distance moved by a given particle of a system from its position of rest when acted upon by a disturbing force. (2) The quantity of fluid displaced by a submerged or partially submerged body. (3) *See* electric displacement.

displacement current. The rate of change of electric flux with respect to time through a dielectric when the applied electric field is varying. When a capacitor is charged the conduction current flowing into it is considered to be continued through the dielectric as a displacement current so that the current is, in effect, flowing in a closed circuit. Displacement current does not involve motion of the current carriers (as in a conductor) but rather the formation of electric dipoles (*dielectric polarization), thus setting up the electric stress. The recognition by Maxwell that a displacement current in a dielectric gives rise to magnetic effects equivalent to those produced by an ordinary conduction current is the basis of his electromagnetic theory of light.

displacement law (Wien). *See* black body radiation.

disruptive discharge. The passage of an electric current through an insulating material when the latter breaks down under the influence of a dielectric stress equal to or greater than the *dielectric strength of the particular insulating material. *See* spark.

disruptive strength. *See* dielectric strength.

dissociation. (1) The breakdown of molecules into smaller molecules or atoms. Most dissociations are reversible; the equilibrium constant for dissociation is often called the dissociation constant. (2) The breakdown of molecules into ions in solution. *See* electrolytic dissociation.

dissonance. *See* consonance.

distance (least) of distinct vision. Conventional distance of 25 cm or 10 in for use in comparing magnifying powers of microscopes.

distortion. The extent to which a system, or part, fails to reproduce accurately at its output the characteristics of the input. (1) (electrical) The modification of a *waveform of voltage, current, etc., by a transmission system or network. It involves the introduction of features that do not appear in the original or the suppression or modification of features that are present in the original. *Attenuation distortion* (or *frequency distortion*) occurs when the gain or loss varies with frequency; *phase distortion* occurs when the phase change introduced is not a linear function of frequency; *harmonic distortion* results from harmonics not present in the input; *amplitude distortion,* due to changes with amplitude of the input, varies the ratio of the r.m.s. input value to r.m.s. output, both waveforms being assumed sinusoidal; *non-linear distortion* results from transmission properties varying with the instantaneous magnitude of the input and gives rise to harmonic and amplitude distortion.

(2) (sound) *Frequency distortion* is the non-uniform transmission of amplitude at different frequencies for a constant amplitude input; *amplitude distortion* results in a non-linear relation between input and output at different amplitudes of the input; *phase distortion* is a phase shift between different components on transmission; *transient distortion* causes the duration of certain components of a note to increase.

(3) (light) The *aberration formed by an optical instrument when the image is not geometrically similar to its object. The lateral magnification (y'/y) is not constant but depends on the size of the object, y. When the magnification decreases with object size, a square object is imaged with *barrel distortion*; the reverse case is *pincushion distortion*. In general, a front stop gives barrel distortion, a rear stop pincushion type;

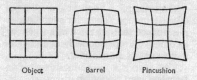

Object   Barrel   Pincushion

Distortion

symmetrical doublets with a central stop for which position the lens is spherically corrected are free from distortion.

distribution function. The mathematical expression of a *frequency distribution.

distribution of velocities. *Maxwell's distribution law* (*Maxwell–Boltzmann distribution*), based on classical statistics,

states that for a gas in equilibrium the number of molecules whose total velocity lies in the range c to $(c + dc)$ is given by the expression

$$dN_c = 4\pi N \left\{ \frac{hm}{\pi} \right\}^{\frac{3}{2}} (e^{-hmc^2}) c^2 \, dc,$$

where N is the total number of molecules, m is the mass of a molecule, h is a constant, equal to $1/(2kT)$, where k is the *Boltzmann constant and T the thermodynamic temperature.

The distribution yields values as follows:

C, root mean square velocity $= \sqrt{3/2hm}$,

$\bar{C}$, the mean velocity $= \sqrt{3/\pi hm}$,

C_p, the most probable
               velocity $= \sqrt{1/hm}$.

The higher the temperature the more scattered is the distribution, but at all temperatures there is theoretically a small number of molecules whose velocity approaches infinity. This equation can also be used to determine the positions and energy distribution of gas molecules. *See also* canonical distribution.

diurnal motion. The apparent motion of celestial bodies across the sky from east to west, caused by the rotation of the earth from west to east.

divergence (div). The *flux per unit volume leaving an infinitesimal element of volume at a point in a vector field; e.g. in an electrostatic field, the divergence of the field is zero unless the volume element contains an electrostatic charge and the vector field is therefore *solenoidal. The divergence of a vector field F is the scalar product (*see* vector) $\nabla \cdot F$, where ∇ is the differential operator *del.

D-layer or region. *See* ionosphere.

D-lines of sodium. Two yellow lines very close together in the *emission spectrum of sodium. D_1 has a wavelength of 589·6 nm and D_2 589·0 nm. Because these lines are bright and easily produced, sodium light is used as a reference line in spectrometry.

domain. *See* ferromagnetism; Bitter patterns.

dominant wavelength. *See* chromaticity.

donor. *See* semiconductor.

doping. The addition of impurities to a *semiconductor to achieve a desired n-conductivity or p-conductivity.

doping compensation. The addition of a particular type of impurity to a *semiconductor to compensate for the effect of an impurity already present.

doping level. In a semiconductor. The number of impurity atoms added to the material to achieve the desired polarity and resistivity. Low doping levels yield a high resistivity material; high doping levels yield a low resistivity material.

Doppler broadening. An effect observed in line spectra when radiation forming a particular spectral line has a spread of frequencies because of the Doppler effect caused by the thermal motion of molecules, atoms, or nuclei. The apparent frequency of light from a single atom of gas depends on the velocity of the atom with respect to the observer. Since the atoms of the gas have a Maxwellian *distribution of velocities the frequencies of radiation received by an observer will have a similar distribution and this gives a single spectral line a *Doppler width*. The effect is also observed in *absorption spectra and in nuclear processes.

Doppler effect. The change in apparent frequency of a source (of light or of sound) due to relative motion of source and observer.

It is illustrated simply by assuming the velocities are in the line joining the source and observer; suppose C is the velocity of sound, u_s the velocity of the source, u_0 the velocity of observer, n the true frequency of the source, and W the velocity of the medium. If S is the initial position of the source and S′ its position one second later, the waves emitted by

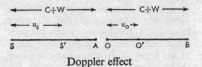

Doppler effect

the source in one second occupy the distance $S'A = C + W - u_s$ which contains n waves. Similarly let O be position of observer; in one second the waves received occupy the distance $O'B = C + W - u_0$ which contains n waves. Then the apparent frequency is

$$n' = n \times \frac{C + W - u_0}{C + W - u_s}.$$

When the medium is still,

$$n' = n \times \frac{C - u_0}{C - u_s}.$$

The principle is applicable to all types of wave motion. Thus, for sound waves it is noticed that the pitch of a whistling locomotive drops suddenly as the locomotive passes an observer.

Doppler radar. *See* radar.

Doppler shift. The magnitude of the change in frequency or wavelength of waves that results from the *Doppler effect. *See* red shift.

dose. A quantity of radiation or absorbed energy. (1) *Absorbed dose* is the energy absorbed per unit mass in an irradiated medium. The unit is the *rad (*r*adiation *a*bsorbed *d*ose). (2) *Exposure dose* is a measure of X- or gamma-radiation to which a body is exposed. It is equal to the total charge collected on ions of one sign produced in unit mass of dry air by all *secondary electrons liberated in a volume element by incident photons stopped in that element. The unit is the *roentgen. (3) *Equivalent dose* is used for protection purposes. The unit is the *rem* (*r*oentgen *e*quivalent *m*an). It is defined by 1 rem = 1 rad × Q.F., where Q.F. is the *quality factor* for a particular type of radiation and is a means of relating absorbed doses of different radiations to give the same biological effect. For X-rays, gamma-rays, and high-energy beta-rays, Q.F. = 1; low-energy beta-rays, Q.F. ≃ 1·8; neutrons, Q.F. = 10.

dosemeter. *Syn.* dosimeter (now deprecated). Any instrument or material used for measuring radiation *dose. *See* dosimetry.

dosimetry. The measurement of radiation *dose, the choice of method being determined by the quantity and quality of radiation delivered, the rate of delivery (*dose rate*), and the convenience. The most common method is to measure the *ionization caused by the radiation, as in an *ionization chamber.

Film dosimetry is a means of measuring dose using photographic film. The degree of blackening on the film after exposure to radiation and development under controlled conditions gives a measure of the dose received.

High energy radiation induces changes in the mechanical, electrical, and optical properties of polymers, such as perspex and PVC. In *perspex dosimetry* a piece of perspex is irradiated producing an increase in *transmission density which is proportional to dose over a certain dose range.

Lithium fluoride dosimetry involves the measurement of the *thermoluminescence from the irradiated phosphor, lithium fluoride. Following irradiation the lithium fluoride is heated and the thermoluminescent output (light) is determined by using a *photomultiplier.

This output is proportional to integrated dose.

In *chemical dosimetry*, measurement of the change in optical density of a particular solution, following irradiation, gives the dose, the change being dependent on radiation used, dose rate, and solute concentration.

double-base diode. *See* unijunction transistor.

double bridge. *See* Kelvin double bridge.

double refraction. *Syn.* birefringence. When near objects are viewed through Iceland spar, they appear doubled. The light is split into two parts: an *ordinary ray* which obeys the ordinary laws of refraction and an *extraordinary ray* which follows a different law. The light in the ordinary ray is polarized at right angles to the light in the extraordinary ray. Because of the crystalline nature of the medium, two groups of Huygens wavelets (*see* Huygens's principle) progress; the ordinary wavefront is developed by spherical wavelets and the extraordinary wavefront is developed by wavelets which are ellipsoids of revolution. Along an optic axis these travel with the same velocity. The measurement of the double refraction of any crystal is given by the difference of its greatest and least refractive indices.

double-sideband transmission. *See* single-sideband transmission.

doublet. A pair of closely spaced lines in a *spectrum. *See* spin.

drag coefficient. When a body and viscous fluid are in relative motion the body experiences a *drag force* (D) parallel to the direction of relative motion but in the opposite direction, and given by $D = k_0 \rho l^2 V^2$, where ρ is the fluid density, V the relative velocity, and l some characteristic length of the body; k_0 is the drag coefficient, a function of *Reynolds number IV/v, where v is the coefficient of kinematic velocity. This is not a unique definition, the term $\frac{1}{2}\rho V^2$ being sometimes used instead of ρV^2.

drain. The electrode in a *field-effect transistor through which *carriers leave the inter-electrode region.

drift mobility. In a *semiconductor, the average velocity of excess *minority carriers per unit electric field. In general, the mobilities of *holes and *electrons are different.

drift transistor. *Syn.* graded-base transistor. A transistor in which the impurity concentration in the *base varies across the base region. A high *doping level at the emitter-base junction reduces across the base to a low doping level at the collector-base junction. Drift transistors have a very high frequency response.

drift tube. *See* linear accelerator.

driver. A circuit whose output is used to provide the input of one or more other circuits. The term is commonly applied to the amplifier stage preceding the output stage of a transmitter or receiver.

driving point impedance. The ratio of the r.m.s. value of the sinusoidal voltage applied to two terminals of an electrical network to the r.m.s. value of the current that flows between the terminals as a result of the applied voltage.

drum. *Syn.* magnetic drum. A direct-access *storage device used in computing that consists of a rapidly rotating cylinder coated with a magnetic iron oxide. Fixed electromagnetic read–write heads are arranged to retrieve and write data on tracks around the circumference of the surface.

drum winding. A type of *winding used in electrical machines. It consists of coils,

usually former-wound, which are housed in slots either on the outer periphery of a cylindrical core or on the inner periphery of a core having a cylindrical bore. Modern machines usually have this type of winding.

dry cell. A primary cell in which the active constituents are absorbed in some porous material so that the cell is unspillable. The usual form consists of a zinc container (forming the negative electrode) lined with a paste of ammonium chloride and plaster of Paris, and having in the centre a carbon rod surrounded by a mixture of ammonium chloride, powdered carbon, zinc sulphate, and manganese dioxide made into a stiff paste with glycerine. Its action is the same as that of the *Leclanché cell; e.m.f. about $1\frac{1}{2}$ volts.

dry ice. Solid carbon dioxide, used as a refrigerant.

Duane–Hunt relation. The shortest wavelength (λ_{min}) generated in an X-ray tube is inversely proportional to the potential difference (V) applied to the tube:

$$Ve = hc/\lambda_{min} = h\nu_{max}$$

where ν_{max} is the maximum frequency emitted. This is a special case of Einstein's law for photon energy.

ductility. A combination of properties of a material which enables it to be drawn out into wires.

Dulong and Petit's law. The product of the mass per mole of a solid element and its specific heat capacity is constant. This product was originally called the atomic heat (equal to atomic weight × specific heat) but it is now known as the *molar heat capacity. According to Dulong and Petit's law the molar heat capacity, in SI Units, is approximately 25 J K^{-1} mol^{-1}. This value may be deduced from the principle of *equipartition of energy, which gives the molar heat capacity for three degrees of freedom as $3R$ (25 J K^{-1} mol^{-1}).

This value holds only for simple substances that crystallize in the regular or other simple systems and at high temperatures. At lower temperatures the value falls below $3R$, being proportional to T^3. This is explained by *Einstein's theory of specific heat capacities.

duplexer. A two channel multiplexer commonly used in *radar, in which a transmit–receive switch functions during the finite time between transmitting a pulse and receiving the return echo, so that the transmitter and receiver are connected in turn to the same aerial system.

Duralumin. A hard light-weight alloy of aluminium containing 4% copper, 5% manganese, 5% magnesium.

Dushman's equation. *See* Richardson's equation.

dust core. A core for magnetic devices consisting of a powdered magnetic material, such as *ferrite, sintered or cemented into a compact block. It is used for minimizing *eddy current loss in high-frequency equipment.

dwarf star. Any of a class of faint stars lying in the main sequence of the *Hertzsprung–Russell diagram that have a high density and small diameter compared to the much brighter class of *giant stars. Both of these distinct types belong to the same spectral classes (G, K, and M). A red dwarf is in the same spectral class as a red giant but is 10 *magnitudes fainter. *See also* white dwarf.

dynamic characteristic. *See* characteristic.

dynamic equilibrium. (1) *See* force. (2) A balanced state of constant change, e.g. if water is sealed in an exhausted vessel and kept at constant temperature, although molecules are constantly being exchanged between the ice, water, and water vapour phases, it will be in equilibrium in so far as the pressure and volume of the phases are concerned.

dynamic friction. *See* friction.

dynamic impedance. *See* rejector.

dynamic range. The range over which a useful output is obtained for a device, expressed as the difference in decibels between the noise level of the system and the overload level.

dynamics. *Syn.* kinetics. The branch of *mechanics concerned with forces that change or produce the motions of bodies.

dynamic similarity. *Syn.* similarity principle. The dimensions of all dynamic quantities (velocity, acceleration, force, etc.) can be expressed uniquely in terms of the fundamental dimensions of mass (M), length (L), and time (T), certain combinations of the dynamical quantities producing non-dimensional numbers. Two systems in motion possess dynamic similarity when, for equal values of some dimensionless grouping of the dynamic quantities, they pass through geometrically similar configurations.

In the motion of fluids two systems are dynamically similar when the body boundaries and the corresponding flow patterns are geometrically similar, the non-dimensional groupings consisting of a combination of one or more of the dimensionless *Reynolds, *Froude, and *Mach numbers.

In hydrodynamics and aerodynamics, the principle of similarity is used extensively in calculating the effect of flow on a system by the observation of the effect of similar flow upon a scale model.

dynamic stability. Of a floating body. The amount of work performed in tilting

115

the body over to a given angle from its position of equilibrium.

dynamic viscosity. *See* kinematic viscosity.

dynamo. A machine for the conversion of mechanical into electrical energy by moving an electrical conductor in a magnetic field. *See* generator.

dynamometer. (1) *See* torquemeter. (2) *See* electrodynamometer.

dynamotor. An electrical machine having a single magnetic field system and a single armature, the latter carrying two independent windings connected to two independent *commutators. The machine operates as a motor with one of the windings and simultaneously as a generator with the other. The armature windings are usually different so that the voltage on the generator side is different from the voltage on the motor side and the machine acts as a rotary transformer.

dynatron. A thermionic valve with the grid placed very close to the anode and the anode treated to be a good emitter of secondary electrons. It has a negative resistance characteristic and has value as an amplifier of current or voltage under suitable conditions, but is generally used as a generator of oscillations.

dyne. Symbol: dyn. A CGS unit of force. 1 dyne = 10^{-5} newton.

dynode. An electrode in an electron tube, whose primary function is to provide *secondary emission of electrons. *See* photomultiplier.

E

e. The charge of an *electron; the natural unit of electric charge. It is equal to $1.602\ 10 \times 10^{-19}$ coulomb or 4.803×10^{-10} e.s.u. or 1.602×10^{-20} e.m.u.

earth. *Syn.* ground. The potential of the earth is taken as the arbitrary zero in the scale of electrical potentials. If current flows from a body to the earth, the body is said to have a positive potential.

earthquakes. *See* seismology.

earth's magnetic field. *See* geomagnetism.

earth's mean density. Using Newton's law of *gravitation, the mean density, ρ, is given by $g = \frac{4}{3}\pi GR\rho$, from which ρ may be determined as $(5.517 \pm 0.004) \times 10^3$ kg m^{-3}. Because the density of solid matter near the earth's surface averages about 2.7 times that of water, the relative density of the core must exceed 5.5. It is calculated to be between 10 and 12, i.e. approximately that of iron-nickel.

east–west effect. *See* cosmic rays.

echelette grating. A *diffraction grating for use primarily with infrared radiation with large grating interval and flat grooves inclined at an angle to reflect the radiation in the direction of the diffracted order intended to be bright.

echelon grating. A diffraction grating capable of high resolution (100 000 to about 1 000 000) for a small portion of a spectrum, e.g. for studying hyperfine structure of lines, Zeeman effect, etc. Some twenty to forty accurately parallel plates of equal thickness (to within a small fraction of a wavelength) are mounted in optical contact and staggered to form a series of steps of width about 1 mm. The grating is used either as a reflection or transmission instrument, the former giving higher resolution.

echo. (1) When a sound pulse is incident upon a surface of large area some part of the sound energy is reflected. If the time interval between the emission of the sound and the return of the reflected wave is more than about one-tenth of a second, the reflected sound is heard after a silent interval and is called an echo, the minimum path difference being about 30 metres. A reflector having a large surface area relative to the wavelength of the sound gives the best echoes. Thus a high pitched sound usually gives a better echo than one of low frequency. The distance of the reflector from the source can be calculated from the time taken between the emission of the sound and the return of the echo. This principle has been extensively used in *echo sounding* to find the depth and also the nature of the sea bed beneath a ship or the distance from the source to the nearest solid surface at which it is reflected. Echoes are very troublesome when they occur in large buildings since the interference they cause prevents the original sound from being heard distinctly. This can be overcome by the use of sound-absorbing materials and by avoiding curved surfaces which act as concave mirrors and thus focus the echoes. (2) In communications, a wave returned to the transmitter with sufficient magnitude and delay to be distinguished from the transmitted wave. (3) In *radar, the portion of the transmitted pulse that is reflected back to the receiver.

echo chamber. *See* reverberation chamber.

eclipse. When the moon passes between the earth and the sun, a solar eclipse occurs. If the angle subtended by the moon is greater than that by the sun and the whole light of the sun is obscured the eclipse is total, otherwise it is partial. If, when the lunar subtense is less than the solar subtense, a ring of illumination from the sun is visible, the eclipse is said to be annular.

A lunar eclipse occurs when the earth intercepts the rays from the sun before they strike the moon; it is a shadow of the earth cast on the moon.

ecliptic. *See* celestial sphere.

eddy current. A current induced in a conductor when subjected to a varying magnetic field. Such currents are a source of energy dissipation (*eddy-current loss*) in a.c. machinery. The reaction between the eddy currents in a moving conductor and the magnetic field in which it is moving is such as to retard the motion, and can be used to produce *electromagnetic damping*.

eddy viscosity. In the turbulent flow (*see* turbulence) of an incompressible fluid, the formation of eddies has the effect of increasing the rate of change of momentum of any portion of the fluid. This may be considered as an increased resistance or as an apparent viscosity of the fluid, greater than that pertinent to non-turbulent motion, called eddy viscosity.

edge dislocation. *See* defect.

edge tones. The sound made when a blade-shaped sheet of gas issues from a linear slit and meets an edge which may or may not be sharp. The distance between the slit and the edge apparently acts as a resonator and stabilizes the *jet tones produced without an edge. The frequency of the sound emitted is related to the number of vortices arriving at the edge per second.

Edison accumulator. *Syn.* nickel–iron or Ni–Fe accumulator. A storage battery having steel grid plates: the positive plate is filled with a mixture of metallic

nickel and nickel hydrate, and the negative plate is filled with iron oxide paste. The electrolyte is a solution of potassium hydroxide of relative density about 1·2. They are lighter than the lead accumulator, but the voltage is lower – 1·3 to 1·4 volts per cell.

effective energy (or wavelength). Of *heterogeneous radiation. The quantum energy (or wavelength) of a beam of *homogeneous radiation that, under the same conditions, is absorbed or scattered to the same extent as the given beam of *heterogeneous radiation.

effective force. *Syn.* inertial force. *See* force.

effective mass. When a potential difference is applied to a conductor, electrons are accelerated by the field produced. They have a mobility that depends on their position in the *energy band. This is described by an effective mass, which is a function of energy and can differ from the true mass.

effective resistance. The resistance of a conductor or other element of an electric circuit when used with alternating current. It is measured in ohms and is the power in watts dissipated as heat divided by the square of the current in amperes. It may differ from the normal value of resistance as measured with direct current since it includes the effects of *eddy currents within the conducting material, *skin effect, etc.

effective value. *See* root-mean-square value.

effective wavelength. *See* effective energy.

efficiency. Symbol: η. The ratio of the useful energy output of a machine or other energy-converting plant to the energy input. In many instances this is the same as the ratio of the useful power output to the power input. It is usually expressed as a percentage.

The efficiency of a heat engine, working between two temperatures, is defined as the ratio of the external work performed by the engine to the heat taken in at the higher temperature, both quantities being measured in the same units. For a reversible engine, the efficiency is given by $(T_1 - T_2)/T_1$, where T_1 and T_2 are the thermodynamic temperatures of the source and condenser respectively. *See* Carnot's theorem.

effusion. The leakage of gas through a fine orifice. *Graham's law applies at ordinary pressures when the mean free path is small compared with the dimensions of the orifice. At low pressures this no longer applies and the volume diffusing per second into a vacuum is given by $s\sqrt{(kT/2\pi m)}$ where s is the area of the orifice, m the molecular weight, and k the Boltzmann constant.

Ehrenfest's rule. The principle that if a system is described by quantized variables and subjected to an adiabatic change then the *quantum numbers of the system must either change suddenly to new values or remain the same. Furthermore if the change occurs very slowly then the quantum numbers must remain constant; the variables are then said to be adiabatically invariant. This implies that the converse may be true: only quantities that are adiabatically invariant can be quantized.

eigenfunction and -value. *See* wave function.

Einstein and de Haas effect. The reverse of the *Barnett effect. When an iron cylinder, which is free to move, is suddenly magnetized it rotates slightly.

Einstein coefficients. Coefficients representing the probability of transitions between electronic states of atoms or molecules. If atoms in a state n are

subjected to a beam of electromagnetic radiation of frequency v they may make a transition to a state of higher energy m by absorbing a photon of energy hv. The number of atoms making this transition is given by $B_{nm}N_n u(v)$, where $u(v)$ is the energy density of radiation of frequency v and N_n the number of atoms in state n. B_{nm} is the Einstein coefficient for absorption. Similarly atoms in state m can interact with the radiation and undergo *stimulated emission of photons in changing to state n. The number of atoms making this change is given by $B_{mn}N_m u(v)$. Atoms in state m can also undergo spontaneous emission to state n with emission of a photon, the number of atoms making this transition being given by $A_{nm}N_m$. The Einstein coefficients are related by the equations:

$$\frac{B_{nm}}{B_{mn}} = \frac{g_m}{g_n},$$

where g_m and g_n are the *statistical weights of state m and n respectively, and $A_{nm} = (8\pi v^3/c^3)B_{nm}$.

Einstein shift. *Syn.* gravitational red shift. A slight *red shift in the lines of a *stellar spectrum due to the gravitational field of that star.

Einstein's law. The law of the equivalence of mass and energy, $E = mc^2$, where c is the velocity of light *in vacuo*. Thus, a quantity of energy E has a mass m, and a mass m has intrinsic energy E. *See also* relativity.

Einstein's photoelectric equation. *See* photoelectric effect.

Einstein's theory of specific heat capacities. Applying the quantum theory to the vibrations of the individual atoms, supposed to have a single frequency v, the specific heat capacity, c_v of a solid is:

$$c_v = 3R\frac{x^2 e^x}{(e^x - 1)^2}$$

where $x = \theta/T$ and $\theta = hv/k$, h being

the Planck constant and k the Boltzmann constant. Einstein's theory has been superseded by that of *Debye.

Einthoven galvanometer. *Syn.* string galvanometer. A sensitive *galvanometer consisting of a single conducting thread strung tightly between the poles of a powerful electromagnet. On passing a current through the thread, it is deflected at right angles to the direction of the magnetic field, and is viewed by a high-power microscope let into the pole piece. It can be used for investigating rapidly fluctuating currents. A current of 10^{-11} A can be detected.

elastance. The reciprocal of *capacitance. It is measured in farad^{-1}, sometimes called a *daraf*.

elastic collision. *See* collision.

elastic constants. Constants, such as Young's modulus (E) and Poisson's ratio (μ), relating *stress to *strain in a homogenous medium. For an isotropic material two constants are required to specify the behaviour and these are related by linear equations. The components of normal stress (σ) and tensile strain (e) in the x direction are related by the equation $e_x = (1/E)(\sigma_x - \mu(\sigma_y + \sigma_z))$. Similar equations apply to the components of strain in the y and z directions. In general an anisotropic solid is described by 21 elastic constants.

elastic deformation. A change in the relative positions of points in a solid body that disappears when the deforming stress is removed.

elasticity. (1) The property of a body or substance by which it tends to resume its original size and shape after being subject to deforming forces. (2) Short for *modulus of elasticity.

elastic limit. The smallest stress that leaves a detectable permanent strain

after removal (a necessarily vague term). *See* Hooke's law; yield point.

elastic modulus. Of an elastic material. The ratio of stress to strain, within the limit of proportionality. *See* elastic constants; modulus of elasticity.

elastic scattering. *See* scattering.

elastoresistance. The change in electrical resistance of materials when they are stressed within their elastic limits. *See* magnetoresistance.

E-layer or region. *Syn.* Heaviside layer; Kennelly–Heaviside layer. *See* ionosphere.

electret. A permanently electrified substance exhibiting electrical charges of opposite sign at its extremities. If it is cut, it separates into two complete electrets, as a permanent magnet does.

electric braking. A method of braking an electric motor by causing it to act as a generator, its output as a generator being either dissipated in a rheostat (*rheostatic braking*) or returned to the supply system (*regenerative braking*). It has a particular application in electric traction.

electric charge. *See* charge.

electric constant. Symbol: ε_0. The absolute *permittivity of *free space, with the formally defined value

$$\varepsilon_0 = 10^7/4\pi c^2 \text{ F m}^{-1}$$
$$= 8.854\,18 \times 10^{-12} \text{ F m}^{-1}$$

(c is the velocity of light in free space, in m s^{-1}.)

electric current. *See* current.

electric degree. One 360th part of an alternating current cycle. Currents or voltages arising in different parts of a circuit may be represented as vectors; the phase difference is the angle, expressed in electric degrees, between the vectors.

electric discharge. *See* conduction in gases.

electric displacement. Symbol: *D*. If an electric field exists in *free space with magnitude *E* and a dielectric is introduced into the field the electric flux per unit area (*electric flux density*) in the medium is *D*, the electric displacement. The permittivity of the medium (*ε*) is given by *D/E*. The divergence of electric displacement equals the surface density of charge. It is measured in coulombs per metre squared.

electric double layer. *See* Helmholtz electric double layer.

electric energy. Energy possessed by a body by virtue of its position in an *electric field. If a body has a charge *Q* and is at a point with electric potential *V* then its electric energy is *QV* and in falling through a potential difference *V* this energy can be converted into kinetic energy. Hence a current *I* flowing for a time *t* between two points differing in potential by *V* will give out energy equal to *VIt*. If no mechanical or chemical work is done by the current the electric energy is transformed into heat in the conductor (i.e. into energy of vibration of the atoms of the conductor). Electric energy is measured in joules.

electric field. The space surrounding an electric charge within which it is capable of exerting a perceptible force on another electric charge.

electric field strength. Formerly called *electric intensity*. Symbol: *E*. The strength of an electric field at a given point in terms of the force exerted by the field on unit charge at that point. It is measured in volts per metre.

electric flux. Symbol: Ψ. The quantity of electricity displaced across a given area in a dielectric. It is defined as the scalar product of the *electric displacement and the area; it is measured in coulombs. A line drawn in the field so that its direction at any point is the direction of the electric flux at that point is known as a *line of flux*. A space bounded by lines of flux forms a tube of electric flux. If the tube is so drawn that the flux across any cross section of it is unity, it is known as a unit tube of flux, or *Faraday tube*. The flux density at any point in a dielectric is equal to the number of unit tubes of flux crossing a unit of area drawn at right angles to the direction of the flux at that point. *See* electric displacement.

electric flux density. *See* electric displacement.

electric intensity. *See* electric field strength.

electric polarization. *Syn.* dielectric polarization. Symbol: *P*. The *electric displacement *D* minus the product of the electric field strength *E* and the permittivity of free space (*electric constant), ε_0, i.e. $P = D - \varepsilon_0 E$. It is measured in C m^{-2}.

electric potential. Symbol: *V*. The electric potential at a point in an electric field is the work required to bring unit positive electric charge from infinity to the point. It is measured in volts. If work of 1 joule is required to move a charge of 1 coulomb to the point its potential is 1 volt. *See also* potential.

electrization. The equation defining *electric polarization *P*,

$$D = \varepsilon_0 E + P,$$

where *D* is the *electric displacement, ε_0 the *electric constant, and *E* the field strength, may be put in the form

$$D = \varepsilon_0(E + E_i)$$

121

where $E_1 = P/\varepsilon_0$. The quantity E_1 is known as the electrization.

electrocardiograph (ECG). A sensitive instrument that records the voltage and current waveforms associated with the action of the heart. The trace obtained is known as an electrocardiogram.

electrochemical equivalent. The mass of any ion deposited from solution by a current of 1 ampere flowing for 1 second.

electrochemistry. The study of processes involving the interconversion of electric and chemical energy.

electrode. In general, a device for emitting, collecting, or deflecting electric charge carriers, especially a solid plate, grid, or wire for leading current into or out of an electrolyte, gas, vacuum, dielectric, or semiconductor. In certain electrolytic cells a liquid mercury electrode is used. *See also* anode; cathode.

electrode dissipation. The heat dissipated by a specified electrode of a thermionic valve in unit time as a result of bombardment by electrons and/or ions.

electrode efficiency. The ratio of the actual yield of metal deposited in an electrolytic cell to the theoretical yield.

electrode potential. The difference of potential between an electrode and the electrolyte with which it is in contact.

electrodialysis. Dialysis assisted by applying a potential difference between electrodes situated on each side of a semipermeable membrane. The ions of any salts present are attracted to the electrodes and diffusion is accelerated.

electrodisintegration. The disintegration of a nucleus by electron bombardment.

electrodynamic instrument. An instrument in which the operating torque is produced by interaction of the magnetic fields produced by currents in a system of movable and fixed coils. The moving system consists of one or more coils which are pivoted so as to move in the magnetic field of the fixed coils and the magnetic circuit is devoid of ferromagnetic material. The currents in all the coils are obtained from a common source. Instruments of this type will operate with either direct or alternating current.

electrodynamics. The branch of science which studies the mechanical forces generated between neighbouring circuits when carrying electric currents.

electrodynamometer. A measuring instrument actuated by the mechanical couple between a moving coil and one or more fixed coils when an electrical current passes through them. The moving coil may be controlled either by a torsional or by a bifilar suspension, and is mounted so that its plane is at right angles to that of the fixed coil when no current is flowing. If the coils are in series the couple is proportional to the square of the current and the instrument can be used to measure either a.c. or d.c. With a high resistance in series it acts as an a.c. voltmeter.

electroencephalograph (EEG). A sensitive instrument that records the voltage *waveforms associated with the brain. The trace obtained is known as an electroencephalogram.

electroendosmosis. *See* electrosmosis.

electrogen. A molecule that emits electrons when illuminated.

electrokinetic potential. *See* zeta potential.

electrokinetic transducer. A *transducer that converts acoustic to electrical energy by using the electrokinetic potential developed when a field streams through a porous body. Sound waves falling on a diaphragm set up oscillatory movement of liquid through a fritted diaphragm, generating an a.c. of the same frequency at electrodes arranged one on each side of the fritted diaphragm.

electroluminescence. *Syn.* Destriau effect. The emission of light by certain phosphorescent substances when subjected to a fluctuating electric field: it can be used for illumination by applying voltages of 400–500 volts across a dielectric coating, about $2 \cdot 5$ μm thick, in which the phosphor is dispersed.

electrolysis. The production of chemical changes in a chemical compound or solution by causing its oppositely charged constituents or ions to move in opposite directions under a potential difference. *See* Faraday's laws of electrolysis.

electrolyte. A substance that conducts electricity in solution or in the fused state because of the presence of ions. *See* electrolytic dissociation.

electrolytic capacitor. A *capacitor consisting of positive and negative electrodes, commonly of aluminium, immersed in an electrolyte. The dielectric of this type of capacitor is provided by a thin insulating film formed on the surface of the positive electrode prior to assembly. It is polarized so that the peak value of an applied a.c. voltage does not exceed the value of the simultaneously applied d.c. voltage. The *power factor and *leakage current are relatively high. In the wet type the electrolyte is a liquid and in the dry type the electrodes are separated by paper or gauze saturated with an electrolyte in the form of a highly viscous liquid or in the form of a paste.

electrolytic conductivity. Symbol: κ. *See* conductivity.

electrolytic dissociation. The reversible separation of certain substances into oppositely charged ions (*anions and *cations) as a result of solution. For example, sulphuric acid molecules break down totally in water ($H_2SO_4 \rightarrow 2H^+ + SO_4^{2-}$). Certain compounds, such as acetic acid, are only partially dissociated in water.

electrolytic polarization. The tendency for the products of electrolysis to recombine. It is measured by the minimum potential difference required to cause a permanent current to pass through the electrolyte. In a primary cell, electrolytic polarization causes a decrease in the effective e.m.f. of the cell, and is counteracted by various depolarizing agents. *See* depolarizer.

electrolytic rectifier. A *rectifier consisting of two electrodes of dissimilar metals immersed in an electrolyte. With certain combinations of metals and electrolytes, the current passes very much more readily in one direction than in the other.

electrolytic tank. A device for the solution of certain problems in electrostatics (or other branches of physics) by analogy, using measurements made on a suitably devised model immersed in a tank of conducting liquid (electrolyte). They have been used to aid design of electrode systems.

electromagnet. An electric circuit wound in a helix or solenoid so that the passage of an electric current through the circuit produces a magnetic field. The space within the windings is almost invariably filled with a core of ferromagnetic substance to enhance the magnetic effect of the current. The strength of the magnet depends greatly on the design and continuity of the core.

electromagnetic damping. *See* eddy current.

electromagnetic deflection. A method of deflecting an electron beam using *electromagnets. It is most often applied to the beam in a *cathode-ray tube using two pairs of deflection coils.

electromagnetic focusing. *See* focusing.

electromagnetic induction. When a conductor is moved so that it cuts the flux of a magnetic field, a potential difference is induced between the ends of the conductor. The magnitude of the induced p.d. depends on the extent of the relative motion, reverting to zero when the motion ceases; the direction depends on the orientation of the magnetic field. A p.d. is also induced in a conductor placed in a region of varying flux.

The *Faraday–Neumann law* states that when a conductor cuts a magnetic flux Φ, the induced potential difference V is proportional to the rate at which the flux changes. *Lenz's law* states that the induced p.d. is in such a direction as to oppose the change producing it. Combining these two laws gives:

$$V = -\frac{d\Phi}{dt},$$

the minus sign indicating the significance of Lenz's law. V is measured in volts when $d\Phi/dt$ is in webers per second. When the conductor is made part of a circuit, the charge Q flowing when the flux changes by $\Delta\Phi$ is given by $Q = \Delta\Phi/R$, R being the total resistance of the circuit.

When the current I in the circuit varies, the associated flux varies in proportion:

$$\Phi = LI$$

thus

$$V = -L\frac{dI}{dt}.$$

The back-electromotive force induced in a circuit when the current in that circuit varies is described as *self-inductance* (formerly, self-induction). L is the co-efficient of self inductance, and is defined as numerically equal to the e.m.f. induced when the current changes at unit rate. L is measured in *henrys when V is in volts and I is in amperes. Similarly the change of current in one circuit can cause an e.m.f. to be induced in a neighbouring circuit due to the flux linkage:

$$\Phi_1 = MI_2,$$

$$V_1 = -M\frac{dI_2}{dt}.$$

M is called the coefficient of *mutual inductance*. The energy stored in an inductive circuit is $\frac{1}{2}LI^2$ (or $\frac{1}{2}MI^2$). For an ideal mutual inductance

$$M^2 = L_1L_2,$$

where L_1, L_2 are the self-inductances of the component inductors. Mutual inductance is the principle behind the action of the *transformer. *Tuned circuits rely on the appropriate values of self-inductances.

electromagnetic interaction. The interaction between *elementary particles arising as a consequence of their associated electric and magnetic fields. The electrostatic force between charged particles is an example. This force may be described in terms of the exchange of virtual photons. Its strength, and thus the lifetime of any relevant decay process, lies between that of *strong and *weak interactions.

The following *quantum numbers have to be conserved in electromagnetic interactions: angular momentum, charge, baryon number, isospin quantum number I_3, strangeness, parity, and charge conjugation parity. *See also* quantum electrodynamics; neutral weak current.

electromagnetic mass. That part of the total inertia of a charged body that arises from its electrical charge. Providing that the velocity of the body is small compared with that of light, the electromagnetic mass of a charge e carried by a sphere of radius a is equal to $\frac{2}{3}\mu(e^2/a)$, where μ is the magnetic permeability of the medium. The effect is due to the fact that the motion of the charge gives rise to a magnetic field, the energy of which is proportional to the square of the velocity of the charge. For velocities approaching that of light the mass increases relativistically.

electromagnetic pump. A pump with no moving parts for use with conducting liquids, such as liquid metals. The liquid is contained in a flattened pipe between two poles of an *electromagnet, a strong magnetic field being applied across the pipe. If an electric current is also passed through the liquid, the liquid will experience a force along the axis of the pipe. This type of pump is used to move the liquid sodium *coolant in *fast breeder reactors.

electromagnetic radiation. Waves of energy that are caused by the acceleration of charged particles; they consist of electric and magnetic fields vibrating transversely and sinusoidally at right angles to each other and to the direction of motion (*see* Maxwell's equations). The waves require no medium for propagation (*compare* sound waves) and travel through free space at the uniform velocity of $2 \cdot 997\ 925 \times 10^8$ metres per second (usually called the *velocity of light, c). This velocity is reduced to a value v if the waves travel through a medium of refractive index, n, where $v = c/n$.

The characteristics of electromagnetic radiation depend on the frequency of the wave motion, the frequency f and the velocity c being related by $c = f\lambda$, where λ is the wavelength. The range of frequencies over which electromagnetic radiation can be propagated is called the *electromagnetic spectrum* (*see* Table 7, page 424). The lowest frequencies are associated with *radio waves. *Infrared radiation, *light, *ultraviolet radiation,

*X-rays, and *gamma rays have progressively higher frequencies.

Although *reflection, *refraction, and *interference can be satisfactorily explained in terms of wave motion, other phenomena, including the *photoelectric effect and the absorption and re-emission of infrared radiation by *black bodies, require an explanation in terms of particles. This concept forms the basis of *quantum theory, in which, under certain circumstances, electromagnetic radiation can be considered as consisting of a stream of particles, or quanta, travelling at the speed of light and having zero *rest mass. The energy E of the quanta (or *photons) is proportional to the frequency of the radiation: $E = hf$, where h is the *Planck constant. *See also* de Broglie waves.

electromagnetic spectrum. *See* electromagnetic radiation.

electromagnetic units (e.m.u.). *See* CGS system of units.

electrometer. A device for measuring potential difference, usually consisting of a very high input impedance amplifier, which draws a negligible amount of current, and may use valves in the circuit, or more commonly, *solid-state devices. *Field-effect transistors are widely used.

electromotive force (e.m.f.). Symbol: E. The algebraic sum of the potential differences acting in a circuit. It is measured by the energy liberated when unit electric charge passes completely round the circuit in the direction of the resultant e.m.f. Thus if a battery sends a current I through an external resistance R joining its terminals, the e.m.f. of the battery is equal to $(R + b)I$, where b is the internal resistance of the battery. The term is sometimes used as equivalent to potential difference; strictly speaking it should be applied only to a source of electric energy.

electron. An *elementary particle having a negative charge $e = 1{\cdot}602\,192 \times 10^{-19}$ coulombs and a mass $m = 9{\cdot}109\,56 \times 10^{-31}$ kg. It is classified as a *lepton and has a *spin of $\frac{1}{2}$. Electrons are liberated in a *gas-discharge tube by the ionization of gas atoms and also by various emission processes. They are constituents of all atoms and as free electrons they are primarily responsible for electrical conduction in most substances.

An electron is acted upon by an electric force in the presence of an electric field. The value of the force is given by: $F_E = Ee$ where E, a vector, is the electric field strength. This forms the basis of the acceleration and *focusing of electron beams. A moving electron constitutes an electric current and accordingly is acted upon by a transverse force in the presence of a magnetic field. This force is given by: $F_H = Bev$, where B is the *magnetic flux density acting at right angles to the velocity vector v. This forms the basis of magnetic focusing and the determination of electron velocities.

The penetration of matter by electrons depends on their velocity. In their interaction with matter, electrons may suffer elastic *collisions leading to deflection or inelastic collisions leading to the loss of discrete amounts of energy and the production of various phenomena dependent on the state of matter involved. With gas atoms, excitation and the emission of light, or ionization is effected, while with solids and liquids, more complex phenomena occur, such as the production of X-rays, fluorescence, *secondary (electron) emission, etc. The energy dissipated in elastic collisions appears as heat and this forms the basis of the localized heating of substances in vacuo. The scattering of a beam of electrons of similar velocities by crystalline matter (*electron diffraction) has regular features which are similar to those associated with an electromagnetic radiation whose wavelength is given by $\lambda = h/mv$, where h is the *Planck constant. This result follows from de Broglie's theory of *wave mechanics. The *antiparticle of the electron is the *positron. *See* atom; Table 8 page 425.

electron affinity. (1) Symbol: A or E_a. The energy released when an electron is attached to an atom or molecule (*electron attachment*). It is thus the energy released for the process $A + e \rightarrow A^-$. The electron affinity of many atoms or molecules is positive, i.e. the negative ion is often a little more stable than the neutral species. *See also* work function.

electron capture. *See* capture.

electron density. (1) The number of electrons per unit mass of a given material. Most light elements (except hydrogen) have an electron density of about 3×10^{26} electrons per kilogramme. (2) The number of electrons per unit volume.

electron diffraction. Owing to the fact that electrons are associated with a wavelength λ given by $\lambda = h/mv$, where h is the Planck constant and (mv) the momentum of the electron, a beam of electrons suffers diffraction in its passage through crystalline material, similar to that experienced by a beam of X-rays. The diffraction pattern depends on the spacing of the crystal planes, and the phenomenon can be employed to investigate the structure of surface and other films. *See* de Broglie waves.

electron gas. The concept of the free electrons in the solid or liquid state as a gas whose state may be compared with that of an actual gas dissolved in a solid or liquid. This model has found application in theories of electric and thermal conduction, thermionic emission, etc. Applying Fermi–Dirac statistics (*see* quantum statistics) to the electron gas, it is shown to be completely degenerate at ordinary temperatures, i.e. it obeys a totally different distribution law from that of an ideal gas.

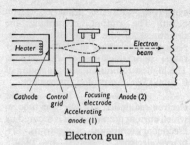

Electron gun

electron gun. A device, consisting of a series of electrodes, that produces an electron beam, usually a narrow beam of high velocity electrons whose intensity is controlled by electrodes in the gun.

Electrons are released from the cathode. The control grid is a cylinder surrounding the cathode with a hole in front to allow passage of the electron beam. It controls the electron beam when its negative potential is varied. The electron beam is accelerated by the positively charged accelerating anode and passes through the focusing electrode before being further accelerated by the second anode.

electronic music. *See* electrophonic instrument.

electronics. The study, design, and use of devices based on the conduction of electricity in a vacuum, a gas, or a semiconductor. Modern electronics is principally concerned with semiconductor devices; vacuum and gas-filled devices are rapidly becoming obsolete, apart from a few specialized uses.

electronic spectrum. *See* spectrum.

electron lens. A device for focusing an electron beam by using either a magnetic field (*magnetic lens*) or an electrostatic field (*electrostatic lens*) in a way that is analogous to the focusing of a light beam by an optical lens. A magnetic lens can only focus electrons of one energy at a particular point. These lenses are used in instruments such as the *electron microscope.

electron microscope. (1) *Transmission electron microscope.* An instrument, closely resembling the optical microscope but using, instead of light, a beam of energetic electrons. The beam is focused by a magnetic lens or sometimes an electrostatic lens and has an energy of 50–100 kV. A sharply focused image in one plane can only be obtained by using electrons of a single energy. To avoid energy losses in this beam the sample must be extremely thin (<50 nm) so that the scattered electrons that form the image are not changed in energy. The thinness of the sample greatly limits the *depth of field and the image therefore appears two-dimensional. A resolution of 0·2–0·5 nm is possible. The maximum magnification is about one million diameters, the image becoming blurred at greater values.

(2) The *scanning electron microscope* has lower resolution and magnification but produces a seemingly three-dimensional image, with great depth of field, from a sample of any convenient size or thickness (Fig. *a*). The sample is

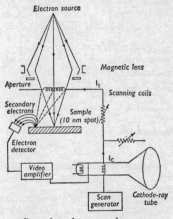

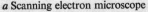

a Scanning electron microscope

scanned by the electron beam, the resulting secondary electrons being proportional to the geometry and other properties of the sample. These electrons are converted, by means of an electron detector, *scintillator, and *photomultiplier, into a highly amplified signal. This signal modulates the intensity.

The magnification of the microscope is determined by the ratio of the variable current I_s in the scanning coils to the current I_c in the deflection coil of the cathode-ray tube. It can vary continuously from 15 diameters to 100 000 diameters. The resolution is about 10–20 nm.

(3) The *scanning-transmission electron microscope* (STEM) combines the high resolution of the transmission instrument with the three-dimensional image of the scanning type. The electron beam, produced by *field emission, is focused to a spot, which is made to scan the sample (Fig. *b*). Two signals are obtained from the elastically and the inelastically scattered electrons. Dividing the elastic signal by the inelastic signal gives an

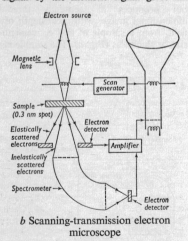

b Scanning-transmission electron microscope

output proportional to *atomic number. This output is fed into a cathode-ray tube whose electron beam scans in synchrony with the primary electron beam. The output, controlling the brightness of the final visual image, responds to changes in atomic number rather than thickness of the sample. The highest resolution is in the region of 0·3 nm. *See also* proton microscope.

electron multiplier. An electron tube in which current amplification is secured by *secondary emission of electrons. Primary electrons (released by photoelectric effect, or otherwise) are accelerated by application of a high potential and made to strike a good secondary emitter (a *dynode) where they produce a greater number of electrons by impact. These are then accelerated on to a further secondary emitter, the process being

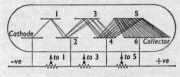

Electron multiplier

repeated several times within the same envelope. The final plate is at a very high potential. *See* photomultiplier.

electron optics. The study of the behaviour and control of an electron beam in magnetic and electrostatic fields. *See also* electron lens.

electron paramagnetic resonance (EPR). *See* electron spin resonance.

electron probe microanalysis. A technique for analysing small quantities of solids by examining the *X-ray spectrum emitted when the sample is bombarded by a fine beam of electrons. The elements in the sample are detected by the *characteristic X-radiation which they emit and the intensity of this radiation depends on the amount of substance present. The electron beam can be focused to a spot with a diameter of about 10^{-6} m and quantities as small as 10^{-16} kg can be detected.

electron shell. A group of electrons in an atom having a given total quantum number n. The innermost or K shell, with $n = 1$, cannot contain more than 2 electrons. The other shells are denoted in sequence by the letters L ($n = 2$), M (3), N (4), ... The electrons in these shells may be grouped into sub-shells, for which the letters s, p, d, f, g, h, ..., are used. The L shell of an atom is filled if it contains $2s$ electrons and $6p$ electrons, making eight in all. The M shell may have a total of 18: $2s$, $6p$, and $10d$ (*see* Pauli exclusion principle).

According to modern ideas, the shells do not represent precise locations in space in that electrons 'belonging' to one shell may well interpenetrate the orbits or tracks of electrons from another shell and even these orbits are no longer regarded as definite paths. *See* atomic orbital.

electron spectroscopy. The measurement of the distribution of electron kinetic energies in a flux of electrons, such as those resulting from *beta decay (β-ray spectroscopy)*, or following inelastic scattering by a solid or gas, or emitted from molecules as a result of an applied stimulus, such as irradiation with photons (*photoelectron spectroscopy*), ions, other electrons, etc. This information is used to determine energy levels in atoms, molecules, solids, nuclei, etc. The technique depends on accurate measurement of electron energies by some form of *electron spectrometer*.

electron spin resonance (ESR). *Syn.* electron paramagnetic resonance. A phenomenon observed when paramagnetic substances containing unpaired electrons are subjected to high magnetic fields and microwave radiation. An unpaired electron has *spin and normally the energy due to this spin is independent of the electron's orientation.

When a strong field is applied the electron can exist in two different energy states because it acts as a small magnet which can either align with the applied magnetic field or oppose it (*space quantization*). The difference in energy between these states is given by $gm_B B$, where g is the *Landé factor of the electron, m_B is the Bohr *magneton, and B the magnetic flux density. Atoms can therefore be raised to a higher energy state by absorption of a photon of microwave frequency v, where $hv = gm_B B$.

Free electrons have a Landé factor of about 2 but in most compounds this is modified by contributions from the orbital and nuclear magnetic moments. Consequently, shifts in the resonant frequency and *hyperfine structure are observed and information is thus obtained on the chemical bonds in the molecule. *See also* nuclear magnetic resonance.

electron stains. Substances such as phosphotungstic acid, osmic acid, silicotungstic acid, and phosphomolybdic acid that have high electron-scattering power and can be used with the *electron microscope in the same way as staining media in optical microscopy.

electron synchrotron. *See* synchrotron.

electron telescope. A type of *telescope in which ultraviolet and infrared radiation can be converted into a visible image. The intensity of faint visible radiation can also be considerably increased. The radiation falls onto a *photocathode surface. The resulting *secondary electrons are accelerated through a series of voltage grids without being deviated and finally fall on a fluorescent screen. An accurate visible image is therefore obtained.

electron temperature. Electrons in the plasma of a discharge tube have a Maxwellian *distribution of velocities.

The electron temperature of the plasma is that temperature at which gas molecules would have the same average kinetic energy as the electrons of the plasma.

electron tube. A device in which the movement of *electrons between two *electrodes, through a gas or a vacuum, takes place in a sealed or continuously exhausted envelope. *See* valve; thermionic valve.

electronvolt. Symbol: eV. A unit of energy extensively employed in atomic physics. It is the energy acquired by an electron in falling freely through a potential difference of one volt. It is equal to $1 \cdot 602 \times 10^{-19}$ joule.

electro-optics. The study of the changes in the optical properties of a dielectric produced by the application of an electric field. *See* Kerr effects.

electrophonic instrument. A musical instrument with the sound created and amplified by electrical or electronic means. The Hammond organ employs tone wheels, approximately circular but with irregular edges, that revolve at various fixed speeds in magnetic fields. The frequencies of the induced currents can be combined and amplified into a wide range of notes. The Compton organ employs fixed insulating discs coated with charged layers, except along certain carefully calculated wavy paths. Each disc is scanned by a second metallic disc, rotating so as to pick up electric potentials from different parts of the first disc at appropriate frequencies. The frequencies are combined and amplified as in the Hammond organ.

The *Moog synthesizer* is an instrument designed to enable the player/operator to produce almost any desired type of sound that can be electronically generated. Many sine- and square-waves are available, either singly or in more or less complex groups, and a large number of filtering circuits are employed. From the outside it appears as a combination of keyboard and telephone exchange, with plug-in facilities for individual potentiometers (*see* patching). The synthesizer can either be set and played (in the conventional sense) or each sound can be prepared separately and at length, the sounds being recorded for reproduction when the complete work has been prepared.

electrophoresis. The migration of fine particles of solid suspended in liquid to the anode (*anaphoresis*) or cathode (*cataphoresis*) when an electric field is applied to the suspension.

electroplating. The practical application of *electrolysis, in which the surface of one metal is covered with another, either for protection or for decoration or both.

electroscope. An electrostatic instrument for the detection of electrical potential differences. The commonest form consists of a pair of gold leaves hanging side by side from an insulated metal support, and enclosed in a draught-proof case. If the support is given a charge the leaves separate, owing to their mutual repulsion. One of the leaves may be replaced by a vertical metal plate. An instrument capable of accurate quantitative indication is usually called an *electrometer.

electrosmosis. *Syn.* electroendosmosis. The passage of an electrolyte through a membrane or porous partition under the influence of an electric field.

electrostatic deflection. A method of deflecting an electron beam using the electrostatic fields produced between two metal electrodes. Most often applied to the beam in *cathode-ray tubes using two pairs of deflection plates.

electrostatic focusing. *See* focusing.

electrostatic generator. A machine for producing electrical charge by electrostatic action, e.g. friction, or (more usually), electrostatic induction. *See* Wimshurst machine; Van de Graaff generator.

electrostatic induction. The production of electric charge on a conductor under the influence of an *electric field. Thus, if an uncharged conductor is placed near a positively charged body, the portion of the conductor nearest to the body becomes negatively charged, the more remote portions being positively charged. If the conductor is insulated, the induced charges are equal in magnitude. If the conductor completely surrounds the charged body, each of the induced charges is numerically equal to the inducing charge.

electrostatic lens. *See* electron lens.

electrostatics. The study of the phenomena associated with electric charge at rest.

electrostatic units (e.s.u.). *See* CGS system of units.

electrostriction. Any body in a medium of relative permittivity different from its own experiences a force of extension or compression, known as electrostriction, in an electric field. If the field is not homogeneous, a body of higher relative permittivity than its surroundings will tend to move into the area of greater field strength and vice versa.

electroviscosity. An effect in which the electrical resistance to shear in certain ionic liquids, due to the effect of an electrical potential gradient of the surface layers, becomes large in relation to the mechanical resistance to shear.

elementary particle. *Syn.* fundamental particle. A collective name for those particles of matter that cannot be sub-divided into smaller particles. Elementary particles are classified by a set of *quantum numbers describing their intrinsic properties e.g. *spin, *isospin, *parity, *charge, and *strangeness. The only stable particles are the *photon, *electron, *neutrino, and *proton. (The *neutron is also stable when it is bound in a nucleus.) All other particles eventually decay into these particles by the emission of other elementary particles.

Particles can be divided into groups according to the kinds of interactions they participate in. *Hadrons, i.e. *baryons and *mesons, are subject to the *strong interaction; *leptons are not subject to the strong interaction but only to the *weak or, if charged, to the *electromagnetic interactions. The photon is in a group by itself, taking part in neither strong nor weak interactions. The mean life of a particle depends on whether it decays by a strong ($\sim 10^{-23}$ s), electromagnetic ($\sim 10^{-16}$ s), or weak interaction (10^{-6} to 10^{-10} s). The mass of an elementary particle is usually measured in units of MeV/c^2 (*see* relativity); 1 MeV/$c^2 = 1.78 \times 10^{-30}$ kg. *See also* quark model; resonances. *See* Table 8 page 425.

ellipsometer. An instrument for studying thin films on solid surfaces. It depends for its action on the fact that if *plane polarized light is incident on a surface it is reflected as elliptically polarized light. (*See* polarization.) The degree of ellipticity in the reflected beam depends on the thickness of the film.

e/m. The ratio of the charge to the mass of an electron; sometimes called the *specific charge* of an electron. Its value decreases (owing to increase in mass) as the velocity of the electron approaches that of light. For slow moving electrons its value is $1.758\ 796 \times 10^{11}$ C kg^{-1}.

emanating power. The rate of emission of radioactive inert gas atoms (radon and thoron) from a given material *e.m.f.*

expressed as a fraction of the rate of their production within the solid.

e.m.f. Abbreviation for electromotive force.

emission. The liberation of electrons or electromagnetic radiation from the surface of a solid or liquid, usually electrons from a metal. Electrons near the surface of a metal with directions of motion out of the surface can leave but then experience a force directing them back to the metal, as the metal is left with a positive charge. There is thus a potential barrier that the electrons must overcome if they are to escape. Emission occurs when sufficient energy is given to the electrons, as in *photoelectric, *thermionic, or *secondary emission, or the potential barrier is distorted, as in *field emission.

emission spectrum. The *spectrum of radiation emitted from a substance as a result of changes in *energy level of its constituent atoms or molecules. The changes occur from an *excited state to a state of lower energy, usually the *ground state. Emission spectra are produced as a result of excitation of atoms by some source of energy, such as heat, electron bombardment, or bombardment with X-rays.

emissivity. Symbol: ε. The ratio of the power per unit area radiated from a surface to that radiated from a black body at the same temperature. Alternatively it can be defined as the ratio of *radiant exitances, $\varepsilon = M_e/M'_e$, where M_e is the radiant exitance of the body and M'_e that of the black body. The emissivity is restricted to radiation produced by the thermal agitation of atoms, molecules, etc. *Compare* absorptivity. *See also* heat transfer coefficient.

emittance. *See* luminous, radiant exitance.

132

emitter. The electrode in a *transistor through which *carriers enter the interelectrode region.

emitter-coupled logic (ECL). A family of integrated *logic circuits. The input stage consists of an emitter-coupled transistor pair (known as a *long-tailed pair) which forms an excellent differential amplifier. The output is via an *emitter-follower buffer. ECL circuits are inherently the fastest logic circuits as the transistors are operated in non-saturated mode and the *delay time is therefore exceedingly short (approximately 1 ns). The basic ECL gate has simultaneously both the function required and its complement.

emitter follower. A type of amplifying circuit employing a bipolar junction *transistor with *common collector connection, the output being taken from the *emitter.

A signal is applied to the *base of the transistor (Fig. *a*), which is suitably biased so that it is non-saturated and conducting. Since the transistor is conducting, the emitter will be one *diode forward voltage from the base at all times, and the emitter follows the signal applied to the base. Since the emitter voltage has a constant value relative to the base voltage the voltage gain on the amplifier is almost unity, but the current gain is high. The amplifier is characterized by high input impedance and low output impedance and is often used as a *buffer.

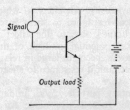

a Simple emitter follower

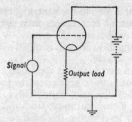

b Simple cathode follower

The analogue in valve circuitry is the *cathode follower* (Fig. *b*) and in FET circuitry the source follower. Neither is as efficient as a unity gain buffer amplifier as the emitter follower.

e.m.u. Abbreviation for electromagnetic units. *See* CGS system of units.

enantiomorphy. A relationship that exists between a left and a right hand, or between any two bodies that can only be brought into coincidence by means of reflection across a plane.

end correction. In the elementary theory of the vibrations in a *column of air, it is supposed that the open end of the pipe is a true antinode. This is not true, for some sound energy escapes at each reflection from the open end and is radiated to the atmosphere in the form of spherical waves. The air beyond the open end of the pipe is in vibration and the effective length of the pipe is greater than the actual length.

A cylindrical closed pipe, of variable length, can be used as a resonator to be tuned to a fork. By finding the first two successive lengths of the tube (say l_1 and l_2) which resound to the fork, the end correction x_0 can be calculated. Since l_2 should be $3l_1$, in the absence of end correction (*see* column of air), $l_2 + x_0 = 3(l_1 + x_0)$. Recent experiments give $0·58r$ for a flangeless tube. The correction is approximately independent of the wavelength of the sound. The magnitude of the correction for other than cylindrical ends depends upon the degree of openness or conductivity of the end.

end-fire array. *See* aerial array.

endothermic process. A process during which heat is absorbed by the system from outside. When a nuclear process results in the absorption of heat it is often called an *endoergic process.*

energy. Symbol: *E*. The property of a system that is a measure of its capacity for doing work. Energy has several forms and is determined by the amount of work it can do. It is measured in joules.

Potential energy. Symbol *U*. The energy possessed by a body or system by virtue of position, equal to the work done in changing the system from some standard configuration to its existing state. For example, a mass *m* placed at a height *h* above a datum level in a gravitational field with an acceleration of free fall *g* has a potential energy given by: $U = mgh$. This is converted into kinetic energy when the body falls between the levels.

Kinetic energy. Symbol: *T*. The energy possessed by virtue of motion, equal to the work that would be required to bring the body to rest. A body undergoing translational motion with velocity *v* has a kinetic energy given by $T = \frac{1}{2}mv^2$, where *m* is the mass of the body. For a body undergoing rotational motion $T = \frac{1}{2}I\omega^2$, where I is the moment of inertia of the body about its axis of rotation and ω is the angular velocity.

Several forms of energy can be distinguished: *electric energy, *heat energy, *chemical energy, *nuclear energy, radiant energy, and mechanical energy. In any closed system energy cannot be created or destroyed, although its form may be changed. This is the law of conservation of energy and in connection with it matter must be regarded as a form of energy. *See* conservation of mass and energy.

133

energy bands. In a single atom, according to *quantum theory, the orbiting electrons can only have certain discrete energies. The atom has a number of associated *energy levels and the electrons occupy the lower levels and obey the *Pauli exclusion principle.

In a solid, as the atoms become closer together the narrow energy levels become wider bands of allowed energies (Fig. *a*), each band consisting of a large number of closely spaced energy levels capable of containing two electrons. The bands of permissible energy are called the *allowed bands*. These may

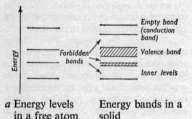

a Energy levels in a free atom   Energy bands in a solid

either be filled or empty depending on whether they correspond to filled or empty levels in the free atoms. The energy regions between these are called *forbidden bands*. The band of energies of the valence electrons in a solid is called the *valence band*. Inner electrons, i.e. electrons close to the nucleus, are not greatly affected when atoms are brought together to form a crystal, being tightly bound to the nuclei.

The theory of these energy bands in solids depends on *quantum mechanics. In general, the *Schrödinger equation is solved for an electron moving in a varying electric potential the periodicity of which is created by the spacing of the ions in the crystal lattice. The allowed solutions give the allowed bands of energy and the energies for which there are no solutions are the forbidden bands.

Within any allowed energy bands the number of constituent discrete energy levels varies with the energy. A curve showing this variation is called a *density of states curve*.

If an electric field is applied to a solid, electrons can be accelerated by the field and they thus gain energy. This can only occur if they can move from their own energy level within the band to an unoccupied level at a higher energy. If the valence band is completely filled and there is a wide forbidden band between it and the next highest empty band then the material is an *insulator. If the valence band is not completely filled or if it overlaps with a higher empty energy band, then there are vacant levels that the electrons can enter. The material is then a good conductor of electricity. This is the situation occurring in most metals.

In *semiconductors there is a small forbidden gap between the valence band and a higher empty band. At absolute zero all the electrons occupy the valence band and the material acts as an insulator. As the temperature is increased some electrons gain enough thermal energy to escape from the valence band and cross the forbidden gap into the *conduction band*, leaving the valence band unfilled. Thus conduction is possible and the conductivity rises with temperature.

At absolute zero all the electrons in a solid occupy the lower energy levels and the valence band is filled to a certain energy, while no higher levels are occupied. This level of maximum energy is called the *Fermi level* (E_F). At temperatures above absolute zero some electrons gain thermal energy and the distribution of electrons in the given energy levels can be derived by Fermi–Dirac statistics (*see* quantum statistics). The probability of finding an electron at a particular energy is its *Fermi function F(E)* (Fig. *b*). The Fermi level is then defined as the energy at which the probability of finding an electron is $\frac{1}{2}$. The Fermi level

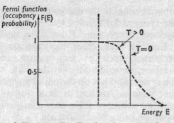

b Energy distribution in a metal

is approximately constant with temperature. In semiconductors the electrons are distributed between the valence band and the conduction band and the Fermi level lies in the forbidden gap between the two (Fig. *c*). In an insulator the Fermi level lies in the valence band. The electron distribution curves in Fig. *c* show how the number of electrons in each band varies with energy.

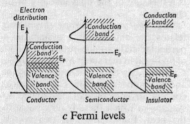

c Fermi levels

energy density. The amount of energy in unit volume.

energy level. According to *quantum theory the energy of an atom or molecule (i.e. the energy due to the motion and electrostatic interactions of the nuclei and electrons) can only have certain fixed values and only change value by an integral multiple of some fixed amount. Thus the electron orbiting around the nucleus in a hydrogen atom can only occupy (according to Bohr's theory of the *atom) certain orbits of different radius. These allowed states of the atom or molecule are called energy levels or, since they result from a change

in the orbiting electron, *electronic energy levels*.

The total energy of an atom is composed of its kinetic energy through space (translational energy) together with this electronic energy. A molecule can also have contributions to the energy from vibrations within the molecule and from its rotation.

The vibrational and rotational energy of molecules can also only have discrete values. For example, in a diatomic molecule the force pulling the atoms together can be thought of as proportional to the distance between the atoms. Thus the vibrations of the molecule are harmonic (*see* simple harmonic motion). It can be shown that the possible energy levels of a harmonic oscillator are given by

$$E_v = (v + \tfrac{1}{2})hf,$$

where h is the *Planck constant and f the frequency of vibration of the molecule. v is the *vibrational quantum number* and can have values 0, 1, 2, etc. When $v = 0$ the lowest energy of the molecule is its *zero-point energy. These energy levels are known as *vibrational energy levels*. In fact molecular vibrations are only harmonic for small internuclear displacements of the atoms. Actual vibrations are anharmonic and the potential energy of the molecule is described by the *Morse equation.

A molecule can also have energy due to its rotational motion and this is also quantized. A diatomic molecule has *rotational energy levels* given by

$$E_R = \frac{h^2 J(J + 1)}{8\pi^2 I}$$

where I is the moment of inertia of the molecule and J the *rotational quantum number*. J can have values of 0, 1, 2, etc. This equation is also an approximation based on the idea that the molecule is not distorted by centrifugal force.

The differences between successive vibrational energy levels are smaller than those between electronic energy

135

levels whereas changes in rotational energy level are smaller still. Thus each electronic energy level has a number of associated vibrational energy levels and each of these has, in turn, a number of rotational levels. Changes in energy level result in the emission or absorption of radiation in the formation of a *spectrum. The lowest energy level of a system is its *ground state, higher levels being called *excited states.

engine. A machine in which heat energy is converted into mechanical work.

enhancement mode. *See* field-effect transistors.

enrich. To increase the *abundance of a particular isotope in a mixture of the isotopes of an element. Applied to a nuclear fuel it means, specifically, to increase the abundance of fissile isotopes.

The *enrichment* is the proportion of atoms of a specified isotope present in a mixture of isotopes of the same element, where this proportion is greater than that in the natural mixture. This is often expressed as a percentage.

enthalpy. *Syn.* heat content; total heat. Symbol: *H*. A thermodynamic function of a system equal to the sum of its internal energy (U) and the product of its pressure (p) and volume (V), i.e. $H = U + pV$. If a system absorbs heat at constant pressure the work done is given by the product of the pressure and the change in volume; the heat absorbed is then equal to the increase in the enthalpy of the system. For *exothermic processes the enthalpy change is taken to be negative.

entrance port, pupil. *See* apertures and stops in optical systems.

entropy. Symbol: *S*. A property of a system that changes, when the system undergoes a *reversible change, by an

amount equal to the energy absorbed by the system (dq) divided by the thermodynamic temperature T, i.e. $dS = dq/T$.

Entropy, like other thermodynamic properties such as temperature and pressure, depends only on the state of the system and not on the path by which that state is reached. It is a quantity with an arbitrary zero, only changes in its value being of significance.

The concept of entropy follows from the application of the second law of *thermodynamics to the *Carnot cycle. In a reversible cycle of this type there is zero entropy change. For an irreversible process in an isolated system the entropy always increases. All practical changes are, to some extent, irreversible and any spontaneous change occurring in a closed system is accompanied by an increase in entropy (*see* heat death). The absolute value of the entropy of a system is a measure of the unavailability of its energy.

The *Boltzmann entropy hypothesis* relates the entropy of a system in a particular state to the probability (W) of finding it in that state: $S = k \log_e W + C$, where k is the *Boltzmann constant and C another constant. This statistical concept of entropy can be applied to systems in which there is no change in the heat. For example, if two vessels are connected, one containing molecules of type A and the other containing molecules of type B, the molecules will mix throughout the vessels. The total system thus goes from one state to a more disordered state. The disordered state can be realized by many more arrangements of the atoms than the more ordered state and thus it has a higher probability of occurring. According to Boltzmann's principle it has a higher entropy and the mixing of the molecules involves an entropy change (the entropy of mixing). The increase in entropy when two types of molecules mix can be thought of as the driving force causing the spontaneous mixing of the molecules. In a perfect crystal at absolute zero the entropy is zero, according to the third law of thermodynamics. A solid that is not perfect has a certain amount of disorder which leads to it possessing a *configurational entropy*. In general, entropy can be thought of as a measure of the disorder of a system. *See also* Carnot–Clausius equation.

epicentre. *See* seismology.

epitaxy. A method of growing a thin layer of material upon a single crystal substrate so that the lattice structure is identical to that of the substrate. The technique is extensively used in the manufacture of *semiconductors when a layer (*epitaxial layer*) of different conductivity is required on the substrate.

epithermal neutron. A neutron with an energy just above thermal energies, often taken to be in the range from 10^{-2} to 10^2 eV ($1 \cdot 6 \times 10^{-21}$ to $1 \cdot 6 \times 10^{-17}$ joule). Epithermal neutrons have energies of the same order of magnitude as the energies of chemical bonds.

equalization. In electronics, the introduction of networks that compensate for a particular type of *distortion over the frequency band required and hence reduce distortion in a system.

equal temperament. *See* temperament.

equation of continuity. *See* continuity principle.

equation of time. *See* time.

equations of state. *Syn.* characteristic equations. Equations showing the relationship between the pressure, volume, and temperature of a substance. (1) For a homogeneous fluid. The most familiar of these equations is the equation $pv = RT$, which only holds good for an ideal gas: if it applied over all ranges of pressure, when the pressure became infinitely great the volume would be zero. To allow for the finite volume occupied by gas particles, the equation should be written $p(v - b) = RT$, where b is the least volume into which the particles can be forced by an indefinitely large pressure. Further, the attractive forces between the particles result in a decreased pressure exerted on the walls of the containing vessel and the equation must be further modified to $(p + k)(v - b) = RT$.

In *Van der Waals equation of state*, $k = a/v^2$, so that the equation becomes $(p + a/v^2)(v - b) = RT$. In the first *equation of Clausius* $k = a/Tv^2$; and in the second equation $k = a/T(v - \beta)^2$. In the first *equation of Dieterici*, $k = a/v^n$, where $n = 5/3$; the second equation is different in type – it is $p(v - b) = RT \exp(-a/RTv)$. There are certain tests which may be applied to these characteristic equations: for example, the critical specific volume, v_c, is equal to about four times the liquid specific volume (or volume of unit mass). Now the constant, b, is approximately equal to the liquid specific volume, so that $v_c = 4b$. Again, the quantity RT_c/p_cv_c is roughly constant for unassociated fluids and is equal to 15/4, so that if the critical constants of the fluids under test are known they should satisfy these values $v_c = 4b$ and $RT_c/p_cv_c = 15/4$. Van der Waals equation gives $v_c = 3b$ and $RT_c/p_cv_c = 8/3$. *See also* reduced equation of state.

(2) For a solid, using the *virial law of Clausius, the equation of state may be written:

$$pV + G(V) = - \frac{\mathrm{d} \log f}{\mathrm{d} \log V} \cdot E,$$

where $G(V) = V \frac{\mathrm{d}}{\mathrm{d}V} W(V)$

and $W(V)$ is the potential energy per mole of the crystal when the atoms are at rest in their mean positions; f is the frequency of oscillation of an atom about its mean position; and E is the total energy of the oscillations given by

$$E = \int_0^T C_v \, \mathrm{d}T$$

where C_v is the molar heat capacity at constant volume. Debye deduced an equation of state for solids based on thermodynamics and statistical mechanics modified to include the quantum theory:

$$pV + V\frac{d\Phi}{dV}$$

$$= -\frac{d\log\theta}{d\log V}9RT\left(\frac{T}{\theta}\right)^3\int_0^{\theta/T}\frac{\xi^3}{e^\xi-1}d\xi,$$

where θ is the characteristic temperature of the body and Φ is the increase in free energy when the body is compressed at absolute zero from a volume V_0 to a volume V. ξ is defined as hf/kT, where h is the Planck constant, k is the Boltzmann constant, and f is the frequency of the vibrations. This equation is essentially the same as that of Clausius. *Grüneisen's law follows from this equation as a first approximation.

equatorial mounting. *See* telescope.

equilibrant. A single force (if one exists) capable of balancing a given system of forces.

equilibrium. (1) A system of coplanar forces is in equilibrium when the algebraic sums of the resolved parts of the forces in any two directions are both zero and the algebraic sum of the moments of the forces about any point in their plane is zero. If the system of forces is not coplanar, then the same results must hold between the components of the forces lying in any plane and also for the components lying in two other different planes.

As any system of forces can be reduced to a single force and a single couple, the condition of equilibrium is also that these shall both vanish.

(2) A body is in stable, unstable, or neutral equilibrium according to whether the forces brought into play following a slight displacement tend to decrease, increase, or not affect the displacement

respectively. Neutral equilibrium is sometimes called *indifferent* equilibrium. These concepts of equilibrium and of stability can be generalized to apply to other physical systems, e.g. a system of electrical charges in a potential field; a soap bubble on the end of a tube connected to a reservoir of air.

(3) In general, the potential energy of a system is a minimum or a maximum if it is stable or unstable respectively. Neutral equilibrium may turn out to be either stable or unstable equilibrium if a large enough displacement be applied. *See* least energy principle.

equilibrium constant. Symbol: K. *See* mass action, law of.

equinoxes. (1) The two points at which the ecliptic intersects the celestial equator (*see* celestial sphere). (2) The two days of the year when the sun is at these points, day and night being of equal length.

equipartition of energy. The mean energy of the molecules of a gas is equally divided among the various *degrees of freedom of the molecules. The average energy of each degree of freedom is equal to $\frac{1}{2}kT$, where k is the Boltzmann constant and T is the thermodynamic temperature.

equipotential. Having the same electrical potential. An equipotential surface is a surface drawn so that all points on it are at the same potential. It cuts the lines of force orthogonally, so that no work is done against electrical forces in moving a small charge in any direction in the surface.

equivalent circuit. An arrangement of simple circuit elements that has the same electrical characteristics as a more complicated circuit or device under specified conditions.

equivalent focal length. The distance from a principal point to its corresponding principal focal point (*see* centred optical systems). With a *zoom lens or variable focal-length lens, the equivalent focal length is a variable. It can be considered as the ratio of the size of an image of a small distant object near the axis to the angular distance of the object in radians.

equivalent length of a magnet. The poles of a magnet are not at its ends. An equivalent length 2*l* can be chosen so that 2*l* times the pole strength is equal to the moment. This length is commonly about $\frac{5}{6}$ of the geometrical length for simple bar magnets.

equivalent network. An electrical network that can be connected in place of another without altering in any way the conditions obtaining in the other parts of the system.

equivalent positions (points). A complete set of points in any given space group that is obtained by performing the symmetry operations of the *space group on a single point (x, y, z).

equivalent resistance. The value of total *resistance that, if concentrated at a point in an electrical circuit, would dissipate the same power as the total of various smaller resistances at different points in the circuit.

equivalent sine wave. A sine wave having the same *root-mean-square value as the given wave and also the same fundamental frequency.

erg. The *CGS unit of energy. 1 erg = 10^{-7} joule.

ergon. A quantum of energy of an oscillator equal to the product of the frequency of oscillation and the *Planck constant.

error equation. The equation

$$y = h\pi^{-\frac{1}{2}} \exp[-h^2(x - a)^2].$$

See frequency distribution.

errors of measurement. (1) Accidental errors. In all physical measurements small errors, due to instrumental imperfections and inaccurate human judgements, always occur. It is often possible and always desirable to estimate the magnitudes of the errors in each part of the experiment and to combine these to find the likely error in the final result. The actual estimated errors in quantities that are added or subtracted should be added in finding the error in the result; the percentage errors should be added if the quantities are combined by multiplication or division. Graphical or arithmetical methods are used to combine observations of a similar type, on the grounds that a better result can be obtained than from one single observation. (*See* probable error.)

Heisenberg's *uncertainty principle shows that there is an irremovable minimum uncertainty in all physical measurements no matter how perfect the instruments or how accurate the observer.

(2) Systematic errors. The foregoing comments do not apply to these errors, which must be removed by suitable design of apparatus and technique. *See* personal equation.

Esaki diode. *See* tunnel diode.

escape velocity. The velocity that a projectile, space probe, etc., must reach in order to escape the *gravitational field of a planet or the moon. It depends on the mass and diameter of the planet or the moon. The escape velocity is about 11 200 m s^{-1} for the earth and about 2370 m s^{-1} for the moon.

e.s.u. Abbreviation for electrostatic units. *See* CGS system of units.

etalon. An interferometer consisting of two semi-silvered glass plates optically flat and fixed accurately parallel to one another with an air separation of a few mm or cm. On account of its sharp

139

fringes and high resolving power it is used for accurate comparison of wavelengths and the study of the *hyperfine structure of spectral lines. A *Fabry–Perot interferometer* is similar but has a variable plate separation.

eta-meson (η). An *elementary particle having zero spin, isospin, and charge, negative parity, and positive G-parity. It has a mass of 549 MeV/c^2.

ether, aether (luminiferous). A now discarded hypothetical medium once thought to fill all space and to be responsible for carrying light waves and other electromagnetic waves. It was assumed to be extremely elastic yet extremely light, to transmit transverse waves with the velocity of light, and to have a greater density in matter than in free space. *See also* Michelson–Morley experiment.

Ettinghausen effect. The establishment of a difference of temperature between the edges of a plate along which an electric current is flowing, when a magnetic field is applied at right angles to the plane of the plate. The effect is very small, and for copper, platinum, and silver is unappreciable.

Euler's angles. A set of three angles (θ, φ, ψ) particularly useful in describing the position of a body moving about a fixed point O. Cartesian axes, OABC, are fixed in the body (OC usually being an axis of symmetry, e.g. the axis of a top) and the motion is described relative to fixed Cartesian axes OXYZ (OZ is usually vertical). θ is the angle between

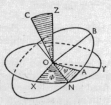

Euler's angles

the axis of the body OC and the axis OZ. The plane OAB in the body intersects the plane XOY (usually horizontal) in the *nodal line* ON. The angle $\varphi = $ XÔN measures the *precession* of the axis OC around the vertical *precession axis* OZ. $\psi = $ AÔN measures the rotation of the body about its own axis OC. Variations in θ are referred to as *nutation*.

Euler's equations. The three differential equations of motion of a rigid body (a) relative to the centre of mass, using the principal axes of the body through the centre of mass as coordinate axes, or (b) about a fixed point using the principal axes through this point as coordinate axes. They are:

(i) $A \dfrac{d\omega_x}{dt} - \omega_y\omega_z(B - C) = G_x$

(ii) $B \dfrac{d\omega_y}{dt} - \omega_z\omega_x(C - A) = G_y$

(iii) $C \dfrac{d\omega_z}{dt} - \omega_x\omega_y(A - B) = G_z$

A, B, and C are the principal moments of inertia, ω_x, ω_y, and ω_z are the components of angular velocity, and G_x, G_y, and G_z are the components of the applied torque about the principal axes OXYZ.

evaporation. (1) The conversion of a liquid to a vapour at a temperature below the boiling point. The process involves cooling of the liquid because it is the fastest molecules that are able to escape, and this lowers the average kinetic energy of those remaining. (2) The conversion of a substance, usually a metal, into a vapour at high temperatures, either from the liquid state or by sublimation from the solid metal. It is used for producing thin films of metal, which are used in *transistors and in studies of surface properties.

evaporator. The part of a refrigerating plant in which the liquid refrigerant is evaporated, taking its latent heat from its surroundings.

even-even nucleus. A nucleus that contains an even number of protons and an even number of neutrons.

even-odd nucleus. A nucleus that contains an even number of protons and an odd number of neutrons. A nucleus, other than that of hydrogen, that has an odd *mass number.

event horizon. *See* Schwarzschild radius.

Ewing's theory of magnetism. The individual atoms or molecules of ferromagnetic substances act as small magnets. In the unmagnetized state of the substance, these elementary magnets arrange themselves in closed chains so that the net effect of their poles externally is zero. Magnetization is produced by a realignment of the elementary magnets with their magnetic axes in the direction of magnetization, and saturation is reached when all have been so aligned. The substance is prevented from following the changes in the magnetizing field owing to the force necessary to break up the molecular chains, thus explaining the phenomenon of magnetic hysteresis. This theory has been partially confirmed by modern investigations. *See* ferromagnetism.

exchange force. (1) A force acting between particles due to the exchange of some property. In *quantum mechanics such forces can arise when two interacting particles can share some property. Exchange forces are an important part of the *nuclear force. There are three types of exchange force which may act between nucleons; each corresponds to the sharing or exchange of different properties: the *Heisenberg force* (exchange of charge), the *Bartlett force* (exchange of spin direction), and the *Majorana force* (exchange of position due to exchange of charge and spin). These exchange forces may be interpreted as being due to the continual emission and absorption of *virtual particles that carry the shared property from one particle to the other. *See also* neutral weak current. (2) *See* ferromagnetism.

exchange relation. The statement

$$(pq - qp = h/2\pi i),$$

in which p and q are matrices replacing momentum and positional coordinates in *matrix mechanics. It replaces the old Wilson–Sommerfeld type of quantum condition. *See* quantum theory; quantum mechanics.

excitation. (1) The production of magnetic flux in an electromagnet by means of a current in a winding. The current is referred to as the *exciting current* and the ampere-turns produced as the exciting ampere-turns. (2) *See* excited state.

excitation energy. *Syn.* critical potential. The energy required to change the *energy level of an atom or molecule to a higher energy level. It is equal to the difference in energy of the levels and is usually the difference in energy between the *ground state of the atom and a specified *excited state.

excitation purity. *See* chromaticity.

excited state. The state of a system, such as an atom or molecule, when it has a higher *energy level than its *ground state.

exciton. An electron in combination with a *hole in a crystalline solid. The electron has gained sufficient energy to be in an *excited state and is bound by electrostatic attraction to the positive hole. The exciton may migrate through the solid and eventually the hole and electron recombine with emission of a photon.

exclusion principle. *See* Pauli exclusion principle.

exclusive OR circuit. *See* logic circuit.

exitance. (1) *See* luminous exitance. (2) *See* radiant exitance.

exit port, pupil. *See* apertures and stops in optical systems.

exosphere. The outermost *atmospheric layer of the earth.

exothermic process. A process during which heat is evolved from the system. When a nuclear process results in the production of heat it is often called an *exoergic process*.

exotic atom. An unstable atom in which an electron has been replaced artificially by another negatively charged particle, such as a muon, pion, or kaon. Following capture the particle drops through the atomic energy levels, causing X-ray photons to be emitted, before colliding with the nucleus. Exotic atoms are studied by means of these X-rays.

expander. *See* volume compressors (and expanders).

expanding universe. Lines in the spectrum of the light from remote galaxies are shifted towards the long wavelength end by an amount which is greatest for those nebulae believed to be farthest away. If this *red shift is interpreted as due to a velocity away from the earth in the line of sight, then those galaxies that are farthest away are moving fastest. Thus the universe appears to be expanding. *See* steady-state theory; big-bang theory.

expansion. *See* coefficient of expansion.

exploring coil. *Syn.* search coil. A coil used for measuring magnetic flux. It is commonly used in conjunction with a *ballistic galvanometer or a *fluxmeter.

exponential decay. The decrease of some physical quantity, usually with time, according to a negative exponential law,

represented by an equation of the type $y = y_0\, e^{-at}$. Examples occur in many diverse branches of physics, e.g. the fall of amplitude in damped harmonic oscillations, the fall in voltage of a charged capacitor leaking through a high resistance, and the fall in activity of a pure radioactive substance with a stable daughter product.

exponential horn. An acoustic horn whose cross sectional area increases from throat to mouth according to the relation

$$S_x/S_0 = \exp mx,$$

where S_x and S_0 are the cross sectional areas distance x from the throat and at the throat, m is a constant determining the rate of flare and the theoretical cut-off frequency.

exposure. (1) *See* light exposure. (2) *See* radiant exposure. (3) The time for which a material is illuminated or irradiated. It is more properly called the *exposure time* and should not be confused with the product of illuminance and time or irradiance and time.

exposure meter. A photographic instrument that measures light intensity by means of a *cadmium sulphide cell or *selenium cell. For a particular type of film it indicates the *f-number required for a given shutter speed, or vice versa, to give the correct exposure.

extensive shower. *See* Auger shower.

extensometer. A device for measuring the small change in length of an arbitrary length of a sample undergoing strain.

external work. Work done by a substance expanding against an external resistance. It is equal to

$$\int_{v_1}^{v_2} p\,\mathrm{d}v$$

where v_1 and v_2 are the initial and final volumes respectively and p is the applied external pressure (*see* diagram). For a cyclic process the external work done per cycle is given by the area enclosed by the cycle.

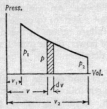

External work done on expansion

extinction coefficient. *See* linear attenuation coefficient.

extraordinary ray. *See* double refraction.

extrapolation. The estimation of the value of a function for a value of the variable lying outside the range of those for which the function is known. This may be done graphically or by calculation as for *interpolation.

extremely high frequency (EHF). *See* frequency band.

extrinsic semiconductor. A *semiconductor in which the charge *carrier concentration is dependent upon impurities or other imperfections.

eye lens. The lens nearer to the eye in an eyepiece of an instrument as distinct from the more remote lens (the field lens).

eyepiece. *Syn.* ocular. The single lens, doublet, or combination of lenses acting virtually as a magnifying lens to examine the image formed by an objective. (*See under* Ramsden, Huygens, Kellner, Fraunhofer eyepieces.) It is usual to arrange that the image from the objective lies in the focal plane of the eyepiece, which thus delivers parallel rays out of the instrument (infinity adjustment). *See* microscope; refracting telescope; reflecting telescope.

F

Fabry–Perot interferometer. *See* etalon.

face-centred. The form of crystal structure in which the atoms occupy the centres of the faces of the lattice as well as the vertices.

facsimile transmission. A system designed to transmit any kind of fixed graphic material so that a recorded likeness of the transmitted images is produced. The system employs facsimile scanning, i.e. a successive analysis of the subject copy, which in turn produces electrical signals capable of transmission to a receiver. Facsimile receivers amplify the incoming signals and convert them into a brightness-modulated light source, which is then used to record the picture elements.

factor of merit. *See* figure of merit.

fading. In communications, variations in the signal strength at the receiver caused by variations in the transmission medium. It is usually caused by destructive interference between two waves travelling to the receiver by two different paths. If all frequencies in the transmitted signal are attenuated approximately equally, the fading is known as *amplitude fading* and results in a smaller received signal. If different frequencies are attenuated unequally, the fading is known as *selective fading* and results in a distorted signal at the receiver.

Fahrenheit scale. The temperature scale on which the ice point is defined as 32° F and the steam point as 212° F. It is no longer in use for scientific purposes.

Fahrenheit's hydrometer. *See* hydrometer.

fail-safe device. An automatic device that causes a system to cease operation when a failure occurs in the supply or control of power, or the overall structure is found defective.

fall-out. (1) Radioactive materials that fall to earth following a nuclear bomb explosion. *Local fall-out* is observed down-wind of the explosion after a few hours, no more than about 500 km from the source; it consists of large particles. During the month or so that follows, a *tropospheric fall-out* of fine particles is observed in various locations at roughly the same latitude as the explosion. The particles that are drawn up to high altitudes often take many years before being deposited all over the surface of the earth, and are referred to as *stratospheric fall-out*. (2) A substance that enters the atmosphere from a source on the earth's surface (e.g. a volcano, nuclear reactor, car exhaust, etc.) that is later deposited as particles either in the vicinity of the source or elsewhere.

fall time. A measure of the rate of decay of a periodic quantity. The time required for the amplitude to fall from 90% to 10% of its peak value.

fan-in. The maximum number of inputs to a *logic circuit.

fan-out. The maximum number of inputs to other circuits that can be driven by the output of a given circuit.

farad. Symbol: F. The *SI unit of *capacitance, defined as the capacitance of a capacitor that acquires a charge of one coulomb when a potential difference of one volt is applied. The farad is far too large a unit for ordinary use and the submultiples microfarad (μF), nanofarad (nF), and picofarad (pF) are generally employed.

Faraday constant. Symbol: *F*. The quantity of electricity equivalent to one mole of electrons, i.e. the product of the *Avogadro constant and the charge on an electron in coulombs. It is, therefore, the quantity of electricity required to liberate or deposit 1 mole of a univalent ion. Its value is $9.648\,670 \times 10^4$ C mol^{-1}.

Faraday cylinder. (1) A closed or nearly closed hollow conductor, usually earthed, placed round electrical apparatus to shield it from the external electrical fields. (2) A similar structure for the collection of a stream of charged particles (electrons or gaseous ions), usually shielded by an earthed cylinder. The inner conductor is insulated and connected to suitable detecting apparatus.

Faraday dark space. *See illustration under* gas-discharge tube.

Faraday effect. The rotation of the plane of polarization experienced by a beam of plane polarized light when it passes in the direction of the magnetic lines of force, through certain substances exposed to a strong magnetic field. It occurs in heavy flint glass, quartz, and water. The direction of rotation is independent of the sense in which the beam traverses the magnetic lines; thus if the beam is reflected back along its course the rotation is doubled. The angle of rotation θ is directly proportional to the strength *H* of the magnetic field and to the length *l* of path in the substance. The quantity θ/lH is called *Verdet's constant*. *See also* Kerr effects.

Faraday–Neumann law. *See* electromagnetic induction.

Faraday's disc. An early model of an electromagnetic generator. It consists of a copper disc that can be rotated (usually by hand) about a horizontal axis through its centre at right angles to the plane of the disc, between the poles of a permanent horseshoe magnet. When the disc is in rotation an e.m.f. is induced between the axis and the circumference, and can be tapped off by sliding contacts or brushes.

Faraday's laws of electrolysis. The mass of any substance liberated from an electrolyte by the passage of current is proportional to the current and to the time for which it flows. If the same current passes for the same time through a series of different electrolytes the masses of the different substances liberated are directly proportional to their atomic weights divided by the charge of the ion carrying the current.

Faraday's laws of induction. (1) Whenever the number of lines of magnetic induction linked with a conducting circuit is changing, an induced current flows in the circuit, which continues only so long as the change is actually taking place. (2) The direction of the induced current in the circuit is such that its magnetic field tends to keep the number of lines linked with the circuit constant. (3) The total quantity of electricity passing round the circuit is directly proportional to the total change in the lines of induction, and inversely proportional to the resistance of the circuit. *See* electromagnetic induction.

Faraday tube. *See* electric flux.

faradmeter. An instrument for the direct measurement of *capacitance.

far infrared or ultraviolet. *See* near infrared or ultraviolet.

fast axis. In negative crystals (e.g. calcite), the vibrations of the extraordinary ray (which travels faster) are parallel to the optic axis which is then referred to as the fast axis. In positive crystals (e.g.

145

quartz) this axis is at right angles to the optic axis.

fast breeder reactor. A fast *nuclear reactor that breeds more fissile material than it consumes (*see also* breeder reactor). These reactors are much more economical than thermal reactors, being able to utilize some 75 % of the uranium ore as it comes from the earth. After the first fuelling of a fast breeder reactor, which requires some 3000 kilogrammes of plutonium per 1000 megawatts of electricity produced, the net fuel requirement is a very small quantity of natural uranium.

Owing to the high temperature in the core (7500° C) a liquid metal (usually sodium) is used as the *coolant.

fast neutron. A neutron with a kinetic energy greater than some specified value, usually above 0·1 MeV (1·6 × 10^{-14} joule). However, it is also applied to neutrons that have an energy greater than the fission threshold in $^{238}_{92}U$, which is about 1·5 MeV. Neutrons of this energy are capable of initiating *fast fission*.

fast reactor. *See* nuclear reactor; fast breeder reactor.

fatigue. The progressive decrease of a property due to repeated stress, e.g. the elasticity of a metal under continuous vibration.

Faure cell. A lead *accumulator cell, the plates of which consist of grids into which a mixture of lead oxide is forced under pressure.

feedback. The process of returning a fraction of the output energy of an energy-converting device to the input. It usually applies to *amplifiers, the gain of the amplifier being either increased or reduced according to the relative phase of the returned energy.

Feedback may occur through one electrical path (single loop) or through several paths (multiple loop). Capacitive feedback employs a *capacitor as the feedback device, and inductive feedback employs an *inductor or inductive *coupling. If the phase of the feedback is such that the input energy is increased, the feedback is known as *positive feedback*. If sufficient feedback is applied the amplifier will oscillate. If the phase is such that the input energy is decreased, the feedback is known as *negative feedback*. This is the type of feedback most commonly employed as it tends to stabilize the amplifier or reduce noise and distortion in the circuit: feedback used for this purpose may also be called *stabilized feedback*.

feeder. An electric line that conveys electrical energy from a generating station to a point of a distributing network. It is not tapped at any intermediate points. *See* transmission line.

Felici balance. A method of determining the mutual inductance between the windings of an inductor by means of an alternating-current bridge circuit.

femto-. Symbol: f. A prefix meaning 10^{-15}, e.g. 1 fm = 10^{-15} metre.

Fermat's principle. The path of a ray in passing between two points during reflection or refraction is the path of least time (*principle of least time*). It is now more usually expressed as the principle of *stationary* time: that the path of the ray is the path of least *or* greatest time. If a reflecting or refracting surface has smaller curvature than the aplanatic surface tangential to it at the point of incidence, the path is a minimum; if its curvature is greater than the aplanatic surface, its path is a maximum.

Fermi age theory. An approximate method of calculating the *slowing-down density of neutrons in a *nuclear reactor, based on the assumption that they lose energy continuously rather than in discrete amounts. The *age equation*:

$$\nabla^2 q - \frac{dq}{d\tau} = 0,$$

relates the slowing-down density q to *neutron age, τ. Because of the assumptions made the theory is least applicable to media containing light elements.

Fermi–Dirac distribution function. In solid state physics, the probability that an *electron will occupy a particular quantum state when thermal equilibrium has been reached. *See also* energy bands; quantum statistics.

Fermi–Dirac statistics. *Syn.* Fermi statistics. *See* quantum statistics.

Fermi gas model. A model of the nucleus in which the neutrons and protons are regarded as independent particles obeying Fermi–Dirac statistics (*see* quantum statistics) but confined within a cube having a volume equal to that of the nucleus. The model is similar to the theory of electrons in solids. It is useful in describing collisions in high-energy nuclear processes.

Fermi level, function. *See* energy bands.

fermion. Any *elementary particle having half integer *spin. Fermions obey Fermi–Dirac statistics (*see* quantum statistics). All particles are either fermions or *bosons; *leptons and *baryons are fermions.

Ferranti effect. An effect occurring in *transmission lines when the load is suddenly reduced. The charging current through the line inductance causes a sharp rise in the voltage at the end of the line.

ferrimagnetism. The property of certain solid substances, such as ferrites, that show both ferromagnetic and anti-

ferromagnetic properties. It is characterized by a small positive magnetic *susceptibility that increases with temperature. It is caused by the presence of two types of ion in the crystal with unequal electron *spins – arranged so that the magnetic dipole moments of adjacent ions are antiparallel. Thus the situation is similar to that in antiferromagnetic materials with the difference that the magnetic moments are unequal.

ferrite. A low density ceramic oxide of iron to which another oxide has been added. The formula for a typical ferrite is $Fe_2O_3 . XO$, where X is a divalent metal such as cobalt, nickel, zinc, or manganese. Ferrites possess insulating properties and exhibit *ferrimagnetism or *ferromagnetism according to the nature of X. They are used in the *dust cores of computers.

ferroelectric crystals. Crystals that behave like Rochelle salt in developing very large values of the piezoelectric and dielectric constants, usually in one particular direction, within a certain temperature range (the Curie region). These properties are in many ways analogous to *ferromagnetism.

ferromagnetism. A property of certain solid substances that, having a large positive magnetic *susceptibility, are capable of being magnetized by weak magnetic fields. The chief ferromagnetic elements are iron, cobalt, and nickel; many ferromagnetic alloys based on these metals also exist. Ferromagnetic materials exhibit *hysteresis. Their relative *permeability is much greater than unity and they achieve *saturation at fairly low magnetic field strengths. At a certain temperature, the *Curie point, there is a change from ferromagnetism to *paramagnetism. The magnetic *susceptibility then varies according to the *Curie–Weiss law.

Ferromagnetics are able to retain a certain amount of magnetization when

147

the magnetizing field is removed. Those materials which retain a high percentage of their magnetization are said to be hard and those which lose most of the magnetization are said to be soft.

The characteristic features of ferromagnetism are explained by the presence of *domains. A ferromagnetic domain is a region of crystalline matter, whose volume may be between 10^{-12} and 10^{-8} m³, which contains atoms whose magnetic moments are aligned in the same direction. The domain is thus magnetically saturated and behaves like a magnet with its own magnetic axis and moment. The magnetic moment of a ferromagnetic atom results from the spin of the electrons in an unfilled inner shell of the atom. The formation of a domain depends upon the strong interatomic forces (*exchange forces*) that are effective in a crystal lattice containing ferromagnetic atoms.

In an unmagnetized volume of a specimen, the domains are arranged in a random fashion with their magnetic axes pointing in all directions so that the specimen has no resultant magnetic moment. Under the influence of a weak magnetic field, those domains whose magnetic axes have directions near to that of the field grow at the expense of their neighbours. In this process the atoms of neighbouring domains tend to be aligned in the direction of the field but the strong influence of the growing domain causes their axes to align parallel to its magnetic axis. The growth of these domains leads to a resultant magnetic moment and hence magnetization of the field. With increasing field strength the growth of domains proceeds until there is, effectively, only one domain whose magnetic axis approximates to the field direction. The specimen now exhibits strong magnetization. Further increases in field strength cause the final alignment and magnetic saturation in the field direction. This explains the characteristic variation of magnetization with applied field strength. The presence

of domains in ferromagnetic materials can be demonstrated by the use of *Bitter patterns or by the *Barkhausen effect. *See also* antiferromagnetism; ferrimagnetism.

fertile. Of an isotope. Capable of being transformed into a fissile material in a *nuclear reactor. Uranium-238 is an example of a fertile isotope.

Féry total radiation pyrometer. A *pyrometer used for the direct measurement of temperature up to 1400° C by measuring the total energy of radiation of all wavelengths from the source.

Fessenden oscillator. An efficient form of electromagnetic or electrodynamic underwater sound generator and receiver. It is commonly used for signalling through sea when a large range is required.

FET. Abbreviation for field-effect transistor.

fetron. A junction *field-effect transistor, mounted in a package so that it can be directly plugged into a circuit as a replacement for a valve, with no special modifications of the circuit.

Feynman diagram and propagator. *See* quantum electrodynamics.

fibre optics system. An optical system using a single glass fibre or an array of fibres as a *light guide* or for transmitting light images. A light guide consists of a single flexible glass rod of high refractive index, usually less than 1 mm in diameter, having polished surfaces coated with material of lower refractive index as protection. Light falling on one end within a certain solid angle will undergo *total (internal) reflection at the cylindrical surface of the glass core. The light is trapped within the core and travels down the length of the fibre with little or no absorption. The fibre can continue to reflect light when it is considerably curved, as long as the reflection angle remains greater than the critical angle.

Images may be transmitted by using a bundle of such fibres, between 0·01–0·5 mm in diameter, in a fixed array. If a pattern of light is displayed at one end, each fibre will transmit light from a small area of the pattern to the other end, and the image will be reassembled on that surface.

Screens on *cathode-ray tubes, *image intensifiers, etc., can be made from parallel glass fibres fused together. There is therefore no loss in definition.

Fick's law. A law expressing the process of *diffusion of liquids and solids in mathematical form. The mass of dissolved substance crossing unit area of a plane of equal concentration in unit time is proportional to the concentration gradient. The constant of proportionality is called the *diffusion coefficient*.

field. A region under the influence of some physical agency. Typical examples are the *electric, *magnetic, and *gravitational fields that result from the presence of charge, magnetic dipole, and mass respectively; these are *vector fields. A field can be pictorially represented by a set of curves, often referred to as *lines of flux* (or *force*); the density of these lines at any given point represents the strength of the field at that point, and their direction represents the direction conventionally associated with the agency.

A field is used to describe the region inhabited by *nucleons, in which *exchange forces are set up. It has also been used in connection with scalar quantities to describe distributions of temperature, electric potential, etc.

field coil. A coil that, when carrying a current, magnetizes a *field magnet of an electrical machine (dynamo or motor).

field-effect transistor (FET). A *transistor in which current flow depends on the movement of majority carriers only. The electrodes are *source, *gate(s), and *drain. There are two main types of FET: *junction field-effect transistors* (JUGFET, JFET), symbol: ⊣╠, and *insulated gate field-effect transistors* (IGFET, MISFET, MIST, MOSFET, MOST), symbol: ⊣╟. The basic structures are shown in Figs. *a* and *b*. If a suitable voltage is ap-

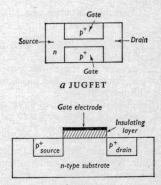

a JUGFET

b IGFET

plied across the transistor, majority carriers move from source to drain through a narrow conducting channel between them. This channel forms part of the structure of JUGFETS. In IGFETS the channel is formed by applying a voltage to the gate electrode when an inverted layer (*see* inversion) is produced at the surface of the semiconductor substrate. *Depletion layers associated with the semiconductor junctions of JUGFETS and the inverted channel of IGFETS determine the size and shape of the conducting channel and are a function of the drain voltage. In both cases a pinch-off condition is reached when the channel cross-section is just zero. Above this *pinch-off voltage* V_p, the channel and therefore the current remains essentially constant until *breakdown occurs. Applying a suitable voltage to the gate(s) causes pinch-off condition to be reached at a lower drain voltage and a family of characteristics, similar to those of a pentode valve, is generated (Fig. *c*).

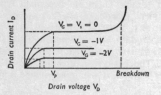

c Characteristic curves of a
JUGFET

The gate voltage is therefore used to modulate the channel conductivity: p-channel devices are those with p-type source and drain regions and n-channel those with n-type regions.

Depletion-mode FETS are those in which conduction occurs with zero gate bias and *enhancement-mode* FETS are those in which a voltage must be applied to the gate before conduction can occur. All JUGFETS are depletion-mode devices. Ideally, all IGFETS are enhancement-mode devices but in n-channel devices a spontaneous inversion layer may exist even with zero gate bias causing such devices to be depletion-mode. In any device the minimum gate voltage for conduction is known as the *threshold voltage*.

field emission. *Syn.* autoemission; cold emission. A kind of *emission in which the presence of a high external electric field reduces the potential barrier at the surface of the emitter (*see* Schottky effect) and allows electrons to escape from the surface. The distortion of the potential barrier at sufficiently large values of the accelerating field results in an effective narrowing of the barrier and allows the *tunnel effect to operate, so liberating more electrons. The current density, *j*, is given by

$$j = aE^2 \exp(-b/E),$$

where E is the electric field and a and b are approximately constant. High electric fields of the order of 10^{10} volts per

metre are necessary for the effect to be observed and these are usually obtained by subjecting very sharp points to high potentials.

field-emission microscope. An instrument for observing the surface structure of a solid by causing it to undergo *field emission under the influence of the

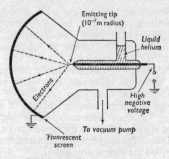

Field-emission microscope

high local electric field. The resulting electrons are accelerated to the screen where they cause fluorescence. Field-emitted electrons leave a surface at right angles and if r_t is the tip radius and r_s its distance from the screen, an image of the surface of the tip is projected onto the screen with a linear magnification of r_s/r_t. The resolution is limited by vibrations of the metal atoms and the tip is therefore usually cooled to liquid-helium or hydrogen temperatures. Individual atoms cannot be resolved (*compare* the field-ion microscope) but a regular pattern of light and dark patches is observed corresponding to areas of different *work function on the tip. These can be interpreted in terms of different crystal planes on the metal surface.

field ionization. Ionization of gaseous atoms and molecules by a high electric field at a solid surface. Electrons can only escape from an atom if they gain sufficient energy to overcome a potential barrier equal to the *ionization potential of the atom. If the atom is close to a solid and there is a high electric field near the surface, the *potential barrier may be distorted to such an extent that an electron can tunnel (*see* tunnel effect) through it from the atom into the metal. The process is similar to *field emission, with the difference that electrons tunnel from atoms or molecules into a metal rather than out of a metal. The fields required are of the order of 10^7 volts per metre and are produced by subjecting very sharp points to very high positive potentials ($\sim$ 10–20 kV). Ions formed at the metal surface are accelerated away by the field.

field-ion microscope. An instrument for observing the surface structure of a metal using *field ionization. It is identical in form to the *field-emission microscope with the difference that a positive voltage is applied to the tip rather than a negative one and the image is formed by positive ions from gas atoms rather than by electrons from the metal itself. Helium is allowed into the microscope at low pressure and helium ions form at the surface of the tip and are accelerated to the screen where they cause fluorescence. The field-ion current from a point depends on the magnitude of the electric field and on the atomic scale there is a local intensification of the field in the region of a surface atom. Consequently a magnified image of the atomic structure of the surface is projected onto the screen, individual metal atoms being resolved.

field lens. Of an eyepiece. The front lens of a two-lens eyepiece which serves to bend the chief rays towards the optical centre of the eye lens.

field magnet. The magnet which provides the magnetic field in an electrical machine. Usually it is an electromagnet but may be a permanent magnet in small machines.

field of view, field stop. *See* apertures and stops in optical systems.

field tube. *See* tube of flux.

figure of merit. *Syn.* factor of merit. Of a galvanometer. The sensitivity of the instrument expressed in mm deflection produced on a scale at a distance of 1 m by a current of 1 μA, after the deflection has been corrected for a coil-resistance of 1 ohm and a period of 10 seconds.

file. *Syn.* data set. A block of data used in computing that has a unique name by which it is accessed from the *storage device on which it is held.

film dosimetry. *See* dosimetry.

film resistor. *See* resistor.

filter. (1) An electrical network designed to transmit freely (i.e. with negligible attenuation) currents having frequencies that lie within one or more bands of frequencies (pass bands), and to attenuate currents of all other frequencies (i.e. frequencies lying within what are called the attenuation bands). The cut-off frequencies are those that separate the several pass and attenuation bands (symbols f_1, f_2, etc., or f_c if there is only one). The four main types of filter and the frequency limits of their pass and attenuation bands are as follows:

Type	Pass band(s)	Attenuation band(s)
Low-pass	0 to f_c	f_c to ∞
High-pass	f_c to ∞	0 to f_c
Band-pass	f_1 to f_2	0 to f_1, f_2 to ∞
Band-stop (or Band-rejection)	0 to f_1, f_2 to ∞	f_1 to f_2

(2) A device for transmitting light (and also infrared and ultraviolet) with restricted ranges of wavelength. Commonly, transparent substances that absorb selectively are used (coloured glasses

or films; *see also* Polaroid). *Interference filters* use a different principle and can be produced to yield a narrower band of wavelength 1–10 nm for half transmission.

filter pump. *Syn.* water aspirator. A fast working vacuum pump in which a jet of water is used to trap and remove air (*see* diagram). The lowest pressure attainable is approximately the vapour pressure of water at the prevailing temperature.

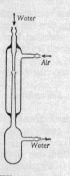

Filter pump

finder. *See* collimator.

fine-structure constant. Symbol: α. A dimensionless quantity formed from the four basic physical constants, electronic charge e, velocity of light c, the *Planck constant h, and the *permittivity of free space ε_0 (electric constant):

$$\alpha = e^2/2hc\varepsilon_0 = 7.297\ 351 \times 10^{-3}$$
$$\simeq 1/137$$

It is a measure of the strength of the *electromagnetic interaction. The equivalent pure number measuring the strength of the *strong interaction is about 1. On this scale the *weak interaction has a strength of 10^{-13} and the gravitational interaction of 10^{-38}.

first point of Aries, Libra. *See* celestial sphere.

152

fissile. Of a nuclide. Capable of undergoing *fission by interaction with *slow neutrons. *Compare* fissionable.

fission. The splitting of a heavy nucleus of an atom into two or more fragments of comparable size usually as the result of the impact of a neutron on the nucleus. It is normally accompanied by the emission of neutrons or gamma rays. Plutonium, uranium, and thorium are the principal fissionable elements. *See* nuclear reactors.

fissionable. Of a nuclide. Capable of undergoing fission by any process. *Compare* fissile.

FitzGerald–Lorentz contraction. *Syn.* Lorentz–FitzGerald contraction. *See* relativity.

five-fourths power law. The law of cooling applicable to free convection. The rate of loss of heat is proportional to the five-fourths power of the excess temperature of the body over the temperature of its surroundings.

fixed points. Reproducible invariant temperatures used to define a temperature scale. They are all either the boiling points or melting points of certain common substances (e.g. water, gold, sulphur) under standard atmospheric pressure. *See* international temperature scale.

flash barrier. A structure of fire-proof material designed to minimize the formation of an electric arc between conductors or to minimize the damage caused by such an arc in an electrical machine.

flashover. *Syn.* sparkover. An abnormal formation of an arc between two electrical conductors.

flashover voltage. *Syn.* sparkover voltage. The dry flashover voltage is the voltage at which the air surrounding a clean dry insulator (especially one supporting electric lines) breaks down completely and *flashover between the electrodes occurs. The wet flashover voltage is the voltage at which flashover occurs across the surface and between the electrodes of a clean insulator which has been sprayed with water (to simulate rain).

flash point. The lowest temperature at which a substance will provide sufficient inflammable vapour (under specified conditions) to ignite upon the application of a small flame.

flaw detection. For the detection of hairline cracks in metals, a short train of ultrasonic waves is sent out and its waveform, as recorded by the receiver, is noted on a cathode-ray oscillograph. Piezoelectric quartz oscillators are placed on two facets of a prismatic specimen. The presence of hairline cracks is shown by a number of secondary echoes which reach the second quartz oscillator before the main reflection from the prism base. Large fissures are more easily detected by X-rays. *See* magnetic crack detection.

F-layer or region, F_1-layer, F_2-layer. *Syn.* Appleton layers. *See* ionosphere.

Fleming–Kennelly law. At a point near magnetic saturation, the *reluctivity of ferromagnetic substances varies linearly with magnetic intensity.

Fleming's rules. Mnemonics for the relation between current, motion, and field in the dynamo and electromotor. *Right-hand rule* (dynamo principle). Hold the thumb, first finger and middle finger of the right hand at right angles to one another. Point the thuMb in the direction of Motion, the First finger along the lines of the Field; the seCond finger will then point in the direction of the induced Current. *Left-hand rule*

(motor principle). Hold the thumb, first finger and middle finger of the left hand at right angles to each other. Point the First finger in the direction of the Field, the seCond finger in the direction of the Current; then the thuMb points in the direction of Motion of the conductor.

flicker photometer. A photometer that presents alternately to the eye two surfaces illuminated by the sources to be compared. If both sources are white and the frequency of alternation is not too high, disappearance of flicker signifies equality of brightness. Flicker photometry is useful when there are colour differences between the lights to be compared, as there occurs a speed of alternation at which brightness flicker exists only while colour flicker is absent.

F-line. A green-blue line in the *emission spectrum of hydrogen, wavelength 486·133 nm. It is used as a reference line for specifying the refractive index and dispersion of optical glass, etc.

flip-flop. A *multivibrator circuit with two stable states and two input terminals, corresponding to the two states. The application of a suitable pulse to one of the inputs causes the circuit to 'flip' into the corresponding state in which it remains until a signal on the other input causes it to 'flop' into the other state. Flip-flops are widely used as counting and storage elements in computing systems, and various types have been developed. Clocked flip-flops have a third input and change state on the application of a clock pulse to this input, according to the signals on the other two inputs. Unclocked flip-flops are triggered directly by the input pulses themselves.

fluence. (1) *Energy fluence.* The sum of the energies, exclusive of *rest mass, of all particles incident in a given time on a small sphere centred at a given point in a space. (2) *Particle fluence.* The number of particles incident in a given time on that small sphere divided by the cross sectional area of the sphere.

fluid. A collective term embracing liquids and gases. A *perfect fluid* offers no resistance to change of shape (i.e. has zero viscosity).

fluid coefficient. The reciprocal of the *viscosity coefficient of a fluid.

fluidics. *Syn.* fluidic logic. The study and use of jets of fluid in specially designed circuits to perform tasks usually carried out by *electronics. Fluidic systems are some million times slower than electronic systems which enables them to be used to advantage in *delay lines, etc. They can generally be used at higher temperatures than electronic systems and they are unaffected by *ionizing radiations; they have therefore been used in *nuclear reactors and spacecraft.

fluorescence. When light strikes a fluorescent substance the latter becomes a source of radiation emitting light of another wavelength usually longer than the exciting radiation (Stokes's law), although it may also be shorter. *See also* luminescence.

fluorescent lamp. A lamp in which light is generated by *fluorescence. The common forms of fluorescent lamp consist of a *gas-discharge tube containing a gas, such as mercury vapour, at a low pressure. The inner surface of the lamp is coated with a *phosphor. When an electric current is passed through the vapour, ultraviolet radiation is produced and this, in striking the phosphor, produces visible radiation. Fluorescent lights of this type are more efficient than normal filament lamps because less of the energy is converted into heat.

fluorescent screen. A screen coated with a luminescent material that fluoresces when excited by electrons, X-rays, etc.

flutter. An undesirable form of *frequency modulation heard in the reproduction of high-fidelity sound and characterized by variations in pitch above about 10 Hz. *See also* wow.

flux. (1) A measure of the strength of a *field of force through a specified area. *See* electric flux; magnetic flux; magnetic flux density. (2) A measure of the power associated with a scalar quantity. *See* luminous flux; sound flux. (3) *See* neutron flux.

fluxmeter. An instrument for measuring changes in magnetic flux. The *Grassot fluxmeter* is essentially a moving coil galvanometer in which the restoring couple on the coil is negligibly small and the electromagnetic damping is large.

flux refraction. When lines or tubes of magnetic flux pass from one region to another of different *permeability they experience an abrupt change of direction, the ratio of the tangents of the angles of incidence and refraction being constant for any pair of media. The same effect is observed when lines of electric force pass across a boundary between media of different dielectric constant.

flying spot microscope. A microscope in which the lens system is used to produce a minute spot of light which, after passing through the object, falls on a photocell for subsequent amplification and display. The spot is made to scan the object and the image is produced on a *cathode-ray tube scanned in synchronization. The contrast of the display can be varied and the resolution is better than that obtained with a photographic plate.

f-number. *Syn.* relative aperture; stop number. The number, used especially in photography, equal to the ratio of the focal length of a particular lens to the effective diameter of the lens opening for a parallel beam of incident light. For a ratio of, say, 4 it is written f/4, f4, f:4, etc. For a given shutter speed, it always corresponds to the same *exposure.

focal length. The distance from the pole of a surface, from the centre of a thin lens, or from the principal point of a system to the principal focal point. In general there are two focal lengths, anterior or first (f) and posterior or second (f'), and $n/f = -n'/f'$ where n and n' are the refractive indexes of the medium on the two sides of the system. When the focal length is measured from the last vertex of a lens it is referred to as the *back focal length.

focal points. *Syn.* focus. *See* centred optical systems.

focus. (1) *See* focal points. (2) *See* seismology.

focusing. (1) Of charged particles. In *accelerators magnets are used to focus the beam of particles. In cyclic accelerators a narrow ring of magnets is used. The magnets usually perform two functions. They bend the path of the particles into a circle, the particles being accelerated by an electric field in the gaps between the magnets. They also focus the beam into a central orbit of small cross section. *Strong focusing* or *alternating gradient* (*AG*) *focusing* is achieved by using pairs of magnets. One member focuses the beam in one plane and defocuses it in the plane at right angles; the other member focuses the defocused plane and defocuses the orthogonal plane. The net effect is a strongly focused beam. The accelerating radio-frequency field in both linear and cyclic accelerators tends to keep the particles in phase with the r.f. field, so that they orbit in bunches. (2) Of the electron beam in a *cathode-ray tube. The principal methods are: (i) *electrostatic focusing*. The beam of electrons is made to converge by the action of electrostatic fields between two or more

electrodes at different potentials. The electrodes are commonly coaxial cylinders and the whole assembly forms an electrostatic *electron lens. The focusing effect is usually controlled by varying the potential of one of the electrodes (called the focusing electrode); (ii) *electromagnetic focusing*. The beam of electrons is made to converge by the action of a magnetic field which is produced by the passage of direct current through a focusing coil. The latter is commonly a coil of short axial length mounted so as to surround the tube and to be coaxial with it.

foot candle. An obsolete unit of illumination in the f.p.s. system, viz. a flux density of one lumen per square foot. 1 foot candle = $10·764$ lux (metre candles).

foot-lambert. *See* lambert.

foot-pound-second system of units (f.p.s. system). The system of units based on the foot, pound, and second. It has now been replaced for scientific and most technical purposes by *SI units.

forbidden band. *See* energy bands.

forbidden transition. A transition of an atom or molecule between two *energy levels, involving a change of *quantum number that is not allowed by the *selection rules.

force. Symbol: F. Any action that alters or tends to alter a body's state of rest or of uniform motion in a straight line. (*See* Newton's laws of motion.)

(1) *Body forces*, e.g. gravity, act throughout a body. Such forces are distinguished from *surface forces* which one solid body can apply to another. Both are called external forces and are transmitted throughout the body, i.e. a force applied at A tends to distort some other part of the body B. Forces between neighbouring parts of a body (such as

that between *A* and *B*) are called internal forces. If the body is in equilibrium under the action of external forces, both external and internal force systems are separately in equilibrium. (*See* stress components.)

(2) *Inertial forces.* If several forces act on a particle of mass *m* and produce an acceleration *a*, the magnitude *F* of the vector sum of the applied forces is equal to *ma*. Thus

$$F - ma = 0.$$

If we regard ($-ma$) as a force (called *effective* or *inertial force* or *kinetic reaction*), we have *d'Alembert's principle* that the impressed forces, together with the inertial forces form a system in equilibrium. The equilibrium is said to be *kinetic* or *dynamic* to distinguish it from static equilibrium.

(3) *Centripetal force* is that force which, directed towards a point, makes a particle of mass *m* describe a circular path of radius *r* with uniform angular velocity ω centred on that point. There is an acceleration of $r\omega^2$ towards the centre, throughout the motion. By d'Alembert's principle the inertial force radially outwards, called the *centrifugal force* = mass × acceleration = $mr\omega^2$, is in equilibrium with the applied centripetal force.

(4) *Coriolis force* is the inertial force associated with a change in the tangential component of a particle's velocity; e.g. suppose a particle moves with a constant speed *v*, outwards along a particular

Coriolis force

radius of a horizontal rotating table whose angular velocity is ω. The tangential velocity of the particle is $r\omega$

(where *r* is the particle's distance from the axis), and is increasing with *r*. Therefore there is a tangential acceleration, which turns out to be $2\omega v$, as well as a centripetal acceleration of $r\omega^2$. Thus the particle, by d'Alembert's principle, is in equilibrium: the real forces causing its motion are balanced by the centrifugal force $mr\omega^2$ and the Coriolis force (= mass × Coriolis acceleration = $2m\omega v$) acting in the direction shown. Coriolis forces are involved in problems concerning projectiles shot from the rotating earth and the direction of the Trade winds.

(5) *Generalized force.* The quotient of the work done by all the forces acting in a system, if one of the generalized co-ordinates alters by an infinitesimal amount while the others remain constant, to the change in that generalized co-ordinate.

forced convection. Ventilated cooling in a strong draught. For a body cooling by this means, *Newton's law applies. *See also* convection (of heat).

forced vibrations (or oscillations). Motion produced when a vibrating system is acted upon by an external vibrating force. The resulting vibrations consist of two components, namely a transient component of frequency given by the natural frequency of the system and a steady component of frequency equal to that of the driving force.

The amplitude of the steady vibration is a maximum when the frequency of the driving force is equal to the natural frequency of the system without the effect of damping. This condition is called *resonance*, and the system is said to resonate with the driving force. Then the forced vibrations lag 90° behind the driving force.

force ratio. *Syn.* mechanical advantage. *See* machine.

Fortin's barometer. *See* barometer.

forward bias or voltage. A voltage applied to a circuit or device in such a direction as to produce the larger current. The term commonly refers to *semiconductor devices.

Foster–Seeley discriminator. *See* frequency discriminator.

Foucault's pendulum. A simple pendulum that demonstrates the earth's rotation. It consists of a lead ball weighing about 28 kg suspended by a fine steel wire 67 m long. The plane of swing is invariable but, owing to the rotation of the earth, it appears to rotate through 360° in T hours, where T is given by $T = 24/\sin \lambda$, where λ is the latitude.

four-dimensional continuum. Einstein's theory of *relativity, by casting doubt on the concept of simultaneity, led to the idea of the three dimensions of space and one of time being taken together to form a reference system. Thus for complete specification an event must be defined in terms of a four-dimensional continuum.

Fourier analysis. It is possible to express any single-valued periodic function as a summation of sinusoidal components, of frequencies which are multiples of the frequency of the function. Such a summation is called a *Fourier series*, and the analysis of a periodic function into its simple harmonic components is a Fourier analysis.

A function of time, $x = \mathrm{f}(t)$, may thus be expressed as follows:

$$x = a_0 + a_1 \cos \omega t + a_2 \cos 2\omega t$$
$$+ a_3 \cos 3\omega t + \ldots$$
$$+ b_1 \sin \omega t + b_2 \sin 2\omega t$$
$$+ b_3 \sin 3\omega t + \ldots$$

The values of the coefficients a_0, a_1, a_2, $a_3, \ldots, b_1, b_2, b_3, \ldots$, may be obtained by integration giving

$$a_0 = \frac{\omega}{2\pi} \int_0^{2\pi/\omega} x \, \mathrm{d}t$$

$$a_n = \frac{\omega}{\pi} \int_0^{2\pi/\omega} x \cos n\omega t \, \mathrm{d}t$$

$$b_n = \frac{\omega}{\pi} \int_0^{2\pi/\omega} x \sin n\omega t \, \mathrm{d}t$$

Fourier number. A dimensionless quantity used in the study of heat transfer. It is defined by the function $\lambda t/c_p \rho l^2$, where $\lambda =$ thermal conductivity, $t =$ time, $c_p =$ specific heat capacity at constant pressure, $\rho =$ density, and $l =$ a characteristic length.

f.p.s. system. *See* foot-pound-second system of units.

frame of reference. (1) A rigid framework relative to which positions and movements may be measured; e.g. latitude and longitude define position on the earth's surface, the earth being used as a frame of reference. (2) A Galilean frame of reference is a rigid framework isotropic with respect to mechanical and optical experiments (used in the special theory of *relativity). *See* Newtonian system.

Fraunhofer diffraction. *See* diffraction of light.

Fraunhofer eyepiece. A terrestrial *eyepiece that has a lenticular erecting system in addition to the optical system of the *Huygens eyepiece or *Ramsden eyepiece.

Fraunhofer lines. Fine dark lines that cross the solar spectrum. They constitute an *absorption spectrum, the continuous bright spectrum from the glowing outer layers of the sun's body having certain wavelengths weakened by traversing gases and vapours in the outer layers of the solar atmosphere. A few lines are due to absorption in the terrestrial atmosphere.

free convection. *Syn.* natural convection. Loss of heat vertically which occurs in the absence of draughts when the surrounding fluid circulates freely. The rate of cooling under these conditions obeys the *five-fourths power law although for a small temperature difference between the body and its surroundings *Newton's law of cooling may be applied. *See* convection (of heat).

free electron. An electron that is not permanently attached to a specific atom or molecule and is free to move under the influence of an applied electric field. *See also* energy bands; semiconductor.

free-electron paramagnetism. *See* paramagnetism.

free energy. A thermodynamic function that gives the amount of work available when a system undergoes some specified change. *See* Gibbs function; Helmholtz function.

free fall. Downward motion in a *gravitational field, the motion being unimpeded by a medium that would otherwise provide the support of buoyancy and viscous retardation. In the earth's gravitational field the standard value for the *acceleration of free fall* (often called the acceleration due to gravity) is $g = 9.806\ 65$ m s^{-2}.

g varies slightly with position on the earth's surface because of greater centrifugal acceleration at the equator, the variation in distance from the earth's centre, and local deposits of heavy or light ores or the sideways attraction of mountains. g is accurately determined from the period of oscillation of a pendulum. *Gravity meters* (*syn.* gravimeters) are used to obtain absolute variations in g or to compare g from place to place. Moderately accurate measurements of variations due to local abnormalities are made with *gravity balances*. These are, in effect, types of

sensitive spring balances in which the change in weight of a fixed mass is measured.

free magnetism. An imaginary magnetic fluid to which the magnetic effects of a magnet are conventionally ascribed. In a bar magnet, the free magnetism is often regarded as being concentrated in the *poles but the actual distribution of free magnetism along the bar can be studied. The algebraical sum of the free magnetism on any specimen is always zero.

free-piston gauge. An absolute device for measuring high fluid pressures. The pressure is applied to one side of a small piston working in a cylinder and the force necessary to keep the piston stationary is a measure of the pressure.

free space. The region, formerly referred to as a vacuum, characterized by the absence of gravitational and electromagnetic *fields, and used as an absolute standard. The values of the properties possessed by free space fall into one of the following classes:

(1) Zero (e.g. temperature).
(2) Unity (e.g. *refractive index).
(3) The maximum possible (e.g. the *velocity of electromagnetic radiation).
(4) A particular, formally defined value (e.g. the *electric and *magnetic constants).

free surface energy. *See* surface tension.

free vibrations (or oscillations). A vibrating system when displaced from its neutral position oscillates about this position with a frequency characteristic of the system – the natural frequency of the system. The amplitude decays gradually, depending on the resistance of the medium to the motion and on the inertia of the system, until the energy supplied by the initial displacement has been expended into the medium. These vibrations are called free vibrations.

The expression for the displacement, x, in a free undamped vibration is given by

$$x = a \sin \sqrt{\frac{\kappa}{m}} . t,$$

where a is the amplitude, κ and m are the elastic and inertia terms respectively, and t is the time.

The corresponding expression for free vibrations with damping is

$$x = ae^{-\alpha t} \sin(\omega t - \delta)$$

where the damping factor $\alpha = \mu/2m$ (μ being the resistive term), and the pulsatance

$$\omega = \sqrt{\frac{\kappa}{m} - \frac{\mu^2}{4m^2}};$$

δ is the angular displacement at $t = 0$ and is called the epoch. *Compare* forced vibrations.

freezing mixture. A mixture of two or more substances that absorb heat when they mix and thus produce a lower temperature than that of the original constituents.

freezing point. *Syn.* melting point. The temperature at which the solid and liquid phases of a substance can exist in equilibrium together at a defined pressure, normally standard pressure of 101 325 Pa.

F-region *See* ionosphere.

Frenkel defect. *See* defect.

frequency (1) Symbol: ν or f. The number of complete oscillations or cycles in unit time of a vibrating system: related to the *angular frequency, ω, by the formula $\omega = 2\pi\nu$.

(2) Of an alternating current. The number of times the current passes through its zero value in the same direction in unit time.

(3) Of *electromagnetic radiation. The frequency, ν, is obtained from the equation $c = \nu\lambda$, where c is the velocity of light and λ is the wavelength of the radiation. In Planck's quantum relation, the quantum energy varies according to the frequency, viz. $h\nu$, where h is the *Planck constant. (1), (2), and (3) are measured in hertz.

(4) The number of values of a statistical variable lying in a given range. *See* frequency distribution.

frequency band. A range of *frequencies forming part of a continuous series of radio frequencies The internationally agreed frequency bands are:

Wavelength	Band	Frequency
1 mm–1 cm	Extremely high frequency; EHF	300–30 GHz
1 cm–10 cm	Super-high frequency; SHF	30–3 GHz
10 cm–1 m	Ultra-high frequency; UHF	3–0·3 GHz
1 m–10 m	Very high frequency; VHF	300–30 MHz
10 m–100 m	High frequency; HF	30–3 MHz
100 m–1000 m	Medium frequency; MF	3–0·3 MHz
1 km–10 km	Low frequency; LF	300–30 kHz
10 km–100 km	Very low frequency; VLF	30–3 kHz

frequency changer. (1) Generally, an electrical machine or circuit for converting alternating current at one frequency to alternating current at another frequency. (2) A heptode, octode, or triode–hexode valve used in the superheterodyne circuit to change incoming signals to the intermediate frequency.

frequency discriminator. A device that produces an output voltage the value of which is substantially proportional to the amount by which the frequency of the input voltage differs from some fixed datum-frequency. It is commonly employed in *automatic frequency control systems and in radio receivers for use with *frequency modulation. The most common type is the *Foster–Seeley discriminator*, which uses a tuned reactance valve followed by a discriminator.

frequency distortion. *Syn.* attenuation distortion. *See* distortion (electrical).

frequency distribution. A table, graph, or equation describing how a particular attribute is distributed among the members of a group, e.g. the distribution of a set of measured quantities about their mean value.

When the *deviations of the members of the set from the true value are the algebraic sum of a very large number of independent small deviations, the resulting frequency distribution is said to be *normal* or *Gaussian*. The graph of a Gaussian distribution following *normalization has the equation (sometimes called the *error equation*):

$$y = h\pi^{-\frac{1}{2}} \exp\left[-h^2(x - a)^2\right]$$

where $y \, . \, \mathrm{d}x$ is the probability of a value of x lying in a small range from x to $x + \mathrm{d}x$; a is the arithmetic mean of all the values of x; h is a constant determining the spread of the distribution. The quantity $s = (h\sqrt{2})^{-1}$ is the standard *deviation of the distribution and is small if the graph is narrow. Frequency distributions which are not normal are said to be *skew*. *See also* Poisson distribution.

frequency divider. An electrical apparatus or circuit the output frequency of which is an exact integral sub-multiple of the frequency of the input. A common form employs a *vibrator.

frequency division multiplexing. A method of *multiplex operation in which a

different frequency band is used for each of the input signals. The transmitted signal consists of a series of carrier waves of different frequencies, each modulated with a different input signal.

frequency function. *Syn.* probability density function. *See* probability.

frequency meter. An instrument for measuring the frequency of an alternating current. A common type consists of a *cavity resonator that measures the frequency of an electromagnetic wave.

frequency modulation. In this type of *modulation the frequency of the *carrier wave is varied above and below its unmodulated value by an amount which is proportional to the amplitude of the modulating signal and at a frequency equal to that of the modulating signal, the amplitude of the carrier wave

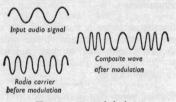

Input audio signal

Radio carrier
before modulation

Composite wave
after modulation

Frequency modulation

remaining constant. A frequency-modulated wave in which the modulating signal is sinusoidal may be represented by:

$$e = E_m \sin\left[2\pi Ft + \frac{\Delta F}{f} \sin 2\pi ft\right]$$

where $E_m =$ amplitude of the carrier wave, $F =$ frequency of the unmodulated carrier wave, $\Delta F =$ the peak variation of the carrier-wave frequency away from the frequency F, caused by the modulation, $f =$ frequency of the modulating signal. Compared with *amplitude modulation frequency modulation has several advantages, the most important of which is improved *signal-to-noise ratio. *Compare* phase modulation.

frequency multiplier. An electrical apparatus the output frequency of which is an exact integral multiple of the frequency of the input. Common forms employ non-linear amplifiers (e.g. *class B or *class C), so that the output is rich in harmonics of the input. The desired harmonic is selected by means of a tuned circuit or a *filter. Another type consists of a *multivibrator which is synchronized by the input so that the oscillations of the multivibrator have a frequency which is an exact integral of the frequency of the input.

fresnel. A unit of frequency equal to 10^{12} hertz.

Fresnel diffraction. *See* diffraction of light.

Fresnel lens. A lens consisting of a large number of steps each one having a convex surface of the same curvature as the corresponding section of a normally shaped convex lens. It was originally

Equal curvature

Fresnel lens

designed for use in lighthouses, to reduce the thickness and weight of the large lenses required. It is now also used as a *field lens in spotlights, camera viewfinders, etc., producing a large increase in image brightness.

Fresnel's rhomb. A glass rhombohedron that, by two internal reflections, changes

*plane polarized light into circularly polarized light.

Fresnel zone. *See* diffraction of light.

friction. (1) Sliding friction. The force needed to keep one solid surface just sliding over another is known as *kinetic* or *dynamic friction.* The force which has to be applied to initiate motion is slightly greater and is called *static* or *limiting friction.* The friction increases approximately in proportion to the total perpendicular force (normal reaction) between the surfaces and its ratio to the normal reaction between the surfaces is called the *coefficient of friction* (symbol: μ). The coefficient of kinetic friction for smooth metal surfaces (both of the same material) ranges from 0·15 to 0·5 and is slightly less usually than the coefficient of static or limiting friction. These coefficients are independent of the area of the surfaces in contact. The kinetic coefficient is also independent of the relative velocity if low, but increases if the speed and normal reactions are high. *See also* angle of friction.

(2) Rolling friction. The force resisting the rolling of a body on a plane and due to the fact that the rolling body is moving up the side of the hollow caused by the elastic deformation of the plane. It is much smaller than sliding friction, especially with hard surfaces, hence the use of wheels and ball bearings.

frictional electricity. *Syn.* triboelectricity. The electric charge produced by rubbing together two dissimilar substances; e.g. ebonite and paper or glass and silk. The charges produced are equal and opposite, one of the substances becoming positively, the other negatively, charged.

fringes. Circular or rectilinear patterns of alternate light and dark or of colour, produced by *interference or *diffraction of light.

front layer photocell. *See* rectifier photocell.

Froude number. In the relative motion of a floating body (e.g. a ship) and a fluid, the resistance force (drag) is dependent on the density of the fluid (ρ), the relative velocity (V), a characteristic length of the body (l), and the acceleration of free fall (g), the last term being due to the action of the gravitational attraction in producing waves. By the method of dimensions the resistance force D is $D \propto \rho l^2 V^2 \varphi(gl/V^2)$ where $\varphi(gl/V^2)$ represents a function of gl/V^2. This drag is the eddy-making and wave-making resistance but excludes the skin friction (due to viscosity of the fluid). The dimensionless number V^2/gl is called the Froude number.

fuel cell. A device for the direct conversion of energy from an oxidation/reduction chemical process to a flow of electricity. The requisite reagents are introduced continuously from outside the cell and react together with the aid of a catalyst. A typical simple fuel cell utilizes hydrogen and oxygen, which are fed to separate porous nickel plates in an electrolyte of weak potassium hydroxide solution; the plate fed by oxygen becomes the anode. The water that is formed from the gases so dilutes the electrolyte that its concentration must be increased from time to time. Fuel cells are able to deliver currents of about 20 A for long periods, but are bulky and have efficiencies of 60% (as opposed to *accumulators, with efficiencies of 75%). The essential difference between a fuel cell and an accumulator is that the former feeds on chemicals and needs no charging, whereas the latter feeds on electricity and its chemicals do not need replenishing.

fuel element. The smallest unit of a *fuel assembly* containing *fissile nuclides for powering a *nuclear reactor. The assembly (consisting of fuel elements and their supporting mechanism) together with the *moderator (if any) form the *core of the reactor.

full load. The maximum output of an electrical machine or *transformer under certain specified conditions, e.g. of temperature rise.

full radiator. *See* black body.

full-wave rectifier circuit. A rectifier circuit in which the positive and negative half-waves of the single-phase a.c. input wave are both effective in delivering unidirectional current to the load.

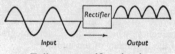

Full-wave rectifier circuit

function generator. A *signal generator producing specific waveforms, which may be used for test purposes, over a wide range of frequencies.

fundamental. Generally that component of a complex vibration constituting a note by which the pitch of a note is described. In a given note it is generally the tone having the lowest frequency.

fundamental particle. *See* elementary particle.

fusion. (1) *Syn.* melting. The change of the state of a substance from solid to liquid which occurs at a definite temperature (melting point) at a given applied pressure. (2) *See* nuclear fusion.

fusion reactor. *Syn.* thermonuclear reactor. A device in which *nuclear fusion takes place and in which there is a net evolution of usable energy. Intense research into the problems of designing such a device has occupied laboratories in many countries. The two central problems are (*a*) containing the *plasma in such conditions that it will yield more energy than is required to raise its temperature and confine it, and (*b*) extracting the energy in a usable form.

Three parameters control the first problem: temperature, *containment time, and plasma density. When fusion occurs the plasma temperature has to be high enough for the fusion energy released to exceed the energy lost by *bremsstrahlung radiation. The temperature above which this occurs is called the *ignition temperature*. The reaction $^2_1H + ^3_1H \rightarrow ^4_2He + n + 17.6$ MeV has the lowest known ignition temperature of 40×10^6 °C.

The problem of confining a plasma for long enough to release fusion energy has proved more difficult. Plasma instabilities have been the main cause of plasma leakage, but a workable plasma containment has now been achieved, though not at the same time as ignition temperature or adequate particle density. (*See* Lawson criterion).

Several types of device have been used for fusion experiments; in most of them a strong pulse of current is passed through the gas to create the plasma. At the same time this current pulse creates a strong magnetic field which makes the charged particles in the plasma travel along helical paths around the lines of force of the field. This causes a contraction of the plasma away from the walls of the tube. This *pinch effect* partially solves the containment

problem, but the confined plasma is not stable and tends to develop kinks. In *zeta pinch* devices, the current is passed axially through the plasma and the magnetic field forms round it. In the *theta pinch*, current-carrying coils run round the plasma and the magnetic field is axial. Both devices are toroidal. Linear devices are often called *magnetic bottles, their ends being 'stoppered' with *magnetic mirrors. Greater stability in these linear devices is achieved by using extra current carriers.

Another experimental device for the creation of plasma uses a pellet of fuel which is ionized instantaneously by a pulse from a high-power *laser. The use of *superconducting magnets might also facilitate the containment of the plasma.

Methods of extracting the energy of fusion reactions fall into two classes. In the deuterium–tritium reaction, some 80% of the energy is carried by the neutrons. In this type of reactor the neutron energy could be absorbed by a liquid lithium *coolant surrounding the reactor tube. In reactions, such as the deuterium–deuterium reaction, in which the energy is carried by charged particles, the kinetic energy of the particles could be converted directly into electrical energy by collecting them on suitably biased positive and negative electrodes.

G

g. Symbol for the acceleration of *free fall (formerly called the acceleration due to gravity).

Gaede molecular air pump. A vacuum pump consisting of a grooved cylinder that rotates in a casing with very little clearance. A fixed comb projects into the grooves, the inlet for gas being on one side of the comb and the outlet on the other. On rotation of the cylinder, the gas is dragged from the inlet to the outlet. Low pressures of the order of 0·001 mmHg can be achieved with a speed of 8000 to 12 000 revolutions a minute.

gain. A measure of the *efficiency of an electronic system. For an amplifier the gain is measured by the ratio of the power delivered by the amplifier to that fed to it. For a directional antenna or aerial the gain is measured by the ratio of the voltage produced by a signal entering along the path of greatest sensitivity to that produced by the same signal entering an omnidirectional antenna: measured in decibels or sometimes in *nepers.

galaxy. An organization of gas, stars, and dust as a separate but not necessarily independent system. Most galaxies are members of a group sharing a common motion.

Galilean telescope. *See* refracting telescope.

Galilean transformation equations. The set of equations

$$x' = x - vt$$
$$y' = y$$
$$z' = z$$
$$t' = t$$

They are used for transforming the

parameters of position and motion from an observer at the point O with co-ordinates (x, y, z) to an observer at O' with coordinates (x', y', z'). The x axis is chosen to pass through O and O'. The times of an event are t and t' in the *frames of reference of observers at O and O' respectively. The zeros of the time scales are the instant that O and O' coincided. v is the relative velocity of separation of O and O'. The equations conform to *Newtonian mechanics. *Compare* Lorentz transformation equations.

Galitzin pendulum. *See* pendulum.

Galton whistle. A whistle producing high frequencies, consisting of a short cylindrical pipe blown from an annular nozzle. The distance of the nozzle from the edge of the pipe can be varied by turning a micrometer screw. By suitable adjustment of this distance and the pressure of the air blast, the pipe is set into resonant vibration at a frequency corresponding to its length and diameter. (*See* edge tones.) Frequencies above the audible limit (normally above 20 000 hertz) can be produced.

galvanic cell. *See* voltaic cell.

galvanometer. An instrument for measuring or detecting small currents, usually by the mechanical reaction between the magnetic field of the current and that of a magnet. For high-frequency currents, use may be made of a *thermogalvanometer* in which the temperature rise in a resistance wire through which the current is passing is employed to measure the current, the temperature rise being measured by means of a thermocouple. *See* astatic system; Broca, Helmholtz, Einthoven, and tangent galvanometers; ammeter.

gamma (γ). (1) The symbol used to denote the ratio of the principal *heat capacities C_p/C_v of a gas, where C_p is the heat capacity at constant pressure and C_v that measured at constant volume. Using the law of *equipartition of energy, the ratio is given by $1 + 2/F$, where F is the number of *degrees of freedom of the molecule. For a monatomic gas ($F = 3$) $\gamma = 1.667$, in agreement with experimental determinations on the rare gases. For polyatomic molecules *quantum theory must be used. *See also* specific heat capacity. (2) The gradient of the linear part of the graph of *density of exposed and processed photographic material against the logarithm of the *exposure.

gamma camera. A device for visualizing the distribution of radioactive compounds in the human body during diagnosis using radioisotopes. It consists of a large thin *scintillation crystal with an array of *photomultiplier tubes mounted above the crystal and connected with it by a section of transparent material.

Radiation, usually from a low energy γ-ray emitter, causes a scintillation at a point X in the crystal, creating pulses in the photomultipliers. The size of the pulses is dependent on the relative position of the tubes and X. The photomultiplier output is fed into a circuit that analyses the pulses produced. The total sum of the pulses gives the intensity of radiation from X, i.e. the energy of the incident radiation; the relative sizes of the pulses gives positional information. The output, after amplification, controls the position of the spot on a *cathode-ray tube. After a suitable time interval a picture of the area below the crystal is built up on the screen and can be photographed.

gamma rays (γ-rays). Electromagnetic radiations emitted spontaneously by certain radioactive substances in the process of a nuclear transition. They are distinguishable from accompanying α- and β-rays by greater penetrating power and absence of deflection in magnetic and electric fields. They are also formed in particle *annihilation. The wavelengths of gamma radiations are characteristic of the substance emitting them and range from 3.9×10^{-10} to 4.7×10^{-13} metre. They form the extreme short-wave end of the known electromagnetic spectrum.

gamma-ray spectrum. A series of wavelengths in the gamma-ray region emitted by a given radioactive source.

gamma-ray transformation. A radioactive disintegration accompanied by the emission of *gamma rays.

Gamow barrier. *See* nuclear barrier.

ganged circuits. Two or more circuits having variable elements operated by a single control so that the circuits can be adjusted simultaneously.

gas. A substance that continues to occupy in a continuous manner the whole of the space in which it is placed, however large or small this space is made, the temperature remaining constant.

gas amplification. *See* gas multiplication.

gas breakdown. A type of *breakdown that occurs when the voltage across a *gas-filled tube reaches a given value. Ions in the gas are accelerated by the field to such energies that further ions are produced by collision but little recombination of ions occurs due to the high kinetic energies. A multiplication effect is present causing breakdown of the gas. The process is analogous to *avalanche breakdown in a *semiconductor.

gas constant. *See* universal gas constant.

gas-cooled reactor. A type of thermal *nuclear reactor in which a gaseous *coolant is used. In the *Magnox

(Mark I) reactors the coolant is carbon dioxide and the outlet temperature is about 350° C: natural uranium fuel is used with a graphite moderator, the fuel elements being encased in Magnox. In the *advanced gas-cooled* reactors (Mark II), the fuel is ceramic uranium dioxide encased in stainless steel. The same coolant and moderator as the Mark I type are used, but the outlet temperature is considerably higher – usually about 600° C.

gas-discharge tube. An *electron tube in which the presence of gaseous molecules contributes significantly to the characteristics of the tube. Normally a gas is a poor electrical conductor but a sufficiently high electric field causes *ionization of molecules and atoms in the immediate vicinity of the electrodes; these *gaseous ions are attracted to the charged electrodes. Collisions with other ions cause excitation and further ionizations, light being produced when excited atoms and ions return to the ground state. Recombination between positive and negative ions also results in a small amount of light emission.

The phenomena observed depend on the pressure of gas in the tube. At relatively high pressures the *mean free path of ions is small; a *positive glow* (or *column*) is observed near the anode and a *negative glow* near the cathode, the centre of the tube being dark. As the gas pressure is reduced the mean free path increases and the positive glow extends across the tube until the whole tube is filled. Such tubes are frequently used for luminous signs, lighting purposes, and for spectral analysis of the gas or vapour in the tube. A further reduction in pressure causes a change in the glow pattern (*see* diagram). Additional dark regions appear in which electrons, produced by ionization and excitation, have insufficient energy for excitation and the probability of recombination is low. The largest potential drop in the tube is across the *Crookes*

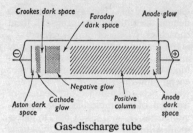

Gas-discharge tube

dark space. Striations in the positive column are caused by alternate ionizations and recombinations in the tube.

At very low pressures the Crookes dark space fills the tube, and very few collisions occur. The high kinetic energies of the ions cause *secondary emission of *cathode rays* (electrons) from the cathode, and at sufficiently high fields secondary emission of positive ions in the form of *anode rays* from the anode. With very high fields *X-rays are emitted from the anode.

gaseous ions. Positively or negatively charged systems formed in gases by the action of *ionizing radiation (e.g. X-rays); when an electric field is applied across the gas, the motion of the gaseous ions under the action of the field conveys an ionization current across the gas. They differ from electrolytic ions in the fact that they are not permanent, but recombine to form neutral molecules within a short time after the ionizing radiation has been cut off.

gas-filled relay. *See* thyratron.

gas-filled tube. An *electron tube containing a gas (or vapour, e.g. mercury vapour) in sufficient quantity to ensure that, once ionization of the gas has taken place, the electrical characteristics of the tube are determined entirely by the gas.

gas laws. Laws governing the variation of physical conditions (temperature, pressure, etc.) of a gas. *See* equations of state; ideal gas.

166

gas multiplication. *Syn*. gas amplification. (1) The process by which, in a sufficiently strong electric field, ions produced in a gas by *ionizing radiation can produce additional ions. (2) The factor by which the initial ionization is multiplied as a result of this process.

gas thermometer. *See* constant pressure gas thermometer; constant volume gas thermometer.

gate. (1) The electrode or electrodes in a *field-effect transistor to which a bias is applied for the purpose of modulating the conductivity of the channel. (2) Digital gate. A digital electronic circuit, with one or more inputs but only one output, frequently used in *logic circuits. The output is switched between two or more discrete voltage levels depending on the input conditions. Symbol =D—. (3) Analog gate. A *linear circuit or device frequently used in radar or electronic control systems that passes signals only for a specified fraction of the input signal. The output is a continuous function of the input signal for the period that the circuit is switched on.

gauss. Symbol: G. The *CGS-electromagnetic unit of *magnetic flux density. $1 \text{ G} = 10^{-4}$ tesla.

Gaussian distribution. *Syn*. normal distribution. *See* frequency distribution.

Gaussian eyepiece. A telescope eyepiece provided with a side window to illuminate the cross-wires and a reflector to transmit the light through the objective.

Gaussian points (or constants). *See* centred optical systems.

Gaussian system of units. *See* CGS system of units.

Gauss's theorem. Total electric flux acting normal to any closed surface drawn in an electric field is equal to the total charge of electricity inside the closed surface. If the surface encloses no charge the total flux over it is equal to zero. Gauss's theorem applies also to surfaces drawn in a magnetic field. Analogous statements of the theorem may be made for gravitational and magnetostatic and fluid-velocity fields; the general mathematical statement is that the total flux of a vector field through a closed surface is equal to the volume integral of the divergence of the vector taken over the enclosed volume.

Geiger counter. A device used for detecting corpuscular or electromagnetic *ionizing radiation (especially *alpha particles) and for counting particles.

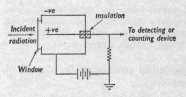

Geiger-counter circuit

(*See* diagram.) It consists essentially of a thin wire anode mounted along the axis of a closed cylindrical cathode which contains a gas at low pressure. A potential difference slightly lower than that required to produce a *discharge through the gas is maintained across the electrodes. The radiation enters through a thin window of mica, glass, etc., and ionizes the gas along its path. The resulting ions, accelerated by the electric field, produce an *avalanche of ions and an ionization current builds up very rapidly. The enclosed gas quenches the discharge, and prevents the production of a continuous gas discharge. Instead a momentary pulse of current is produced. Halogen-quenched tubes have working potentials of 300–400 volts. The use of a rare gas enables the working potential

167

to be raised to over 1000 volts. The energy of the ionization current is quickly dissipated through a high resistance connected between the wire and earth, the momentary current being registered, usually after amplification, by a detecting or counting device. From one particle to several thousand particles per second can be counted.

Geiger–Nuttall relation. The relation, discovered empirically, between the range, R, of an α-particle emitted by a given radioactive substance and its *decay constant λ: $\log \lambda = A + B \log R$, where B has the same value for all four radioactive series, while the constant A has a different value for each series. The law is of only approximate validity.

Geissler tube. A *gas-discharge tube specially designed to demonstrate the luminous effects of an electrical discharge through a rarefied gas.

generalized coordinates. *See* degrees of freedom.

generalized force. *See* force.

generator. A machine for converting mechanical into electrical energy. In the electromagnetic generator (dynamo), a coil is moved so as to cut the lines of induction in a magnetic field. In the electrostatic generator (*see* Van de Graaff generator; Wimshurst machine), mechanical energy is expended in separating equal and opposite electrical charges produced by electrostatic induction or by friction. *See also* superconductivity.

geoid. A surface defined by the term sea-level, the ocean being imagined taken to any desired point by means of canals and to be free from tides. The geoid is thus a surface in the earth's gravitational field and is approximately an oblate spheroid in shape.

geomagnetism. The study of the earth's magnetic field and its variations. At any point on the earth's surface three magnetic elements are defined: B_0, the horizontal component of the *magnetic flux density at the location; the *dip δ, the angle between the vector B_0 and the resultant flux density at the location; the *declination α, the angle between B_0 and the geographic true north. The vertical component of the earth's magnetic flux density, B_v, is $B_0 \tan \delta$ and the resultant, B_R, is $B_0 \sec \delta$.

Two main kinds of variation in these elements are observed. Secular variations take place slowly and are associated with periodic and semiperiodic terrestrial and solar phenomena. Abrupt changes, termed *magnetic storms*, are the result of solar phenomena, e.g. flares. The approximate value of the magnetic elements in the UK are

$$B_0 = 1 \cdot 88 \times 10^{-5}\,\text{T}$$

$$\alpha = 9 \cdot 8^\circ\,\text{W}$$

$$\delta = 66 \cdot 7^\circ\,\text{N}$$

$$B_v = 4 \cdot 35 \times 10^{-5}\,\text{T}.$$

The present locations of the earth's magnetic poles (i.e. the points on the earth's surface where $\delta = 90^\circ$) are

N magnetic pole
= latitude 76° N, longitude 102° W;

S magnetic pole
= latitude 68° S, longitude 145° E.

Due to the slow change with time of the angle of declination, the position of the magnetic poles is changing with time. At times of great magnetic disturbance (usually linked with increased solar activity) the poles can be displaced by 150 km in short periods of time. The magnitude of the earth's magnetic dipole moment is $8 \cdot 1 \times 10^{15}$ weber metres. *See also* palaeomagnetism.

geometrical moment of inertia. *See* moment of inertia.

geometric image. *See* image.

geometric optics. The study of reflection and refraction of rays of light without reference to the wave or physical nature of light. Graphical methods are used for determining the positions of images formed by lenses and mirrors.

geophysics. The physics of the earth (especially geophysical prospecting and *seismology).

getter. A material with a strong chemical affinity for other materials. Such materials may be used to remove unwanted atoms or molecules from an environment; for example barium may be used in a sealed vacuum system to remove residual gases or phosphorus may be introduced into oxide layers on silicon to remove mobile impurities such as sodium. This latter is particularly important in the stabilization of MOS *field-effect transistors.

g-factor. *See* Landé factor.

giant star. A star of large dimensions in comparison with average (main sequence) stars like the sun. A typical giant star will have a diameter ten times that of the sun (i.e. 1.4×10^9 m), although *supergiant stars may be as much as 500 times the sun's diameter. Since its mass will be about seven times the sun's its density will be only 10^{-4} of the sun. The luminous output is equivalent to 800 times that of the sun, and giant stars are situated above the main sequence in the *Hertzsprung–Russell diagram. *See also* red giant.

Gibbs function. *Syn.* Gibbs free energy; thermodynamic potential. Symbol: *G*. A thermodynamic function of a system given by its *enthalpy (*H*) minus the product of its *entropy (*S*) and its thermodynamic temperature (*T*), i.e. $G = H - TS$. In a *reversible change occurring at constant temperature and

pressure the change in the Gibbs function of a system is equal to the work done on it. If a system is considered at constant pressure and temperature and the only work done is that caused by changes in volume, the system is in equilibrium when *G* has a minimum value.

Gibbs–Helmholtz equation. The thermodynamic expression for the internal energy (*U*) in terms of the free energy (*F*) and its variation with thermodynamic temperature:

$$U = F - T\left(\frac{\partial F}{\partial T}\right)_v.$$

giga-. Symbol: G. The prefix meaning 10^9, e.g. 1 GHz = 10^9 hertz. In the US, the symbol B is sometimes used.

gilbert. Symbol: Gb. The *CGS-electromagnetic unit of magnetomotive force or magnetic potential. A point has a magnetic potential of one gilbert if the work done in bringing a unit positive pole up to that point is one erg. One turn of wire carrying a current of 1 ampere produces a magnetomotive force of $4\pi/10$ gilberts.

Giorgi units. Units based on the metre, kilogramme, and second as fundamental mechanical units, together with one electrical unit of practical size. When first proposed (in 1900) the ohm was the fourth unit chosen, although in 1950 this was replaced by the ampere. In 1954 Giorgi's system was superseded by *SI units. As well as unifying mechanical, thermal, and electrical units, Giorgi recognized and recommended the principle of *rationalization.

Gladstone–Dale law. If the density, ρ, of a substance is altered by compression or by increasing its temperature, there is a corresponding rise in the refractive index, *n*, given by $(n - 1)/\rho = k$, where *k* is a constant.

glide. The movement of one atomic plane over another in a crystal. It is the process by which a solid undergoes plastic deformation.

glide plane. In metal physics, a plane upon which glide can take place upon application of a suitable shearing stress. Sometimes the glide is in a particular direction (the glide direction) in the plane.

glow discharge. An electric discharge through a gas, usually at a relatively low pressure, in which the gas becomes luminous. *See* gas-discharge tube.

gluon. Hypothetical particle exchanged between quarks, binding them together.

gnomonic projection. From a point within a crystal (the pole of projection) lines are drawn normal to the crystal faces (or sets of planes in the crystal) and these produced will meet any plane in a pattern of points which is the gnomonic projection of the crystal on that plane.

gold-leaf electroscope. *See* electroscope.

goniometry. The measurement of interfacial angles for the comparison of crystals of different development.

goniophotometer. *See* photometry.

G-parity. A quantum number associated with *elementary particles that have zero *baryon number and *strangeness. It is conserved in *strong interactions only.

graded-base transistor. *See* drift transistor.

gradient (grad). The gradient of a scalar field $f(x, y, z)$ at a point is the *vector pointing in the direction of the greatest increase in the scalar with distance (i.e. perpendicular to the level surface at the

point in question). It has components along the coordinate axes that are the partial derivatives, f_x, f_y, f_z of the function with respect to each variable:

$$\text{grad } f = \nabla f = if_x + jf_y + kf_z,$$

where ∇ is the differential operator and i, j, and k are unit vectors along the x-, y-, and z-axis. Electric field is the negative gradient of electrical potential. *See* potential gradient.

Graetz number. Symbol: (G_z). A dimensionless coefficient, $(G_z) = q_m c_p / \lambda l$, where $q_m =$ mass flow rate, $c_p =$ specific heat capacity at constant pressure, $\lambda =$ thermal conductivity, and $l =$ a characteristic length.

Graham's law of diffusion. The rates of efflux of different gases through a fine hole at the same temperature and pressure are inversely proportional to the square roots of their densities. Knudsen showed that the law is only true when the mean free path in the issuing gas is at least ten times the diameter of the hole. *See* effusion.

gramme (or **gram**). $\frac{1}{1000}$ of the mass of the International prototype *kilogramme.

gramme-atom or -molecule. The former name for a *mole.

Gramme winding. *See* ring winding.

Grashof number. *Syn.* free convection number. The dimensionless group $(l^3 g \alpha \rho^2 \theta / \eta^2)$ occurring in the dimensional analysis of convection in a fluid due to the presence of a hot body; l is a typical dimension of the body, g is the acceleration of free fall, α is the temperature coefficient of density of the fluid, ρ is the density of the fluid, η is the viscosity of the fluid, and θ is the temperature difference between the hot body and the fluid. *See* convection (of heat).

Grassot fluxmeter. *See* fluxmeter.

graticule. A network of fine lines set at the focal point of the *eyepiece of a microscope or telescope, and therefore in focus simultaneously with the object viewed. It acts as a field reference system and may be used for the purpose of measurement. It consists either of fine wires or threads, or of a transparent glass disc with the lines engraved on it.

grating. *See* diffraction grating.

gravimeter. *See* free fall.

gravitation. The universal effect as a result of which all bodies attract one another, quantitatively summed up in the law of universal gravitation (Newton): the force F of attraction between two bodies of mass m_1, m_2 separated by a distance x is given by

$$F = Gm_1m_2/x^2.$$

G is the constant of universal gravitation (or *gravitational constant*) and has a value of $(6 \cdot 6732 \pm 0 \cdot 0031) \times 10^{-11}$ N m^2 kg^{-2}. It has been predicted that G is not constant but is decreasing with time by about 1 part in 10^{10} per year, due to the expansion of the universe. Experimental evidence has not disproved this. For the solar system, Newton's law of gravitation can be shown to be a corollary of *Kepler's laws.

The size of a gravitational field at any point is given by the force exerted on unit mass at that point. The field intensity at a distance x from a point mass m is therefore Gm/x^2, and acts towards m. Gravitational field intensity is measured in newtons per kilogramme. The gravitational potential V at that point is the work done in moving a unit mass from infinity to the point against the field. Due to a point mass,

$$V = Gm \int_{\infty}^{x} \mathrm{d}x/x^2$$
$$= -Gm/x$$

V is a scalar measured in joules per kilogramme. The following special cases are also important: (a) Potential at a point distance x from the centre of a hollow homogeneous spherical shell of mass m and outside the shell, $V = -Gm/x$. The potential is the same as if the mass of the shell is assumed concentrated at the centre. (b) At any point inside the spherical shell the potential is equal to its value at the surface, $V = -Gm/r$, where r is the radius of the shell. Thus there is no resultant force acting at any point inside the shell (since no potential difference acts between any two points). (c) Potential at a point distance x from the centre of a homogeneous solid sphere and outside the sphere is the same as that for a shell: $V = -Gm/x$. (d) At a point inside the sphere, of radius r, $V = -Gm(3r^2 - x^2)/2r^3$. The essential property of gravitation is that it causes a change in motion, in particular the acceleration of *free fall (g) in the earth's gravitational field. According to the general theory of *relativity, gravitation can be explained by the curvature or warping of space and time around a massive body.

gravitational constant. *See* gravitation.

gravitational field. The space surrounding a massive body in which another massive body experiences a force of attraction. *See* gravitation.

gravitational force. One of the four fundamental forces believed to account for all observed interactions of matter. The gravitational force (*see* gravitation) influences all matter and acts over an infinite range, possibly by means of *graviton exchange. *See also* strong, weak, electromagnetic interactions.

gravitational potential. *See* potential.

gravitational red shift. *See* Einstein shift.

gravitational unit. A unit of force, pressure, work, power, etc., involving g, the acceleration of *free fall. The *slug is an example.

graviton. A hypothetical *elementary particle responsible for the effects of gravity; the quantum of gravitation. It is postulated to be its own *antiparticle, to have zero charge and rest mass, and a spin of 2.

gravity. The resultant effect of the gravitational attraction and centrifugal repulsion between any body of matter and a planetary body as measured by the *weight of the body near the planet; and the acceleration with which the body freely falls towards the planet: commonly denoted by g. *See* free fall.

gravity balance. *See* free fall.

gravity cell. A primary electric cell in which two electrolytes are kept apart by their different densities.

gravity meter. *See* free fall.

gravity wave. A wave occurring in the surface of a liquid, the wave being controlled by gravity and not by the surface tension of the liquid. For example, for shallow sea waves the velocity v depends on the wavelength λ according to $v = (g\lambda)^{\frac{1}{2}}$, where g is the acceleration of free fall.

grease-spot photometer. A design of *photometer head consisting of a thin white opaque paper with a translucent spot at the centre. Lights illuminate both sides. The intensity of illumination is assumed to vary inversely as the square of the distance. Any convenient auxiliary source is fixed on one side. The two sources to be compared (C_1 and C_2) are moved along a bench until the spot disappears for each in turn. Then $C_1/C_2 = (d_1/d_2)^2$. Alternatively the two sources C_1 and C_2 are on opposite sides and the distances d_1 and d_2 when disappearance occurs on one side, and d'_1

and d'_2 for disappearance on the other side, are measured. Then, $C_1/C_2 = d_1d'_1/d_2d'_2$.

Grenz rays. X-rays of long wavelength produced in a *Grenz tube*. This is a tube with a low-absorption window so that X-rays produced at voltages below about 10^4 volts can be transmitted.

grey body. A body that emits radiation of all wavelengths in constant proportion to the *black-body radiation of the same wavelengths at the same temperature.

grid. (1) *See* control electrode. (2) The high-voltage transmission line system which interconnects many large generating stations. Voltages of 275 kV, or in some cases 400 kV, are commonly used, though in some countries voltages as high as 735 kV are used.

grid bias. A polarizing potential difference applied between the cathode and control grid of a thermionic valve to cause it to operate on any desired part of its characteristic curve, or to modify its cut-off values.

grid leak. A high resistance between the grid of a thermionic tube and its cathode to prevent a charge accumulating on the grid.

ground. *See* earth.

ground plane. A conducting sheet in any electrical circuit that is at earth potential and provides a low impedance earth connection throughout the circuit.

ground state. The state of a system in its lowest *energy level. For example, when the electron of a hydrogen atom is in the orbit of smallest radius the energy of the atom is lowest; this is the ground state of the atom. The ground state of a molecule is its *zero-point energy. *Compare* excited state.

ground wave. An electromagnetic radio wave which is radiated from a transmitting aerial on the surface of the earth, and which travels along the surface of the earth.

group velocity. In certain forms of wave motion the *phase velocity (i.e. the velocity of a wave of given wavelength) varies with the wavelength. As a result of this a non-sinusoidal wave appears to travel with a velocity distinctly different from the phase velocity.

The phenomenon is most readily seen with waves on the surface of water. Considering the group of waves resulting from a stone dropped into water, it may be observed that the waves within the group travel faster than the group itself, fresh waves appearing at the rear of the group as the existing waves vanish at the leading edge. The velocity of the group is called the group velocity while that of the waves within the group is the phase velocity. Since wave velocities are usually measured by the arrival of the disturbance caused by the wave at different points in its path, it is seen that measurements usually give the group velocity of the wave and not the phase velocity.

An expression for group velocity may be obtained by considering the propagation of two sinusoidal waves of slightly different wavelengths, λ and $\lambda - \delta\lambda$, say, the corresponding phase velocities being c and $c - \delta c$. The superposition of these waves produces beats which travel with the group velocity U, given by

$$U = \frac{c\delta t - \lambda}{\delta t} = c - \frac{\lambda}{\delta t} = c - \lambda \frac{\delta c}{\delta\lambda}.$$

In the limit, for $\delta\lambda = 0$, this equation becomes $U = c - \lambda \, dc/d\lambda$. Or $U = d\nu/d\nu'$, where ν is the frequency and $\nu' = 1/\lambda$, the reciprocal wavelength or wave number.

If the phase velocity does not vary with wavelength then the group velocity and the phase velocity become identical. There is then absence of dispersion of velocity, e.g. in the case of light in a vacuum. The direct measurement of light velocity in dispersing media measures group velocity.

Grove cell. A two-fluid primary cell in which the negative element consists of a zinc rod in dilute sulphuric acid, and the positive element, which is separated from the negative by a porous partition, consists of a platinum plate immersed in fuming nitric acid. The e.m.f. is 1·93 volts.

grown junction. A *semiconductor junction formed by changing the types and amounts of impurities that are added to the semiconductor, while the crystal is being grown from the melt.

Grüneisen's law. A law derived from the *equation of state for solids that states that the ratio of the coefficient of linear expansion of a metal to its specific heat capacity is a constant independent of the temperature at which the measurements are made.

guard ring. (1) (electrical). A large metal plate surrounding and coplanar with a small metal plate from which it is separated by a narrow air gap. It produces a uniform and calculable field over the area of the smaller plate, which can be treated as an infinite plane, since the variations in the field which occur as the edge of the plane is approached affect only the guard ring. An extra electrode, equivalent to a guard ring, is commonly used in semiconductor devices and vacuum tubes. (2) (heat). A similar device used in experiments on heat flow. It produces a temperature gradient in the region all round the specimen identical to that down the specimen so that heat losses from the latter are eliminated.

guard wires. Earthed conductors placed beneath overhead-line conductors so

173

that if the latter break, they will be earthed before they reach the ground. A series of guard wires arranged to form a net is known as a *cradle guard* and is used where a high-voltage line crosses a telephone wire or a thoroughfare.

Guillemin effect. A type of *magnetostriction in which a bent bar of a *ferromagnetic material tends to straighten out under the influence of a magnetic field applied along its length.

Gunn effect. If a d.c. electric field is applied across short n-type samples of gallium arsenide, at values above a threshold value of several thousand volts per cm, coherent microwave output is generated. A two-terminal device operated in this way is known as a *Gunn diode*. The effect is caused by the *carriers breaking up into domains under the influence of the electric field. Some of the conduction electrons move from a low energy, high mobility state into a higher energy, low mobility state causing domains of low mobility to be set up.

gyrator. A component, usually used at microwave frequencies, which reverses the phase of signals transmitted in one direction but has no effect on the phase of signals transmitted in the opposite direction. The gyrator may be entirely passive or contain active components.

gyrocompass. A nonmagnetic compass using a *gyroscope fitted with a pendulous weight or some equivalent to induce precession due to gravity. The subsequent damped motion of the gyro aligns this with the true N–S direction.

gyrodynamics. The study of rotating bodies, particularly when subject to precession.

gyromagnetic effects. The relationships between the magnetization of a body and its rotation. *See* Barnett effect; Einstein and de Haas effect.

gyromagnetic ratio. Symbol: γ. The ratio of the *magnetic moment of a system to its *angular momentum. An orbiting electron has a value of $e/2m$, where e is the electron charge and m its mass. The gyromagnetic ratio of an electron due to its *spin is twice this value.

gyroscope. A device in which a suitably mounted flywheel or rotor is spun at high speed. The mounting, usually of gimball type, allows the axis of rotation to be in any direction in space.

If a couple is applied to the frame of the gyroscope, the resulting motion of *precession tends to align the gyro with the axis of the couple. The rate of turning or precession is proportional to the moment of the applied couple and inversely proportional to the angular momentum of the gyro. In the absence of disturbing couples, the direction in space of the spin axis stays constant. They are widely used in automatic guidance devices. Large gyros are used on some ships to achieve stability against rolling.

gyrostat. A *gyroscope, especially a version intended primarily to indicate or to use the constancy of direction of axis of a fast-running gyroscope.

H

h. Symbol used for the Planck constant. *See also* Dirac constant.

hadron. An *elementary particle that can take part in *strong interactions. All elementary particles except *leptons and the photon are hadrons.

hair hygrometer. A hygrometer that depends for its action on the increase in length of a hair occurring when the relative *humidity of the surrounding air increases.

halation. The luminous patch that surrounds the spot on the screen of a *cathode-ray tube, generally resulting from internal reflections in the glass of the screen.

half-cell. One electrode of an electrolytic cell and the electrolyte with which it is in contact.

half-life. *Syn.* half-value period. Symbol: $T_{\frac{1}{2}}$, $t_{\frac{1}{2}}$. The time in which the amount of a radioactive nuclide decays to half its original value, given by $T_{\frac{1}{2}} = (\log_e 2)/\lambda = 0.693\ 15/\lambda$ where λ is the *decay constant, or by $T_{\frac{1}{2}} =$ *mean life $\times$ 0.693 15.

half-value thickness. The thickness of a uniform sheet of material which, when interposed in a beam of radiation, will reduce the intensity or some other specified property of the radiation passing through it to one half: often used as a means of defining the quality of the radiation.

half-wave dipole. An *aerial consisting of a straight conductor which is approximately half a wavelength long. When the dipole is excited it has a voltage node and current antinode at its centre, and a voltage antinode and current node at

each end. The feeder is commonly, but not always, connected across a small gap in the centre of the dipole. *See also* dipole aerial.

half-wave plate. A thin piece of quartz or mica cut parallel to the optic axis of such thickness as to introduce a phase difference of 180° between the ordinary and extraordinary rays. *Plane polarized light incident normally on the plate has its plane of polarization rotated through twice the angle between the axis and the incident vibrations.

half-wave rectifier circuit. A rectifier circuit in which alternate half waves of the single-phase a.c. input wave are effective in delivering unidirectional current to the load.

half-width. (1) Half the width of a spectrum line measured at half its height. (2) In some branches of spectroscopy the half-width is used for the full width of the line at half its height.

Hall effect. If a current-carrying conductor is placed in a magnetic field and orientated so that the field is at right angles to the direction of the current, an electric field is produced in the conductor at right angles to both the current and the magnetic field. The field produced is related to the current density j and magnetic flux density B by the relation

$$E_H = -R_H(j \times B).$$

The constant R_H is the *Hall coefficient*. In metals and degenerate semiconductors the force due to the induced field just opposes the force due to motion in the magnetic field:

$$Ee = -Bev,$$

where v is the drift velocity of the charge carriers. Current density is given by $j =$

175

nev, where *n* is the number of carriers per unit volume. Thus R_H is equal to $1/ne$.

Hall mobility. Of a semiconductor or conductor. Symbol: μ_H. The product of the Hall coefficient R_H (*see* Hall effect) and the electrical conductivity κ.

Hamiltonian function. *Syn.* Hamiltonian. Symbol: H. A function that expresses the energy of a system in terms of momenta, p, and positional coordinates, q; e.g. $(p^2/2m + \mu q^2/2)$ expresses the energy of a body in *simple harmonic motion. It may also involve the time. It is much used in *wave mechanics.

Hamilton's equations. A restatement of *Lagrange's equations with emphasis on momenta rather than forces. Much used in advanced mechanics including *quantum mechanics. They involve the Hamiltonian function H, which in ordinary cases is the total energy expressed as a function of the generalized coordinates q_i and momenta p_i.

$$\frac{dq_i}{dt} = \frac{\partial H}{\partial p_i}, \quad \frac{dp_i}{dt} = -\frac{\partial H}{\partial q_i}.$$

Hamilton's principle. If the configuration of a system is given at two instants, t_0 and t_1, then the value of the time-integral of the *kinetic potential is a maximum or minimum for the path actually described in the motion compared with any other infinitely near paths which might be described (for instance under constraints) in the same time between the same configurations. That is,

$$\delta \int_{t_0}^{t_1} (T - V)\, dt = 0,$$

where T = total kinetic energy, V = total potential energy. This is for a conservative system, but the principle is of general application.

hardness. Of a crystal. The resistance of a crystal face to scratching, usually varying with direction. It can be measured by the *Brinell test*, which measures the load required to produce an indent of measured dimensions on the material. *Moh's scale* of hardness uses ten selected solids arranged in such an order that a substance can scratch all substances below it in the scale, and cannot scratch those above it: (1) talc, (2) rock salt, (3) calcspar, (4) fluorspar, (5) apatite, (6) felspar, (7) quartz, (8) topaz, (9) corundum, (10) diamond. The scale is not quantitative.

hard radiation. *Ionizing radiation with a high degree of penetration: most commonly applied to X-rays of relatively short wavelength.

hard vacuum tube. *Syn.* high vacuum tube. A *vacuum tube in which the degree of the vacuum is such that ionization of the residual gas has a negligible effect upon the electrical characteristics.

hardware. The physical components of a *computer system, such as the *CPU, *memory, and *peripheral devices.

Hare's hydrometer. *See* hydrometer.

harmonic. An oscillation of a periodic quantity or a tone of a series constituting a *note, whose frequency is an integral multiple of the fundamental frequency. The full set of harmonics is a Fourier series, which represents the complex waveform of the note.

harmonic analyser. A device that evaluates the coefficients of the Fourier series (*see* Fourier analysis) corresponding to a particular function.

harmonic distortion. *See* distortion (electrical).

Hartmann formula. A formula giving the variation of refractive index n of a medium with the wavelength of light:

$$n = n_\infty + c/(\lambda + \lambda_0)^\alpha.$$

n_∞, λ_0 and a are constants. For common forms of glass it is usual to take $a = 1$.

Hartmann generator. An apparatus for producing ultrasonic edge tones on the principle of the *Galton whistle. It differs from this mainly in the greater blast velocity employed whereby the energy of the output is markedly increased. Frequencies up to 100 000 hertz can be produced.

hartree. *See* atomic unit of energy.

h-bar. *See* Dirac constant.

health physics. A branch of *medical physics concerned with the health and safety of personnel in medical, scientific, and industrial work. It is most particularly concerned with protection from *ionizing radiation and from neutrons.

Problems involved in radiation protection include the detection and measurement of ionizing radiation, decontamination of both personnel and surfaces affected by radioactive substances, disposal of radioactive waste, design of laboratories and the shielding of equipment for radiation work, and the supervision of tolerance *doses received by personnel in the course of their duties.

hearing. *See* resonance theory of hearing.

heat. Symbol: Q, q. That form of energy transferred between two bodies as a result of a difference in their temperatures, and governed by the laws of *thermodynamics. Provided that there is no change in phase the heat required to raise the temperature of a mass m by a temperature θ is given by $Q = mc\theta$, where c is the *specific heat capacity. At the transition temperature heat is absorbed or evolved when a change of phase occurs: $Q = ml$, where l is the *specific latent heat.

Radiant heat energy (*infrared radiation) is one form in which heat can be transferred. It occupies the electromagnetic spectrum between light and radio

waves (i.e. in the wavelength range 740 nm to 0·3 mm approximately). The other two important transfer processes are *conduction and *convection. Heat is now measured in *joules.

heat capacity. Symbol: C. Formerly, thermal capacity. The quantity of heat required to raise the temperature of a body through one degree. It is measured in joules per kelvin. *See also* specific heat capacity.

heat content. *See* enthalpy.

heat death. The condition of any isolated system when its *entropy is a maximum. The matter present is then completely disordered and at a uniform temperature, there is therefore no energy available for doing work. If the universe is a closed system it should eventually reach this state. This is called the *heat death of the universe*.

heat engine. A device that transforms heat into mechanical energy. Heat engines operate by a cycle in which they absorb heat from a reservoir at one temperature and give heat to a *heat sink at a lower temperature. *See* Carnot cycle; Diesel cycle; Otto cycle; efficiency.

heat exchanger. A device for transferring heat from one fluid to another without the fluids coming in contact. Its purpose is either to regulate the temperatures of the fluids for optimum efficiency of some process, or to make use of heat that would otherwise be wasted. The simplest form consists of two concentric pipes, the inner one finned on the outside to maximize the contact area, with the fluids moving through the pipes in opposite directions.

heating effect of a current. *Syn.* Joule effect. When an electric current I passes through a resistor a rise of temperature is observed. If all the electrical energy is turned into heat energy Q, $Q = I^2Rt$,

177

where R is the resistance at the temperature involved, and t is the time for which the current passes. Q does not increase indefinitely with t since a temperature is reached at which the rate of emission of heat from the surface of the resistor is equal to its rate of generation.

heat pump. A device for extracting heat from large quantities of material, such as air or water, at a low temperature and supplying it at a higher temperature. In accordance with the second law of *thermodynamics, mechanical work must be performed to accomplish this process. A volatile liquid is expanded and evaporates, thus extracting heat from the material. It is then compressed and gives up its heat. The principle is similar to that in a *refrigerator.

heat sink. (1) A device employed, especially in electronic components, when it is essential to dispose of unwanted heat and prevent a damaging rise in temperature. It generally consists of a set of metal plates in a fin-like formation that conducts and radiates the heat away. (2) A system that is considered to absorb heat at a constant temperature. The concept is useful in *thermodynamics, as in the operation of a heat engine.

heat transfer coefficient. The heat flow per unit time through unit area divided by the temperature difference. When applied to conduction of heat through a body it is called the *thermal conductance* and has the symbol K. When applied to the emission of heat from a surface it is sometimes loosely called the *emissivity and has the symbol E or α. It is measured in watt metre^{-2} kelvin^{-1}.

Heaviside layer. *See* ionosphere.

heavy-water reactor (H.W.R.). A type of thermal *nuclear reactor in which heavy water (deuterium oxide, D_2O) is used as the moderator, and sometimes also as the *coolant.

hecto-. Symbol: h. The prefix meaning 100, e.g. 1 hm = 100 metres.

Heisenberg force. *See* exchange force.

Heisenberg uncertainty relation. *See* uncertainty principle.

Helmert's formula. An empirical formula that provides a value for the gravitational acceleration $g_{\varphi,H}$ at any latitude φ and altitude H (in metres): $g_{\varphi,H} = 9.806\,16 - 0.025\,928 \cos 2\varphi + 6.9 \times 10^{-5} \cos^2 2\varphi - 3.086 \times 10^{-6}H$.

helmholtz. A unit of dipole moment per unit area equal to 3.335×10^{-10} C m^{-1}.

Helmholtz electric double layer. When a body is brought into contact with another body composed of a different material the two bodies become oppositely electrified, the substance with the higher dielectric constant becoming positive. Helmholtz postulated that a film one molecule thick forming a double layer of positive and negative charges is set up and maintained by the inherent electrical forces of matter. Lenard extended the theory by suggesting that at the surface of any solid or liquid the molecules show orientation of the dipoles, negative charge outwards, forming an electrical double layer. In materials of high dielectric constant, the attraction between the opposite charges is smaller, and a substance of small dielectric constant can thus remove free negative charges from one of greater constant. Contact needs to be close for this to happen. On separation of the charges, which initially were at molecular diameters apart, the lines of force are considerably extended, and the potential difference thus produced may be made very large.

Helmholtz function. *Syn.* Helmholtz free energy; work function. Symbol: A, F. A thermodynamic function of a system given by its internal energy (U) minus the product of its entropy (S) and its thermodynamic temperature (T), i.e. $A = U - TS$. If a system undergoes a *reversible change at a constant temperature, the Helmholtz function increases by an amount equal to the work done on it. The change in A (ΔA) between any two states of a system gives the maximum work that could be obtained from the system during this change, if the optimum pathway were to be followed. If this change is negative, work is obtained from the system. *See also* Gibbs function.

Helmholtz galvanometer. A modification of the simple *tangent galvanometer in which the single coil is replaced by a pair of equal and similar coils mounted coaxially with their centres at a distance apart equal to the radius of either coil. The magnet is mounted at a point half way between the centres of the two coils. The arrangement produces a uniform and calculable field throughout the space in which the magnet rotates. It is obsolete as a current-measuring device.

Helmholtz resonator. An acoustic resonator in the form of an air cavity contained in a spherical or cylindrical bulb, connecting with the atmosphere through a neck whose length is negligible compared with its diameter.

The air in the neighbourhood of the neck is assumed to act like a piston, alternately compressing and rarefying the air in the cavity; the wavelength of the vibrations in the free air is assumed large compared with the dimensions of the cavity. The resonance frequency n is that for which the reactance term disappears, i.e.

$$n = \frac{c}{2\pi} \sqrt{\frac{S}{lV}},$$

where c is the velocity of sound, l is the length of the neck, S is its cross-section area, and V is the volume of the cavity.

henry. Symbol: H. The *SI unit of self and mutual inductance, defined as the

inductance of a closed loop that gives rise to a magnetic flux of one weber for each ampere of current that flows.

heptode. A thermionic *valve having five grids between the cathode and anode, usually employed as a frequency-changer (mixer).

Herschel–Quincke tube. *Syn.* Quincke's tube. An apparatus to demonstrate the *interference of sound. It consists of a tube which divides into two tubes of different lengths the ends of which join together to form one tube again. One of the tubes can usually be varied in length by means of an arrangement similar to the slide of a trombone. A source of sound is placed at one end of the apparatus and the sound travels along the two different paths, the resultant at the other end depending on the path difference.

hertz. Symbol: Hz. The *SI unit of *frequency, defined as the frequency of a periodic phenomenon that has a period of one second.

Hertzian oscillator. An electrical system for the production of electromagnetic waves (*Hertzian waves*). It consists of two capacitors, e.g. two plates or spheres joined by a conducting rod in which there is a small spark gap. If the two halves of the oscillator are raised to a sufficiently high potential difference a spark passes across the gap, rendering it temporarily a conductor, and an oscillatory discharge takes place, the period of the oscillations being equal to $2\pi\sqrt{LC}$, where L is the self inductance and C the capacitance of the system. Electromagnetic waves of the same period are given off during the discharge. The oscillator is usually activated by a small induction coil, and a group of waves is emitted at each discharge. Owing to the resistance of the spark gap, the waves are highly damped. Their wavelength is usually of the order of a few metres.

Hertzsprung–Russell diagram. A diagram showing the variation of brightness in stars against spectral class (*see* stellar spectra). The great difference in luminosity between giant and *main sequence stars*

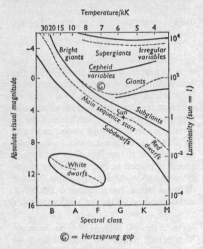

Hertzsprung–Russell diagram

Ⓖ = Hertzsprung gap

derives from a difference of density rather than of mass: a *giant star of spectral class K will have a mass about eight times that of a K *dwarf star but its density will be about one four-thousandth of the dwarf. The radius *r* of a main-sequence star is related to its luminosity *L* and temperature *T* by the theoretical formula:

$$\log r = 0.5 \log L - 2 \log T + 1.57.$$

The diagram can therefore be traversed with equal-radius contours. The mass and temperature of a star are related to its chemical composition.

The youngest stars (say 10^7 years old) lie on the upper end of the main sequence and have a magnitude range of from say −7 to +4. The oldest clusters on the main sequence have a magnitude as low as +16 for stars 10^{10} years old. The giant branches contain more clusters of old stars. As a star burns up its hydrogen

core, converting it into helium, its radius increases and the star 'moves' across from the main sequence to the giant region. This movement occupies only a relatively short length of time, and thus there is a space (known as the *Hertzsprung gap*) between the two regions. After eventually becoming red supergiants the stars tend to develop a variation in magnitude (*see* variable star), and they occupy the lower lefthand part of the giant region. In due course the stars become *white dwarfs, *pulsars, or *black holes.

heterodyne reception. *See* beat reception.

heterogeneous radiation. A particular type of radiation, such as X-rays or gamma rays, having a variety of wavelengths or quantum energies.

heterogeneous reactor. A type of *nuclear reactor in which the fuel is separated from the moderator.

heterogeneous strain. *See* homogeneous strain.

heterojunction. *See* semiconductor diode laser.

heteropolar generator. A *generator in which the active conductors pass through magnetic fields of opposite sense in succession. Most modern generators are of this type. An alternating e.m.f. is induced in each conductor so that a direct-current generator of this type must be fitted with a *commutator.

hexagonal system. *See* crystal systems.

hexode. A thermionic *valve having four grids between the cathode and anode, commonly employed as a frequency-changer.

high frequency (HF). *See* frequency bands.

high tension (H.T.). High voltage, especially when applied to the anode supply of thermionic valves; usually in range 60 to 250 volts.

high voltage. In electrical power transmission and distribution, a voltage in excess of 650 volts.

Hilbert space. A multidimensional space in which the proper (eigen) functions of *wave mechanics are represented by orthogonal unit vectors.

histogram. A graphical representation of a frequency distribution: rectangular areas standing on each interval into which the observations are grouped show the frequency of observations in that interval.

Hoffmann electrometer. A sensitive *electrometer using only a half-vane (*see* diagram) moving in two half-segments of a closed metal box, but otherwise working on the same principle as the

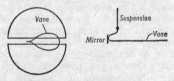

Hoffmann electrometer

*quadrant electrometer. Very heavy copper shields are used to minimize thermal variations which might affect the needle, and the instrument is usually operated with the pressure reduced to a few mmHg.

hole. In a solid, an unfilled vacancy in an electronic *energy level. These vacancies behave as if they were positive electronic charges with positive mass and are mathematically equivalent to the *positron. In a p-type *semiconductor electrical conduction is due to holes, which are the *majority carriers.

hole conduction. A mechanism of conduction in an *extrinsic semiconductor in which *holes in a crystal lattice are in effect propagated through the lattice under the influence of an electric field. The process is one of continuous exchange with adjacent electrons, and the apparent movement of the holes is equivalent to a movement of positive charges in the same direction.

holography. A technique for the reproduction of a stereoscopic image without cameras or lenses. A monochromatic, coherent, and highly collimated beam of light from a *laser is separated into two beams, one of which is directed to a photographic plate coated with a film of high resolution. The second beam hits the subject and is diffracted to the plate where a *hologram* is formed, consisting of an interference pattern (rather than a collection of light and dark areas as with a conventional photographic negative). The original subject may be recreated by placing the hologram in a beam of coherent light, generally from the same laser; the hologram behaves as a *diffraction grating, producing two beams of diffracted radiation, one giving a real image that may be recorded on a photograph, and the other a stereoscopic virtual image.

homocentric. Converging to or diverging from a common point.

homogeneous radiation. Radiation that has constant wavelength or quantum energy.

homogeneous reactor. A type of *nuclear reactor in which the fuel and moderator present a uniform medium to the neutrons, e.g. the fuel, in the form of a salt of uranium, may be dissolved in the moderator.

homogeneous solids. Those in which the physical and chemical properties are the same about every point; they may be amorphous or crystalline.

homogeneous strain. When a body is strained, a particle whose Cartesian co-ordinates with respect to axes fixed outside the body are (x, y, z) is displaced to a new position (x', y', z'). If the following relations (in which the a's, b's, and c's are nine constants) exist, the *strain is said to be homogeneous and uniform:

$$x' = a_1x + a_2y + a_3z$$
$$y' = b_1x + b_2y + b_3z$$
$$z' = c_1x + c_2y + c_3z.$$

In a uniform homogeneous strain, a plane in the body remains a plane but changes its position, a parallelogram becomes a parallelogram in a different plane and with different angles. A sphere becomes an ellipsoid whose three mutually perpendicular axes are derived from three mutually perpendicular diameters of the sphere by their elongation and rotation.

If the relations between (x', y', z') and (x, y, z) are not linear, the strain is *heterogeneous*; if the a's, b's, and c's vary with (x, y, z), the strain is not uniform.

Hooke's law. The law forming the basis of the theory of elasticity and in its most general form states that, for a certain range of stresses, the strain produced is proportional to the stress applied and independent of the time and disappears completely on removal of the stress. The point on the graph of stress versus strain for a real material, where it ceases to be linear, is known as the *limit of proportionality*. *See* yield point; elastic limit.

horse-power (H.P.). A unit of power in the f.p.s. system equal to 33 000ft.-lb per min. or 746 watts.

hot. Highly radioactive. A *hot atom* is one in an excited state or having kinetic energy above the thermal level of the surroundings, usually as a result of nuclear processes.

hot-cathode tube. A discharge tube in which the supply of electrons for carrying the discharge is provided by thermionic emission from a heated element.

hot-wire ammeter. An instrument in which the thermal expansion of a wire or strip due to the heat liberated by a current passing through it is employed to measure the current. Some mechanical device is used to magnify the actual increase in length of the wire, and to cause it to rotate a pointer over a circular scale. The scale is not uniform and the instrument must be calibrated empirically; but since the heating effect varies as the square of the current, the hot-wire ammeter can be used both for direct and for alternating current. It can be used as a voltmeter by adding suitable resistances in series, as in the *Cardew voltmeter*.

hot-wire anemometer. An instrument that measures the velocity of a fluid in motion by virtue of the convective cooling it experiences when exposed to the fluid. It has the advantage over other *anemometers that it can be made to occupy a very small space. It may, for example, take the form of 25 μm of nickel wire of a few centimetres diameter mounted on a fork and heated to 50° C above its surroundings (in still air or water). The change of temperature of the wire when exposed to the flow is measured in terms of the change in its electrical resistance, recorded on a *Wheatstone bridge.

A similar apparatus can be used to measure a fluctuating velocity by replacing the galvanometer of the Wheatstone bridge with a cathode-ray oscillograph.

hot-wire gauge. A pressure gauge depending on the cooling by the gas of a hot filament. *See* Pirani gauge.

hot-wire microphone. A device for the measurement of the intensity and amplitude of sound waves, based on the decrease in the resistance of an electrically heated fine wire when subjected to sound waves.

hour-angle. *See* celestial sphere.

Hubble constant. According to the theory of the *expanding universe, the *red shifts observed in the spectra of stars in external galaxies represent recessional velocities. The Hubble constant H is defined as the ratio of recessional velocity to distance. Whether H is truly constant is still open to argument. The value of the constant is between about 50–100 (km s^{-1})/megaparsec or $1 \cdot 6 \times 10^{-18}$ to $3 \cdot 2 \times 10^{-18}$ s^{-1}. If the universe has been expanding at a constant rate the reciprocal of these figures gives an upper limit to its age as 20×10^9 years. The radius of the observable universe is c/H, where c is the velocity of light. This fraction has an upper value of 6×10^{10} parsecs or $1 \cdot 85 \times 10^{26}$ metres.

hue. *See* colour.

hum. In an amplifier. Extraneous alternating currents that appear in the output of the amplifier and have their origin in an associated or nearby electric power circuit.

humidity. A measure of the degree of wetness of the atmosphere. *Absolute humidity*, d, is the mass of water vapour present in unit volume of moist air and is measured in kg/m^3. It is related to the actual vapour pressure e (in pascals) and the absolute temperature T (in kelvin) by $d = 0 \cdot 002\ 17\ e/T$. Because the absolute humidity of a volume of air is strongly dependent on temperature, a more useful measure is the *relative humidity*, U, defined as the ratio of the actual vapour pressure to the saturation vapour pressure over a plane liquid water surface at the same temperature (symbol: e''), expressed as a percentage: $U = 100\ e/e''$. As the temperature of the air is reduced the water vapour concentration is in-

creased until, at the *dew point θ_d, the air becomes saturated. Because only temperature has been altered, the actual vapour pressure at a temperature θ must equal the saturation vapour pressure at the dew point, and the formula reduces to $U = 100\ e''(\theta_d)/e''(\theta)$. Because values of e'' for water vapour are well known, the relative humidity can be easily found. The *specific humidity* is the mass of water vapour divided by unit mass of moist air. The *mixing ratio*, r, is the ratio of the mass of water vapour to the mass of dry air that contains it. If p is the total atmospheric pressure (in pascals) $r = 0 \cdot 622e/(p - e)$. Humidity, either relative or absolute, is measured with a *hygrometer. A rough indication of the humidity is given by a *hygroscope.

hunting. Variation of a controlled quantity such as the temperature of a thermostat above and below the desired value. Time-lags or bad positioning of regulating devices may lead to violent hunting. It can be eliminated by damping.

Huygens eyepiece. An *eyepiece consisting of two planoconvex lenses facing the incident light with focal lengths and separation in the proportion of $2:3:4$ = field lens f : separation d : eye lens f. This is modified somewhat on occasion, but is commonly used with telescopes and microscopes. Although it corrects chromatic differences of magnification it shows longitudinal *chromatic aberration, pin cushion *distortion, and other aberrations.

Huygens's principle. A wave theory of light based on the concept of wavelets or *secondary waves* spreading from each point affected by a disturbance and conspiring to give a fresh wavefront which envelops the wavelets which create it. The amplitude in a secondary wavelet falls off in proportion to $(1 + \cos \theta)$, where θ is the angle with the forward direction. Huygens conceived the waves as longitudinal in nature and could not explain polarization.

hybrid. *See* integrated circuit.

hybrid computer. *See* computer.

hydrated electron. *Syn.* aqueous electron. Symbol: e_{aq}^-. When an aqueous solution is irradiated with *ionizing radiation, the water molecules become ionized and secondary electrons are released. Such an electron rapidly loses its energy by ionizing and exciting neighbouring water molecules. After about 10^{-11} seconds from its formation, the water molecules have sufficient time to orientate themselves around the electron without it escaping, and a region of radial polarization results, trapping the electron in the centre. (The water molecule is polarized such that the hydrogen atom is slightly more positive than the oxygen atoms.) This species is called the hydrated electron, the electron existing in a *potential well. It is an extremely reactive species.

hydraulic press. A device for producing large forces, consisting basically of two cylinders, one much wider than the other, fitted with pistons A and B and connected by a pipe C, the whole being filled with water. A force f applied downwards at A develops a pressure equal to f/A where A is the area of cross section of A. This pressure is transmitted throughout the fluid (*see* Pascal's principle) and is thus applied at B. The total force upwards on B equals the pressure times the area of $B = fB/A$. Hence a much larger force appears at B if B is much larger than A. Also if A moves downwards, B moves upwards by a much smaller distance and the work done on B never exceeds that done on A.

hydrodynamics. A branch of the science of deformable bodies, being a study of the motion of fluids (liquid and gaseous). The classical theory of hydrodynamics is concerned with the mathematical treatment of perfect fluids. This theory is subject to modification to include the effect of the viscosity of a real fluid.

hydroelectric power station. A power station in which electrical energy is produced by conversion from hydraulic energy. Usually, the potential energy of water falling from a high to a low level is converted into kinetic energy in a water turbine. This kinetic energy is then converted into electrical energy by a generator.

hydrogen bomb. *See* nuclear weapons.

hydrogen electrode. An electrode system in which hydrogen is in contact with a solution of hydrogen ions. It consists of a *half-cell in which a platinum foil is immersed in a dilute acid solution. Hydrogen gas is bubbled over the foil, which is usually coated with finely divided platinum to increase absorption of the hydrogen. Hydrogen electrodes are used in cells to measure standard *electrode potentials.

hydrogen spectrum. The *emission spectrum of hydrogen contains a large number of lines in the visible region of the spectrum. These lines form a series, the *Balmer series*, represented by the empirical equation:

$$k = R\left(\frac{1}{4} - \frac{1}{m^2}\right),$$

where k is the *wave number of the line, m an integer, and R a constant, equal to $1.096\,775 \times 10^7\ \text{m}^{-1}$, called the *Rydberg constant*. The lines get closer together at lower wave numbers.

The formation of this series was explained by Bohr in his theory of the *atom. The hydrogen atom can exist in a number of energy states given by:

$$E = -me^4/8h^2\varepsilon_0^2 n^2,$$

where n is an integer, ε_0 the *electric constant, and m, e, and h have their usual meanings. When electrons of an excited hydrogen atom move to a lower energy state, photons are released of energy $h\nu$, where ν is the frequency of the radiation. The Balmer series results from electrons moving into the second orbit. The frequencies ν_m are given by:

$$h\nu_m = \frac{me^4}{8h^2\varepsilon_0{}^2}\left(\frac{1}{2^2} - \frac{1}{m^2}\right),$$

where m is an integer greater than 2, i.e. $m = 3, 4, 5$, etc. The equation clearly has the same form as Balmer's empirical equation and the theoretical value of the Rydberg constant is $me^4/8h^3\varepsilon_0{}^2c = 1\cdot097$ $373 \times 10^7\,\mathrm{m}^{-1}$. The fact that this agreed so well with the experimental value of R was a great success for Bohr's theory of the atom. There are in fact four series of lines in the emission spectrum of hydrogen depending on the orbit of the electron in the final state of the atom, specified by the *principal quantum number, n. When $n = 1$ the *Lyman* series is found in the visible region. There are also two series of lines in the infrared region, the *Paschen series* for which $n = 3$ and the *Brackett series* for which $n = 4$.

hydrometer. *Syn.* aerometer. An instrument for determining relative densities (specific gravities) usually of liquids. *Hare's hydrometer* consists of two vertical glass tubes, one standing in a vessel of water, the other in the liquid under test. The tubes are connected at their upper ends by a glass T-piece, and by applying suction the liquids may be raised in the tubes; the relative densities are inversely proportional to the height to which the liquids are raised in the tubes.

In hydrometers of constant immersion, the hydrometer consists of a glass tube blown out to two bulbs at its lower end. The lower bulb contains mercury, so that the hydrometer may float vertically in whatever it is immersed, and the graduated scale which is fixed to the tube will indicate the relative density of the liquid in which it floats. The hydrometer scale may be graduated in different ways. In hydrometers of constant immersion, the instrument carries a pan at its upper end and is adjusted by means of weights put into the pan until the hydrometer is sunk to a fixed mark on its neck; the relative density of the liquid may be obtained from a knowledge of the weights required, first in water, and then in the liquid under test. In this form the hydrometer is known as *Fahrenheit's hydrometer*. In *Nicholson's hydrometer*, the lower end of the instrument carries a scale pan and this addition permits the determination of the relative density of a solid. *Sikes's hydrometer*, which is much used in alcoholometry, consists of a graduated brass rod carrying a weighted bulb at its lower end. The range of the hydrometer may be increased by adding brass weights to a platform below the bulb.

hydrophone. An instrument for detecting sounds under water.

hydrostatic balance. *See* balance.

hydrostatic equation. *See* barometric formula.

hydrostatics. *See* statics.

hygristor. An electronic component with an electrical *resistance that varies with *humidity. It is used as the basis of some recording *hygrometers.

hygrograph. An instrument for measuring and recording the relative *humidity of the air.

hygrometer. An instrument for the measurement of the *humidity of air. The main types are the *chemical hygrometer, in which the dew point is measured and the relative humidity obtained from the ratio of the saturation pressure of water vapour at the dew point to that at the temperature of the air; *wet and dry bulb hygrometers, and recording instruments, such as the *hair hygrometer, in which an indicator gives the relative humidity directly.

hygroscope. A device for giving a rough guide to the *humidity of the atmosphere. A very simple form of hygroscope is a card impregnated with chemicals that change colour when the moisture content increases above a certain level, e.g. cobalt chloride (changing from blue to pink).

hypercharge. Symbol: *Y*. A *quantum number associated with an elementary particle. It is the sum of its *baryon number and *strangeness and is conserved in strong and electromagnetic interactions.

hyperfine structure of spectral lines. Some spectral lines (apparently single lines at ordinary resolution) consist of a multiple system with differences of wavelength of the order of a thousandth of a nanometre. These can only be resolved by using high resolution (10^6) gratings, etc., e.g. the Fabry–Perot *etalon or *Lummer–Gehrcke plate.

hypermetropia. *Syn.* long sight. *See* refraction.

hypernucleus. *See* lambda particle.

hyperon. The collective name given to long-lived *baryons other than the proton and neutron. Long-lived in this context is taken to mean not decaying in the usual decay time of the *strong interaction, i.e. particles with lifetimes much greater than 10^{-23} seconds. The lambda, sigma, xi, and omega-minus particles are hyperons. *See* elementary particle; strangeness.

hypersonic velocity. A velocity not less than five times the velocity of sound through a medium at the same level and under the same physical conditions, i.e. not less than *Mach 5.

hypsometer. An apparatus for the determination of the upper fixed point of a thermometer. The thermometer T is placed in the steam above the water

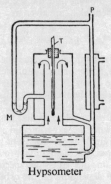

Hypsometer

boiling under a known pressure, usually atmospheric, applied at P, the manometer M being used to ensure that the water is not being boiled too vigorously. The central space is enclosed by a steam jacket from which any condensed liquid flows back to the boiler. The boiling point under the measured pressure is deduced from tables and the reading of the thermometer T corrected.

hysteresis. (1) (magnetic) A phenomenon shown by ferromagnetic substances, whereby the magnetic flux through the medium depends not only on the existing magnetizing field, but also on the previous state or states of the substance. The existence of permanent magnets is due to hysteresis. The phenomenon necessitates a dissipation of energy when the substance is subjected to a cycle of magnetic changes. This is known as the magnetic *hysteresis loss. *See* hysteresis loop. (2) (dielectric) *See* dielectric hysteresis. (3) (torsional) When a wire is subject to many twists and untwists between the limits $+\theta$ and $-\theta$, it settles down to a condition in which the couples called into play by the twists $+\theta$ and $-\theta$ have definite values, and the couple for an intermediate twist θ' has two values, one corresponding to the passage from $+\theta$ to $-\theta$ and the other to the passage from $-\theta$ to $+\theta$. The wire is in a cyclic state and the twist lags behind the couple: this has been called torsional hysteresis.

hysteresis loop (magnetic). A closed curve obtained by plotting *either* the magnetic induction, B, *or* the intensity of magnetization, I, of a ferromagnetic material against the corresponding value of the magnetizing field H. The area enclosed by the I/H loop is equal to the *hysteresis loss in joules per unit volume in taking the specimen through the pre-

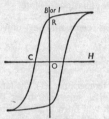

Hysteresis loop

scribed magnetizing cycle. The area of the B/H loop is equal to that of the I/H loop multiplied by 4π. The general form of the hysteresis loop for a symmetrical cycle between H and $-H$ is shown in the diagram, but any complete magnetizing cycle, say between the limits $H + h$ and $H - h$ will give rise to a hysteresis loop. The area enclosed by the loop varies with the nature and heat treatment of the magnetic substance, being a minimum for electrolytic iron and reaching a value some twenty times greater for tungsten steel. *See* ferromagnetism.

hysteresis loss. (1) (magnetic) The dissipation of energy which occurs, due to magnetic hysteresis, when the magnetic material is subjected to changes (particularly cyclic changes) of magnetization. *See* hysteresis loop. (2) (dielectric) The dissipation of energy which occurs, due to *dielectric hysteresis, when the dielectric is subjected to a varying (in particular, an alternating) electric force. (3) (elastic) The dissipation of energy through torsional hysteresis.

I

ice. The solid form of water, the transition point at one atmosphere being defined as $0°$ C (*see* ice point). The specific latent heat of fusion is 0.3337 MJ kg^{-1}. Its density at $0°$ C is 916.0 kg m^{-3}, compared to water at $0°$ C with a density of 999.8 kg m^{-3}. There are several allotropic forms of ice, mostly stable only under high pressure.

ice calorimeter. *See* Bunsen ice calorimeter.

ice line. *Syn.* solidification curve. A curve expressing the relation between the melting point of ice and the applied pressure. It may be calculated by using the *Clausius–Clapeyron equation.

ice point. The temperature of equilibrium of ice and water at standard pressure. Its former importance was as the lower fixed point on the Celsius scale of temperature. Now, however, *thermodynamic temperature and the kelvin are based on the *triple point of water, and its value (273.16 K) has been chosen so as to make the ice point equal to $0°$ C within the limits of experimental measurement. *Compare* steam point.

ideal crystal. The crystal structure considered as perfect and infinite, that is, ignoring all questions of crystal texture.

ideal gas. *Syn.* perfect gas. A gas that obeys Boyle's law and has an internal energy independent of the volume occupied, i.e. it obeys Joule's law of internal energy. These two requirements are, from the point of view of the kinetic theory, both equivalent to saying that the intermolecular attractions are to be negligible, but the first requires also that the molecules shall be of negligible volume. An ideal gas in fact obeys Boyle's law, Charles's law, Joule's law of internal energy, Dalton's law of partial pressures, and Avogadro's hypothesis exactly, whereas real gases obey them only as their pressure tends to zero. The equation of state for 1 mole of an ideal gas is given by

$$pV = RT,$$

R being the *universal gas constant. The isothermals of a perfect gas therefore form a family of rectangular hyperbolas. For a treatment of gases that are not ideal, *see* equations of state.

ideal gas constant. *See* universal gas constant.

idle component. *See* reactive current.

ignition temperature. (1) The temperature to which a substance must be heated before it will burn in air (or some other specified oxidant). (2) *See* fusion reactor.

ignitron. An electronic rectifying tube controlled by a subsidiary igniter rod. The tube has an anode and a mercury

Ignitron

pool in which a rod of semiconductor such as silicon carbide is immersed. The voltage applied to the anode is insufficient to strike an arc, but if a current is passed between the igniter and the mercury a hot spot forms which is sufficient to enable the arc to strike.

illuminance. *Syn.* illumination; intensity of illumination. Symbol: E_v, E. The *luminous flux incident on a given surface per unit area. At a point on a surface the illuminance is given by: $E_v = d\Phi_v/dA$, where Φ_v is the luminous flux and A is the area. It is measured in lux. *Compare* irradiance.

illumination. (1) *See* illuminance. (2) The extent to which a surface is illuminated or the application of visible radiation to a surface.

image. From the geometrical optics point of view an image point is the point to which rays are converged (*real image*) or from which they appear to diverge (*virtual image*) after reflection or refraction. The real object point from which rays have diverged (and the virtual object point to which incident rays may be converging), and the corresponding image, are said to be *conjugate. If the pencils do not reunite to foci in the image, the latter suffers from *aberration. The greatest concentration of ray intersections is the *geometric image*. If the blur circles are sufficiently small (say 0·1 mm for viewing at 25 cm), the image formation may be regarded as being sharp. This means that there is an allowable *depth of focus of the image. From the physical optics point of view the distribution of light in the image is considered in relation to phase and path differences, which gives the image a focal depth, throughout which there is little deterioration of quality. The *image space* is a convenient mathematical conception to describe where images may lie; it may be real or virtual.

image converter. An *electron tube for converting an infrared, or other invisible image, into a visible image. The infrared image is focused on to a semitransparent photocathode, and the electrons released are attracted to a fluorescent anode screen which is positively charged. They are focused on to the screen by an electron optical system and thus produce a visible image.

image impedances. Of a *quadripole. The two impedances Z_{i1} and Z_{i2} that satisfy both the following conditions: (1) When Z_{i2} is connected across one pair of

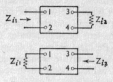

Image impedances

terminals, the impedance between the other pair is Z_{i1}. (2) When Z_{i1} is connected across the other pair of terminals, the impedance between the first pair is Z_{i2}.

image intensifier. A device for increasing the *luminance of the spot produced when a beam of X-rays hits a fluorescent screen.

image orthicon. *See* camera tube.

image potential. If a charged particle (electron or ion) is a distance r from a metal surface it experiences an electrostatic force. The interaction is equivalent to the interaction between the particle and an image of the particle a distance r below the surface. The potential energy of the particle is then $e^2/16\pi\varepsilon_0 r^2$, where e is its charge and ε_0 the *electric constant.

image space. *See* image.

image-transfer coefficient. Of a *quadripole. The quantity

$$\log_e \sqrt{\frac{E_1 I_1}{E_2 I_2}} = \tfrac{1}{2}\log_e \frac{E_1 I_1}{E_2 I_2},$$

where E_1 and I_1 are the voltage and current respectively at the input terminals, and E_2 and I_2 are the corresponding quantities at the output terminals under steady state conditions when the network is terminated in its *image impedance. The voltages and currents are expressed in vector (e.g. complex) form and the coefficient is in general complex.

immersion objective. Microscope objectives use the principle of aplanatic refraction and to reduce the refraction at the front lens of the objective for higher powers, cedar wood oil (refractive index 1·517) is placed between the cover glass (index 1·51, say) and the plane surface of the front lens of higher index (*see* diagram). Besides aiding aplanatism the *numerical aperture is increased by this process, which therefore increases *resolving power.

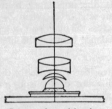

Immersion objective

immittance. A term used to include both the terms *impedance and *admittance.

IMPATT transistor. Abbreviation for *Imp*act ionization *A*valanche *T*ransit *T*ime. A diode transistor that provides a very powerful source of microwave power. The diode consists of either a p–n junction, or a p–i–n junction where i is a region of almost *intrinsic semiconductor sandwiched between p and n regions. The diode is biased so that a region of *avalanche breakdown exists. An increment in differential voltage causes an increase in differential current, which will be out of phase with the voltage because of the transit time of carriers between generation and collection at the electrodes. If the total delay in current exceeds one quarter of a cycle, the in-phase component of the current becomes negative and in an appropriate circuit the device may oscillate spontaneously.

impedance. In general the ratio of one sinusoidally varying quantity (e.g. force or voltage) to a second quantity (e.g.

velocity or current) that measures the response of the system to the first quantity.

(1) (electrical). Symbol: Z. If an alternating e.m.f. is applied to an electric circuit the *alternating current produced is opposed by the capacitance and inductance of the circuit as well as its resistance. This extra opposition is the *reactance of the circuit and the total opposition to current flow is the impedance. It is the ratio of *root-mean-square voltage to root-mean-square current and is equal to $\sqrt{R^2 + X^2}$, where R is the resistance and X the reactance.

The magnitude of an alternating current varies with time according to the equation $I = I_0 \cos(2\pi ft)$, where f is the frequency and I_0 the maximum current. The e.m.f. in the circuit will not be in phase with the current if reactance is present, i.e. $V = V_0 \cos(2\pi ft + \varphi)$, where φ is the phase angle. Thus

$$I = I_0 \, e^{i\omega t}$$
and
$$V = V_0 \, e^{i(\omega t + \varphi)}.$$

where ω is $2\pi f$. The real parts of these are the instantaneous current and voltage. The impedance is then the complex voltage divided by the complex current, i.e. $Z = V/I$, and is thus equal to $|Z|e^{i\varphi}$, where $|Z|$ is $\sqrt{R^2 + X^2}$. This quantity is sometimes called the complex impedance. It is given by $Z = R + iX$.

(2) (acoustic). Symbol: Z_a. The complex ratio of the alternating *sound pressure to the rate of volume displacement of the surface that is vibrating to produce a simple sinusoidal source of sound. It is related to acoustic resistance (R_a) and reactance (X_a) by

$$Z_a = R_a + iX_a.$$

The *specific acoustic impedance* (Symbol: Z_s) is the product of acoustic impedance and the area. It is the complex ratio of the sound pressure to the *particle velocity in the medium. Acoustic impedance has units of pascal second per metre squared.

(3) (mechanical). Symbol: Z_m; ω. The complex ratio of the force acting in the direction of motion to the velocity. It is related to *mechanical resistance* (R_m) and *reactance* (X_m) by $Z_m = R_m + iX_m$ and is measured in newton second per metre.

impedance drop (or rise). *See* voltage drop.

impedance magnetometer. An instrument for measuring local variations of the magnetic field of the earth (e.g. in a building) by measurement of the change in impedance of a nickel–iron wire of high permeability caused by the axial component of the field in which the wire is placed.

impedance matching. The matching of impedances or parts of an electrical system to ensure maximum transfer of power. For maximum power to be transferred from an *amplifier to a load, the load impedance is made the conjugate of the amplifier output impedance. In transmission lines, the line impedance is made equal to the generator-output impedance and also to the terminal-load impedance to ensure no reflection in the transmission line. If transmission lines of differing impedance are joined in a system, a section of line, one quarter of a wavelength long, is used to couple the lines and effect matching. Such a section is termed a *quarter-wavelength transformer* (or *line*).

impedance voltage. *See* voltage drop.

impulse. Of a constant force F. The product, Ft, of the force and the time t for which it acts. If the force varies with time, the impulse is the integral of the force with respect to the time during which the force acts. In either case, impulse of force = change of momentum produced by it. An *impulsive force* is one which is very large but acts only for a very short time; it can be represented by a *Dirac function.

impulse generator. *Syn.* surge generator. An electronic circuit for producing single pulses, usually by charging and discharging a capacitor.

impulse noise. *See* noise.

impulse voltage (or current). A unidirectional voltage (or current) that rises rapidly to a maximum value without appreciable superimposed oscillations and then falls to zero more or less rapidly. The diagram below shows a typical waveshape which is described as a T_1/T_2 wave.

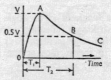

Waveshape of impulse voltage (or current)

Relevant terms are as follows. *Peak value*: maximum value, V. *Wavefront*: rising portion, OA. *Wavetail*: falling portion, ABC etc. *Duration of the wavefront*: time interval (T_1) for the voltage (or current) to rise from zero to its peak value (usually measured in microseconds). *Time to half value of the wavetail*: time interval (T_2) for the voltage (or current) to rise from zero, pass through its peak value (V) and then fall to half its peak value (0·5 V) on the wavetail (usually measured in microseconds).

impulsive force. *See* impulse.

impurities. In a *semiconductor. Foreign atoms, either naturally occurring or deliberately placed in the semiconductor. They have a fundamental effect on the amount and type of conductivity.

incandescence. The emission of visible radiation from a substance at a high temperature. The term also refers to the radiation itself. *Compare* luminescence.

incandescent lamp. An electric lamp in which light is produced by the heating effect of a filament of carbon, osmium, tantalum, or (more usually) tungsten. Inert gas fillings are often used to suppress disintegration of the filament at the high temperature (> 2600° C), and efficiency is often increased thermally by winding the filament into a close spiral, and then this into a second close spiral (coiled-coil) to reduce heat loss by conduction through the gas.

incidence (angle of). The angle between the ray striking a reflecting or refracting surface (i.e. the incident ray) and the normal to the surface at the point of incidence.

inclination, magnetic. *See* dip.

inclinometer. An instrument for measuring the magnetic inclination (dip). *See* dip circle.

incoherent. Not *coherent. Radiation from any source other than a *laser is incoherent.

indeterminacy principle. *See* uncertainty principle.

index error. *Syn.* zero error. A scale error on a measuring instrument such that the instrument shows a reading x when it should show zero reading.

indicator diagram. The cycle traced out during the motion of a piston in the cylinder of an engine. Vertical displacements represent the pressure and horizontal displacements the volume of the working substance. The area enclosed by the diagram gives the work done per cycle and is used in estimating the efficiency of the engine.

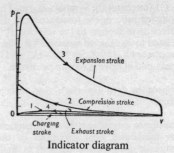

Indicator diagram

indicator tube. A minute *cathode-ray tube in which the shape or size of the image on the screen varies with the input voltage V in such a manner that it is used to measure V, and hence can indicate the value of a varying signal.

indifferent equilibrium. *See* equilibrium.

indirect stroke. *See* lightning stroke.

inductance. *See* electromagnetic induction.

induction. *See* electromagnetic, electrostatic induction; magnetic flux density.

induction coil. A device for producing high potential and approximately unidirectional current by *electromagnetic induction. It consists of a primary circuit of a few turns of wire, wound on an iron core A, and insulated from a secondary coil S of many turns which surrounds it coaxially. The primary is supplied with an interrupted current. Owing to the high resistance introduced into the primary circuit by each break of the circuit the *time constant of the primary is much smaller at break than when the contact is remade, and the

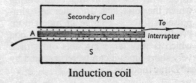

Induction coil

induced e.m.f. in the secondary is consequently much higher. The efficiency of the coil thus depends on the sharpness of the break. The output from the secondary consists of a succession of sharp pulses, corresponding to the breaks in the primary circuit, with much smaller inverse pulses produced when the current is remade.

induction flowmeter. The rate of flow of a conducting liquid passing through a tube T (*see* diagram) in a magnetic field can be measured by the e.m.f. induced

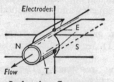

Induction flowmeter

across a diameter, between electrodes E. The relationship is $e = BLv \times 10^{-16}$, where e is the e.m.f. in volts, B is the flux density in tesla, L is the length of the conductor in metres, v is the velocity in $m s^{-1}$, and B, e, and v are mutually perpendicular.

induction heating. The heating effect arising from *eddy currents in conducting materials, often used for melting metals.

induction instrument. An instrument in which the deflecting force or torque is produced by the interaction of *eddy currents induced in a movable conducting disc or cylinder and the magnetic field of an electromagnet.

induction motor. An a.c. motor consisting of a *stator and a *rotor in which the current in one member (usually the rotor) is generated by *electromagnetic induction when alternating current is supplied to a winding on the other member (usually the stator). The torque is produced by interaction between the

rotor current and the magnetic field produced by the current in the stator. For motors used industrially there are two main types of rotor: (i) *squirrel-cage rotor* in which all the rotor conductors are permanently short-circuited at both ends of the rotor by means of end-rings; (ii) *slip-ring rotor* (or wound rotor) which carries a *polyphase winding connected to *slip rings.

inductive coupling. *See* coupling.

inductive load. *See* lagging load.

inductive reactance. *See* reactance.

inductive tuning. *See* tuned circuit.

inductor. *Syn.* reactance coil. A coil or other piece of apparatus possessing *electromagnetic inductance and selected for use because of that property.

inelastic collision. *See* collision.

inelastic scattering. *See* scattering.

inertance. *See* acoustic inertance.

inert cell. A *primary cell that is inert until water is added to produce an electrolyte. It contains the chemicals and other necessary ingredients in solid form.

inertia. The property of a body by virtue of which it tends to persist in a state of rest or uniform motion in a straight line. *See* Newton's laws of motion; force.

inertial force. *Syn.* effective force. *See* force.

information theory. An analytical technique for determining the optimum (generally minimum but sufficient) amount of information required to solve a specified problem in communication or control.

infrared radiation (i.r.). Long-wave (heat) radiation emitted by hot bodies, with

193

wavelengths ranging from the limit of the red end of the visible spectrum, about 740 nm, to about 1 mm. The shorter wave or near infrared is examined by a spectroscopic method using the thermopile, bolometer, or radio micrometer, with fluorite or other material prisms in place of glass, and concave reflectors in place of lenses. This is because glass is absorbent at wave length 2 μm. The quartz limit is 4 μm, fluorite 10 μm, rocksalt 15 μm, sylvin 23 μm. Photographic methods can be used to about 1 μm; photoconductive cells, using *semiconductors, are extensively used in the range 1–3 μm.

To examine the far infrared (to about 75 μm) the method of selective reflection, using the residual rays, is employed. Focal isolation methods are used for the extremely long radiations whose wavelengths link up with radio waves produced electronically.

infrared window. *See* atmospheric windows.

infrasound. Vibrations of the air below a frequency of about 16 hertz, recognized by the ear as separate pulses rather than as sound.

injection. (1) In general, the technique of applying a signal to an electronic circuit or device. (2) The process of introducing *carriers into a semiconductor so that the total number of carriers exceeds the number present at thermal equilibrium. The carriers may be introduced in various ways, e.g. across a forward-biased junction or by irradiation.

in parallel. *See* parallel.

in phase. *See* phase.

in-phase component. *See* active current.

input. The signal or driving force applied to a circuit, device, machine, or other plant. Also the terminals to which this is applied.

in series. *See* series.

instantaneous axis. That straight line in a rigid body about which it may be regarded as rotating at any instant. If a rigid body is constrained to rotate about a fixed point O (*compare* Poinsot motion), the instantaneous axis will occupy different positions in the body but will always pass through O.

instantaneous frequency. The rate of change of phase of an electric oscillation in radians per second, divided by 2π. It has particular applications in connection with *frequency and *phase modulation.

insulated gate field-effect transistor (IGFET). *See* field-effect transistor.

insulating resistance. The resistance between two electrical conductors or systems of conductors that are normally separated by an insulating material. It is usually expressed in megohms or, in the case of cables, in megohms per mile (or kilometre).

insulator. A substance that provides very high resistance to the passage of an electric current; an appliance made of insulating material and used to prevent the loss of electric charge or current from a conductor. *See also* energy bands.

integrated circuit. A complete circuit manufactured in a single package. In *hybrid* integrated circuits separate components and/or circuits are attached to a ceramic substrate and interconnected. The complete circuit, bearing some resemblance to a circuit made from discrete components, is enclosed in a single package. It cannot be modified without destroying the whole circuit. In *monolithic* integrated circuits all the components are manufactured into or on top of a *chip of silicon. They are formed by selective diffusion of the appropriate type of impurity into a layer of semiconductor. Interconnections between individual components are made by means of metallization patterns and the individual components are not separable from the complete circuit.

Bipolar integrated circuits are based on bipolar junction *transistors, and *M O S integrated circuits* on insulated gate *field-effect transistors; both are monolithic circuits. MOS circuits have several advantages compared to bipolar circuits. Relatively fewer processing steps are required, the MOS transistors are self-isolating and therefore smaller than bipolar transistors, no separate process is required to form resistors, and *pulse operation of the circuits is easily obtainable, reducing the power dissipated in the circuit. Large chips may therefore be easily made, increasing the functional packing density and reducing the cost of the device. The complexity of circuits which may be produced on a single chip has led to the evolution of descriptive terms: *small scale integration* (SSI) describes fairly simple circuits, *medium scale integration* (MSI) describes circuits of medium complexity e.g. a decade counter, and *large scale integration* (LSI) describes very complex circuits e.g. 100 bit (or more) *shift register.

integrating galvanometer. A *galvanometer in which inertia and control of the moving system are so chosen that the change in flux produced in an exploring coil can be measured even though the changes last over a period of several minutes.

integrating meter. A measuring instrument that integrates the measured quantity with reference to time.

integrating photometer. In order to measure the mean spherical *luminous intensity of a source, a large sphere is painted white inside with a matt or opal window whose brightness can be matched with a standard lamp on an outside photometer bench. The lamp under test is completely surrounded by the sphere; the internal brightness and that of the window are proportional to the total flux emitted by the lamp.

integrator. A mechanical or electrical device for performing the mathematical operation of integration, e.g. the d.c. current i, flowing into a capacitor C gradually builds up a voltage on the capacitor equal to $1/C \int i \, dt$, i.e. an integration of i with respect to time is performed.

intensifier. A substance used to strengthen the image on a negative or positive photographic medium.

intensifying screen. A screen, coated with calcium tungstate crystals, that emits light under the action of X-rays and reduces the exposures needed in radiography by a factor of about 100. There is, however, some reduction of definition as the screen impresses its own grain on the film.

intensity. (1) Of sound. Symbol: I. The rate of energy transfer per unit area normal to the direction of propagation, at any given point. The total energy per unit volume can be given by $\frac{1}{2}\rho_0 a^2 f^2$, where ρ_0 is the mean density, a is the amplitude, and f the frequency. The intensity is then:

$$I = \frac{\text{energy passing in one period}}{\text{time of one period}}$$

$$= \frac{\frac{1}{2}\rho_0 a^2 f^2 \lambda}{1/f} = \frac{1}{2}\rho_0 a^2 f^3 \lambda = \frac{1}{2}\rho_0 c a^2 f^2.$$

Converted to terms of the maximum alternating pressure, p_{max} at the point under consideration, the expression becomes $\frac{1}{2}(p^2_{max}/\rho_0 c)$.

(2) *See* magnetic field strength; electric field strength. (3) *See* illuminance; cosine law.

intensity modulation. Of a *cathode-ray tube. The variation of the brilliance of the spot on the screen in accordance with the magnitude of a signal. It is often referred to as *z-modulation*.

intensity of magnetization. For a uniformly magnetized body, the ratio of its magnetic moment to its volume.

interaction. In general, an exchange of energy between one particle and a second particle or an electromagnetic wave. The four fundamental interactions of matter are the *strong interaction, *weak interaction, *electromagnetic interaction, and *gravitational force.

interelectrode capacitance. The capacitance between specified *electrodes of an electronic device, in which the electrodes form a small capacitor, e.g. between *emitter and *base of a *transistor. These capacitances may have a significant effect on the operation of such devices.

interfacial angles. Angles between the normals to crystal faces.

interference. (1) Of light. If light from a source S passes through a pinhole and falls on two further pinholes A and B (Fig. *a*), light and dark fringes appear on

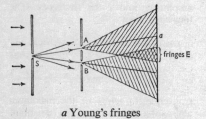

a Young's fringes

the screen where the resultant pencils of light overlap. The pencils of light *interfere* and produce *interference fringes*, first observed by Thomas Young in 1801. These and similar fringes were used by Fresnel and Young to establish the wave theory of light.

For interference to occur the light

beams must be *coherent. This originally meant that beams had to be obtained from a single source; two *lasers can now be used. The angle of intersection of the beams must not be too great and the beams must not be polarized in planes at right angles to each other. They must also be of approximately equal intensity.

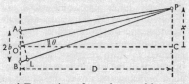

b Formation of interference fringes

A bright fringe will be observed at P (Fig. *b*) if the path difference $BP - AP = n\lambda$ where n is an integer. The beams reinforce each other at P and *constructive interference* occurs, the beams being in phase. If the beams are 180° out of phase, i.e. if $BP - AP = \frac{1}{2}n\lambda$, *destructive interference* occurs and a dark fringe results. For slits $2b$ apart the separation of successive bright fringes is $\lambda D/2b$, where D is the distance between screen and pinholes.

Thin films (e.g. soap bubbles; oil on water) often display brilliant colourations when reflecting white light and show fringes when in monochromatic light. Here light reflected from the front and back surfaces may be out of step by various amounts, destructive interference and consequent darkness occurring in some directions while constructive interference or reinforcement occurs in others. The irregular appearance of the coloured bands results from the uneven thickness of the film.

Parallel-sided layers give *fringes of equal inclination*, visible by eye or telescope focused on infinity; thin films give fringes of equal thickness, effectively contours, located in or near the film. *Newton's rings*, formed between a convex lens face and a plane glass slab, are of the latter type. Fringes become much sharper when formed by multiple reflections between surfaces of high reflecting power, e.g. if the film is between surfaces thinly silvered so that light can enter and leave the interspace.

In an *interferometer* fringes are produced and used to make accurate measurements of wavelength. *See* etalon; echelon grating; Michelson–Morley experiment; Lummer–Gehrcke plate.

(2) Of sound. The superposition of two or more waves originating from a common source, but traversing different paths, results in regions in the transmitting medium at which there is a minimum intensity (*nodes) and in other regions at which there is a maximum intensity (antinodes). This phenomenon is called interference, and the resulting pattern in the field of radiation is called an *interference pattern*. Interference can also be produced by waves originating from two or more different sources. It can be demonstrated in the *Herschel–Quincke tube. *See also* Kundt's tube.

(3) In a communication system. A disturbance caused by undesired signals, *atmospherics, *hum, whistle, etc. Electrical apparatus and machinery commonly give rise to it.

interference figure. A pattern of coloured rings and black bands given by a crystal in convergent polarized light between crossed *Nicol prisms.

interference filter. *See* filter.

interference microscope. *See* microscope.

interferometer. (1) *See* interference. (2) *See* radio telescope.

intermediate frequency. *See* superheterodyne receiver.

intermediate vector boson. *See* W-particle.

intermodulation. Modulation of the component sinusoidal waves of a complex wave by each other. The resulting wave contains, in particular, frequencies which are equal to the sum of and also the difference between the frequencies, taken in pairs, of all the components of the original complex wave.

internal absorptance. Symbol: α_i. A measure of the ability of a substance to absorb radiation as expressed by the ratio of flux absorbed between the entry and exit surfaces of the substance to the flux leaving the entry surface. Internal absorptance does not apply to loss of intensity by scattering or to reflection of radiation at the surface of the substance. (*Compare* absorptance.)

The internal absorptance is related to the *internal transmittance (τ_i) by:

$$\alpha_i + \tau_i = 1.$$

internal conversion. The process in which a nucleus in an *excited state decays to a lower state and gives up energy to one of its orbital electrons, usually a K-electron. If this energy is large enough to overcome the binding energy of the electron then it is ejected from the atom as a *conversion electron*. The process is independent of *gamma-ray emission; it is not the production of a γ-ray photon which then knocks the electron out by the photoelectric effect.

internal energy. *Syn.* thermodynamic energy. Symbol: U or E. A thermodynamic function of a system that changes by an amount equal to the algebraic sum of the heat received by the system (δq) and the work done on it (δw): $dU = \delta q + \delta w$. It is necessary to suppose that a system possesses internal energy in order to apply the principle of conservation of energy to thermal systems (*see* thermodynamics). The above equation is a symbolic representation of the first law. If a system changes from one state to another the heat change and work change both depend on the path taken but the change in internal energy is only dependent on the initial and final states, not on the way the change is made. The internal energy is never absolutely determined; only changes in its value are important. The internal energy of a system is equal to the sum of all the kinetic and potential energies of the molecules. *See also* Joule's law of internal energy.

internal forces. *See* force.

internal friction. The effect that causes a damping of elastic vibrations in a solid and similar effects. It is analogous to viscosity in liquids and results from the *anelasticity of the material.

internal resistance. Of a cell, accumulator, or dynamo. The resistance in ohms obtained by dividing the difference in volts between the generated e.m.f. and the potential difference between the terminals of the cell by the current in amperes.

internal transmission density. *Syn.* absorbance. Symbol: D_i. A measure of the ability of a body to absorb radiation, expressed by

$$D_i = \log_{10}(1/\tau_i),$$

where τ_i is the internal transmittance.

internal transmittance. Symbol: τ_i. A measure of the ability of a material to transmit radiation as expressed by the ratio of the flux reaching the exit surface of the body to the flux leaving the entry surface. It only applies to regular transmission and not to substances that scatter light or to reflection at the surfaces of the body. (*Compare* transmittance.) It is related to the *internal absorptance (α_i) by:

$$\tau_i + \alpha_i = 1.$$

internal work. The work done in separating the molecules of a system against their forces of attraction. Its value is zero for an *ideal gas.

international ampere. *See* ampere.

international candle. A unit of luminous intensity superseded (in 1948) by the *candela.

international steam table calorie (I.T. calorie). A heat unit formerly adopted by international agreement as being $4 \cdot 1868 \times 10^7$ ergs to avoid errors due to the variation of the specific heat capacity of water with temperature. It is now replaced by the joule; 1 cal$_{IT}$ = $4 \cdot 1868$ ioules. *See* calorie.

international system. A former system of units for measuring electrical quantities, based on the international *ohm and the international *ampere. It has now been replaced by SI units.

international temperature scale. A practical scale of temperature, based on the meaning of *thermodynamic temperature, and employing experimentally determined values of particular temperatures (known as the primary fixed points) and particular experimental methods for measuring temperature between and beyond these fixed points on the International Practical Temperature Scale of 1968; the following eleven fixed points are defined:

triple point of equilibrium hydrogen	$-259 \cdot 34°C$
boiling point of equilibrium hydrogen at a pressure of $\frac{25}{76}$ atmosphere	$-256 \cdot 108$
boiling point of equilibrium hydrogen	$-252 \cdot 87$
boiling point of neon	$-246 \cdot 048$
triple point of oxygen	$-218 \cdot 789$
boiling point of oxygen	$-182 \cdot 962$
triple point of water	$0 \cdot 01$
boiling point of water	$100 \cdot 0$
freezing point of zinc	$419 \cdot 58$
freezing point of silver	$961 \cdot 93$
freezing point of gold	$1064 \cdot 43$

(Equilibrium hydrogen is an equilibrium

mixture of ortho-hydrogen and para-hydrogen.)

Temperatures below 630° C are measured by means of a platinum resistance thermometer; between 630° and 1064° C a platinum–platinum/rhodium thermocouple is used; above 1064° C a *radiation pyrometer is used based on Planck's law of radiation.

interpolation. Estimation of the value of a function, $y(x)$, for a value of the variable, x, which lies between those for which the function is known. This may be done graphically or by using an interpolation formula. *Compare* extrapolation.

intersecting storage ring (ISR). A very high vacuum device in which two beams of high-energy particles, such as protons, circulate in opposite directions being built up from pulse to pulse by a process called stacking. The beams can be arranged to collide at several points

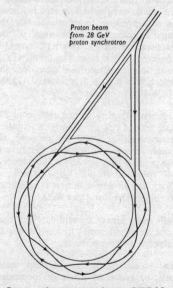

Proton beam from 28 GeV proton synchrotron

Intersecting storage ring at CERN

within the device, leading to the production of very high energies. The ISR at CERN will eventually produce energies of about 1700 GeV. The rate at which proton–proton interactions occur however is only about one millionth the rate at which the CERN beam interacts with a stationary target.

interstage coupling. In a multi-stage *amplifier, employing several amplifying stages in *cascade, the system that effects the transfer from the output of one stage to the input of the next. Common types of *coupling are direct, resistance, capacitive, etc.

interstellar matter. Matter in interstellar space tends to be gathered into clouds of irregular shape and distribution, composed of dust and gas. Interstellar gas causes slight absorption of starlight and strong polarization effects. The mean density is of the order of 10^{-18} grains/m³ at a temperature of about 25 K. Interstellar gas consists mainly of neutral hydrogen and some ionized hydrogen. The mean density is about 10^{-21} kg/m. The kinetic temperature can range from 120 K to very high values. The neutral hydrogen gives rise to the best known radio astronomy wavelength of 210 mm.

interstitial structures. Crystalline arrangements in which small atoms occupy some of the interstices between large atoms, which themselves form a regular crystalline pattern. They are of considerable importance in connection with the structure of steels and other alloys as well as *semiconductors. *See* defect.

interval. The difference in frequency between two notes of a scale, the difference being expressed either as a ratio or logarithmically. If the ratio form is used it is conventionally written as a value greater than one. The most common units of interval expressed in a logarithmic form are the *millioctave* and the *cent*. An interval I in millioctaves between frequencies f_1, f_2 is

$$I = (10^3/\log_{10} 2) \log_{10} (f_1/f_2)$$

In cents the interval is

$$I = (1200/\log_{10} 2) \log_{10} (f_1/f_2)$$

See also temperament.

intrinsic mobility. The mobility of *carriers in an *intrinsic semiconductor. Electrons are approximately three times as mobile as *holes.

intrinsic pressure. Assuming intermolecular forces of attraction, the inward force on the molecules near the surface of a fluid, which decreases rapidly as the distance from the surface increases. It is the term a/v^2 in Van der Waals' *equation of state.

intrinsic (i-type) semiconductor. A pure *semiconductor in which the *electron and *hole densities are equal under conditions of thermal equilibrium. In practice absolute purity is unattainable and the term is applied to nearly pure materials.

Invar. An alloy of iron with 36% of nickel, which has a very small coefficient of thermal expansion. It is used in making clocks and accurate standards of length.

inverse gain. Of a transistor. The *gain of a *bipolar junction transistor when it is connected with the emitter as the collector, and vice versa. It is usually less than the gain normally observed, as the emitter has a higher *doping level than the collector and therefore a higher *injection efficiency into the base than the collector.

inverse-speed motor. *See* series-characteristic motor.

inverse square law. A law relating the intensity of an effect to the reciprocal of the square of the distance from the cause. The law of *gravitation is an inverse square law, as are the laws relating the

forces associated with static electric charges and magnetic poles (*see* Coulomb's law).

inverse Zeeman effect. *See* magnetic effects; Zeeman effects.

inversion. A reversal in the usual direction of a process, as in the change of density of water at 4° C or, in meteorology, an increase in temperature with altitude as opposed to the normal decrease. It also applies to the production of a layer of opposite type in the surface of a *semiconductor, usually under the influence of an applied electric field. The presence of mobile minority carriers is necessary for inversion to take place. The phenomenon is utilized in the formation of the *channel in an insulated gate *field-effect transistor.

inversion temperature. (1) If one junction of a *thermocouple is kept at a constant low temperature, the temperature to which the other junction must be raised in order that the thermoelectric e.m.f. in the whole circuit shall be zero is known as the inversion temperature. For the same thermocouple, the sum of the temperatures of the two junctions is a constant, at the inversion point. If the inversion temperature is exceeded, the direction of the e.m.f. is reversed. (2) *See* Joule–Kelvin effect.

inverter. (1) Any device that converts d.c. into a.c., particularly a rotating machine designed for the purpose. (2) *Linear inverter.* An amplifier that inverts the polarity of a signal, i.e. introduces a 180° phase shift. (3) *Digital inverter.* A *logic circuit whose output is low when the input is high and vice versa.

Ioffe bars. Heavy current-carrying bars used in experimental fusion devices to increase *plasma stability.

ion. An electrically charged atom, molecule, or group of atoms or molecules. *See* anion; cation; gaseous ions.

ionic atmosphere. In an electrolyte, cations tend to accumulate anions around them (and the converse), this being known as an ionic atmosphere. When an electric field is applied the ions migrate in the reverse direction to their ionic atmosphere, and the symmetry of the atmosphere with respect to the ion is disturbed in such a manner that the ion is retarded. *See also* Wien effect.

ionic conduction. The movement of charges within a semiconductor due to the displacement of ions within the crystal lattice. An external contribution of energy is required to maintain such movement.

ionic mobility. The velocity attained by an ion when acted on by an electric field of unit strength. It is usually measured in m/s per V/m, i.e. $m^2\,V^{-1}\,s^{-1}$.

ionic semiconductor. A solid in which the electrical conductivity due to the flow of *ions predominates over that due to the movement of *electrons and *holes.

ion implantation. A technique used in the manufacture of *integrated circuits and *transistors in which the semiconductor material is bombarded by high-velocity ions under controlled conditions. The ions penetrate the surface of the semiconductor and can be made to assume lattice positions within the semiconductor crystal.

ionization. The process of forming ions. Ionization occurs spontaneously when an electrolyte dissolves in a suitable solvent. Ionization in gases requires the action of some *ionizing radiation; e.g. X-rays, α-, β-, or γ-rays. *See* conduction in gases.

ionization chamber. A chamber containing two oppositely charged electrodes so arranged that when the gas in the chamber is ionized, e.g. by X-rays, the ions formed are drawn to the electrodes,

creating an ionization current. This is used as a measure of the intensity of the *ionizing radiation. The sensitivity of an ionization chamber is dependent on the mass of gas enclosed in the sensitive volume.

ionization gauge. A vacuum pressure gauge consisting basically of a three-electrode thermionic tube and used for measuring small gas pressures of as low

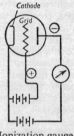

Ionization gauge

as 10^{-8} mmHg. The tube is fused to the gas system to be measured, and is connected up as shown. Electrons are accelerated between the cathode and grid, but cannot reach the plate since it is at negative potential. Some electrons, however, pass through the grid and collide with gas molecules and ionize them, leaving them positively charged. The positively charged gas molecules then go to the plate and the plate current produced provides a measure of the number of molecules present.

ionization potential. Symbol: *I*. The minimum energy necessary to remove an electron from a given atom or molecule to infinity. It is thus the least energy that causes an ionization: $A \rightarrow A^+ + e^-$, where the *ion and the electron are far enough apart for their electrostatic interaction to be negligible and no extra kinetic energy is produced by the ionization. The electron removed is that in the outermost orbit, i.e. the least strongly bound electron. It is also possible to consider removal of electrons from inner orbits in which their binding energy is greater. The minimum energy required to remove the second least strongly bound electron from a neutral atom is called its second ionization potential. *Compare* electron affinity.

ionizing radiation. Any radiation that causes ionization or excitation of the medium through which it passes. It may consist of streams of energetic charged particles, such as electrons, protons, alpha particles, etc., or energetic ultraviolet radiation, X-rays, or γ-rays. A large number of ions, secondary electrons, and excited molecules are produced in the medium by particles; electromagnetic radiation produces a lower number by processes such as the *photoelectric effect, *Compton effect, and *pair production.

Ionizing radiation occurs naturally as *cosmic rays and the *solar wind, and is emitted by *radioisotopes. It is produced artificially by X-ray machines and particle *accelerators. Its effects can be observed visually by using such apparatus as the *bubble chamber or *spark chamber, or by examination of the tracks made in photographic emulsion. More quantitative measurements are made with *counters. *See also* dosimetry.

ionosphere. A spherical shell of ionized air surrounding the earth extending from about 50 km (the top of the stratosphere) to over 1000 km (*see* atmospheric layers). Nitrogen and oxygen molecules are split into atoms, ions, and free electrons by *ionizing radiation from space, especially ultraviolet radiation and X-rays from the sun. Radio transmission is achieved by reflection of radio waves from these charged particles.

The ionosphere can be divided into three distinct layers or regions. The thickness of these regions can change between day and night, and shows seasonal and latitude variations.

The *D-layer or region* is the lowest

ionospheric layer, lying approximately 50–90 km above the earth; it contains a low concentration of free electrons and reflects low-frequency waves.

The *E-layer or region* (*Syn.* Heaviside layer; Kennelly–Heaviside layer) lies approximately 90–150 km above the earth and reflects medium-frequency waves.

The *F-layer or region* (*Syn.* Appleton layer) is the highest layer, approximately 150–1000 km above the earth. During the day it splits into the F_1-*layer* (lower) and F_2-*layer*. It has the highest concentration of free electrons.

At night the electron concentrations in the D- and E-layers fall owing to the absence of sunlight and the consequent recombination of electrons and ions. In the higher F-layer the density is lower and collisions between electrons and ions are less frequent. The F-layer can therefore be used for radio transmission at all times.

Radio waves deflected by the electrically conducting ionospheric layers are called *ionospheric waves* (or sky waves). Some wavelengths, lying in the radio window between 8 mm and 20 m, are transmitted through the ionosphere; radio and television, broadcast at high frequencies, must thus be reflected by artificial *satellites.

ion pump. A type of vacuum pump in which the gas is ionized by a beam of electrons and the positive ions attracted to a cathode. It is only operated at very low pressures (less than about 10^{-6} Pa) and the gas is not completely removed from the system but simply trapped on the cathode. The pump thus saturates after a certain time. The capacity of ion pumps can be increased by continuously evaporating a film of metal onto the cathode during its operation.

ion source. A device that provides ions, especially for use in a particle *accelerator. A minute jet of gas, such as hydrogen or helium, is ionized by bombardment with an electron beam and the resulting ions are ejected into the accelerator.

ion trap. In a *cathode-ray tube, a device to prevent the *ions present in the tube impinging on the phosphor coating of the screen and so causing blemishes.

iris diaphragm. The variable diaphragm used as an aperture stop in optical instruments.

I²R loss. *Syn.* copper loss. The power loss in watts due to the flow of electric current in the windings of a machine or transformer.

iron loss. *See* core loss.

irradiance. Symbol: E_e, E. The *radiant flux of electromagnetic radiation, Φ_e, incident on a given surface per unit area, A. At a point on the surface the irradiance is given by: $E_e = d\Phi_e/dA$. It is measured in joules per square metre. *Compare* illuminance.

irradiation. The exposure of a body or substance to *ionizing radiation, either electromagnetic (X-rays and gamma rays) or corpuscular (alpha particles, electrons, etc.).

irreversible change. *See* reversible change.

irrotational motion. Of a fluid. Motion such that the equation of relative motion of any element of a finite portion of the fluid does not include rotational terms, i.e. *curl $V = \nabla \times V = 0$ where V is the vector velocity of an element of the fluid. When the motion is irrotational, there exists a *velocity potential and conversely when a velocity potential exists the motion is irrotational. If once irrotational, then the motion of a fluid under conservative forces is always irrotational. Any motion of a fluid in which the component angular velocities of rotation do not vanish together is called rotational

and a velocity potential does not then exist.

isenthalpic process. A process that takes place without any change of *enthalpy, i.e. so that the total heat energy (internal plus external) remains constant.

isentropic process. *See* adiabatic process.

isobar. (1) A line on a map passing through places of the same atmospheric pressure. (2) One of two or more nuclides that have the same *mass number but different *atomic numbers.

isochore. A curve representing two variables involved in an isometric (constant volume) thermodynamic change, e.g. pressure/temperature, temperature/entropy.

isoclinal. A curve drawn in such a manner that all places on the curve have the same magnetic *dip. *See* aclinic line.

isodiapheres. Two or more nuclides with the same *isotopic number.

isodynamic. A curve drawn in such a manner that the total magnetic field strength of the earth's magnetic field is identical at all points on the curve.

isogam. A line on a map joining points at which the acceleration of free fall is constant.

isogonal. A curve drawn in such a manner that the magnetic *declination (or variation of the compass) is the same at all places on the curve. *See* agonic line.

isolating transformer. A *transformer used to isolate any circuit or device from its power supply.

isolator. A device that allows microwave energy to pass in one direction while absorbing power in the reverse direction.

203

isomagnetic lines. Lines joining points at which the magnetic force is equal.

isomers. (1) Compounds of the same molecular weight and percentage composition differing in some or all of their chemical and physical properties. (2) *See* nuclear isomer.

isometric change. A change in a gas that takes place at constant volume.

isomorphism. Similarity of crystalline form or of structure in substances that are chemically related.

isospin. *Syn.* isotopic spin. Symbol: *I*. A *quantum number associated with *elementary particles. It is found experimentally that the *strong interaction between two protons and between two neutrons is the same. This also applies to the three pions π^+, π^0, and π^-. As electromagnetic interactions are about 100 times weaker than strong interactions they can often be ignored. *Hadrons differing only in their charge can thus be combined into groups (called *multiplets*) which can be regarded as different states of the same object: mass differences between multiplet members arise from energy differences associated with their differing charge.

It is found that to each hadron two quantum numbers I and I_3 may be assigned. The quantum number I, which can take values $0, \frac{1}{2}, 1, \frac{3}{2}, 2, \ldots$, is called the isospin and is the same for all particles in a multiplet. The *isospin quantum number* I_3 can have values $-I, -I + 1, \ldots, I - 1, I$ and labels the particles in a multiplet. Examples of isospin multiplets are the nucleon doublet and the pion and sigma triplets:

	I	I_3		I	I_3		I	I_3
n	$\frac{1}{2}$	$-\frac{1}{2}$	π^-	1	-1	Σ^-	1	-1
p	$\frac{1}{2}$	$\frac{1}{2}$	π^0	1	0	Σ^0	1	0
			π^+	1	1	Σ^+	1	1

In general, the charge Q of any elementary particle is related to its *hyper-charge Y and the quantum number I_3 by the equation:

$$Q = I_3 + \frac{Y}{2}.$$

Both quantum numbers are conserved in strong interactions. For electromagnetic interactions there is a dependence on the charge of the particles and I is no longer conserved although I_3 is.

isothermal. A line joining all points on a graph that correspond to the same temperature.

isothermal process. A process that occurs at a constant temperature. For example, if a gas is expanded in a cylinder by a piston its temperature can be kept constant by supplying heat from a thermostatically controlled source during the expansion. In such a process the wall separating the gas from the source has to allow them to remain in thermal equilibrium with each other. It is then called a *diathermic* wall. *Compare* adiabatic process.

isotopes. Two or more nuclides having an identical nuclear charge (i.e. same atomic number) but differing in atomic mass. Such substances have almost identical chemical properties but differing physical properties, and each is said to be an isotope of the element of given atomic number. The difference in mass is accounted for by the differing number of *neutrons in the nucleus.

isotopic number. *Syn.* neutron excess. The difference between the number of neutrons and the number of protons in a nuclide.

isotropic. A body is isotropic if its properties are the same in all directions.

iterative impedance. Of a *quadripole. The impedance presented by the quadripole at one pair of terminals when the other pair is connected to an impedance of the same value. In general, a quadripole has two iterative impedances, one for each pair of terminals. Sometimes the two iterative impedances are equal and in this case their common value is called the *characteristic impedance* of the network. *Compare* image impedance.

i-type semiconductor. *See* intrinsic semiconductor.

J

J. The symbol for the mechanical equivalent of heat.

Jamin refractometer. *See* refractive index.

jamming. Interference in radio reception caused by an undesired signal which is so strong that the desired signal cannot be understood.

Jansky noise. High-frequency static disturbance of cosmic origin.

jet propulsion. Propulsion in which the propulsive force is the reaction of one or more jets of hot gases issuing at high velocity from backwardly directed nozzles. Jet engines are, therefore, devoid of reciprocating parts; air is drawn through an intake into a compressor, whence it passes to a combustion chamber, where it mixes with an oil fuel. The products of the combustion are expanded into the jet, driving the compressor on their way by means of a turbine.

jet tones. The rather unsteady tones produced when a stream of air is projected into still air from an orifice. The moving fluid tends to curl outwards into the stationary fluid forming alternate vortices on each side of the jet. Instability in jets is, however, very high and where the velocity of efflux and fluid are suitably chosen to give sufficient vortices per second for an audible sound the tones produced are weak, uncertain, and fluctuating. The sound, generally of high frequency, is more suitably described as a variable hiss.

jitter. A short term instability in either the amplitude or phase of a signal, particularly the signal on a *cathode-ray tube.

Johnson–Rahbeck effect. If a semiconducting plate of material such as slate or agate is placed against a metal plate, the two hold strongly together during the application of a potential of about 200 volts. The plate and stone are only in actual contact at a few points through which a very small current flows to equalize a high potential difference. This potential difference is therefore applied across a very small distance and the forces of attraction are correspondingly great.

Joly's steam calorimeter. A calorimeter for the determination of the specific heat capacities of solids. A pan is suspended from one arm of a chemical balance by a fine wire passing through a plaster plug, G, in an enclosure through which steam can be passed. The balance is counterpoised both with and without the specimen giving m_1 the mass of the specimen at temperature t_1. Steam at temperature t_2 is then passed through the chamber, condensation at G being prevented by a small heating coil encircling the wire. On reweighing, the mass of steam m_2 condensed on the pan (of *water equivalent W) and specimen is found and so

$$m_1 c(t_2 - t_1) = m_2 L - W(t_2 - t_1),$$

where c is the specific heat capacity of the specimen and L the specific latent heat of steam at temperature t_2. W is determined by a similar experiment carried out with the pan empty. All weighings must be corrected for the buoyancy of the air and steam.

Josephson effect. An effect observed in two superconductors that are separated by a thin dielectric when a steady potential difference V is applied. An oscillatory current is set up with a frequency proportional to V.

joule. Symbol: J. The *SI unit of all forms of *energy (mechanical, thermal, and electrical), defined as the energy equivalent to the work performed as the point of application of a force of one newton moves through one metre distance in the direction of the force. In electrical theory one joule equals one watt second. The joule has replaced the calorie as a unit of heat energy, one calorie being equal to 4·1868 joules.

Joule calorimeter. An electrically heated calorimeter.

Joule effect. The liberation of heat by the passage of a current through an electric conductor, due to its resistance. *See* heating effect of a current.

Joule–Kelvin effect and coefficient. *Syn.* Joule–Thomson effect. A change in temperature observed when a gas undergoes an adiabatic expansion without doing external work. It indicates a departure from *Joule's law (def. 2). Joule and Kelvin performed an experiment in which they throttled gas through a porous plug from a high to a low pressure in an insulated system. The expansion of the gas occurred at constant *enthalpy and it was found that most gases were cooled on expansion. This is because real gases have attractive forces between their molecules and work is done against this attraction during the expansion. The change in temperature with pressure at constant enthalpy, H, is called the *Joule–Kelvin coefficient* and is given by

$$\mu = \left(\frac{\partial T}{\partial P}\right)_H = \frac{T\left(\frac{\partial V}{\partial T}\right)_p - V}{c_p}$$

where V is the volume, P the pressure, T the thermodynamic temperature, and c_p the specific heat capacity at constant pressure. Most gases undergo a change in the sign of their Joule–Kelvin coefficient at a certain temperature, the *inversion temperature*, which, with the exception of helium, is higher than room temperature. The Joule–Kelvin effect is used in the *liquefaction of gases and in *refrigerators.

Joule's equivalent. The *mechanical equivalent of heat.

Joule's law. (1) The heat produced by an electric current I flowing through a resistance R for a fixed time t is given by I^2Rt. If the current is in amperes, the resistance in ohms, and the time in seconds, then the heat produced is in joules. (2) The *internal energy of a gas is independent of its volume. It only applies to *ideal gases, i.e. when there are no intermolecular forces.

Joule–Thomson effect. *See* Joule–Kelvin effect.

J particle. *See* psi particle.

junction. (1) A contact between two different materials, e.g. two metals, as found in a *rectifier or *thermocouple. (2) In a *semiconductor device. A transition region between semiconducting regions of differing electrical properties. (3) A connection between two or more conductors or sections of transmission lines.

junction field-effect transistor (JUGFET, JFET). *See* field-effect transistor.

junction transistor. *See* transistor.

just intonation. *See* temperament.

Juvin's rule. When a capillary tube of radius r stands vertical in a liquid of density ρ and surface tension γ the liquid rises a distance h up the tube, given by

$$h = 2\gamma \cos \alpha / rg\rho$$

where α is the angle of contact between the liquid and the walls of the tube and g is the acceleration of free fall. For a liquid that does not wet glass α exceeds 90° and h is negative: the liquid is depressed in the bore below the general level.

K

k. The symbol for the Boltzmann constant.

kaon. *Syn.* k-meson. *See* meson.

K-capture. *See* capture.

keeper. *Syn.* armature. The regions near the ends of a magnet produce an induced flux within it opposing the original magnetizing flux, the effect being greatest for the shortest magnets. Permanent magnets are provided with soft iron keepers, kept in position across the poles of a horseshoe magnet or between opposite poles of a pair of bar magnets, when the magnets are not in use. The flux induced in the keepers is opposite in direction to that in the magnet itself, and thus the demagnetizing effect in the magnet is neutralized.

Kellner eyepiece. A *Ramsden type of eyepiece with a cemented eye lens which corrects *chromatic aberration and distortion inherent in the original design. It is commonly used as an eyepiece in prism binoculars.

kelvin. Symbol: K. The *SI unit of *thermodynamic temperature, defined as 1/273·16 of the thermodynamic temperature of the *triple point of water. The kelvin is also used as a unit of temperature difference on the Kelvin and Celsius scales, where 1 K = 1 deg C.

Kelvin balance. A type of *current balance instrument that consists of six coils, four fixed and two which move between them on a balanced rod. The suspension consists of two flexible multiple copper ribbons which serve to carry current to the coils in the manner shown, so that each fixed coil tends to displace the balanced arm in the same direction when current flows. The scale

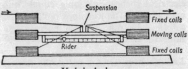

Kelvin balance

divisions are unequal as the displacement of the rider is proportional to the square of the current. The instrument can measure d.c. and a.c. and can also be adapted to read wattage.

Kelvin contacts. A method used when testing or measuring electronic circuits or components. Double leads are used to test points, one lead carrying the test signal and the other lead going to the measuring instrument. This removes the effect of the resistance of the leads on the measurement.

Kelvin double bridge. A special development of the d.c. *Wheatstone bridge for precision measurement of low resistances. A is the low resistance to be measured

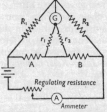

Kelvin double bridge

and B is a known low resistance of the same order. R_1/R_2 is kept equal to r_1/r_2 but they are varied until no current can be detected by the galvanometer, G. Then,

$$\frac{A}{B} = \frac{R_1}{R_2} = \frac{r_1}{r_2}.$$

The method eliminates possible errors due to contact resistance and the resistance of leads.

Kelvin effects. *See* thermoelectric effects.

Kelvin's formula. The approximate formula, $T = 2\pi\sqrt{LC}$, relating the period to the inductance (L) and capacitance (C) of an electric circuit with negligible resistance.

Kennelly–Heaviside layer. *See* ionosphere.

Kepler's laws. Of planetary motion. (1) Every planet moves in an ellipse, of which the sun occupies one focus. (2) The radius vector drawn from the sun to the planet sweeps out equal areas in equal times (i.e. the areal velocity is constant). (3) The squares of the times taken to describe their orbits by two planets are proportional to the cubes of the major semiaxes of the orbits.

Kepler telescope. *Syn.* astronomical telescope. *See* refracting telescope.

kerma (*k*inetic *e*nergy *r*eleased in *ma*tter). The sum of the initial kinetic energies of all charged particles produced by the indirect effect of *ionizing radiation in a small volume of a given substance divided by the mass of substance in that volume.

Kerr effects. Two effects concerned with the optical properties of matter in electric and magnetic fields. The *electro-optical* effect refers to certain liquids and gases that become doubly refracting when placed in an electric field at right angles to the direction of the light. The substance acts as a *uniaxial crystal with optic axis parallel to the field. If n_1 and n_2 are the refractive indexes of light with planes of polarization respectively parallel and perpendicular to the field, then:

$$n_1 - n_2 = k\lambda E^2,$$

where k is *Kerr's constant*, λ the wavelength of the light, and E the electric field strength. The *Kerr cell* consists of two parallel plates immersed in a liquid that shows a marked electro-optical

effect. Polarized light passes through the cell and can be interrupted by the application of an electric field. (*See also* Pockel's effect.)

The *magneto-optical effect* refers to the production of a slight elliptic polarization when plane polarized light is reflected from the polished pole face of an electromagnet. The incident light is plane-polarized in, or normal to, the plane of incidence. *See also* Faraday effect.

Kew magnetometer. A type of *magnetometer used to make accurate measurements of the earth's magnetic field and the magnetic declination. The magnetic needle is a steel tube with a graduated transparent scale on one end and a lens on the other. Its precise position can be observed with a coaxial telescope.

kilo-. (1) Symbol: k. Prefix meaning 10^3, e.g. 1 km = 1000 metres. (2) In computing. Prefix meaning 2^{10} (1024), e.g. 1 kilobyte = 1024 *bytes.

kilogramme (or kilogram). Symbol: kg. The *SI unit of mass represented by the international prototype kilogramme at the International Bureau of Weights and Measures at Sèvres in France. It consists of a cylinder whose height is equal to its diameter and which is made from an alloy consisting of 90% platinum and 10% iridium.

kilowatt-hour. Symbol: kWh. A unit of energy equivalent to the energy produced when power of 1 kilowatt is expended for 1 hour.

kinematics. The branch of *mechanics dealing with the motion of bodies without reference to mass or force.

kinematic viscosity (coefficient of). Symbol: ν. The ratio of the coefficient of viscosity (μ) to the fluid density (ρ). It is used in modifying the equations of motion of a perfect fluid to include the terms due to a real fluid. The units are metres squared per second. At room temperature water has a kinematic viscosity of $10^{-6} \, m^2 \, s^{-1}$. The ordinary viscosity coefficient is often called the coefficient of *dynamic viscosity*.

kinetic energy. *See* energy.

kinetic equilibrium. *See* force.

kinetic friction. *See* friction.

kinetic potential. *Syn.* Lagrangian function. An expression for the kinetic minus the potential energy in a conservative system. *See* Hamilton's principle.

kinetic reaction. *Syn.* inertial force. *See* force.

kinetics. *See* dynamics.

kinetic theory. The work of Rumford, Joule, and others led to the establishment of the concept of heat as a form of *energy. The kinetic theory combines this conclusion with the molecular theory of chemistry and interprets the heat content of a body as being the energy of the motions of the molecules of which the body is made up. The basis of the theory is in fact that of the kinetic theory of matter as a whole, namely, that the particles of matter in all states of aggregation are in a violent state of agitation, the vibratory motions becoming more energetic with increase of temperature. Evidence of molecular agitation is provided by diffusion and *Brownian movement.

During their motion gas molecules collide with the walls of the vessel containing them, delivering momentum to them and giving rise to an exertion of pressure. For an *ideal gas the pressure is given by

$$p = \tfrac{1}{3}mvC^2,$$

where m is the mass of the molecules, v is the number of molecules per m^3, and C is the *root-mean-square velocity of the molecules.

Maxwell's law of the *distribution of velocities gives the actual distribution of velocity among the molecules in a steady state, and is based on the main concepts of classical statistics, which lead also to the principle of equipartition of energy, namely that the total energy of a system is equally divided between the different degrees of freedom, and that each degree of freedom possesses a mean energy $\tfrac{1}{2}kT$, where k is the Boltzmann constant, and T is the thermodynamic temperature.

The application of kinetic theory leads to the relation for gases

$$\gamma = 1 + \frac{2}{n},$$

where γ is the ratio of the principal *specific heat capacities and n is the number of *degrees of freedom for each molecule.

In the case of solids it leads to *Dulong and Petit's law that the *molar heat capacity of a solid is constant and equal to $3R$. The simple kinetic theory of specific heat capacities is quite unable to account for the variation of specific heat capacity with temperature both in solids and in gases, and the classical concepts of equipartition had to be replaced by those of the *quantum theory.

Kirchhoff formula. A formula for the variation of *vapour pressure with temperature:

$$\log p = A - B/T - C \log T,$$

where A, B, and C are constants. It is valid over limited temperature ranges.

Kirchhoff's law (for radiation). The principle that at a given temperature the spectral *emissivity of a point on the surface of a *thermal radiator in a given direction is equal to the spectral *absorptance for incident radiation coming from that direction. The adjective *spectral* implies that the emissivity or absorptance is considered for monochromatic radiation.

Kirchhoff's laws (for an electric circuit). (1) The algebraic sum of the electric currents which meet at any point in a network is zero. (2) In any closed electrical circuit the algebraic sum of the products of current and resistance in each part of the network is equal to the e.m.f. in the circuit.

klystron. An *electron tube that employs *velocity modulation of the electron beam, and is usually used at high frequencies for either the amplification or generation of high-frequency waves. The electron beam passes through a resonant cavity and if high-frequency waves are used to excite the cavity, these interact with the beam and cause velocity

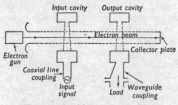

Two-cavity klystron amplifier

modulation of the beam. (*See* diagram.) After travelling some distance from the cavity, bunching of the electron beam will occur and the beam current will be modulated. If this now interacts with another resonant cavity, the cavity will be excited and high-frequency waves generated in it. Amplification of the original wave in the input cavity will thus occur, power being taken from the electron beam. If positive feedback is employed between the two cavities, the tube will emit waves of the resonant frequency of the output cavity. This may be tuned to the frequency of the input cavity or to a desired harmonic of it.

k-meson. *Syn* kaon. *See* meson.

Knudsen flow. *See* molecular flow.

Knudsen gauge. A device for the absolute measurement of very low pressures

Knudsen gauge

where the mean free path of the molecules is large compared with the dimensions of the apparatus. Two cold plates, B_1, B_2, at a temperature T_2 are free to rotate in the evacuated vessel about a vertical quartz suspension. Stationary plates, A_1, A_2, are electrically heated to a temperature T_1. The gas molecules striking B from the side A have greater momentum than those striking the other side of B and so the vanes B_1, B_2 experience a force per unit area equal to F in the direction shown. F is calculated from the measured deflection of the suspended system and the torsion constant of the fibre. The pressure p of the gas is given by

$$p = \frac{2F}{\sqrt{\frac{T_1}{T_2}} - 1}$$

Kundt's rule. The principle that the refractive index of a medium does not vary continuously with wavelength in the region of absorption bands. *See* anomalous dispersion.

Kundt's tube. An apparatus to measure the velocity of sound in gases under different controllable conditions of temperature, density, and humidity. A column of gas in a tube D is closed at one end R and has a source of sound, such as a rod clamped at its centre C, at the other; in between there is a dry powder such as lycopodium or cork or pith dust for detecting resonance. If the piston is adjusted so that the length of the gas column gives an exact number of stationary waves, the dust will be

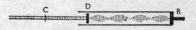

Kundt's tube

211

violently disturbed at the antinodes and will form a series of striations. As the wavelength is equal to 2*d*, where *d* is the distance between two nodes or antinodes, the velocity of sound *c* can be determined.

The determination of the ratio of the specific heat capacities of a gas (γ), especially those supplied in small quantities as rare gases, can be found from the relation $c = \sqrt{\gamma p/\rho}$ where p and ρ are the pressure and density of the gas.

L

ladder filter. A network consisting of a succession of series and shunt impedances, usually acting as a transmission line with a known attenuation or delay.

laevorotatory. *Syn.* laevorotary. Capable of rotating the plane of polarization of polarized light in an anticlockwise direction as viewed against the direction of motion of the light. *See* optical activity.

lag. (1) Of a periodically varying quantity. The interval of time or the angle by which a particular phase in one wave is delayed with respect to the similar phase in another wave. *Compare* lead. (2) The time elapsing between the transmission and reception of a signal.

lagging current. An alternating current that, with respect to the applied e.m.f. producing it, has a *lag.

lagging load. *Syn.* inductive load. A *reactive load that takes a *lagging current.

Lagrange law. *See* sine condition.

Lagrange's equations. A set of second order differential equations for a system of particles which relate the kinetic energy T of the system to the generalized coordinates q_i, the generalized forces Q_i, and the time t. There is one equation for each of the n degrees of freedom possessed by the system.

$$\frac{\mathrm{d}}{\mathrm{d}t}\left(\frac{\partial T}{\partial q_i}\right) - \frac{\partial T}{\partial q_i} = Q_i, (i = 1, 2 \dots n).$$

Lagrangian function. *See* kinetic potential; Hamilton's principle.

Lalande cell. A *primary cell with zinc and iron electrodes in caustic soda solution as electrolyte and with copper oxide as depolarizer.

lambda particle. Uncharged *elementary particle, a *hyperon, that can replace a neutron in a nucleus to form an extremely unstable *hypernucleus*.

lambda point. *See* superfluid.

lambert. A unit of *luminance, no longer used, equal to 1 lumen of flux emitted per square cm of a surface assumed to be perfectly diffusing. The *foot-lambert* is a luminance of 1 lumen per sq. ft.

$$1 \text{ lambert} = \frac{1}{\pi} \text{ cd cm}^{-2} = \frac{1}{\pi} \text{ *stilb.}$$

Lambert's law. (1) *Syn.* cosine law. The luminous intensity of a small element of a perfectly diffusing surface in any direction is proportional to the cosine of the angle between the direction and the normal. The law is used to define the perfect diffuser, and since brightness is defined as the luminous intensity in a prescribed direction per unit area projected perpendicular to the direction, such a surface will have the same photometric luminance in different directions. *See* photometry. (2) *See* linear absorption coefficient.

Lamb shift. A small difference in energy between the energy levels of the $^2P_{\frac{1}{2}}$ and $^2S_{\frac{1}{2}}$ states of hydrogen, explained by a correction to the energy levels on the basis of the interaction of electromagnetic fields with matter in which the fields themselves are quantized.

laminar flow. Steady flow in which the fluid moves in parallel layers or laminae, the velocities of the fluid particles within each lamina not being necessarily equal. In the motion of a fluid through a straight horizontal pipe the velocities of the particles within each lamina are the same until the *critical velocity is attained and the motion changes from laminar to turbulent. When a velocity potential exists the flow is called *potential flow* and is essentially laminar flow, although the laminae are not necessarily plane.

lamination. The core of a transformer, transductor, relay, choke, or similar apparatus, when it is intended to be used with alternating currents, is formed of a pile of thin iron or steel stampings called laminations. These are oxidized on the surface, or lightly varnished, to increase the electrical resistance from one to another. Their purpose is to reduce losses by preventing *eddy currents circulating in the core.

Lamy's theorem. If a particle is in equilibrium under the action of three forces P, Q, and R, then

$$\frac{P}{\sin \alpha} = \frac{Q}{\sin \beta} = \frac{R}{\sin \gamma},$$

where α is the angle between Q and R, β the angle between R and P, and γ the angle between P and Q.

Landé factor. *Syn.* g-factor. A constant factor used in expressions for changes in energy level in a magnetic field. It is a correction for the fact that there is not a simple relationship between the total magnetic moment of an atom, nucleus, or particle and its angular momentum. The Landé factor is necessary to explain fine structure in spectral lines due to coupling between orbital and spin angular momenta. It is also used in the magnetic moments of particles resulting from their *spin. For example a nucleus with a spin *quantum number I has a magnetic moment given by $g\sqrt{I(I+1)}.M_N$, where M_N is the nuclear *magneton and g is a constant for a particular nucleus.

langley. A unit of energy density formerly used to express solar radiation; it is equal to one calorie per cm² or $4 \cdot 1868 \times 10^4 \, \text{J m}^{-2}$.

Langmuir effect. An ionization that occurs when atoms of low *ionization potential come into contact with hot metal of high *work function. It has been used in the production of intense beams of ions of such elements as the alkali metals.

Laplace equation. A linear differential equation of the second order:

$$\frac{\partial^2 V}{\partial x^2} + \frac{\partial^2 V}{\partial y^2} + \frac{\partial^2 V}{\partial z^2} = 0.$$

V may, for example, be the potential at any point in an electric field where there is no free charge.

Laplace equation (for velocity of sound). An equation relating the velocity of sound (c) in a gas to the density (ρ), pressure (p), and ratio of heat capacities (γ) of the gas. It has the form:

$$c = \sqrt{\frac{\gamma p}{\rho}}.$$

See dispersion of sound.

Laplace operator. The differential operator

$$\left(\frac{\partial^2}{\partial x^2} + \frac{\partial^2}{\partial y^2} + \frac{\partial^2}{\partial z^2} \right),$$

often represented by the symbol ∇^2. *See* del.

Laplace's coefficients. Spherical harmonics that are the analogues in three dimensions of *Legendre polynomials.

lapse rate. The rate of change of atmospheric temperature with altitude.

Larmor precession. A uniform magnetic field applied to a plane electron orbit of an atom causes the plane to precess about the direction of the field in such a way that the normal to the plane traces a cone with its axis in the field direction. The frequency of precession is given by

$$\nu = \frac{e}{m} \frac{H}{4\pi c}$$

e being the electron charge and *m* its mass, *H* the field strength, and *c* the velocity of the electron.

laser (*l*ight *a*mplification by *s*timulated *e*mission of *r*adiation). *Syn.* optical maser. A source of intense monochromatic coherent radiation in the visible, ultraviolet, and infrared regions of the spectrum. It operates by *stimulated emission*, which is a process whereby an incoming photon of energy hv (where h is the *Planck constant and v the frequency) can stimulate an electron in a high energy state E_1 to jump to a lower energy state E_2, where $E_1 - E_2 = hv$. The photon resulting from this process has the same frequency, $v = (E_1 - E_2)/h$, as the stimulating photon and travels in the same direction. If there are sufficient electrons in the high energy level, both stimulating and stimulated photons can cause further stimulated emission and a narrow beam of monochromatic radiation results, the intensity of which increases exponentially. The beam is coherent and has a very high energy density.

A laser beam is produced by stimulated emission but can only operate efficiently if a large number of electrons are in a particular high energy state. This condition, called *population inversion*, is a non-equilibrium state and power must be fed into the system to maintain the inversion.

Laser action has been achieved in gaseous, solid, and liquid media. The ruby laser consists of a cylinder of ruby, about 5 cm long and 1 cm in diameter, the ends being polished flat and parallel, one end having a silvered reflecting surface and the other end having a semi-silvered surface. Chromium ions in the ruby lattice are excited by an intense flash of light. Electrons, raised to a high energy state, decay immediately to a slightly lower *metastable state, and thus population inversion occurs. The level slowly depopulates by fluorescence and this spontaneous emission triggers stimulated emission of the same frequency of 694·3 nm, the photons being reflected along the crystal axis with a small percentage emerging from the semi-silvered end. The ruby laser beam is usually pulsed. Although the overall efficiency is less than 1 % the energy density is very high, the peak power being between 10 and 100 kW.

The population inversion in gas lasers is achieved by a continuous electric discharge in a *gas-discharge tube. The helium–neon laser operates at wavelengths including 1·153 μm, 3·391 μm, and 632·8 nm. The output and efficiency are both low. The output and efficiency of the carbon dioxide laser, at 10·6 μm, is much higher. The *semiconductor diode laser has also a large efficiency.

A gas laser can be made to act as an electrical *oscillator by adding two reflecting surfaces, often at the *Brewster angle, outside both ends of the laser tube thus forming a *cavity resonator. One of the reflectors is totally reflecting, the other partially reflecting. The parallel silvered ends of a solid laser, such as the ruby laser, serve the same purpose. The laser radiation oscillates between the mirrors, being built up by additional stimulated emission so that it emerges through the partially-reflecting mirror at a much greater power.

The laser is not truly monochromatic but has a linewidth of the order of 10^4 hertz. This is much narrower than other radiation sources, the best monochromatic beams having a linewidth between 10^8–10^9 Hz. *See also* holography.

latent heat. Symbol: L. The quantity of heat absorbed or released in an isothermal transformation of phase. The quantity of heat released or absorbed per unit mass is now called the *specific latent heat. The quantity of heat absorbed or released per unit amount of substance (per mole) is now called the *molar latent heat*.

latent image. *See* photography.

lateral aberration. *See* chromatic aberration.

lateral magnification. The inverse ratio of the size (y) of an object perpendicular to the axis of a reflecting or refracting system, to the size (y') of the image, i.e. $m = y'/y$. According to the sign convention adopted, the algebraic sign of m will determine whether the image is erect or inverted.

lattice. (1) A regular periodically repeated three-dimensional array of points that specifies the positions of atoms, molecules, or ions in a crystal. *See* Bravais lattice; crystal systems. (2) The internal structure of the *core of a *nuclear reactor, consisting of a regular geometric pattern of fissile material and non-fissile material, especially a moderator.

lattice constant. The length of edge or the angle between the axes of the *unit cell of a crystal. It is usually the edge length of a cubic unit cell.

Laue diagram. When a heterogeneous beam of X-rays, electrons, or neutrons falls on to a thin crystal, the different atomic planes give rise to a series of symmetrically arranged spots on a photographic plate placed behind the crystal. This pattern, called a Laue diagram, is used to determine the type of crystal and its structure.

Lauritsen electroscope. An electroscope in which a metal wire carries a metal-coated quartz fibre, which is attracted to the wire when under charge. A T-piece on the fibre is viewed by a microscope with an eyepiece scale.

Lawson criterion. The product of the particle density of a *plasma (in particles per cm³) and the *containment time (in seconds) at or above its *ignition temperature, such that the fusion energy released equals the energy required to produce and confine the plasma. For the deuterium–tritium reaction the value of the Lawson criterion is 10^{14} s/cm³. *See* fusion reactor.

lead. (1) An electrical conductor. (2) Of a periodically varying quantity. The interval of time or the angle by which a particular phase in one wave is in advance of the similar phase in another wave. *Compare* lag.

lead equivalent. A measure of the absorbing power of a radiation screen expressed as the thickness of metallic lead (usually in mm) that could give the same protection as the given material under the same conditions.

leader stroke. The initial discharge that establishes the track of a *lightning flash.

leading current. An alternating current that, with respect to the applied e.m.f. producing it, has a *lead.

leading load. *Syn.* capacitive load. A *reactive load that takes a *leading current.

leakage. (1) The flow of an electric current, due to imperfect insulation, in a path other than that intended. The current is small compared to that of a short circuit. (2) *See* magnetic leakage.

leakage flux. In any electrical machine or transformer, in which there is a magnetic circuit. The flux which is outside the useful portion of the flux circuit.

leakage reactance. Reactance caused in a transformer by the leakage inductance associated with losses due to some of the magnetic flux cutting one coil but not the other.

least action principle. In a conservative dynamic system, the motion between two points has a stationary value for the actual path as compared with various paths between the same points for which the total energy has the same constant value, i.e. $\delta\int_{t_0}^{t_1} 2T\,dt = 0$, where T is the kinetic energy of the system at time t. *Compare* Hamilton's principle.

least energy principle. A dynamic system is in stable equilibrium only if the potential energy of the system considered as a whole is a minimum. *See* Le Chatelier's rule.

least squares, method of. A technique for finding the equation that gives the best fit for a set of experimental data. A simple example is in fitting a linear equation $y = ax$ to a set of measurements of the dependent variable y in terms of the independent variable x. A value of a is chosen and the deviation of experimental values can be obtained. The best fit is considered to occur for a value of a at which the sum of the squares of these deviations is a minimum.

least time principle. *See* Fermat's principle.

Le Chatelier's rule (or principle). When a constraint is applied to a dynamic system in equilibrium, a change takes place within the system, opposing the constraint and tending to restore equilibrium.

Leclanché cell. A primary cell in which the anode is a rod of carbon and the cathode a zinc rod, which may be amalgamated. The electrolyte is 10–20 % NH_4Cl solution. The depolarizer consists of manganese dioxide mixed with graphite or crushed carbon, contained in a fabric bag or porous pot. The e.m.f. is about 1·5 volts, but falls off fairly rapidly on closed circuit as the depolarizer is slow in action. In the *agglomerate cell* the internal resistance is reduced by having the depolarizer made into solid blocks held to a carbon plate by rubber bands. In this variant the cathode is usually a large Zn cylinder surrounding the blocks. *See* dry cell.

Leduc effect. *Syn.* Righi effect. When heat flows through a metal strip in a magnetic field that is at right angles to the strip, a temperature difference appears across the strip. *See* Nernst effect.

Lee's rule. A formula for calculating moments of inertia I, given by:

$$I = \text{mass} \times \{a^2/(3 + n) + b^2/(3 + n')\},$$

where n and n' are the numbers of principal curvatures of the surface that terminates the semiaxes in question and a and b are the lengths of the semiaxes. Thus, if the body is a rectangular parallelepiped, $n = n' = 0$, and $I = \text{mass} \times (a^2/3 + b^2/3)$. For an axis through the centre of a cylinder, perpendicular to the cylinder axis, $n = 0$ and $n' = 1$ and $I = \text{mass} \times (a^2/3 + b^2/4)$. If I is desired about the axis of the cylinder, then $n = n' = 1$ and $a = b = r$, where r is the radius of the cylinder, and $I = \text{mass} \times (r^2/2)$.

left-hand rule. For electric motors. *See* Fleming's rules.

Legendre equation and polynomials. The differential equation of the form

$$\frac{d}{dx}\left((1 - x^2)\frac{dy}{dx}\right) + ay = 0.$$

The solutions of this equation are known as Legendre polynomials.

Lenard–Jones potential. *See* Van der Waals forces.

Lenard's mass absorption law. The absorption of electrons moving with a velocity at least $\frac{1}{5}$ of that of light is determined only by the mass of absorbing matter traversed and is unaffected by its chemical nature.

lens. (1) A piece of transparent substance (commonly glass, plastic, quartz, etc.)

bounded by two surfaces of regular curvature. A lens is used to change the curvature of wavefronts so that light may be focused to a desired position. They may be convergent or divergent. Some lenses (spherical and parabolic) are intended to be stigmatic, uniting rays to point foci. Others (cylindrical and toric) have a different converging effect in meridians at right angles, producing two focal lines instead of one point focus – such lenses are astigmatic. A *thin lens* is one whose thickness is small compared with the focal lengths of its surfaces or the focal length of the lens: the powers of the individual surfaces add up to the power of the lens. *See also* lens formula; blooming of lenses. (2) *See* electron lens.

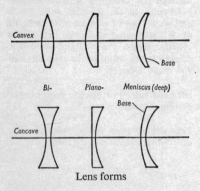

Convex

Base

Bi-   Plano-   Meniscus (deep)

Base

Concave

Lens forms

lens formula. The relationship between object distance, u, and image distance, v, from a thin lens is given by $(1/v + 1/u) = 1/f$ where f is the focal length. For a *real object or image, v and u are positive; for a virtual object or image, v and u are negative. For a convex lens, f is positive; it is negative for a concave lens. For thick lenses, refraction must be taken into account. The relation for refraction at a single curved surface is: $(n_2/v + n_1/u) = (n_2 - n_1)/2f$, where n_2 and n_1 are the refractive indexes of the lens material and the medium. *See also* optics sign conventions.

Lenz's law. *See* electromagnetic induction.

lepton. A collective name given to *fermions which do not take part in *strong interactions. The only known members of the group are the electron, muon, the two neutrinos, and their antiparticles. It is possible to define two *quantum numbers l_e and l_μ called *lepton numbers* as follows:

Particle	l_e	$l\mu$
e^-, ν_e	1	0
$e^+, \bar\nu_e$	−1	0
μ^-, ν_μ	0	1
$\mu^+, \bar\nu_\mu$	0	−1
others	0	0

In *weak interactions the total lepton numbers l_e^{TOT} and l_μ^{TOT} (obtained by adding up the values of l_e and l_μ for the individual particles) are conserved. Leptons do not have a quark substructure. *See* Table 8, page 425.

lethargy. Symbol: u. The negative natural logarithm of the ratio of the energy (E) of a neutron to a specified reference energy (E_0).

Lewis number. Symbol: (Le). A dimensionless number used in problems involving both heat and mass transfer. It is equal to $\lambda/\rho Dc$, where λ is the thermal conductivity, ρ is the density, D is the *diffusion coefficient, and c is the *specific heat capacity.

Leyden jar. An early form of capacitor consisting of a glass jar with metal foil on the lower outside and inside surfaces.

Lichtenberg figure. A complex symmetrical star-shaped pattern that is formed by dust particles adhering to a solid dielectric when it is under a high potential. It can also be produced on a photographic plate placed between electrodes.

lifetime. (1) In a *semiconductor. The mean time interval between generation and recombination of a charge *carrier. (2) *See* mean life.

lift coefficient. For a body and a fluid of density ρ in motion with a relative velocity V, the lift coefficient of the body is the ratio of the component of resistance force perpendicular to the direction of relative motion (lift) to the quantity $\rho l^2 V^2$, where l is some characteristic length of the body. The coefficient is a function of the *Reynolds number and is dependent on the circulation round the body.

light. The agency that causes a visual sensation when it falls on the retina of the eye. Light forms a narrow section of the electromagnetic spectrum and can be interpreted as a wave motion in electromagnetic theory or a stream of energy quanta or *photons in quantum theory, both aspects being complementary. Most phenomena involving the interaction of light with light can be explained by wave theory; with energy interactions, such as the *photoelectric effect, quantum theory must be used.

The wavelength range of light in nanometres is approximately 400 (violet) to 740 (red). The red end of the spectrum can be extended to almost 900 nm if very high power light sources are used. When light frequencies are multiplied by the *Planck constant (h), 6.626×10^{-34} Js, the energy of the light quantum for the frequency concerned is obtained. The *velocity of light in free space is $2.997\,925 \times 10^8$ m s^{-1}. *See* also colour.

light-emitting diode (LED). A *diode formed from certain *semiconductor materials, e.g. gallium arsenide, in which direct radiative recombination of electron–hole pairs is possible. If a p–n junction is formed from such materials and *forward biased, the light given off will be proportional to the bias current. The useful light obtained will be dependent on the optical quality of the crystal surfaces, and the colour will depend on the particular material used. *See also* semiconductor diode laser.

light exposure. Symbol: H_v, H. (1) The surface density of the total quantity of light received by a material. (2) A measure of the total amount of light energy incident on a surface per unit area, expressed as the product of the *illuminance and the time for which it is illuminated. When the intensity of the light varies over the period of illumination the exposure is given by: $H_v = \int E_v \, dt$, where E_v is illuminance and t is time. It is measured in lux second. *Compare* radiant exposure.

light guide. *See* fibre optics system.

lightning conductor. A system having an air termination and a single conductor connected to earth, used to protect buildings from lightning.

lightning flash. A complete lightning discharge along a single discharge path. It may be made up of more than one *lightning stroke, in which case it is described as a multiple stroke.

lightning stroke. A discharge that is a component of a complete *lightning flash. It is the discharge of one of the charged regions of a thunder cloud. The polarity of a lightning stroke is the polarity of the electric charge that is brought to earth. A lightning stroke to any part of a power or communication system is described as a *direct stroke*. It is an *indirect stroke* if it induces a voltage in that system without actually striking it.

light-year. A unit of distance employed in astronomy and equal to the distance travelled by light *in vacuo*, in one year. It equals 5.8785×10^{12} miles, 9.4607×10^{15} metres, or 0.307 *parsec.

limiter. A device that automatically prevents some output characteristic from exceeding a certain value. For example, in a frequency modulation receiver it is a device for eliminating or reducing any amplitude modulation of the received signal.

limiting current. *Syn.* diffusion current. In electrolysis the rate of diffusion of ions towards the electrodes may not keep pace with their deposition. There is thus a limiting value of current that can be passed under the particular conditions of ionic concentration and characteristics of the electrolyte.

limiting friction. *See* friction.

limit of proportionality. *See* Hooke's law.

Linde process. For the liquefaction of air. Air is compressed by the pump A, and

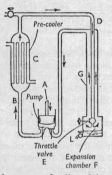

Linde process for liquefying air

passes through B to the cooler C where the heat of compression is removed. The compressed air passes through D and expands through a throttle valve E into the vessel F at a pressure of about 40 atmospheres. The cooled air then returns through the heat exchanger G to the pump chamber A, cooling the oncoming air in DE, until finally liquid air is formed in F and may be withdrawn at L.

linear. (1) Having its components arranged in a line, such as a *linear

accelerator. (2) Having an output that is directly proportional to its input as in a linear amplifier.

linear absorption coefficient. *Syn.* absorption coefficient. Symbol: *a*. During its passage through a medium radiation is absorbed to an extent that depends on the wavelength of the radiation and the thickness and nature of the medium. If $d\Phi$ is the change in *radiant or *luminous flux of a parallel beam of monochromatic radiation in passing through a small thickness dl of an absorbing medium, then

$$a = \frac{1}{\Phi}\frac{d\Phi}{dl}, \text{ i.e. } \frac{\Phi_x}{\Phi_0} = e^{-ax},$$

where Φ_0 is the initial flux and Φ_x the flux after a distance x.

This equation is known as *Bouguer's law* or *Lambert's law* of absorption. It only applies in practice if factors such as reflection and scattering are negligible or can be corrected for. (*See also* linear attenuation coefficient.) Units: m^{-1}.

For X-ray absorption it is often more convenient to consider the mass per unit area, rather than the thickness of the absorbing radiation. The corresponding coefficient is known as the *mass absorption coefficient*. It is equal to a/ρ, where ρ is the density of the material.

linear accelerator (linac). A particle *accelerator in which electrons or protons are accelerated along a straight evacuated chamber by an electric field of radio frequency produced by a *klystron or *magnetron. In older machines, cylindrical electrodes (or *drift tubes*) of the r.f. supply are aligned coaxially with the chamber. Keeping in phase with the r.f. supply, the charged particles are accelerated in the gaps between the electrodes.

Modern high-energy linacs are usually travelling-wave accelerators in which particles are accelerated by the electric component of a *travelling wave set up ın a *waveguide. No drift tubes are used, the r.f. being boosted at regular intervals along the chamber length by means of klystrons. Only a small magnetic field, supplied by magnetic lenses between the r.f. cavities, is required to focus the particles and maintain them in a straight line. Typical rates of energy gain in a linac are 7 MeV per metre (electrons) and 1·5 MeV m^{-1} (protons).

linear attenuation coefficient. *Syn.* (linear) extinction coefficient. Symbol: μ. A measure of the ability of a medium to diffuse and absorb radiation. If a collimated beam of radiation is passing through the medium it loses intensity due to absorption and scattering. The linear attenuation coefficient is defined by the equation

$$\mu = -\frac{1}{\Phi}\frac{d\Phi}{dl},$$

where $d\Phi$ is the decrease in *luminous or *radiant flux Φ passing through a section dl of the material perpendicular to its face; μ has units of m^{-1}. The part of the linear attenuation coefficient not due to absorption is sometimes called the *scattering coefficient*. *Compare* linear absorption coefficient.

linear circuit. *Syn.* analog circuit. A circuit in which the output is a continuously varying function of the input. *Compare* digital circuit.

linear extinction coefficient. *See* linear attenuation coefficient.

linear inverter. *See* inverter.

linear motor. A type of *induction motor in which stator and rotor are linear and parallel rather than cylindrical and coaxial.

linear stopping power. *See* stopping power.

line defect. *See* defect.

line frequency. *See* television.

line of flux (or of force). An imaginary line whose direction at all points along its length is that of the electric or magnetic field at those points. *See* field; vector field.

line spectrum. *See* spectrum.

line voltage. *See* voltage between lines.

linkage. Of magnetic flux. A measure of the flux and the number of turns of the coil or circuit with which it links. Quantitatively, it is the product of the number of lines of magnetic flux and the number of turns of the coil or circuit through which they pass. This is sometimes called a *line-turn* (or *maxwell-turn*).

liquefaction of gases. The following methods for the liquefaction of gas are available: (1) The application of high pressure after cooling the gas below its critical temperature as in *cascade liquefaction. (2) The Joule–Kelvin effect in which gas at high pressure is cooled by expansion through a porous plug or throttle valve as in the *Linde process. (3) Adiabatic expansion in which a compressed gas is cooled by performing external work. (4) Adiabatic desorption in which the gas is adsorbed in cooled charcoal and further cooling produced when the gas is removed adiabatically.

liquid column manometers. Open liquid column *manometers are based on the U-tube of liquid which measures the pressure difference between the two sides. If the difference in vertical level of the surfaces of the liquid is h and its density is ρ, the applied pressure difference is $h\rho g$ (g being the acceleration of free fall).

The mercury *barometer is a special case in which one pressure is zero. When measuring very high pressures (e.g. 100 atmospheres) which would need a prohibitively great difference in height, several U-tubes of mercury are used in tandem

221

with either compressed air or a light liquid in between.

liquid drop model. A model of the nucleus in which the nuclear matter is regarded as being continuous. The interactions between *nucleons are thought of as being analogous to those between molecules in a liquid. As in a liquid drop, the net effect of the interaction of particles near the surface of the nucleus is interpreted as a *surface tension which maintains the shape of the nucleus. The liquid drop model is most applicable to heavy nuclei and is used in the theory of nuclear *fission.

Lissajous's figures. The displacement pattern traced out by the superposition of two vibrations in directions at right angles to each other. These figures can be constructed graphically; or they may be obtained practically using either a mechanical device or a cathode-ray oscilloscope. Examples are illustrated for various frequency ratios and for phase differences between 0 and π. The figures can be used to identify phase

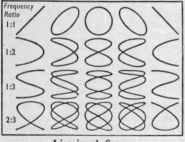

Lissajous's figures

relationship of two vibrations of the same frequency and in verifying that two given vibrations are of the same frequency.

lithium fluoride dosimetry. *See* dosimetry.

litre. A unit of volume formerly defined as the volume occupied by a mass of 1 kg of pure water at its maximum density and under standard atmospheric pressure. This volume is equal to 1·000 028 decimetres cubed. Subsequently the litre was defined as a special name for the decimetre cubed, but owing to confusion between the two definitions the unit is not recommended for scientific purpose, although the millilitre (ml) is still used synonymously with the cc where great accuracy is not implied.

Lloyd's mirror. A mirror for producing interference fringes in overlapping beams – one direct and the other after grazing reflection.

load (electrical). (1) A device or material in which signal power is dissipated or received, i.e. a device which receives or absorbs power from a *transducer, machine, generator, or electronic circuit, or the material to be heated by dielectric and induction heating. (2) The power delivered by a machine, generator, or electronic circuit or device.

loaded concrete. Concrete containing material of high atomic number or capture cross section, such as barium, iron, or lead, to increase its effectiveness as a radiation shield in *nuclear reactors.

load impedance. The *impedance presented by a *load to the *driver circuit.

load line. A line drawn on the graph of a family of *characteristics, showing the graphical relationship between voltage and current for the particular *load of the circuit under consideration.

local oscillator. *See* superheterodyne receiver.

logarithmic decrement. Symbol λ. The natural logarithm of the ratio of the amplitudes of successive oscillations that are decaying due to the presence of frictional forces; i.e.

$$\lambda = \log_e a_1 - \log_e a_2 = \log_e a_2 - \log_e a_3$$
$$= \log_e a_{n-1} - \log_e a_n$$

and therefore

$$\lambda = \frac{\log_e a_1 - \log_e a_n}{n - 1}.$$

logic circuit. A circuit designed to perform a particular logical function based on the concepts of 'and', 'either-or', 'neither-nor', etc. Normally these circuits operate between two discrete voltage levels, i.e. high and low logic levels, and are described as binary logic circuits. Logic using three or more logic levels is possible but not common. Binary circuits are extensively used in *computers to carry out instructions and arithmetical processes, and may be formed from discrete components or, more commonly, from *integrated circuits. Families of integrated logic circuits exist based on bipolar transistors or *field-effect transistors. The basic *gates are:

(1) *AND circuit*. A circuit with two or more inputs and one output in which the output signal is high if and only if all the inputs are high simultaneously.

(2) *Inverter (NOT gate)*. A circuit with one input whose output is high if the input is low and vice versa.

(3) *NAND circuit*. A circuit with two or more inputs and one output, whose output is high if any one or more of the inputs is low, and low if all the inputs are high.

(4) *NOR circuit*. A circuit with two or more inputs and one output, whose output is high if and only if all the inputs are low.

(5) *OR circuit*. A circuit with two or more inputs and one output whose output is high if any one or more of the inputs are high.

(6) *Exclusive OR circuit*. A circuit with two or more inputs and one output whose output is high if any one or more of the inputs (but not all) are low.

These circuits are for use with *positive logic*: that is the high voltage level represents a logical 1 and low a logical 0.

Negative logic has high level representing a logical 0 and low a logical 1. The same circuits may be used in negative logic, but become the complements of the positive logic circuits, i.e. a positive OR circuit becomes a negative AND circuit.

longitudinal aberrations. Aberration distances measured along the principal axis. In *chromatic aberration it is the distance between the foci for the two standard colours, e.g. F and C. In *spherical aberration, it is the distance from the paraxial focus to the intersection of a zonal ray with the axis.

longitudinal mass. In special *relativity theory. The ratio of force to acceleration in the direction of the existing velocity of a particle, expressed by

$$m_l = \frac{m_o}{(1 - \beta^2)^{\frac{1}{2}}}.$$

where m_o is the rest mass of the particle and $\beta = v/c$ is its velocity expressed as a fraction of the velocity of light. *Compare* transverse mass.

longitudinal strain. *See* strain.

longitudinal waves. Waves in which the particles of the transmitting medium are displaced along the direction of propagation. The velocity, c, of longitudinal waves in a bar is given by $c = \sqrt{E/\rho}$ where E is Young's modulus and ρ is the density; the corresponding equation for longitudinal waves in a fluid is $c = \sqrt{k/\rho}$ where k is the bulk modulus. Sound waves in a gas form the chief example of longitudinal wave motion. *See* velocity of sound.

long-tailed pair. Two matched *bipolar transistors that have their *emitters coupled together, with a common emitter bias resistor acting as a constant current source. The larger the bias resistance, the more nearly it resembles a constant current source (because of the relatively large voltage developed across it). Originally the name was given to matched thermionic valves with the cathodes connected to a common cathode bias resistor. The long-tailed pair forms the basis of most *differential amplifiers.

loop (feedback and control). A closed circuit in the form of a loop between the input and output terminals of a control system, by means of which part of the output signal may be fed back to the input signal to control the output in a desired manner.

loop aerial. *Syn.* frame aerial. An *aerial that is essentially a coil having one or more turns of wire and having an axial length which is usually small compared with its other linear dimensions. It is commonly employed in radio direction finders and in small portable radio receivers.

Lorentz–Fitzgerald contraction. *See* relativity.

Lorentz force. The force acting on a moving charge q in magnetic and electric fields is given by:

$$F = q(E + v \times B)$$

where F is the force, E the electric field, and $v \times B$ the *vector product of the particle's velocity and the *magnetic flux density.

The magnetic contribution to this force is often called the Lorentz force and this, in non-vector notation, is given by:

$$F = qvB \sin \theta,$$

where θ is the angle that the direction of motion of the particle makes with the magnetic field. The force acts in a direction that is perpendicular to both the direction of motion and the magnetic field.

Lorentz transformation equations. A set of equations for transforming the posi-

tion-motion parameter from an observer at a point $O(x, y, z)$ to an observer at $O'(x', y', z')$, moving relative to one another. The equations replace the *Galilean transformation equations of Newtonian mechanics in *relativity problems. If the x-axis is chosen to pass through OO' and the time of an event is t and t' in the *frame of reference of the observers at O and O' respectively (where the zeros of their time scales were the instant that O and O' coincided) the equations are

$$x' = \beta(x - vt)$$
$$y' = y$$
$$z' = z$$
$$t' = \beta(t - vx/c^2)$$

where v is the relative velocity of separation of O, O', c is the velocity of electromagnetic radiation, and β is the function $(1 - v^2/c^2)^{-\frac{1}{2}}$.

Loschmidt's number. The number of molecules present in 1 cm^3 of an ideal gas at S.T.P. ($2 \cdot 687\ 19 \times 10^{19}$ per cc.) *See* Avogadro constant.

loss. *See* core loss.

loss angle. Of a capacitor or dielectric when subjected to alternating electric stress. The angle by which the angle of *lead of the current is less than 90° when the applied voltage is sinusoidal. It is due mainly to dielectric *hysteresis loss.

loss factor. (1) The ratio of the average power loss to the power loss at peak load in a line, circuit, or device. (2) The product of the *power factor and the relative *permittivity of a *dielectric. It is proportional to the heat generated in a material in a given alternating field.

lossy. Of or relating to a material or device, such as a dielectric or transmission line, that dissipates energy with a high degree of attenuation.

loudness. The magnitude of the sensation produced when a sound reaches the ear.

Although related to intensity there is no simple connection between the two. The basis of loudness scales is the *Weber–Fechner law* which states that the sensation is proportional to the logarithm of the stimulus. In the decibel scale of intensity level, the intensity of a sound is logarithmically related to the threshold intensity at the same frequency. This suffers from the disadvantage that the sensitivity of the ear to changes of intensity varies with frequency. The *phon scale of equivalent loudness overcomes this by relating the intensity of a sound to a fixed reference tone of defined intensity and frequency. The phon scale is widely used.

loudness level. A measure of the strength of a sound as expressed by the *sound pressure level of a pure tone of specified frequency that is judged, by a normal listener, to be equally as loud as the sound.

loudspeaker. A device in which electrical energy is converted into sound energy. It is the final unit in any broadcast receiver or sound reproducer. Although its action is the reverse of that of the microphone it is designed to handle far greater power so that its sound output is audible over a considerable area. In the most common types of loudspeaker the current is passed through a small coil fixed to the centre of a diaphragm and moving in an annular gap across which is a strong magnetic field. Alternating current in the coil causes the diaphragm to vibrate at the same frequency and emit sound waves. For high efficiency a small diaphragm is used at the mouth of a large *exponential horn. Although the horn gives suitable loading to the diaphragm it is impractical for most indoor work on account of its size. Instead, a speaker is used having a conical diaphragm, of elliptical or circular cross section, with the speech coil at its apex. The cone is made of stiff paper and is supported round its edge by a metal frame. The magnetic field is produced either by a permanent magnet or an electromagnet and the coil is held in position in the centre of the gap. The cone should be set in a large *baffle to prevent direct passage of sound from front to back and so improve the low frequency response. In most commercial sound reproducers the cabinet forms the baffle.

lower sideband. Of an amplitude-modulated wave. The *sideband containing all the frequencies below the frequency of the *carrier wave.

low frequency (L F). *See* frequency band.

low-pass filter. *See* filter.

low voltage. In electrical power transmission and distribution. A voltage which does not exceed 250 volts.

lumen. Symbol: lm. The *SI unit of *luminous flux, defined as the luminous flux emitted by a uniform point source, of intensity one candela (cd), in a cone of solid angle one steradian. Thus 1 lm = $(1/4\pi)$ cd.

luminance. Symbol: L_v, L. The brightness, for a specified direction, of a point source of light or a point on a surface that is receiving light. For sources of light it is defined as the luminous intensity, I_v, per unit projected area, i.e. $L_v = dI_v/dA. \cos \theta$, where A is the area and θ is the angle between the surface and the specified direction. For illuminated surfaces it is defined as the illuminance (E_v) per unit solid angle (Ω), $L_v = dE_v/d\Omega$. The illuminance is taken over an area perpendicular to the direction of the incident radiation. The general equation of luminous intensity, applying to both a point source and a point receptor, is

$$L_v = \frac{d^2\Phi_v}{d\Omega . dA . \cos \theta},$$

where Φ_v is the *luminous flux. Luminance is measured in candela per square metre. *Compare* radiance.

luminance signal. *See* colour television.

luminescence. The emission of electromagnetic radiation from a substance as a result of any non-thermal process. The term is also applied to the radiation itself and is usually used for visible radiation. Luminescence is produced when atoms are excited, as by other radiation, electrons, etc., and then decay to their *ground state. If the luminescence ceases as soon as the source of energy is removed the phenomenon is *fluorescence*. If it persists the phenomenon is *phosphorescence*.

If certain solids are subjected to ionizing radiation electrons may be released within the solid and trapped at *defects. These electrons may be released when the solid is heated and the energy produced is emitted as visible radiation. This is known as *thermoluminescence*.

Luminescence can also be produced by the friction of solids (*triboluminescence*) and chemical reaction (*chemiluminescence*). *Compare* incandescence.

luminosity. The attribute of a source of light that gives the visual sensation of brightness. The luminosity depends on the power emitted by the source, i.e. on the *radiant flux, and also on the fact that the sensitivity of the eye varies for different wavelengths. *See also* luminous quantities.

luminous efficacy. A property relating *luminous flux to *radiant flux for radiation or for a source.

(1) Symbol: K. The ratio of the luminous flux, Φ_v, of a radiation to its radiant flux, Φ_e. If monochromatic radiation is considered the property is called *spectral luminous efficacy*. Symbol: $K(\lambda)$.

$$K(\lambda) = K_m V(\lambda),$$

where $V(\lambda)$ is the *spectral luminous efficiency. K_m is the spectral luminous

efficacy when $V(\lambda) = 1$, i.e. the maximum spectral luminous efficacy.

(2) Symbol: η_v, η. The ratio of the luminous flux emitted by a source to the power it consumes. (*Compare* radiant efficiency.)

Luminous efficacy is measured in lumen per watt.

luminous efficiency. Symbol: V. A property of *polychromatic radiation defined by the equation:

$$V = \frac{\int \Phi_{e\lambda} V(\lambda)\, d\lambda}{\int \Phi_{e\lambda}\, d\lambda},$$

where $\Phi_{e\lambda}$ is the *radiant flux of a particular wavelength λ and $V(\lambda)$ the *spectral luminous efficiency of this wavelength. The term $\int \Phi_{e\lambda} V(\lambda)\, d\lambda$ weighs the radiant flux of the radiation according to the sensitivity of a standard observer for its wavelengths. It is dimensionless.

luminous energy. Symbol: Q_v, Q. The product of luminous flux and its duration: $Q_v = \int \Phi_v\, dt$. It is measured in lumen-seconds.

luminous exitance. Symbol: M_v, M. The *luminous flux leaving a surface per unit area. It was formerly called the *luminous emittance*. It is measured in lumen per square metre. *Compare* radiant exitance.

luminous flux. Symbol: Φ_v, Φ. The rate of flow of radiant energy as evaluated by the luminous sensation that it produces. The luminous flux is obtained from the *radiant flux of the source corrected according to the effect it has on the observer, i.e. according to the spectral sensitivity of the receptor. For monochromatic radiation the luminous flux is given by: $\Phi_v = K_m \Phi_e V(\lambda)$, where K_m is a constant relating the units of luminous flux to those of radiant flux. Φ_e is the radiant flux, and $V(\lambda)$ the *spectral luminous efficiency. For polychromatic radiation the radiant flux will generally vary with wavelength, and luminous flux can be defined by:

$$\Phi_v = K_m \int \frac{d\Phi_e}{d\lambda} V(\lambda) \, d\lambda$$

where $(d\Phi_e/d\lambda) \, d\lambda$ is the radiant flux of light with wavelengths in the range $\lambda \to \lambda + d\lambda$. The constant K_m has the value of 680 lumens per watt (for photopic vision). It is the maximum spectral *luminous efficacy. Luminous flux is measured in lumens.

luminous intensity. Symbol: I_v, I. The *luminous flux emitted per unit solid angle by a point source in a given direction. It is measured in candela. A source may radiate unequally in different directions and the direction has to be specified. If the luminous intensity is averaged over all directions it is called the *mean spherical intensity*. For extended sources the luminous intensity per unit area, or *luminance, is used. *Compare* radiant intensity.

luminous quantities. Physical quantities used in *photometry, such as *luminous flux, *luminance, etc., in which energies of light are evaluated by an observer (*see* luminosity). They are distinguished from their corresponding *radiant quantities by adding a subscript v (for visual) to their symbols.

Lummer–Brodhun photometer. *See* photometry.

Lummer–Gehrcke plate. An interferometer using a parallel-sided glass or quartz plate of considerable thickness in which multiple reflections occur, giving rise to interference effects. It gives a *resolving power of the order of 10^6.

lumped parameter. Any parameter of a circuit which, for the purposes of circuit analysis, can be treated as a single parameter throughout the frequency range under consideration, e.g. inductance, capacitance, resistance, etc.

lux. Symbol: lx. The *SI unit of *illumination, defined as the illumination of one lumen uniformly over an area of one metre squared.

Lyman series. *See* hydrogen spectrum.

M

Mach angle. If a body moves, with a supersonic velocity V, through a fluid from a point X to a point Y in time t, then when the body is at Y the spherical

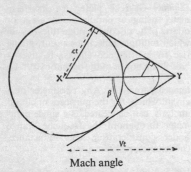

Mach angle

pressure wave originating from X will have a radius ct where c is the local velocity of sound in the fluid. Similarly the pressure waves from the other points between X and Y will have corresponding radii such that all the spherical pressure waves combine to form a right-conical wave front with its vertex at Y. The semiangle of the cone (β) is called the Mach angle, where

$$\beta = \sin^{-1}\frac{ct}{Vt} = \sin^{-1}\frac{c}{V} = \sin^{-1}\frac{1}{M},$$

and M is the *Mach number.

machine. A device for doing work. In a machine a comparatively small force called the *effort* is used to overcome a larger force (e.g. the weight lifted by a system of pulleys) called the *load*.

The ratio

$$\frac{\text{distance moved by effort}}{\text{distance moved by load}}$$

is the *velocity ratio* of the machine. The ratio

$$\frac{\text{load}}{\text{effort}}$$

is the *mechanical advantage* or *force ratio*.

The fraction

$$\frac{\text{work done on load}}{\text{work done by effort}}$$

is the *efficiency* and is necessarily less than 1. It is usually multiplied by 100 and expressed as a percentage.

$$\text{Efficiency} = \frac{\text{load's motion} \times \text{load}}{\text{effort's motion} \times \text{effort}}$$

$$= \frac{\text{mechanical advantage}}{\text{velocity ratio}}$$

Mach number. Symbol: M. The ratio of the relative velocity of a body and fluid to the local velocity of sound in the fluid. A Mach number in excess of 1 indicates a supersonic velocity; in excess of 5 it is said to be hypersonic. It appears in all problems of flow in which compressibility is of importance. The resistance to motion of a body moving at high speed in a fluid of small viscosity is in general a function of both Mach and Reynolds numbers. *See also* Mach angle.

McLeod gauge. A mercury-in-glass vacuum pressure gauge in which a known large volume of gas is compressed into a small volume at which the pressure, now much larger, is measured. Being based on Boyle's law, the gauge cannot be used when condensable vapours are present. It will work down to 10^{-5} mm of mercury and is an absolute instrument.

magic numbers. Certain values of the number of protons (Z) in a nucleus and/or the number of neutrons (N) which produce unusual stability in that nucleus. These values of Z and/or N are 2, 8, 20, 28, 50, 82, and 126. The energy required to remove a nucleon from a nucleus with magic N or Z is higher than for neighbouring nuclei with non-magic values. *See also* shell model.

magnet. A body possessing the property of *magnetism. Magnets are either temporary or permanent. *See also* electromagnet.

magnetic amplifier. A *transductor so arranged that a small controlling d.c. input can produce large changes in coupled a.c. circuits. This a.c. can be wholly or partially rectified, and if necessary fed back in a positive or negative direction, to give wide variations in the controlling conditions and output.

magnetic balance. A device used for the direct determination of attraction or repulsion between poles. A long bar magnet is suspended on a knife edge system so that it takes up a horizontal position, and the force is applied to one end by bringing a magnet pole near to it, the magnet being restored to horizontal by direct addition of weights or the action of a movable rider.

magnetic bottle. Any configuration of magnetic fields used to confine a *plasma, especially a linear device in which the ends are stoppered with *magnetic mirrors. *See* fusion reactor.

magnetic circuit. The completely closed path described by a given set of lines of *magnetic flux.

magnetic constant. Symbol: μ_0. The absolute *permeability of *free space, with the formally defined value:

$$\mu_0 = 4\pi \times 10^{-7} \text{ H m}^{-1}$$
$$= 1 \cdot 256\,64 \times 10^{-6} \text{ H m}^{-1}.$$

See rationalization of electric and magnetic quantities.

magnetic crack detection. If a magnetizing field is applied to a ferromagnetic body there is often leakage of lines of force, or uneven distribution of magneti-

zation, at points where discontinuities occur at or near the surface. These discontinuities become evident when the surface is painted with a magnetic fluid consisting of very finely divided particles of iron or of magnetic oxide of iron dispersed in oil. The particles concentrate above the discontinuities. *See also* flaw detection.

magnetic difference of potential. The difference between the magnetic states of two points in a magnetic field. It equals the line-integral of the magnetizing force between the two points.

magnetic disk. *See* disk.

magnetic drum. *See* drum.

magnetic effects. Optical phenomena resulting from the presence of a magnetic field, such as the *Zeeman, *Kerr, *Faraday, *Voigt, and *Cotton–Mouton effects.

magnetic element. *See* geomagnetism.

magnetic equator. *See* aclinic line.

magnetic field. The *field of force surrounding a magnetic pole or a current flowing through a conductor, in which there is a *magnetic flux.

magnetic field strength. Symbol: H. Formerly called magnetic intensity. The magnitude of a *magnetic field, measured in A m^{-1}. *See also* magnetomotive force.

magnetic flux. Symbol: Φ. A measure of the total size of a *magnetic field, defined as the scalar product of the flux density and the area. It is measured in *webers.

magnetic flux density. *Syn.* magnetic induction. Symbol: B. The magnetic flux passing through unit area of a *magnetic field in a direction at right angles to the magnetic force. The vector product of the magnetic flux density and the current in a conductor gives the force per unit length of conductor. It is measured in teslas.

magnetic hysteresis. *See* hysteresis, magnetic.

magnetic induction. *See* magnetic flux density.

magnetic intensity. *See* magnetic field strength.

magnetic interval. *See* palaeomagnetism.

magnetic leakage. The loss of *lines of force from the core of a transformer or transductor, which reduces the overall efficiency of operation. The *magnetic leakage coefficient* (σ) is defined by:

$$\sigma = \frac{\text{total magnetic flux}}{\text{effective (or useful) magnetic flux}}.$$

σ usually exceeds unity on account of magnetic leakage. It follows that:

$$\sigma = \frac{\text{useful flux} + \text{leakage flux}}{\text{useful flux}}$$

$$= 1 + \frac{\text{leakage flux}}{\text{useful flux}}.$$

A typical value for σ in electrical machines is 1·2.

magnetic lens. *See* electron lens.

magnetic meridians. Imaginary lines drawn along the earth's surface in the direction of the horizontal component of the earth's field at all points along their length. They converge on the magnetic poles of the earth. *See* geomagnetism.

magnetic mirror. A region of high magnetic field strength that reflects particles from a plasma back into a *magnetic bottle. *See* fusion reactor.

magnetic moment. Symbol: *m*. A property possessed by a *permanent magnet

or a current-carrying coil, used as a measure of the magnetic strength. *Magnetic dipole moment* is the torque experienced when the magnet or coil is set with its axis at right angles to a magnetic field of unit size. It is measured in weber metres. *Electromagnetic moment* is the torque experienced when the magnet or coil is set with its axis at right angles to a magnetic flux density of unit size. It is measured in ampere metres squared. *See also* magneton.

magnetic monopoles. Hypothetical magnetic particles (analogous to the electrical particles, the electron and proton) with a magnetic charge of either north or south. They have been postulated on conservation and symmetry principles: an electric particle gives rise to an electric field and when set into motion gives rise to a magnetic field; a magnetic particle should give rise to a magnetic field and, in motion, produce an electric field. Neither *quantum theory nor classical electromagnetic theory bars the existence of the magnetic monopole but it would have profound effects on the theoretical basis of *quantum electrodynamics. *Maxwell's equations would prove completely symmetrical if such particles did exist.

magnetic potential. *See* magnetomotive force.

magnetic quantum number. *See* atomic orbital; spin.

magnetic recording. A continuously moving iron oxide impregnated plastic tape is longitudinally magnetized so that variations in magnetization represent variations that occur in the audio-frequency currents. If the tape is fed past suitable electromagnets, currents are induced in the coils corresponding to the original magnetizing currents. In practice microphone currents are amplified electronically and fed to coils surrounding magnetic poles shaped so that a very small length of the recording medium completes the *magnetic circuit. The recording medium is moved at a uniform speed past the recording head. A reproducing head of similar design to the recording head is used to transfer the magnetic flux variations into small current variations which are then amplified and fed to a loudspeaker system.

magnetic resistance. *See* reluctance.

magnetic saturation. *See* saturation.

magnetic screening. An area may be screened from magnetic effects by enclosing it with material of high*permeability.

magnetic shell. A thin iron sheet magnetized across its thickness. It can be considered as an infinite number of small bar magnets.

magnetic shunt. A piece of magnetic material mounted near a magnet in an electrical measuring instrument, and having means whereby its position relative to the magnet can be adjusted so that the useful *magnetic flux of the magnet can be varied.

magnetic storms. *See* geomagnetism.

magnetic susceptibility. *See* susceptibility.

magnetic tape. A plastic strip coated with iron oxide, used for *magnetic recording or on which binary information can be stored in the form of rows of magnetized dots, typically 7 or 9 across the tape, and 200 to 1600 per inch along it.

magnetic viscosity. In most ferromagnetic substances there is a time lag between application of a magnetic field and the resulting magnetization, which is accounted for by the eddy currents induced in the substance. In some materials, however, the persistence and magnitude of the change of magnetization are much too great to be accounted for in this way,

and this phenomenon is called magnetic viscosity.

magnetic well. A configuration of magnetic fields for containing a *plasma in experimental fusion devices. *See* fusion reactor.

magnetism. All materials have some magnetic properties. *Diamagnetism is a weak effect common to all substances and results from the orbital motion of electrons. In certain substances this is masked by a stronger effect, *paramagnetism, due to electron *spin. Some paramagnetic materials, such as iron, also display *ferromagnetism. *See also* ferrimagnetism; antiferromagnetism; palaeomagnetism.

magnetization. Symbol: M. The difference between the ratio of the *magnetic flux (B) to the *magnetic constant (μ_0) and the *magnetic field strength (H): $M = B/\mu_0 - H$. It is measured in amperes per metre.

magnetization curves. The magnetic properties of ferromagnetic substances are usually studied by drawing curves relating the magnetization of the material to the strength and variations of the magnetizing field.

magneto. An electrical generator, usually one in which the *magnetic field is provided by a permanent magnet.

magnetocaloric effect. *Syn.* thermomagnetic effect. A fall in temperature occurring when a substance suffers *adiabatic demagnetization. It increases as the initial temperature of the substance is lowered so that the effect has been used for the production of temperatures in the neighbourhood of absolute zero.

magnetodamping. An increase in internal damping of acoustic vibrations in a metal such as nickel when it is subjected to a strong magnetic field.

magnetohydrodynamics (MHD). The branch of physics dealing with the behaviour of a conducting fluid under the influence of a *magnetic flux. The motion of the fluid gives rise to an induced electric field that interacts with the applied magnetic field, causing a change in the motion itself.

A magnetohydrodynamic (or *magnetoplasmadynamic*) *generator* is a source of electrical power in which a flame or plasma flows between the poles of a magnet. The free electrons in the flame constitute a current when they flow, under the influence of the magnetic field, between electrodes in the flame. The concentration of free electrons in the flame is increased by adding elements of low *ionization potential, such as sodium or potassium.

magnetometer. An instrument for comparing *magnetic field strengths (H) at different places, or for comparing *magnetic moments (m). It usually consists of a short magnet, freely suspended by a jewelled pivot as in a compass needle, and carrying a long pointer which moves over a graduated circle. The pivoted needle is deflected from its N–S direction by a magnet placed near to it. In the broadside position (with the magnet in an E–W direction, due N or S of the needle) $m/H = (d^2 + l^2)^{\frac{3}{2}} \tan \theta$, where d is the distance of the centre of the magnet from the needle, $2l$ the length of the magnet between its poles, θ the angle of deflection of the needle. If l is small compared with d then $m/H = d^3 \tan \theta$. In the end-on position (with the magnet in an E–W direction and due E or W of the needle) $m/H = \{(d^2 - l^2)^2/2d\} \tan \theta$, or, if l is small compared with d then $m/H = (d^3 \tan \theta)/2$. By measuring θ for various positions of the magnetometer, using the same magnet, or by using two or more magnets in the same positions with respect to the needle, the measurements mentioned above can be made by use of the equations given.

magnetomotive force (mmf). Symbol: F_m. Formerly called *magnetic potential*. The circular integral of the *magnetic field strength round a closed path:

$$F_m = \oint H \, dx.$$

It is measured in amperes or ampere-turns.

magneton. A fundamental constant for the intrinsic *magnetic moment of an electron. The circulatory current created by the angular momentum p of an electron moving in its orbit produces a magnetic moment $\mu = ep/2m$ where e and m are the charge and mass of the electron. By substituting the quantized relation $p = jh/2\pi$ (h = the Planck constant; j = magnetic quantum number), $\mu = jeh/4\pi m$. When j is taken as unity the quantity $\mu_B = eh/4\pi m$ is called the *Bohr magneton*, its value being $9.274\,096 \times 10^{-24}$ A m^2. Exactly the same moment is produced by electron spin if the electron has angular momentum $\frac{1}{2}h/2\pi$. The *nuclear magneton* is given by $\mu_N = (m_e/m_p)\mu_B$, where m_p is the mass of the proton. The value of the nuclear magneton is 5.0503×10^{-27} A m^2. The magnetic moment of a proton is, in fact, $2.792\,45$ nuclear magnetons. The magneton is also often given a symbol m_B or m_N.

magnetoplasmadynamic generator. See magnetohydrodynamics.

magnetoresistance. The change in electrical resistance which ferromagnetic substances undergo when magnetized. It is closely associated with the change in resistivity (*elastoresistance) caused by tension within the elastic limit of the materials, and is also associated with their *magnetostriction.

magnetosphere. The elongated region enclosing the earth's magnetic field and radiation belts and occurring as a result of the interaction of the *solar wind and the magnetic field. A bow-shaped wave separates the magnetosphere boundary (the *magnetopause*) from the solar wind. The interaction causes the magnetosphere to extend a considerable distance in the direction away from the sun.

magnetostriction. The mechanical deformation of a ferromagnetic material when it is subject to a magnetic field. The change occurs in a direction parallel to the field. Conversely, a mechanical extension or compression increases or decreases the permeability of a ferromagnetic rod. Various types of oscillator and transducer are operated by magnetostriction.

magnetron. An *electron tube that produces high-frequency microwave oscillations. A cylindrical cathode is surrounded by a coaxial cylindrical anode with *cavity resonators in its inner surface. The tube is in a magnetic field *B*, parallel to the cylindrical axis. Electrons from the heated cathode travel radially to the anode in the absence of a magnetic field. A sufficiently large magnetic field turns most of the electrons back towards the cathode resulting in a sheath of electrons rotating about the cathode. Due to the structure of the anode, the fields associated with this electron cloud induce radio-frequency fields in the resonant cavities and this field further interacts with the electrons. Depending on the

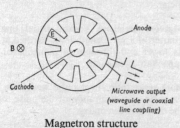

Magnetron structure

point of interaction with the R F field electrons either travel towards the anode

and give up kinetic energy to the field, or they are turned back towards the cathode. The kinetic energy received from electrons by the R F field is greater than the power required to turn electrons back to the cathode and the result is a net power gain. The closed nature of the circuit provides built-in positive feedback and oscillations can occur. The frequency of the oscillations depends critically on the geometrical structure of the anode and the magnitudes of the electric and magnetic fields. The electrons returned to the cathode cause *back heating* of the cathode reducing the heater current required when the tube is running, and also stimulate *secondary emission of electrons, which forms a significant portion of the total electron emission.

magnetron effect. *See* thermionic valve.

magnification. (1) *Syn.* lateral magnification. The ratio y'/y where y is the height of the object perpendicular to the axis, and y' the corresponding height of the image. (2) *See* magnifying power.

magnifying glass. *Syn.* magnifier. *See* microscope.

magnifying power. *Syn.* instrument magnification. The ratio of the size of the retinal image of an object seen with an instrument to the size of the retinal image of the object seen with the unaided eye; that is, the ratio of the angle subtended at the eye by the image of the object as seen through the instrument, to the angle subtended by the object (*a*) *in situ* for *telescopes (*b*) when placed 25 cm from the eye for *microscopes.

magnitude. A means of expressing the brightness of astronomical bodies on a logarithmic scale. Two bodies of luminous intensities I_1, I_2 will have magnitudes m_1, m_2 related by

$$m_1 - m_2 = 2 \cdot 5 \log (I_2/I_1).$$

Thus a decrease of five magnitudes

means a hundred fold increase in luminous intensity.

An *apparent magnitude* is the magnitude as observed, correcting for atmospheric absorption. The reference point of the scale has been fixed as $m = 0$ (in the visible region of the spectrum) when $I = 2.65 \times 10^{-6}$ lux.

An *absolute magnitude* M is the apparent magnitude the body would have at a distance of 10 parsecs from the observer. Thus $M = (m - 5) + 5 \log x$ where x is the distance of the body in parsecs.

Magnox. A group of proprietary magnesium alloys used to encase the *fuel elements in certain types of *nuclear reactors. (*See* gas-cooled reactor.) Magnox A consists of magnesium containing 0.8 % aluminium with 0.01 % beryllium.

Magnus effect. If a cylinder or sphere rotates about its axis while at the same time it is in relative motion with a fluid, there is a resultant force on the cylinder or sphere perpendicular to the direction of relative motion. A spinning object, such as a golf ball, will thus be deflected from its flight path.

main sequence star. *See* Hertzsprung–Russell diagram.

main store. *See* memory.

Majorana force. *See* exchange force.

majority carrier. In a *semiconductor. The type of *carrier constituting more than half of the total charge carrier concentration.

making-current. Of a switch, *circuit-breaker, or similar apparatus. The peak value of the current (including any d.c. component) during the first cycle after the circuit is closed on a short-circuit.

Maksutov telescope. A telescope consisting of a concave spherical mirror, the *spherical aberration of which is reduced by a convexo-concave *meniscus positioned in front of the mirror.

Malter effect. If a layer of semiconductor of high *secondary emission ratio (e.g. caesium oxide) is separated by a thin film of insulator (e.g. aluminium oxide) from a metal plate, it can become strongly positively charged on electron bombardment. The potential may be up to 100 volts with an insulating layer of about 0.1 μm thick.

Malus's law. The intensity of transmitted light through a polarizer placed at an angle with the analyser varies as the square of the cosine of the angle.

Manganin. An alloy of 15–25 % Mn, 70–86 % Cu, and 2–5 % Ni that has a high electrical resistivity and low temperature coefficient of resistance. It is used for electrical resistances.

Mangin mirror. A diverging meniscus lens, silvered on the outer convex surface. A combined refraction and reflection results in a system corrected for spherical aberration and coma. It is used to throw out a parallel beam from a light source or to bring parallel light to a reasonably good focus.

manometer. A device for measuring a fluid pressure. *See* pressure gauges; liquid column manometers; micromanometer.

Marconi aerial. A vertical aerial one quarter of a wavelength long, earthed at its lower end through an inductive or capacitative reactance.

mark space ratio. In a pulse waveform, the ratio of the duration of the pulse to the time between pulses.

maser (*m*icrowave *a*mplification by *s*timulated *e*mission of *r*adiation). A class of microwave amplifiers and oscillators that operate by the same principles and have the same characteristics as the *laser, the beam occurring in the microwave region of the spectrum. They generate less *noise than other types of amplifier.

mask. In the manufacture of *semiconductor components and *integrated circuits, a means of shielding selected areas of the semiconductor during the various processing steps. The circuit layout is described on a set of photographic masks which are used during *photolithography processes to define the patterns of openings in the oxide layer through which the various diffusions are made, the windows through which the metal contacts are formed, and the pattern in which the desired metal interconnections are etched.

Mason's hygrometer. A *hygrometer of the wet and dry bulb type used as the standard British instrument. The instrument must be exposed to an air draught of 1 to 1·5 metres/second.

mass. The quantity of matter in a body, indicating how many times larger or smaller is the acceleration experienced by the body than that which would be experienced by a standard mass, e.g. the International Prototype kilogramme, under otherwise identical conditions. (*See also* weight.)

Mass varies with velocity in accordance with the principle of *relativity. Mass and *energy are interconvertible by Einstein's law.

mass absorption coefficient. *See* linear absorption coefficient.

mass action, law of. In a chemical reaction $aA + bB \rightarrow cC + dD$, the concentrations [A], [B], [C], and [D] at equilibrium are related by the equation:

$$\frac{[C]^c[D]^d}{[A]^a[B]^b} = K,$$

where K is the *equilibrium constant* for that reaction at a given temperature.

mass defect. The mass equivalent of the *binding energy of a nucleus.

Massieu function. Symbol: J. The negative of the *Helmholtz function divided by the thermodynamic temperature.

mass-luminosity law. A theoretical law relating the mass m and total outflow of radiation, or luminosity, L of normal stars: $\log L = 3·3 \log m$, where m and L are in *solar units.

mass moments. *See* centre of mass.

mass number. *Syn.* nucleon number. Symbol: A. The number of *nucleons in the nucleus of a particular atom. It is the number nearest to the atomic mass of a nuclide.

mass reactance. *See* reactance (acoustic).

mass resistivity. The product of the mass and electrical resistance of a conductor, divided by the square of its length.

mass spectrometer. An apparatus for separating streams of positive rays by application of electrostatic and electromagnetic deflecting fields. The stream is separated into a spectrum corresponding to particles with different ratios of charge to mass. J. J. Thomson used parallel electric and magnetic fields which produced parabolic traces the shape of which was dependent on the ratio of mass to charge. Aston, in his mass spectrometer, used fields at right angles to each other, the magnetic field being adjusted to give twice the deflection of the electric field, but in the opposite direction so that it focused the rays to form a sharp image of the slit. Different positions of the marks photographed on a plate in the focal plane correspond to particles with different ratios of charge to mass. Spectra of first, second, and third order are produced with atoms carrying one, two, and three positive charges respectively. The instrument provides an accurate method of determining the atomic weight of any element which can be made to produce a stream of positive rays.

mass stopping power. *See* stopping power.

master oscillator. An oscillator of high inherent frequency stability, used to establish the carrier frequency in radio transmission.

matched. In a network or transmission line. Having no *reflected waves at a termination or, in a waveguide, at any of the transverse sections.

materialization. The direct conversion of energy E into mass m according to Einstein's equation $E = mc^2$ (c = velocity of light), as in *pair production.

Mathiessen's rule. The product of the *resistivity and temperature coefficient of resistance of a metal is the same whether the metal be pure or impure. Normally impurities and alloying elements increase the resistance of a metal markedly, but this effect is accompanied by a corresponding decrease in change of resistance with temperature.

matrix mechanics. A branch of mechanics that originated simultaneously with but independently of *wave mechanics. It is equivalent to wave mechanics but in it the *wave functions of wave mechanics are replaced by *vectors in a suitable space (Hilbert space) and the observable things of the physical world, e.g. energy, momenta, coordinates, etc., are represented by matrices. The theory involves the idea that a measurement on a system disturbs, to some extent, the system itself. If two successive observations are made on an atomic system the result depends on the order in which the observations are made. Thus if p denotes

an observation of momentum and q an observation of position then $pq \neq qp$. Here p and q are not physical quantities but operators. In matrix mechanics they are matrices and obey the relationship $pq - qp = ih/2$. This leads to the quantum conditions for the system. The matrix elements are connected with the transition probabilities between various states of the system.

matter waves. *See* de Broglie waves.

maximum and minimum thermometer. An alcohol thermometer due to Six which records both the highest and the lowest temperatures reached since setting the thermometer. Movement of the mercury in the U-tube, due to the expansion or contraction of the alcohol in A, causes the mercury to push tiny steel indicators I along the tubes. These indicators remain in position if the mercury meniscus recedes, being held against the walls of the tube by tiny springs. The thermometer is reset by using an external magnet.

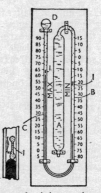

Maximum and minimum thermometer

maximum density of water. When water at 0° C is heated it contracts until the temperature is 4° C after which it expands normally. Owing to the hydrogen

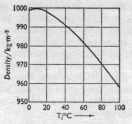

Maximum density of water

bonds between water molecules ice crystals have a very open three-dimensional tetrahedral structure. When ice melts, this structure collapses and the water molecules become closer packed; small aggregates of molecules can however continue to survive up to 4° C. Thus water has a maximum density at 4° C.

maxwell. Symbol: Mx. The *CGS-electromagnetic unit of magnetic flux, now replaced by the *weber. 1 Mx = 10^{-8} weber.

Maxwell–Boltzmann (or Maxwell's) distribution. *See* distribution of velocities.

Maxwell's bridge. An early form of inductance bridge. If the battery key K_1 is closed first followed by the ballistic galvanometer key K_2, no ballistic throw is observed for the balance condition

$$R_1 R_3 = R_2 R_4.$$

If K_2 is now closed before K_1 and there is still no ballistic throw, the balance condition

$$L = R_2 R_4 C$$

Maxwell's bridge

has been achieved and the value of L may be deduced. If the ballistic balance is not perfect the ratio R_1/R_2 must be altered and the double balancing repeated. The circuit may be set up using an alternating current source of electricity and headphones for detection.

Maxwell's demon. An imaginary creature to whom Maxwell assigned the task of operating a door in a partition dividing a volume containing gas at uniform temperature. The door was opened to enable fast molecules to move (say) from left to right through the partition. In this way, without expenditure of external work, the gas on the right could be made hotter than before and that on the left made cooler. This supposed violation of the second law of *thermodynamics has no material basis and is therefore extremely unlikely to occur.

Maxwell's equations. A series of classical equations connecting vector quantities applying to any point in a varying electric or magnetic field. The equations are:

$$\text{curl } H = \frac{\partial D}{\partial t} + j$$

$$\text{div } B = 0$$

$$\text{curl } E = -\frac{\partial B}{\partial t}$$

$$\text{div } D = \rho.$$

H is the *magnetic field strength, D is the *electric displacement, t is time, j is the current density, B is the *magnetic flux density, E is the *electric field strength, and ρ is volume density of charge. The equations apply to empty space, apart from the presence of dielectrics, conductors, or magnetizable bodies.

From these equations, Maxwell showed the interrelationship between electricity and magnetism: where a varying electric field exists there is also a varying magnetic field induced at right angles, and vice versa; the two form an electromagnetic field. He thus

237

demonstrated that each field vector obeys a wave equation and he deduced that light is propagated as electromagnetic waves. *See also* magnetic monopole.

Maxwell's formula. A formula connecting the relative permittivity ε_r of a medium with its refractive index n. If the medium is not ferromagnetic the formula is $\varepsilon_r = n^2$.

Maxwell's thermodynamic relations. The equations relating the four thermodynamic variables S, p, T, and V, referring to a given mass of a homogeneous system, namely

$$\left(\frac{\partial T}{\partial V}\right)_S = -\left(\frac{\partial p}{\partial S}\right)_V, \quad \left(\frac{\partial T}{\partial p}\right)_S = \left(\frac{\partial V}{\partial S}\right)_p,$$

$$\left(\frac{\partial V}{\partial T}\right)_p = -\left(\frac{\partial S}{\partial p}\right)_T, \quad \left(\frac{\partial S}{\partial V}\right)_T = \left(\frac{\partial p}{\partial T}\right)_V,$$

where S is the entropy, V is the volume, p is the pressure, T is the thermodynamic temperature.

maxwell-turn. *See* linkage.

mean current density. *See* current density.

mean deviation. *See* deviation.

mean free path. Symbol: λ. The mean distance that a molecule moves between two successive collisions with other molecules. It is related to the molecular cross section $\pi\sigma^2$ by the relationship:

$$\lambda = 1/\sqrt{2}\pi n\sigma^2$$

where n is the number of molecules per unit volume. The most important means of determining λ is through its connection with viscosity η. According to *kinetic theory

$$\lambda = k\eta/\rho u$$

where ρ = density and u = mean molecular velocity. The value of k lies between $\frac{1}{3}$ and $\frac{1}{2}$ according to the degree of approximation introduced into the theory.

mean life. *Syn.* average life or lifetime. Symbol: τ. (1) The average time for which the unstable nucleus of a radioisotope exists before decaying. It is the reciprocal of the *decay constant and is equal to $T_{\frac{1}{2}}/0{\cdot}693\,15$, where $T_{\frac{1}{2}}$ is the *half-life. (2) The average time of survival for an elementary particle, ion, etc., in a given medium or a charge carrier in a *semiconductor.

mean sidereal or solar time. *See* time.

mean spherical intensity. *See* luminous intensity.

mean square velocity. The average value of the square of all the velocities of a system of particles, given by the relation

$$C^2 = (n_1c_1{}^2 + n_2c_2{}^2 + \ldots + n_rc_r{}^2)/n,$$

where n_1 particles have velocity c_1, n_2 particles have velocity c_2, etc., and n is the total number of molecules.

Its value for a gas may be calculated on the *kinetic theory from the expression $p = \frac{1}{3}\rho C^2$, where p and ρ are the pressure and density respectively of the gas. For an ideal gas $C^2 = 3rT$, where r is the gas constant for 1 g of the gas. This expression shows that the mean velocity is dependent only on the temperature of a given gas.

By the Maxwell *distribution of velocities, for the molecules of a gas in a steady state, the mean square velocity has the value

$$C^2 = \frac{3kT}{m}.$$

mean sun. *See* time.

mean velocity. The average value of the velocities of a system of particles, given by the relation

$$\bar{C} = (n_1c_1 + n_2c_2 + \ldots + n_rc_r)/n,$$

where n_1 particles have velocity c_1, n_2 particles have velocity c_2, etc., and n is the total number of particles.

The Maxwell *distribution of velocities for the molecules of a gas in a steady state yields a value

$$\bar{C} = \frac{2}{\sqrt{(\pi h m)}}, \text{ where } h = \frac{1}{2kT}.$$

mechanical advantage. *Syn.* force ratio. *See* machine.

mechanical equivalent of heat. *Syn.* Joule's equivalent. Symbol: *J*. A constant relating the former unit of heat energy, the *calorie, to the units of mechanical energy, the *joule and erg. Formerly given as the ratio of an amount of mechanical energy in ergs to the amount of thermal energy in calories into which it could be converted, it now has formally defined values (for the different 1 deg C ranges) that represent the experimentally determined values very closely. For the fifteen-degree calorie

$J = (4 \cdot 1855 \pm 0 \cdot 0005) \times 10^7 \text{ erg cal}_{15}^1$
$\quad = 4 \cdot 1855 \pm 0 \cdot 0005 \text{ J cal}_{15}^1.$

mechanical equivalent of light. *Radiant flux expressed in mechanical units, which are equivalent to the unit of *luminous flux, at the wavelength of maximum visibility. It is 0·0015 watts per *lumen at 555 nm. Its reciprocal is also quoted with the same title (660 lumens per watt).

mechanical impedance. *See* impedance.

mechanical rectifier. A rectifier that consists essentially of a rotating or oscillating commutator, operated synchronously so that alternate half waves of the input alternating current are inverted thereby producing a unidirectional output current.

mechanics. The branch of science, divided into dynamics, statics, and kinematics, that is concerned with the motion and equilibrium of bodies in a particular frame of reference. *See also* wave mechanics; quantum mechanics; statistical mechanics.

mechanomotive force. In any machine that develops an alternating force, the *root-mean-square value of the force developed.

medical physics. The application of physics to medicine, as in *radiotherapy, *nuclear medicine, and medical electronics.

medium frequency (MF). *See* frequency bands.

mega-. Symbol: M. The prefix meaning 10^6, e.g. 1 MΩ = 10^6 ohms. In computing it is sometimes used to mean 2^{20} (1 048 576), e.g. 1 megabyte = 1 048 576 *bytes.

megaphone. An instrument for amplifying and directing sound. It consists of a conical or rectangular horn about a foot long, the small end of which is held near the mouth of the speaker. The horn increases the efficiency of the voice by providing a suitable loading for it. Provided the solid angle of a conical horn is not large, the wave front of the sound emerging from the open end is almost plane.

Meissner effect. *See* superconductivity.

melting point. *See* freezing point.

memory. *Syn.* main store; core store. The part of a *computer that stores information in units of *words or *bytes for immediate use by the *CPU. The memory may consist of magnetic *cores or may be a *solid-state memory* in which *bits of information are stored as one of the two states of integrated circuit bistable *multivibrators. It is smaller and faster than core memory but when the supply voltage is removed the information is lost.

meniscus. (1) A concave or convex upper surface of a liquid column that is due to capillary action. (2) A convexo-concave or concavo-convex *lens.

mercury barometer. *See* barometer.

mercury in glass thermometer. A type of thermometer in which mercury acts as the thermometric fluid in a glass bulb attached to a graduated fine capillary tube. During manufacture all air is excluded from the capillary tube, a small bulb being left at the top of the tube as a safeguard against breakage should the thermometer be raised to a temperature beyond the highest value on the graduated scale. The thermometer is calibrated by immersion first in melting ice then in steam in a *hypsometer, the positions of the mercury meniscus being marked. In the Celsius (centigrade) thermometer, the distance between the marks is divided into 100 equal parts, each part corresponding approximately to a Celsius degree on the mercury in glass scale. Although it has the advantage of giving

Celsius and Fahrenheit thermometers

a direct reading which is easily read, for accurate work the platinum *resistance thermometer is used. Since the coefficient of expansion of mercury is not independent of temperature and since the expansion of the glass is not negligible, the thermometer readings can only be corrected to the gas scale by a direct comparison with a *gas thermometer. The chief errors for which correction is

necessary are non-uniformity of the bore of the capillary tube; errors in marking the ice and steam points; hysteresis of the glass causing a change in the ice point; the effect of external pressure on the bulb; the emergent stem correction. *See also* international temperature scale.

mercury switch. A switch in which contact is established between two mercury surfaces usually enclosed in a glass tube. Arcing is often suppressed by filling the tube with an inert gas and sometimes a porcelain tube is fused in at the point of contact to eliminate breakage from heat shock. There are many types. Usually they are operated by tilting, and may have delayed make, or break, or both, by the mercury having to flow through a constriction in a side tube.

mercury vapour lamp. An incandescent arc of mercury vapour between mercury electrodes in an enclosed tube. The light is rich in ultraviolet radiation and in *fluorescent lamps some of this is converted to visible wavelengths by fluorescent powders coated on to the interior of the tube.

mercury vapour rectifier. An electron tube rectifier in which a discharge passes in one way only from a hot wire cathode to an anode via an atmosphere of ionized mercury vapour.

meridian circle. *Syn.* transit circle. *See* telescope.

mesa transistor. A type of *bipolar transistor in which the *base region is first diffused into the substrate, the areas surrounding the base region being etched to leave a plateau above the substrate to form the *collector. The *emitter may be either alloyed into the base or diffused into it. The latter is a double-diffused transistor.

mesh. *See* network.

mesh connection. A method of connection used in *polyphase a.c. working in which the windings of a transformer, a.c. machine, etc., are all connected in series to form a closed circuit so that a polygon may be used to represent them diagrammatically. A special form is the *delta connection. *Compare* star connection.

meson. A collective name given to *elementary particles that can take part in *strong interactions and that have integral spin. By definition, mesons are both *hadrons and *bosons and can be created or annihilated freely as they are not subject to Fermi–Dirac statistics. *Pions* and *kaons* are mesons. Mesons are thought to be composed of a tightly bound quark and antiquark. *See* Table 8, page 425.

mesosphere. *See* atmospheric layers.

metacentre. The point at which a vertical line through the centre of *buoyancy B′ of a tilted ship, or other floating body, intersects the line joining the centre of mass G and the centre of buoyancy B of the upright ship. If G is below M, the

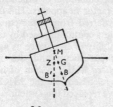

Metacentre

force of buoyancy (upwards through B′) together with the weight of the ship (downwards through G) tends to rotate the ship back to the upright position.

metadyne. (1) Metadyne generator. A commutator-type d.c. generator producing a constant output current. It has, in addition to the usual brushes supplying the load, a set of brushes that are either short-circuited or connected together through stator windings of low resistance. The extra brushes have a position intermediate between the others on the commutator. The current in the circuit containing the additional brushes produces the whole or a substantial part of the magnetic flux which gives rise to the output voltage. The output can be controlled by additional windings.

(2) Metadyne converter. A machine that is similar in construction to a metadyne generator. The additional brushes are not, however, connected together but are connected to an independent d.c. supply (usually of constant voltage). Fundamentally, this machine converts the input power from the d.c. supply at constant voltage into output power at constant current (i.e. output current is independent of load resistance), the mechanical power required to drive the armature being very small. It is used in the control of d.c. motors particularly in electric traction.

metallizing. The covering of an insulating material with a film of metal or other substance to render it electrically conducting. The technique is widely used in solid-state electronics. The conducting film is etched and forms interconnections on *integrated circuits. It is also used in forming *bonding pads for integrated circuits and discrete components.

metal rectifier. A *rectifier that depends for its action upon the fact that when a metal is placed in contact with a suitable solid (usually an oxide or other compound of the metal), the resistance offered to the passage of an electric current is very much less when the current flow is in one direction (e.g. from the solid to the metal) than it is in the other direction. Typical examples are the copper-oxide and selenium rectifiers, comprising respectively cuprous oxide on copper, and selenium on copper. The potential applied must not exceed a few volts so that for high voltages a series of

241

elements is required. The current passed depends on the area of contact.

metastable state. (1) Symbol: m. A comparatively stable *excited state of a radioisotope that decays into a more stable lower energy state with the emission of gamma-rays. The isotope technetium-99m decays into technetium-99, the half-life being 6 hours. It is often an excited state from which all possible transitions to lower states are *forbidden transitions according to the relevant *selection rules. (2) A comparatively stable electronically *excited state of an atom or molecule.

meteor. A lump of matter from space that enters the earth's atmosphere and is detected either optically by virtue of its luminosity as a result of friction with air particles, or by radio means by virtue of the trail of ionized gas left in its wake.

Since the surface of a typical meteor reaches a temperature of the order of 3000 K, very few reach the earth's surface. Such specimens, called *meteorites*, are made up largely of iron and nickel alloys, although some have a stony constitution or contain a mixture of metals and minerals.

meteorograph. A device for recording some or all of the following: temperature, relative humidity, pressure, and wind force. It is usually carried into the upper air by a balloon or kite.

meteorology. The science of the atmosphere, especially with respect to weather and climate.

method of mixtures. A method of calorimetry in which a substance is added to a calorimeter at a different temperature, the mixture being stirred to reach equilibrium at an intermediate temperature. The unknown heat capacity may be calculated by equating the heat lost by one part of the system to the heat gained by the remainder of the system since the

law of conservation of energy applies, if there is allowance made for heat exchange with the surroundings.

metre. Symbol: m. The *SI unit of length, defined as 1 650 763·73 wavelengths in vacuum of the radiation corresponding to the transition between the levels $2p_{10}$ and $5d_5$ of the krypton-86 atom. In 1960 this definition replaced the former International prototype metre bar. The metre was originally intended to be one ten-millionth of the quadrant from the equator to the north pole through Dunkirk, but the original measurements were found to be in error.

metre bridge. A form of the *Wheatstone bridge in which a uniform resistance wire 1 metre long, which can be tapped at any point along its length, takes the place of two of the four resistors.

metre-kilogramme-second electromagnetic system of units (MKS units). A system of absolute units in which the fundamental units are the metre, the kilogramme, and the second and in which the permeability of free space is 10^{-7} henries per metre. In many electromagnetic equations of practical importance, a factor 4π appears. This factor can be transferred from these equations to others less commonly used by taking the permeability of free space as $4\pi \times 10^{-7}$ henries per metre and this gives the *rationalized* MKS system of units. *SI units are based on the MKS system and have replaced this system.

metre slug. *See* slug.

metrology. The branch of science concerned with the accurate measurement of the three fundamental quantities: mass, length, and time. It is often extended to mean the systematic study of weights and measurements.

mho. The reciprocal ohm, formerly used as a unit of conductance. This unit is now replaced by the *siemens.

mica. A mineral consisting of complex silicates, characterized by a perfect basal cleavage enabling the crystals to be split into very thin plates. It has a low thermal conductivity and high dielectric strength, being widely used for electrical insulation.

Michelson–Morley experiment. An experiment (1887) that attempted to measure the velocity of the earth through the *ether. Using a *Michelson interferometer* (*see* diagram) Michelson and Morley attempted to show that there is a difference in the velocity of light as measured in the direction of the earth's rotation compared to the velocity at right angles to this direction. If there was such a difference the interference fringes observed in the interferometer would be shifted when the instrument was turned through 90°. This shift would correspond to a change of optical pathlength of approximately $2dv^2/c^2$, where v is the velocity of the earth with respect to the ether in the direction OM_2. No shift was observed indicating the absence of an ether wind. This fact was of considerable

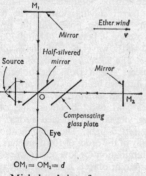

$OM_1 = OM_2 = d$

Michelson's interferometer

importance and was responsible for the downfall of the ether concept. The explanation was finally provided by the Lorentz–Fitzgerald contraction which, in turn, led to the special theory of *relativity.

micro-. Symbol: μ. The prefix meaning 10^{-6}, e.g. 1 μm = 10^{-6} metre.

microbalance. A *balance capable of weighing very small masses (e.g. down to 10^{-5} mg). The beam is made to balance by varying the air pressure in the balance case so altering the upward buoyant force on a bulb fixed on one end of the beam. A manometer is provided for measuring the pressure when the beam is balanced; if the temperature is constant the density of the gas (and thus the upward buoyant force) is proportional to the pressure.

microcalorimeter. A differential calorimeter used for the measurement of very small quantities of heat, such as that evolved by a small quantity of radioactive substance.

microdensitometer. A device for automatically measuring and recording small changes in *transmission density across a sample, such as a photographic plate.

microelectronics. The branch of electronics concerned with the design, production, and application of electronic components, circuits, and devices of extremely small dimensions.

micromanometer. A device for the measurement of very small pressure differences. The U-tube manometer has one arm of the U nearly horizontal so that pressure changes causing only a small difference in vertical height produce easily visible movements of liquid in this arm. In diaphragm gauges two pressures are applied on either side of the diaphragm and optical methods are used to measure the tiny displacement.

micrometer eyepiece. An eyepiece, generally a *Ramsden eyepiece, provided with cross-wires which can be displaced by means of a *micrometer screw. It is used for the measurement of small objects or small separations of objects, lines, etc.

micrometer screw. A device for measuring small and/or accurate distances. Such instruments are fitted with a drum that when rotated advances a screw of known pitch; the drum is calibrated in fractions of a revolution which can be interpreted in terms of the distance advanced by the screw.

micron. Symbol: μ. A former name for the micrometre; 10^{-6} m.

microphone. A device for converting sound energy into electrical energy. It forms the first element of the telephone, the broadcast transmitter, and all forms of electrical sound recorders. The types of microphone most generally used are the carbon, crystal, moving-coil, capacitor, and ribbon. (*See* articles under these headings.) Many other types exist for specialized purposes however, such as the magnetostriction, moving iron, and hot-wire microphones. In most of these, a thin diaphragm is used which vibrates under the influence of the sound waves. The diaphragm is mechanically coupled to some device, the motion of which produces electrical energy. The force exerted by the sound against the diaphragm is usually proportional to the sound pressure, but in the case of the ribbon microphone it is proportional to the particle velocity. For good quality reproduction, resonance in the mechanical system of the microphone should be avoided. This is done by making the resonant frequency of the moving parts either much higher or much lower than the frequency of the sound to be reproduced. Lack of sensitivity is not a great disadvantage since it is usual to amplify the output from the microphone.

microradiography. *See* microscope.

microscope. (1) An optical instrument for producing an enlarged image of small objects. The *simple microscope* (or *magnifying glass*) consists of a strong converging lens system, corrected for chromatic and spherical aberrations, and used for low power work. The object is usually placed at the focus of the lens system, producing an image at infinity. The *magnifying power is the ratio $25/f$ (where f is in cm).

The *compound microscope* (Fig. *a*) consists essentially of two lens systems and gives a much greater magnification, up to about 1000 diameters. A very short

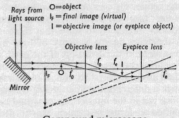

a Compound microscope

focal length *objective forms a magnified real image of the object which is further magnified by the *eyepiece acting as a simple microscope. The total magnification is the product of the objective and eyepiece magnification. Greater magnification can be obtained with oil immersion (*see* resolving power). The maximum *resolving power of the optical microscope is between 200 and 300 nm (i.e. half the wavelength of blue or orange light). The *binocular microscope* has two eyepieces. Light from the objective is split into two beams by using prisms. The *stereoscopic microscope* has two eyepieces and two objectives, the object being viewed by reflected rather than transmitted light. The magnification is usually of the order of 100 diameters.

Illumination for low power work with transparent objects is achieved by using a mirror mounted below the object to reflect light from a light source onto the object. For higher magnifications, a substage *condenser, such as the *Abbe condenser, is necessary. The optical microscope can be focused sharply only in one plane so that a two-dimensional image is obtained. If the object is fairly transparent, different depths can be brought into focus, but since material above and below the plane of focus can interact with the light, the image may be blurred. The microscope therefore works best with thin samples viewed by transmitted light, or with flat samples viewed by reflected light. The shape of the object can only be obtained at low magnifications of about 200 diameters.

Details in objects are seen because of varying density regions. With a strongly lit background, a small transparent object is very difficult to observe. *Dark-field illumination* increases the visibility of small objects. An opaque disc is placed over the centre of the condenser so that the borders of the object are illuminated by marginal rays which do not enter the objective. Some light is refracted by the specimen, some of which enters the objective. A bright image is thus obtained against a dark background; however, little detail can be seen.

The refractive index of a transparent specimen varies slightly from point to point. These variations give rise to *diffraction patterns in the focal plane of the objective. The diffracted light passing through the object is one quarter of a wavelength out of *phase with undiffracted light, which has not been transmitted through the object. In *phase-contrast microscopy* a phase-contrast plate is used to produce a quarter wavelength shift in the undiffracted light. The plate is placed at the focal plane of the objective (Fig. *b*) onto which the image of a substage annular diaphragm falls. The final image has higher contrast due to interference between the diffracted and undiffracted beams.

In *interference microscopy* a transparent object is placed between two semi-silvered surfaces. Light passing through the object interferes with light that has not passed through, and interference patterns can be observed. It is possible to view opaque objects in a similar way. *Reflecting microscopes* use a reflecting objective rather than the conventional lens system and can focus wavelengths ranging from infrared to ultraviolet at the same point. In *ultraviolet microscopy* (*see* resolving power) the resolving power of the microscope is increased to 100 nm by using ultraviolet radiation. The image is made visible by using a photographic plate to record it.

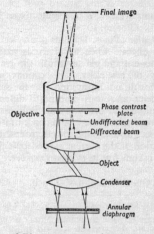

b Phase-contrast microscope

X-ray microscopy (or *microradiography*) further increases the resolution, the image being recorded on film or on a fluorescent screen.

(2) *See* electron microscope.

microwave. An electromagnetic wave with a wavelength in the approximate range 1 mm to 0·3 m, i.e. between infrared radiation and radio waves. *Radar uses these wavelengths.

Mie scattering. Scattering of light by spherical particles of diameters comparable with the wavelength; an extension of *Rayleigh scattering.

migration area. The area required for a neutron to slow down from fusion energy to thermal energy plus that required to diffuse the energy. The

245

former area is one-sixth of the mean square distance between the source and the point where the neutrons reach mean energy. The diffusion area is one-sixth of the mean square distance between the point where the neutron is in thermal equilibrium with the surroundings and the point where it is captured. The *migration length* is the square root of the migration area. *See also* neutron age.

migration of ions. The ions of an electrolyte migrate when a current is passed through it and play a part in the transport of electricity. The cations and anions do not always move at the same velocity and thus transport different fractions of the current. Progressive changes take place in the concentration of electrolyte around the electrodes. The fraction of the current carried by either ion is known as its *transport number*.

mil. One thousandth of an inch.

Miller effect. In an electronic device the *interelectrode capacitance may provide a feedback path between the input and output circuits. This can affect the total input admittance of the device and is called the Miller effect. The total dynamic input capacitance of the device will always be equal to or greater than the sum of the static electrode capacitances because of this effect.

Miller indices. *See* rational intercepts, law of.

milli-. Symbol: m. The prefix meaning 10^{-3}, e.g. 1 mm $= 10^{-3}$ metre.

minimum deviation. *See* deviation.

Minkowski space–time. *See* relativity.

minority carrier. In a *semiconductor, the type of carrier constituting less than half of the total charge carrier concentration.

minute. (1) Of time. $\frac{1}{1440}$ of the mean solar day (unless the context indicates that the sidereal day is meant). *See* time. (2) Symbol: '. A unit of angle equal to $\frac{1}{60}$ degree.

mirror. An optical device for producing reflection, generally having surfaces that are plane, spherical, paraboloidal, ellipsoidal, or aspheric. Concave mirrors are hollowed out, convex mirrors are dome-shaped. The *mirror formulae* generally describe the conjugate focus relations for spherical mirrors. The commonest form is $1/v + 1/u = 2/r = 1/f$, in which u is the object distance, v the image distance, r the radius of curvature, f the focal length. Objects and images lying in front of the mirror are real and the distances are taken as positive. For a virtual image, v is negative. For a concave mirror f is positive, for a convex mirror it is negative. The value of $m = v/u$ is positive for inverted images. (*See also* optics sign conventions.)

A *thick mirror* is a lens with the back surface silvered or it may apply to a lens in combination with a curved mirror with or without separation.

Although mirrors are free from chromatic aberration, in general they suffer from spherical aberration. The paraboloid form focuses parallel rays accurately (used with reflecting telescopes, searchlight mirrors, etc.); the ellipsoidal mirror focuses light from one focus to the other focus (both foci are real); the hyperboloid mirror reflects light directed to one focus (virtual) to the opposite focus (real). *See also* magnetic mirror; Mangin mirror.

mirror nuclides. Two nuclides having the same number of nucleons each, but where the number of protons (or neutrons) in one is equal to the number of neutrons (or protons) in the other. The nuclides will have the general form ^m_nX and $^m_{m-n}Y$, and will be the source and product nuclides in *beta decay. In the special case of the pair $^{2n+1}_{n}X$ and $^{2n+1}_{n+1}Y$, they are known as *Wigner nuclides*.

MISFET, MIST. *See* field-effect transistor.

mismatch. The condition arising when the impedance of a *load is not equal to the output impedance of the source to which it is connected.

mixer. *Syn.* frequency changer. A device used in conjunction with a beat-frequency oscillator to produce an output having a different frequency from the input. The amplitude of the output bears a fixed relationship to the amplitude of the input (usually approximately linear) and the device is used in a *superheterodyne receiver for changing the frequency of an amplitude-modulated *carrier wave while retaining the modulation characteristics.

mixing ratio. *See* humidity.

MKS system. *See* metre-kilogramme-second system of units.

mmHg. Abbreviation for millimetres of mercury. A unit of pressure measured by the height in mm of a mercury column supported by the pressure when the mercury density is 13 595·1 kg m^{-3}, under standard g. One standard atmosphere is equal to 760 mmHg.

mobility. *See* Hall mobility.

mode. (1) One of several wave frequencies that an oscillator can generate or to which a resonator can be tuned. (2) The value of the abscissa corresponding to the maximum ordinate of a *frequency distribution curve.

modem. Abbreviation of modulator-demodulator. A device that converts the signals from one particular type of equipment into a form suitable for use in another.

moderator. *See* nuclear reactors.

modulated amplifier. The amplifier stage in a transmitter in which the modulating signal is introduced for the purpose of *modulation of the carrier wave.

modulated wave. *See* carrier wave.

modulating wave. *See* carrier wave.

modulation. The process of impressing one wave system upon another of higher frequency. The term is usually used to cover impressing an audio-frequency, or other desired signal-transmitting wave, onto a higher frequency *carrier wave for radio transmission. *See* amplitude, frequency, phase, and velocity modulation.

modulation factor. *See* amplitude modulation.

modulator. (1) Any device that effects the process of *modulation. (2) A device used in radar for generating a succession of short pulses to act as a trigger for the *oscillator.

modulator electrode. An electrode used for modulating the flow of current in an electrode device. In a *cathode-ray tube it is the electrode controlling the intensity of the electron beam. In a *field-effect transistor it is the *gate electrode(s) controlling the conductivity of the *channel.

modulus of decay. In a system exhibiting *damped oscillations of the form $a = a_0 e^{-\alpha t}$, where a_0 is the initial amplitude and a its value after time t, then the modulus is equal to the time t_1 at which the amplitude has fallen to $1/e$ of its initial value. It is the reciprocal of the damping factor α.

modulus of elasticity. The ratio of *stress to *strain for a body obeying *Hooke's law. There are several moduli corresponding to various types of strain:

(1) Young's modulus $(E) =$

$$\frac{\text{applied load per unit area of cross section}}{\text{increase in length per unit length}};$$

it applies to tensional stress when the sides of the rod or bar concerned are not constrained. *See* Poisson's ratio.

(2) Bulk modulus (or volume elasticity) $(K) =$

$$\frac{\text{compressive (or tensile) force per unit area}}{\text{change in volume per unit volume}};$$

it applies to compression or dilation, e.g. when a body is subject to changes in hydrostatic pressure. Fluids, as well as solids, have bulk moduli.

(3) Rigidity (or shear) modulus $(G) =$

$$\frac{\text{tangential force per unit area}}{\text{angular deformation}}.$$

Since strain is a ratio and so dimensionless, the moduli have the dimensions of stress, i.e. force/area. The various moduli and Poisson's ratio for an isotropic solid are interrelated. The moduli given in Physical Tables and most often used are measured under isothermal conditions; the adiabatic values are always greater.

If stress is not proportional to strain (as in cast metals, marble, concrete, wood), the moduli have to be defined as the ratio of a small change in stress to a small change in strain at a particular value of the stress.

modulus of torsion. The couple required to give a wire a twist of one radian per cm of length.

Moh's scale. *See* hardness.

moiré pattern. The pattern produced by overlying sets of parallel threads or lines, the sets being slightly inclined to one another. The overlaps produce the appearance of dark bands running athwart the individual lines. If the two sets are perfectly regular these bands are straight but deviations in either or both give wavy lines as in the characteristic appearance of moiré silk. Transparent diffraction gratings and replicas from them may be compared by superposing them and examining the resulting moiré pattern.

molar. Divided by *amount of substance. In practice this means 'per mole'.

molar heat capacity. Symbol: C_m. The *heat capacity of unit *amount of substance of an element, compound, or material. The amount of substance is usually expressed in moles and molar heat capacities are measured in joules per kelvin per mole.

molar latent heat. *See* latent heat.

molar polarization. When a molecule is subjected to an electric field there is a small displacement of electrical centres which induces a *dipole in the molecule. If $m = \alpha E$, where m is the electrical *dipole moment induced by a field strength E, then the constant α is called the *polarizability* of the molecule.

molar volume. The volume occupied by 1 mole of a substance. According to *Avogadro's hypothesis all gases have the same molar volume of $22 \cdot 4$ dm^3 at STP.

mole. Symbol: mol. The *SI unit of *amount of substance, defined as the amount of substance of a system that contains as many elementary entities as there are atoms in $0 \cdot 012$ kilogrammes of carbon-12. The elementary entities must be specified and may be atoms, molecules, ions, electrons, other particles, or specified groups of particles.

molecular beam. A collimated beam of atoms or molecules at low pressure, in which all the particles are travelling in the same direction and few collisions occur between them.

molecular flow. *Syn.* Knudsen flow. A type of gas flow occurring at low pressures, when the *mean free path of the gas molecules is large compared with the dimensions of the pipe through which the gas is flowing. The rate of gas flow is determined by collisions between the molecules and the wall of the tube rather than by collisions between molecules. Thus the flow does not depend on the viscosity of the gas.

molecular gauges. *Syn.* viscosity gauges or manometers. At pressures of a fraction of a mm of mercury, the viscosity of a gas is dependent on pressure and this effect is used in molecular gauges for measuring pressure. In one gauge, a disc is turned rapidly at a uniform speed and a second disc parallel to the first tends to follow its rotation due to the viscous drag of the air. The couple acting on the second disc is a measure of the pressure. The instrument works from 10^{-3} mm to 10^{-7} mm and is usually calibrated with reference to a *McLeod gauge.

In another form, a flat quartz fibre fixed at one end vibrates in the gas and the damping, which is observed, depends on the viscosity. This instrument, called a *decrement gauge* or *quartz-fibre manometer*, is most useful from 10^{-2} to 10^{-4} mm of mercury.

molecular orbital. In an atom the electrons moving around the nucleus have *atomic orbitals that are often represented as a region around the nucleus in which there is a high probability of finding the electron. When molecules are formed, the valence electrons move under the influence of two or more nuclei and their *wave functions are known as molecular orbitals. These can also be represented by regions in space. It is usual to think of molecular orbitals as formed by a combination of atomic orbitals. Two atomic orbitals combine to give two molecular orbitals of different energies and forms.

molecular pump. *See* pumps, vacuum.

molecular spectrum. *See* band spectrum.

molecular weight. *Syn.* relative molecular mass. The sum of the atomic weights of all the atoms contained in a molecule.

moment. (1) *Syn.* torque. The moment of a force about an axis is the product of the perpendicular distance of the axis from the line of action of the force, and the component of the force in the plane perpendicular to the axis. The moment of a system of coplanar forces about an axis perpendicular to the plane containing them is the algebraic sum of the moments of the separate forces about that axis (anticlockwise moments are taken conventionally to be positive and clockwise ones negative).

(2) The moment of a vector about an axis is similarly defined. It is a scalar and is given a $+$ve or $-$ve sign as in (1) above. When dealing with systems in which forces and motions do not all lie in one plane, the concept of moment about a point is needed. The moment of a vector **P** (e.g. force or momentum) about a point A (*see* diagram) is a vector **M** equal to the vector product of **r** and **P**, where r is any line joining A to any point B on the line of action of **P**. (The vector product $\mathbf{M} = \mathbf{r} \times \mathbf{P}$ is independent of the position of B.)

Moment of a vector

The relation between the scalar moment about an axis and the vector moment about a point on that axis is that the scalar is the component of the vector in the direction of the axis.

moment of inertia. (1) Symbol I. Of a body about an axis. The sum of the products of the mass of each particle of the body and the square of its perpendicular distance from the axis. (This addition is replaced by an integration in the case of a continuous body.) The *kinetic energy of the body rotating about that axis with angular velocity ω is $\frac{1}{2}I\omega^2$, which corresponds to $\frac{1}{2}mv^2$ for the kinetic energy of a body of mass m translated with velocity v. *See also* Routh's rule; product of inertia; theorem of parallel axes.

(2) Of a surface about an axis. The moment of inertia of an imaginary sheet of matter whose mass/unit area is unity and which coincides with and has the same boundaries as the surface considered. This is known as the *geometrical moment of inertia* of the surface.

moment of momentum. *See* angular momentum.

momentum. (1) Linear momentum of a particle. Symbol: p. The product of the mass and the velocity of the particle. It is a vector quantity directed through the particle in the direction of motion. The linear momentum of a body or of a system of particles is the vector sum of the linear momenta of the individual particles. If a body of mass M is translated (*see* translation) with a velocity V, its momentum is $MV =$ momentum of a particle of mass M at the centre of gravity of the body. (*See* Newton's laws of motion, II; conservation of momentum.) (2) *See* angular momentum.

monochord. *Syn.* sonometer. A thin metallic wire stretched horizontally or vertically over two bridges by means of a weight hanging over a pulley or by a spring tensioning device. The string and bridges are mounted on a hollow box, which acts as a sounding board, increasing the sound volume. The string is made to vibrate by plucking, bowing, striking, etc. *See* stretched string.

monochromatic radiation. Radiation restricted to a very narrow band of wavelengths: ideally one wavelength. *See* laser.

monochromator. *See* spectrometer.

monoclinic system. *See* crystal systems.

monolithic. *See* integrated circuits.

monostable. *Syn.* single-shot. A type of circuit having only one stable state, but which can be triggered into a second quasi-stable state by the application of a trigger pulse. A resistive–capacitive coupled *multivibrator forms a monostable. Such circuits are used to provide a fixed duration pulse and can be utilized for pulse stretching or shortening or as a delay element.

Moog synthesizer. *See* electrophonic instruments.

Morse equation. An empirical equation giving the potential energy V of two atoms in a molecule as a function of their separation. It has the form:

$$V = D_e(1 - e^{-\beta(r-r_0)})^2,$$

where β is a constant, r is the distance between the atoms, and r_0 is the equilibrium distance, i.e. the bond length. At small separations the energy is very high because of repulsion between the nuclei. At large separations the energy is constant with separation because the molecule has dissociated into two atoms. D_e is the energy from the minimum to the dissociation level.

MOS. Abbreviation for metal oxide semiconductor. *See* MOS logic circuit; field-effect transistor.

mosaic electrode. The light-sensitive surface of a *camera tube.

Moseley's law. The *X-ray spectrum of a particular element can be split into several distinct line series: K, L, M, and N. Moseley's law states that for certain elements the square root of the frequency f of the characteristic *X-rays of one of these series is directly proportional to the atomic number Z. A graph of Z against $\sqrt{f}$ is called a *Moseley diagram*.

MOSFET, MOST. *See* field-effect transistor.

MOS integrated circuit. *See* integrated circuit.

MOS logic circuit. *Logic circuits constructed in MOS integrated circuits. They consist of combinations of MOS *field-effect transistors in series or in parallel that perform the logic functions (e.g. act as AND or OR gates). These are coupled to other MOS transistors that determine the output voltages of the circuit. The logic functions are switches, the combination switch being 'on' when the required input conditions are fulfilled.

Mössbauer effect. When nuclei emit gamma-ray photons the photon energy corresponds to the difference between two energy states of the nucleus and, in principle, is sharply defined. However, a part of the energy is often taken up in the recoil of the nucleus and this leads to a spread of gamma-ray energies. Mössbauer found that in certain solids the recoil momentum is taken up by the solid as a whole rather than by lattice vibrations. The gamma-ray photon has then the correct energy to be absorbed by another nucleus in a similar process.

An example of the Mossbauer effect is shown by the gamma-ray emission from ^{57}Co nucleus. This decays first to a *metastable state of ^{57}Fe, which decays to its *ground state by a recoilless transition to give a gamma-ray photon of 14·4 keV energy. If an iron sample is placed close to this emitting source these gamma rays can be absorbed in exciting iron nuclei from their ground state to an excited state.

By moving the source the gamma-ray frequency can be changed by the *Doppler effect. Again, by the general theory of *relativity, the energy can be increased by causing the beam to be emitted downwards for several hundred feet. The gravitational effect can thus be counteracted by an upward movement of the source, a fact used in testing general relativity.

motor. A machine that converts electrical energy into mechanical energy. *See* induction motor; synchronous-induction motor; synchronous motor; universal motor; superconductivity.

moving-coil, moving-iron instruments. *See* ammeter.

moving-coil microphone. A type of *microphone in which the diaphragm is connected to a coil and moves it backwards and forwards in a stationary magnetic field, thus inducing a voltage.

multichannel analyser. A test instrument that splits an input waveform into a number of channels in respect of a particular parameter of the input. A circuit that sorts a number of pulses into selected ranges of amplitude is known as a *pulse height analyser*. A circuit that splits an input waveform into its frequency components is known as a *spectrum analyser*. In general a multichannel analyser will have facilities for carrying out both these operations.

multi-electrode valve. A valve that contains two or more sets of electrodes within a single envelope, each set of electrodes having its own independent stream of electrons. The sets of electrodes may have one or more common electrodes (e.g. a common cathode). A typical example is the double-diode-triode which contains the electrode assemblies of two diodes and one triode.

multiple reflection. The reflection of light and the formation of a number of images when two or more mirrors reflect light several times in succession.

multiplet

multiplet. (1) A group of spectrum levels specified by the values of the quantum numbers L (vector sum of orbital and angular momenta of individual electrons) and S (vector sum of spin momenta of individual electrons). The group of levels gives rise to a set of spectrum lines. (2) A set of quantum-mechanical states of *elementary particles having the same value of certain *quantum number(s). Individual members of the set are distinguished by having different values of other quantum numbers. The word multiplet is most commonly used in connection with sets of states which are transformed into each other by operations which form the elements of a group. *See* isospin; unitary symmetry.

multiplex operation. The use of a single path for the simultaneous transmission of several signals without any loss of identity of an individual signal. The various signals are fed to a *multiplexer* which allocates the transmission path to the input according to some parameter (e.g. *frequency-division multiplexing or *time-division multiplexing). At the receiving end a *demultiplexer*, operating in sympathy with the multiplexer, reconstructs the original signals at the outputs. The transmission path may be in any of the available media, i.e. wire, waveguide, or radio waves.

multiplication constant or factor (effective). Symbol: k_{eff}. In a nuclear reactor. The ratio of the total number of neutrons produced by *fission in a given time to the total number absorbed or leaking out in the same period.

multipolar. Having a *field magnet with more than two poles.

multivibrator. A form of oscillator consisting of two *inverters coupled so that the input of one is derived from the output of the other. The type of multivibrator is determined by the coupling

used. (1) Capacitive coupling. This gives an astable circuit with two quasi-stable states, which can generate a continuous waveform without any trigger. (2) Capacitive-resistance coupling. This gives a *monostable circuit. (3) Resistive coupling. (*See* diagram.) This gives a

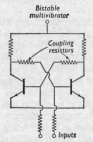

Multivibrator using resistive coupling

bistable circuit with two stable states, which can change state on the application of a trigger pulse. *See* flip-flop.

mu-meson. *See* muon.

muon. Formerly called mu-meson. Symbol: μ. A *lepton similar to the electron except for its mass, which is 207 times greater than that of the electron. It has a lifetime of 2×10^{-6} seconds, decaying into electrons and neutrinos thus: $\mu^- \rightarrow e^- + \bar{\nu}_e + \nu_\mu$. Its antiparticle decays: $\mu^+ \rightarrow e^+ + \bar{\nu}_\mu + \nu_e$. It was originally thought to be a *meson, hence its name. *See* elementary particles.

musical scale. A series of notes progressing from any given note to its octave by prescribed *intervals chosen for musical effect. The *diatonic scale* is an eight-note scale consisting of five *tones and two semitones and is produced by playing the white keys of a keyboard instrument. It forms the basis of the major and minor scales of Western music. The *chromatic scale* is a 13-note scale resulting from the division of the tones of the diatonic scale into semitones. The *wholetone scale* consists of six notes to the octave, there being no semitones. The *pentatonic scale* with five notes to the octave has the spacing: tone, $1\frac{1}{2}$ tones, tone, tone, $1\frac{1}{2}$ tones. *See also* temperament.

mutual capacitance. The extent to which two *capacitors can affect each other, expressed in terms of the ratio of the amount of charge transferred to one, to the corresponding potential difference of the other.

mutual conductance. *Syn.* transconductance. Symbol: g_m. Of an amplifying device or circuit. The ratio of the incremental change in output current, I_{out} to the change in input voltage, V_{in} causing it, the output voltage remaining constant.

mutual inductance. *See* electromagnetic induction.

myopia (short sight). *See* refraction.

N

nabla. *See* del.

nadir. *See* celestial sphere.

NAND circuit. *See* logic circuit.

nano-. Symbol: n. The prefix meaning 10^{-9}, e.g. $1nm = 10^{-9}$ metre.

natural abundance. *See* abundance.

natural convection. *See* convection (of heat).

natural frequency. *See* free vibrations (or oscillations).

near infrared or ultraviolet. Parts of the infrared or ultraviolet regions of the spectrum of *electromagnetic radiation that are close to the visible region. The regions that are far from the visible region and close to the X-ray and micro-wave regions are called the *far ultra-violet* and *far infrared* respectively. The near infrared is usually the region in which molecules absorb radiation by making transitions between vibrational *energy levels. The far infrared is usually the region in which absorption is due to changes in rotational energy levels.

near point. Of the eye. The nearest point for which, with accommodation fully excited, clear vision is obtained. It should not be confused with the con-ventional distance of distinct vision (25 cm or 10 in.).

Néel temperature. *See* antiferromag-netism.

negative electron. *Syn.* negatron; nega-ton. An electron with a negative charge as opposed to the positively charged elec-tron or *positron.

negative feedback. *See* feedback.

negative glow. *See* gas-discharge tube.

negative logic. *See* logic circuit.

negative principal and nodal points. *See* antiprincipal, antinodal points.

negative resistance. In certain devices, the point at which the voltage–current characteristic has a negative slope, i.e. the current decreases as the voltage increases. Such devices include the *silicon-controlled rectifier, the *magne-tron, and the *tunnel diode.

negative specific heat capacities. Certain substances under stated conditions need heat to be extracted from them if their temperature is to be raised. The most familiar example is a saturated vapour, for which

$$c = (c_p)_1 + \frac{dL}{dT} - \frac{L}{T},$$

where $(c_p)_1$ is the specific heat capacity of the liquid at the boiling point T and L is the specific latent heat of vaporization. When the vapour rises in temperature it must simultaneously be compressed to keep it saturated since the density of saturated vapour rises with increasing temperature. For steam, the heat of com-pression is so great that the vapour becomes superheated so that heat must be extracted from it. This occurs through the evaporation of more water, the specific latent heat for this evaporation coming from the supersaturated steam.

negatron or negaton. *See* negative electron.

neon tube. A gas-discharge tube con-taining neon at low pressure, the colour of the glow being red. The striking voltage is between 130 and 170 volts and within a range of current the voltage across the tube remains constant so that for small currents (up to about 100 milliamps) it can be used as a voltage stabilizer. Electrodeless neon tubes will easily glow in the presence of high-frequency currents of high voltage.

neper. Symbol: N or Np. A logarithmic unit used for comparing two currents, usually those entering and leaving a transmission line or other transmission network. Two currents I_1 and I_2 are said to differ by N nepers when $N = \log_e |I_1/I_2|$. *See also* bel.

neptunium series. *See* radioactive series.

Nernst effect. When heat flows through a strip of metal in a magnetic field, the direction of flow being across the lines of force, an e.m.f. is developed perpendicular to both the flow and the lines. The direction of the current the e.m.f. produces depends on the nature of the metal of which the strip is composed. *See* Leduc effect.

Nernst heat theorem. Also known as the third law of *thermodynamics. If a chemical change occurs between pure crystalline solids at absolute zero, there is no change in *entropy, i.e. the entropy of the final substance equals that of the initial substances. Planck extended this by stating that the value of the entropy for each condensed phase is zero at absolute zero.

net radiometer. An instrument for measuring the difference in intensity between radiation entering and leaving the earth's surface. The radiation can be direct, diffuse, and reflected solar radiation or infrared radiation from the sky, clouds, and ground. A similar thermopile system is used to that found in *solarimeters, except that both sides of the thermopile are exposed to radiation and the resulting e.m.f. is pro-

portional to the difference in intensity of the incoming and outgoing radiation. *See also* pyrheliometer.

network. A number of electrical conductors connected together to form a number of interrelated circuits. The conductors include resistors, inductors, and capacitors in all forms. The *network parameters* (or constants) are the actual resistances, inductances, etc., in the network. They are *linear* or *non-linear* respectively according to whether or not their values are independent of the magnitude of the current in them. They are *bilateral* or *unilateral* respectively according to whether or not they will pass currents in both directions. A network is described as *passive* if it contains no source or sink of energy (the latter does not include energy dissipated in the resistance elements of the network); otherwise it is described as *active*. A point in the network at which more than two conductors meet is called a *branch point* and a conducting path between two branch points is called a *branch*. A *mesh* is the portion of the network included in any closed conducting loop in the network.

Neumann's law. *See* electromagnetic induction.

neutral current. *See* neutral weak current.

neutral equilibrium. *See* equilibrium.

neutral filter. A light filter that absorbs equally all wavelengths: it reduces light intensity without change of relative spectral distribution.

neutralization. The provision of negative *feedback in an amplifier to a degree sufficient to neutralize any inherent positive feedback. Positive feedback in an amplifier is usually undesirable since it may give rise to the production of oscillations. Neutralization is commonly

255

employed with radio-frequency amplifiers to counteract the *Miller effect, and also with *push–pull operation to avoid *parasitic oscillations.

neutral temperature. For a *thermocouple with one junction maintained at $0°$ C, the temperature θ of the hot junction causes the e.m.f. E to vary according to the formula $E = \alpha\theta^2 + \beta\theta$, where α, β are constants. The maximum value of E occurs when $\theta = -\beta/2\alpha$; this is called the neutral temperature. It is usual to restrict the use of the thermocouple to the range between $0°$ C and θ.

neutral weak current. In an *electromagnetic interaction between two moving charged particles, a photon is exchanged. An alternative description is that the motion of one charged particle gives rise to a current that attracts or repels a similar current associated with the other particle. The force thus operates between the two currents, called *neutral currents*, since the charge of each particle is unchanged.

In a *weak interaction, the force is thought to operate through the exchange of a massive particle, the hypothetical *W-particle, which may be charged or neutral. When a proton is struck by a neutrino of the muon type (ν_μ), the proton is disrupted into a debris of other particles and either a negative muon or a ν_μ is present in the final state. In the first interaction charge is exchanged, through a W^+ particle, and the process is a *charged current* process. In the second interaction charge is conserved, a W° being exchanged, and the process is a neutral weak current one.

The existence of neutral weak currents would provide evidence for the theory that electromagnetic and weak interactions are aspects of the same force. They have been detected in experiments with beams of high-energy neutrinos and antineutrinos.

neutrino. A stable elementary particle with *spin $\frac{1}{2}$ that only takes part in *weak interactions. Neutrinos are thought to have zero mass and according to the theory of *relativity must therefore always travel at the speed of light. The neutrino's existence was first postulated in order to explain an apparent violation of the laws of conservation of energy and angular momentum in *beta decay. Two kinds of neutrino are now known; one is associated with the electron (ν_e) and the other with the muon (ν_μ). Two examples of reactions involving these particles are:

$$n \to p + e^- + \bar{\nu}_e \quad \text{(beta decay)}$$
$$\pi^- \to \mu^- + \bar{\nu}_\mu$$

Here $\bar{\nu}_e$ and $\bar{\nu}_\mu$ are the *antiparticles of $\bar{\nu}_e$ and $\bar{\nu}_\mu$. *See also* lepton; Table 8, page 425.

neutron. An elementary particle, having zero charge and a rest mass of $1 \cdot 674\,92 \times 10^{-27}$ kg ($939 \cdot 6$ MeV/c^2), that is a constituent of the atomic *nucleus. The absence of charge allows the neutron to penetrate the open structure of the atom but makes it difficult to detect. Free neutrons are unstable and decay by *beta decay with a mean life of 932 s. Although this decay is a *weak interaction it is considerably slower than the usual weak decay, which can be as short as 10^{-21} s. The difference in mass between the proton and neutron, representing available energy for the decay, is only about $1 \cdot 3$ MeV and it is this that slows down the decay. However, when bound in a nucleus, the neutron is stable. The neutron has *spin $J = \frac{1}{2}$, *isospin $I = \frac{1}{2}$, and positive *parity. *See also* Table 8, page 425.

neutron age. One sixth of the mean square displacement of a neutron as it slows down, through a specified energy range, in an infinite homogeneous medium. *See* Fermi age theory.

neutron diffraction. A technique for determining the crystal structure of solids by diffraction of a beam of neutrons. It is similar in principle to *electron diffraction and can be used in place of *X-ray crystallography. The wavelength of a neutron is related to its velocity by the *de Broglie equation, a neutron with a velocity of about 4×10^3 m s^{-1} having a wavelength of about 10^{-10} m.

neutron excess. *See* isotopic number.

neutron flux. *Syn.* neutron flux density. The product of the number of free neutrons per unit volume and their mean speed. The neutron flux in a *power reactor lies in the range 10^{16}–10^{18} per square metre per second.

neutron number. Symbol: N. The number of neutrons present in the nucleus of an atom. The neutron number is obtained by subtracting the *atomic number from the *mass number.

neutron star. After exhausting the nuclear sources of energy a star contracts under gravitation to a stage of electron *degeneracy. If the star is massive enough (greater than about 1·4 solar masses) the density exceeds 10^5 kg m^{-3} and the electrons become relativistic. The pressure increases at a slow rate and further contraction can occur. When the density exceeds 10^7 kg m^{-3} equilibrium between protons, electrons, and neutrons shifts in favour of the neutrons until at densities of 5×10^{10} kg m^{-3} 90% of the protons and electrons have interacted to form neutrons. If the mass of the star is less than 2·0 solar masses, strong repulsive forces between neutrons are set up causing a rapid rise in pressure. Contraction is halted and a stable neutron star is formed. *Pulsars are examples of neutron stars.

new candle. *See* candela.

newton. Symbol: N. The *SI unit of *force, defined as the force that provides

a mass of one kilogramme with an acceleration of one metre per second per second.

Newtonian fluid. A fluid in which the amount of strain is proportional both to the stress and to the time. The constant of proportionality is known as the coefficient of viscosity. *See* viscosity; anomalous viscosity.

Newtonian force. *Syn.* Coulomb force. A force between points which falls off as the inverse square of the distance between them.

Newtonian frame of reference. *See* Newtonian system.

Newtonian mechanics. *See* Newton's laws of motion.

Newtonian system or frame of reference. Any frame of reference relative to which a particle of mass m, subject to a force F moves in accordance with the equation $F = kma$ where a is the acceleration of the particle, m its mass and k a universal positive constant equal to unity in *SI units.

Such a frame of reference is one in which the centre of mass of the solar system is fixed, and which does not rotate relative to the fixed stars. Any other frame of reference which moves relative to this with a uniform velocity is also a Newtonian system; this is the classical principle of *relativity. For non-Newtonian systems, e.g. a frame of reference fixed to the earth's surface, Newton's equation $F = kma$ can be made to hold if the fictitious inertial forces are added to F.

Newtonian telescope. *See* reflecting telescope.

Newton's formula (for a lens). The distances p and q between two conjugate points and their respective foci are related by $pq = f^2$. For a mirror, the foci coincide but the relationship is unaltered.

Newton's law of cooling. The rate of loss of heat from a body is proportional to the excess temperature of the body over the temperature of its surroundings. Strictly the law applies only if there is *forced convection, but provided the temperature excess is small the law is fairly well obeyed even in the case of free or natural convection.

Newton's law of gravitation. *See* gravitation.

Newton's laws of fluid friction. (1) The force of resistance, D, opposing the relative motion of a body and a fluid is proportional to the square of the relative velocity, the density of fluid, and to some projected area of the body, i.e. $D = k_0 A V^2 \rho$ (*compare* drag coefficient). The law was formulated from considerations of the change of momentum in the direction of relative motion. (2) The shearing force between two infinitesimal layers of viscous fluid is proportional to the rate of shear in a direction perpendicular to the direction of motion of the layers. This force is expressed: $F = \eta \partial u / \partial y$, where u is the velocity in the direction of motion and y is perpendicular to the direction of u. η is called the coefficient of viscosity, and in classical hydrodynamics is a factor peculiar to the molecular nature of the fluid alone. *See* viscosity.

Newton's laws of motion. The three fundamental laws of motion which are the basis of *Newtonian mechanics*:
  Law I. Every body perseveres in its state of rest or uniform motion in a straight line except in so far as it is compelled to change that state by forces impressed on it. This may be regarded as a definition of force.
  Law II. The rate of change of linear momentum is proportional to the force applied, and takes place in the straight

line in which that force acts. This definition can be regarded as formulating a suitable way by which forces may be measured, that is, by the acceleration they produce,

$$F = \frac{\mathrm{d}}{\mathrm{d}t}(mv);$$

i.e.

$$F = ma + v\frac{\mathrm{d}m}{\mathrm{d}t}$$

where F = force, m = mass, v = velocity, t = time, and a = acceleration. In the majority of non-relativistic cases, $\mathrm{d}m/\mathrm{d}t = 0$ (i.e. the mass remains constant), and then

$$F = ma.$$

  Law III. An action is always opposed by an equal reaction: the mutual actions of two bodies are always equal and act in opposite directions.
  A more general system of mechanics has been given by Einstein in his theory of *relativity. This reduces to Newtonian mechanics when all velocities relative to the observer are small compared with those of light.

Newton's rings. Circular interference fringes formed between a lens and a glass plate with which the lens is in contact. There is a central dark spot around which there are concentric dark rings. The radius of the nth ring is given by $r_n = \sqrt{n\lambda R}$, where λ is the wavelength and R the radius of curvature of the lens.

Nicholson's hydrometer. *See* hydrometer.

Nichrome. A heat-resistant alloy used in electrical heating elements. The composition varies but is approximately 62 % Ni, 15 % Cr, and 23 % Fe.

nickel–iron accumulator. *See* Edison accumulator.

Nicol prism. A prism made of calcite used for polarizing light and analysing

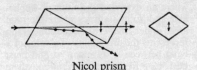

Nicol prism

plane-polarized light, e.g. in polarized microscopes. The crystal is cut in a special direction, sliced and recemented together with Canada balsam. Light entering one face is doubly refracted; the extraordinary ray passes straight forward through the balsam, whereas the ordinary ray is reflected out of the way (*see* diagram). The emerging extraordinary ray is plane-polarized with vibrations parallel to the short diagonal of the rhomb-shaped section as viewed from the emergent face.

night glasses. *See* refracting telescope.

nit. Symbol: nt. A unit of *luminance, defined as one candela per metre squared. The unit is identical with the *SI unit of luminance, but the name has not received international recognition.

Nixie tube. *See* digitron.

nodal line. *See* Euler's angles.

nodal points. *See* centred optical systems.

node. (1) A point or region in an interference pattern at which some characteristic of the wave motion, such as particle displacement, particle velocity, or pressure amplitude, has a minimum (or zero) value. Nodes commonly occur in *standing waves. *Compare* antinode. (2) A point at which the current or voltage is zero, e.g. a point of zero amplitude on a radio wave, or a junction point in a *network. (3) The two points at which the orbit of a celestial body intersects the ecliptic (*see* celestial sphere).

node voltage. Of a network. The voltage of some point in the network with respect to a *node.

noise. (1) (general) Sound that is undesired by the recipient, usually a discordant sound which is neither music nor speech. The frequency components of a noise can be determined with a sound analyser but it is usually only necessary to know its loudness. This is expressed either in decibels or phons.

(2) Spurious unwanted energy (or the associated voltage) in an electronic or communication system. *Interference often produces noise. There are two main types of noise, *white noise* and *impulse noise*. White noise has a wide frequency spectrum and is usually *thermal noise* or *random noise*. Thermal noise is due to the thermodynamic interchange of energy in a material or between a material and its surroundings. Random noise is due to any random transient disturbances. White noise in a communication system gives rise to loudspeaker hiss or television screen snow. Impulse noise is due to a single momentary disturbance or a number of such disturbances when they are separated from one another in time. In audiofrequency amplifiers this type of noise gives rise to clicks in the loudspeaker. *See also* Schottky noise; Jansky noise.

noise factor. A measure of the *noise introduced into a circuit or device. It is defined as the ratio of the *signal-to-noise power ratio at the source to the corresponding ratio at the output, i.e. the ratio of the actual noise at the output to the noise at the output due only to the source.

no-load. Of an electrical machine, transformer, etc. Operation with no output but under rated conditions of voltage, speed, etc.

nondegeneracy. The normal state of matter, i.e. matter not raised to a very high temperature nor subject to excessive stress such that the density is abnormally high. A nondegenerate gas is characterized by Maxwell's law of the *distribution of velocities.

nonlinear distortion. *See* distortion (electrical).

nonlinear optics. The study of the electro-optical effects produced by the electric fields of very intense light beams and causing changes in the optical properties of the medium through which they pass. For instance the local refractive index of glass can be increased by the passage of an intense laser beam, making the beam narrower and thus even more intense. The resulting electric field may eventually shatter the glass. If two intense laser beams are sent through a suitable crystal the nonlinear effects can result in the production of radiation whose frequency is equal to the sum or the difference of the original frequencies.

non-Newtonion fluid. *See* anomalous viscosity.

nonreactive. An electric circuit or winding in which, for the purpose in view, the *reactance is negligible.

nonreactive load. A *load in which the alternating current is in phase with the terminal voltage. *Compare* reactive load.

nonvortical field. *See* curl.

NOR circuit. *See* logic circuit.

normal. The normal to any surface at a point is the line perpendicular to the tangent plane at that point.

normal distribution. *Syn.* Gaussian distribution. *See* frequency distribution.

normalization. The process of introducing a numerical factor into an equation $y = f(x)$ (in which $y \to 0$ as $x \to \pm\infty$) so that the area under the corresponding graph (if finite) shall be made equal to unity. The process is of importance (a) in quantum mechanics

where an extended definition is applicable and (b) in statistics where the total area under the error equation graph represents the probability of a value of x lying between $+\infty$ and $-\infty$ and must be 1. (*See* frequency distribution, where $h\pi^{-\frac{1}{2}}$ is the *normalizing factor*.)

note. (1) A musical sound of specified pitch (frequency) produced by a musical instrument, voice, etc. (2) A sign in a musical score representing pitch and time value of a musical sound.

NOT gate. *See* logic circuit.

nova. A faint *variable star that can undergo a considerable explosion during which the *luminosity increases by up to 100 000 times. The luminosity then slowly decreases to its original value.

n–p–n transistor. *See* transistor.

NTP. Normal temperature and pressure. *See* STP.

n-type conductivity. Conductivity in a *semiconductor caused by a flow of electrons.

n-type semiconductor. An *extrinsic semiconductor in which the density of conduction *electrons exceeds that of mobile *holes.

nuclear barrier. *Syn.* Gamow barrier. A region of high potential energy that a charged particle must pass through in order to enter or leave an atomic nucleus.

nuclear energy. The energy released during a *nuclear fusion or *fission process. *See* binding energy.

nuclear energy change. *See* Q-value.

nuclear fission. *See* fission.

nuclear force. *Syn.* strong nuclear interaction. An extremely strong attractive force binding pairs of *nucleons together inside a nucleus. It acts over a distance that is less than 10^{-15} m and is of sufficient magnitude to overcome electrostatic repulsion between protons, being about 137 times stronger. The force exhibits *charge independence*; i.e. the force appears to be unaffected by the charge on a proton and is of the same magnitude between any two nucleons (proton–proton, neutron–neutron, proton–neutron), provided they have the same angular momentum and spin. It is thought to result from the exchange of a *virtual pion between the nucleons, within about 10^{-24} seconds, the reactions being:

$$n \rightleftharpoons p + \pi^-$$
$$p \rightleftharpoons n + \pi^+$$
$$n \rightleftharpoons n + \pi^0$$
$$p \rightleftharpoons p + \pi^0$$

See also strong interactions; isospin.

nuclear fusion. A *nuclear reaction between light atomic nuclei in which a heavier nucleus is formed with the release of energy (*see* binding energy). This process is the basis of the production of energy in stars (*see* carbon cycle). It was first demonstrated on earth when the first hydrogen bomb was exploded. Considerable efforts are now being made to produce a controlled thermonuclear reaction in *fusion reactors.

The principal fusion reactions that are likely to be used in any future fusion reactors are:

$${}^2_1H + {}^2_1H \rightarrow {}^3_2He + n \quad\quad + 3\cdot2\ \text{MeV}$$
$${}^2_1H + {}^2_1H \rightarrow {}^3_1H + {}^1_1H \quad\quad + 4\cdot0\ \text{MeV}$$
$${}^2_1H + {}^3_1H \rightarrow {}^4_2He + n \quad\quad + 17\cdot6\ \text{MeV}$$
$${}^2_1H + {}^3_2He \rightarrow {}^4_2He + {}^1_1H \quad + 18\cdot3\ \text{MeV}$$
$${}^6_3Li + {}^1_1H \rightarrow {}^3_2He + {}^4_2He \quad + 4\cdot0\ \text{MeV}$$
$${}^6_3Li + {}^3_2He \rightarrow {}^4_2He + {}^4_2He$$
$$\quad\quad\quad\quad\quad\quad + {}^1_1H + 16\cdot9\ \text{MeV}$$
$${}^6_3Li + {}^2_1H \rightarrow {}^7_3Li + {}^1_1H \quad\quad + 5\cdot0\ \text{MeV}$$
$${}^6_3Li + {}^2_1H \rightarrow {}^3_2He + {}^4_2He$$
$$\quad\quad\quad\quad\quad\quad + n + 2\cdot6\ \text{MeV}$$
$${}^6_3Li + {}^2_1H \rightarrow 2{}^4_2He \quad\quad\quad + 22\cdot4\ \text{MeV}$$
$${}^7_3Li + {}^1_1H \rightarrow 2{}^4_2He \quad\quad\quad + 17\cdot5\ \text{MeV}$$

nuclear heat of reaction. *See* Q-value.

nuclear isomers. When nuclei exist with the same mass number and atomic number (*see* isobar; isotopes) but show different radioactive properties, they are said to be nuclear isomers. They represent different energy states of the nucleus.

nuclear magnetic resonance (NMR). An effect observed when radio-frequency radiation is absorbed by matter. A nucleus with a *spin has a nuclear *magnetic moment. In the presence of an external magnetic field this magnetic moment precesses (*see* precession) about the field direction. Only certain orientations of the magnetic moment are allowed and each of these has a slightly different energy.

If the nucleus has a spin I there are $2I + 1$ different energy levels due to this quantization; each is characterized by a different value of the magnetic quantum number m which can have values $I, I - 1, \ldots -(I - 1), -I$. The difference in energy levels depends on the strength of the applied magnetic field. The nucleus can make a transition from one level to another with the emission or absorption of electromagnetic radiation according to a selection rule that $\Delta m = 1$. The technique used is to apply a strong magnetic field (~ 2 tesla) to the sample, which is usually a liquid or solid. An RF field (1–100 MHz) is imposed at right angles and a small detector coil is wound around the sample. As the magnetic field is varied the spacing of the energy levels changes and at a certain value of the magnetic field this spacing is such that radio-frequency radiation is strongly absorbed. This *resonance produces a signal in the detector coil. A plot of the detected signal against the magnetic field gives an NMR spectrum which can be used for determining nuclear magnetic moments. The energy levels of the nuclei depend to some extent on the surrounding orbital electrons and this is useful in studying chemical compounds. *See also* electron spin resonance.

nuclear magneton. *See* magneton.

nuclear medicine. The branch of medicine concerned with the use of radioisotopes in the diagnosis and treatment of disease, especially cancer. A radioisotope will follow the same path inside the body as a non-radioactive normally-ingested isotope of the same element, and will accumulate in the same areas. Measurement of the radioactivity at these areas will indicate any abnormal activity in the body. A high level of radioactivity means that there are overactive cancer cells present. The most common uses of radioisotopes are the diagnosis and treatment of thyroid disorders, kidney studies, and liver studies.

Equipment commonly used includes *scintillation counters, *Geiger counters, *scanners, and *gamma cameras, often with computer analysis of the outputs of this equipment.

nuclear power station. A power station in which *nuclear energy is converted into electrical energy in a *nuclear reactor. *Compare* thermal power station; hydroelectric power station.

nuclear reaction. A reaction between an atomic *nucleus and a bombarding particle or photon leading to the creation of a new nucleus and the possible ejection of one or more particles. Nuclear reactions are often represented by enclosing within a bracket the symbols for the incoming or outgoing particles or quanta, the initial and final nuclides being shown outside the bracket. For example:

$$^{14}N(\alpha, p)^{17}O$$

represents the reaction:

$$^{14}_{7}N + {}^{4}_{2}He = {}^{17}_{8}O + {}^{1}_{1}H.$$

nuclear reactors. 1. *Energy from nuclear fission.* On the whole, the nuclei of atoms of moderate size are more tightly held together than the largest nuclei, so that if the nucleus of a heavy atom can be induced to split into two nuclei of moderate mass, there should be a considerable release of energy (*see* binding energy). The uranium isotope of mass number 235 will readily accept a neutron but the nucleus ^{236}U so formed is very unstable and almost instantaneously splits up. In this *fission, two or three neutrons are released and these and the fission fragments carry away much of the energy released as kinetic energy while some is radiated as gamma-radiation. The total energy released is about 3×10^{-11} joule per atom or 7.5×10^{13} joules per kilogramme (by comparison, coal releases about 4×10^7 joules per kilogramme).

To extract energy in a controlled manner from fissionable nuclei, arrangements must be made for a sufficient proportion of the neutrons released in the fissions to cause further fissions in their turn, so that the process is continuous (*see* chain reaction). At present, the energy released is made available as heat and is used in the same way as ordinary fuel in order to raise steam, etc.

2. *Types of reactor.* A reactor with pure ^{235}U or plutonium ^{239}Pu as fuel uses the fast neutrons as they are liberated from the fission; such a reactor is called a *fast reactor*. Natural uranium contains 0.7% of ^{235}U and if the liberated neutrons can be slowed down before they have much chance of meeting ^{238}U atoms, the latter are not likely to absorb them. A high proportion of the neutrons will then travel on until they meet a ^{235}U atom and then cause another fission. To slow the neutrons, a *moderator* is used containing light atoms to which the neutrons will give kinetic energy by collision. As the neutrons eventually acquire energies appropriate to gas molecules at the temperature of the moderator, they are then said to be *thermal neutrons and the reactor is a *thermal reactor*.

3. *Thermal reactors.* In a typical thermal reactor, the fuel elements are rods embedded as a regular array in the bulk of the moderator. The typical neutron from a fission process has a good chance of escaping from the relatively thin fuel rod and making many collisions with nuclei in the moderator before again entering a fuel element. Suitable moderators are pure graphite, heavy water, and ordinary water. The reactor *core is surrounded by a *reflector* made of suitable material to reduce the escape of neutrons from the surface. Each *fuel element is encased (e.g. in an aluminium can) to prevent escape of radioactive fission products. The *coolant, which may be gaseous or liquid, flows along the channels over the canned fuel elements. The assembly is surrounded by a massive *biological shield, with an inner iron *thermal shield* to protect the concrete from the high temperature of the reactor core.

To keep the power production steady, *control rods are moved in or out of the assembly. These contain material which captures neutrons readily (e.g. cadmium or boron). The power production can be held steady by allowing the currents in suitably placed *ionization chambers automatically to modify the settings of the rods. Further absorbent rods, the shut-down rods, are driven into the core to stop the reaction, as in an emergency if the control mechanism fails. To attain high thermodynamic efficiency so that a large proportion of the liberated energy can be converted into electrical energy, the heat should be extracted from the reactor core at a high temperature. *See* gas-cooled, boiling-water, pressurized water, and heavy water reactors.

4. *Fast reactors.* In fast reactors no moderator is used, the frequency of collisions between neutrons and fissile atoms being increased by enriching the natural uranium fuel with ^{239}Pu or additional ^{235}U atoms which are fissioned by fast neutrons. The fast neutrons thus build up a self-sustaining chain reaction. In these reactors the core is usually surrounded by a blanket of natural uranium into which some of the neutrons are allowed to escape. Under suitable conditions some of these neutrons will be captured by ^{238}U atoms, which will be converted to $^{239}_{94}$Pu. As more plutonium can be produced than is required to enrich the fuel in the core, these are called *fast breeder reactors.

nuclear recoil. The mechanical recoil suffered by the residual nucleus of an atom on radioactive or other disintegration. It can lead to physical effects such as abnormally high volatilities, or to chemical effects such as initiation of polymerization or molecular rupture. *See also* Mössbauer effect.

nuclear weapons. The first nuclear weapon was the *atom bomb* or *A-bomb*, which consisted of two small masses of fissile material each of which was below the *critical mass. When the bomb was detonated the two subcritical masses were brought rapidly together to form a super-critical mass within which a single *fission set off an uncontrollable *chain reaction. This first bomb consisted of only a few kilogrammes of uranium-235, but it had an explosive effect of 20 000 tons (20 kilotons) of TNT. Later models of the A-bomb used plutonium to even greater effect, but these weapons are small compared with the *hydrogen* or *fusion* or *H-bomb*, which consists of a fission bomb surrounded by a layer of solid hydrogeneous material, such as lithium deuteride. The fission bomb elevates the temperature of the hydrogen to its *ignition temperature so that a *nuclear fusion reaction takes place with the evolution of enormous quantities of energy – equivalent to tens of megatons of TNT.

nucleon. The collective term for a proton or neutron, *i.e.* for a constituent of an atomic nucleus. *See* isospin.

nucleon number. *See* mass number.

nucleonics. The practical applications of nuclear science and the techniques associated with these applications.

nucleor. The postulated core of a *nucleon, thought to be surrounded by a cloud of *pions.

nucleus. The most massive part of the atom having a positive charge given by Ze, where Z is the *atomic number of the element and e the charge on an electron. The radius (in metres) has been shown to be related to the mass number A of an atom by the formula: $r = c \cdot A^{\frac{1}{3}}$, where c is a constant equal to $1 \cdot 5 \times 10^{-15}$.

Nuclei consist of protons and neutrons collectively called *nucleons. The number of protons in nuclei of the same element is equal to the atomic number Z. The number of neutrons N associated with the Z protons varies within limits, the different numbers of neutrons giving rise to the various isotopes of that element. The total number of nucleons in a given isotopic nucleus is called the mass number A.

A nucleus is completely defined by the value of its atomic number Z and mass number A. This allows an abbreviated form of nomenclature in which a given nucleus is represented by its chemical symbol with Z and A as subscript and superscript respectively, e.g. the common uranium isotopes are $^{235}_{92}U$ and $^{238}_{92}U$.

The nucleons are maintained within a roughly spherical volume by *nuclear forces. These attractive binding forces act between pairs of nucleons being operative over a distance that is less than the nuclear radius. Various theories, such as the *liquid drop model and the *shell model, have been put forward to explain the structure of the nucleus.

The mass of a given nucleus is always less than the sum of the rest masses of the constituent nucleons. This is due to the conversion of mass into energy on creation of the nucleus. The energy equivalent of the mass lost (mass defect) is indicative of the degree of cohesion of the nucleons and is known as the *binding energy of the nucleus.

Most naturally occurring atoms have stable nuclei. The naturally occurring radioactive atoms have unstable nuclei giving rise to nuclear transmutations in which the atomic number is altered and the product atom is chemically different. Artificial nuclei are produced by bombarding stable nuclei with high energy charged particles such as protons, deuterons, etc., or with neutrons. The collision process which occurs is called a *nuclear reaction. *See also* radioactivity; elementary particles.

nuclide. An atom as characterized by its *atomic number, *mass number, and nuclear energy state.

null method. *Syn.* balance method. A method of measurement in which the quantity being measured is balanced by another of a similar kind so that the indicating instrument reading is adjusted to zero (e.g. *Wheatstone bridge).

number of poles. Of a switch, circuit-breaker, or similar apparatus. The number of different electrical conducting paths that the device closes or opens simultaneously. The device is described as single-pole, double-pole, triple-pole, or multipole if it is suitable for making or breaking an electrical circuit on one pole, two poles, three poles, or more than one pole respectively.

numerical aperture (N.A.). A parameter used to express the angle of view of *objectives used in *microscopes and also the light-gathering power of these lenses. It is the product of the refractive index of the medium in which the objective is situated (air, oil, etc.) and the sine of half the angle of view of the objective. As the numerical aperture is increased, the *resolving power of the microscope improves.

Nusselt number. The dimensionless group $(hl/\lambda\theta)$, where h is the rate of loss of heat per unit area of a hot body immersed in a fluid, l is a typical dimension of the body, θ is the temperature difference between the body and the fluid, and λ is the thermal conductivity of the fluid. *See* convection (of heat).

nutation. *See* Euler's angles.

Nyquist noise theorem. The law that relates the power P due to thermal *noise in a resistor to the frequency f of the signal. At ordinary temperatures T,

$$dP = kT\,df$$

where k is the *Boltzmann constant.

O

O.A.S.M. system. A system of fundamental units based on the ohm, ampere, second, and metre.

object. Extended natural objects consist of points, self-luminous or otherwise, that deliver diverging pencils of light. They are classed as real objects when they are delivering rays to some optical system under consideration. Commonly an optical system may focus an image real or virtual in front of a second system – this image becomes a real object for the second system. If the second system lies in such a position as to intercept the rays before they have converged to a focus, the real image from the first system becomes the virtual object for the second system. Incident rays are convergent when a virtual object is under consideration. The *object space* is a mathematical conception covering both the region lying in front of the system (real) and behind the system (virtual) in which real or virtual objects may lie, and possessing the same refractive index throughout – that of the preceding region. It completely coexists with the similarly conceived image space.

objective. The lens (generally compound), in an optical instrument, that lies nearest to the object viewed.

observable. The name used for the measurable things of physical science. In *quantum mechanics they are represented by matrices (matrix mechanics) or, alternatively, by operators (wave mechanics).

occultation. The passage of the moon in front of a star or planet thus obscuring its light, radio emission, etc. Planets can sometimes occult stars and also their satellites. Occultations by the moon give an accurate determination of the moon's position.

octave. An *interval having the frequency ratio 2:1.

octode. A *thermionic valve having five grids between the cathode and the main anode and an additional anode between the two innermost grids (i.e. a total of eight electrodes). It is usually employed as a combined *mixer and *beat oscillator.

ocular. *See* eyepiece.

odd–even nucleus. A nucleus that contains an odd number of *protons and an even number of *neutrons.

odd–odd nucleus. A nucleus that contains an odd number of both *protons and *neutrons. Most of these nuclei are unstable.

oersted. Symbol: Oe. The *CGS electromagnetic unit of magnetic field strength. $1 \text{ Oe} = 10^3/4\pi \text{ A m}^{-1}$.

ohm. Symbol: Ω. The *SI unit of electric *resistance, defined as the resistance between two points on a conductor through which a current of one ampere flows as a result of a potential difference of one volt applied between the points, the conductor not being a source of electromagnetic force. This unit replaced the *international ohm* (Ω_{int}), defined as the resistance of a column of mercury of mass 14·4521 grammes, length 106·300 cm at 0° C, and uniform cross section. $1 \; \Omega_{int} = 1·000 \; 49 \; \Omega$.

ohmic contact. A contact in which the potential difference across it is proportional to the current flowing through it.

ohmic loss. Power dissipation in an electrical circuit arising from its resistance rather than from other causes such as back e.m.f.

Ohm's law. The electrical current in any conductor is proportional to the potential difference between its ends, other factors remaining constant. As the ratio of potential difference to current in a conductor is termed the resistance of the conductor, Ohm's law is often expressed as $I = V/R$, where I is the current, V is the potential difference, and R the resistance.

oil-immersion (microscope). *See* resolving power; immersion objective.

Olbers's paradox. The idea of an infinite number of stars, uniformly distributed in space, was once thought to mean that the night sky should glow with uniform brightness. The assumption of a finite number of stars is unnecessary to explain the dark night sky as the recession of galaxies, as indicated by their *red shifts, causes the brightness of distant stars to be greatly diminished.

omega–minus (Ω^-) particle. An *elementary particle classified as a *hyperon. *See* unitary symmetry.

omni-aerial. An aerial of any type which is essentially non-directional, i.e. which is equally effective as a radiator (or collector) of energy in all directions having the same angle of elevation.

opacity. The ratio of the *radiant flux incident on the subject (e.g. part of an exposed and processed photographic plate) to the flux transmitted. It is the reciprocal of *transmittance.

open circuit. *See* circuit.

operating point. Of a *transistor or *valve. The point on the family of *characteristic curves representing the

magnitudes of voltage and current for the particular operating conditions under consideration.

operational amplifier. A high gain, high input-impedance, *direct-coupled amplifier invariably used with considerable external *feedback which completely determines its transfer *characteristics. It normally has a differential stage at the input allowing a choice of inverting and non-inverting inputs and is usually supplied as a complete packaged unit either of hybrid construction or more commonly as a single monolithic *integrated circuit. It is used in a very wide range of instrumentation and control applications.

Oppenheimer–Phillips (O–P) process. *See* stripping.

opposition. Any two celestial bodies are in opposition with respect to a third body, such as the earth, when they lie on diametrically opposite sides of the third body (*see* diagram). The sun and moon are in opposition at full moon. Any two

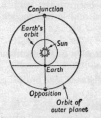

Opposition and conjunction

celestial bodies are in *conjunction* when a third reference body lies on an extension of the line joining the two bodies. The sun and moon are in conjunction at new moon.

optical activity. The ability of certain solutions and crystals to rotate the plane of polarization of plane polarized light in proportion to the length of substance traversed and to the concentration in the case of solutions. When looking towards the oncoming light, if the rotation is clockwise the optical activity is called right-handed (*dextrorotatory*); if anticlockwise, it is called left-handed (*laevorotatory*).

optical (or optic) axis. (1) The path of rays passing through the centres of the entrance pupil and exit pupil of an optical system. The cardinal points lie on this line. (2) The direction (not a single line) in a doubly refracting crystal in which the ordinary and extraordinary rays apparently do not exhibit *double refraction, while their velocities are equal, i.e. the direction in a crystal along which the polarized components of a ray of light will be transmitted with a single velocity.

optical centre. A point on the surface of a lens where the optical axis intersects the surface. For thicker lenses it is defined as that axial point through which all undeviated rays pass (incident and emergent rays parallel with or without lateral displacement). Its position depends only on the surface radii and thickness, and is independent of wavelength.

optical density. *See* transmission density.

optical distance. *See* optical path.

optical flat. A surface which is so flat that there are no irregularities of surface flatness greater than a fraction of the wavelength of light. The surface is tested by observing interference fringes when a known flat is placed in contact (*optical contact*).

optical glass. Glass with which special precautions are taken during manufacture to avoid mechanical and optical defects (density, strain, heterogeneity, colour, refractive index, etc.). The prescribed refractive indexes and dispersions must be measured to a high degree of accuracy in order to provide lenses corrected to various degrees of accuracy for chromatism and spherical aberration.

optically negative crystal. A crystal in which the ordinary refractive index (ω) is greater than the extraordinary (ε) for uniaxial crystals; or in which β is nearer to γ than to α in biaxial crystals. In an *optically positive crystal* $\omega < \varepsilon$ for uniaxial, or β nearer to α than to γ in biaxial crystals. Here, α, β, γ are the principal refractive indices, written in ascending order ($\alpha < \beta < \gamma$).

optical maser. *See* laser.

optical path. *Syn.* optical distance. The distance traversed by light multiplied by the refractive index of the medium (nd). When light passes through different media the total optical path is the sum $n_1d_1 + n_2d_2 + \ldots$ relating to each of the media. It is the distance in a vacuum that light would travel in the same time that it takes to pass through the distance d in the medium; it would contain the same number of waves in the vacuum as occur in the actual path in the medium, so that the optical paths between two wavefronts are all the same.

optical pyrometer. A *pyrometer in which the luminous radiation from the hot body is compared with that from a known source. The instrument therefore measures the temperature of a luminous source without thermal contact. The two chief types are the *disappearing filament pyrometer and the *polarizing pyrometer.

optical window. *See* atmospheric windows.

optic axis. *See* optical axis.

optics. A branch of physics concerned with the study of light, its production, propagation, measurement, and properties. The ray treatment of light is called *geometrical optics* as distinct from *physical optics*, which attempts to explain the objective phenomena of light.

optics sign conventions. In geometric optics two sign conventions are in use. In the *real-is-positive convention* (used in this dictionary) distances, measured from a lens or mirror to an object, image, focal point, etc., are considered positive if the objects, images, etc., are real and negative if they are virtual. The focal distance and the radius of curvature of a converging surface are considered positive and those of a diverging surface negative. In the *Cartesian sign convention* light is drawn moving left to right. Distances measured from the lens or mirror to an object, image, etc., are considered positive when in the same direction as the incident light and negative when against it. Transverse distances (heights, etc.) are considered positive if above the axis and negative if below it.

orbit. A curved path, such as that described by a planet or a comet in the field of force of the sun, or by a particle in a field of force. The term is especially used for the locus of an extra-nuclear electron in an *atom in the Rutherford–Bohr atomic model.

orbital. (1) *See* atomic orbital. (2) *See* molecular orbital.

orbital velocity. The velocity required by a *satellite or spacecraft to enter and maintain a particular orbit around the earth or some other celestial body. The orbital velocity needed for a 24-hour orbit (*see* synchronous orbit) around the earth is approximately 3·2 kilometres per second, at an altitude of about 36 000 km.

OR circuit. *See* logic circuit.

order of interference or diffraction. A whole number that characterizes a position of an interference fringe according to whether there is interference arising from one, two, three, etc., wavelength difference of path, or according to the direction of the maxima of illumination produced by diffraction.

ordinary ray. *See* double refraction.

orthochromatic film. Photographic film that is sensitive to green as well as to the blue end of the spectrum.

orthogonal. (1) Mutually perpendicular, as in orthogonal axes. (2) Having or involving a set of mutually perpendicular axes as in orthogonal crystals.

orthorhombic system. *See* crystal systems.

oscillation. (1) A vibration. (2) If the electrical equilibrium of a circuit possessing *self inductance and *capacitance is disturbed, an oscillating current may, under certain conditions, be produced in the circuit giving rise to electrical oscillations.

oscillator. An electric circuit in which electrical *oscillations occur freely. Usually the circuit is designed specifically for this purpose.

oscillogram. The record produced by a recording *oscillograph, or the reading from an *oscilloscope.

oscillograph. An *oscilloscope, especially one equipped to make a permanent record of the parameter being measured.

oscilloscope. An instrument used to produce a visual image of one or more rapidly varying electrical quantities. The *cathode-ray oscilloscope is the most usual type.

osmosis. A process in which certain kinds of molecules in a liquid are preferentially transmitted by a *semipermeable membrane; e.g. parchment will allow water

269

molecules to pass but will hinder sugar molecules. The hydrostatic pressure that balances osmosis, preventing solvent flow through a membrane, is the *osmotic pressure*. At great dilution and if the solute molecules do not dissociate, the osmotic pressure of a solution is equal to the pressure that the solute molecules would exert if they were a gas of the same volume. Thus the osmotic pressure (Π) of a solution is given by $\Pi V = RT$, where V is the volume of solution containing unit amount of solute. *See also* Van't Hoff factor.

osmotic pressure. *See* osmosis.

Ostwald viscometer. An instrument for measuring or comparing the viscosities of liquids, consisting of two bulbs at different heights connected by a capillary tube. The times t_1 and t_2 taken for each liquid to flow out of the upper bulb is measured. The viscosity is then given by $\eta_1/\eta_2 = \rho_1 t_2/\rho_2 t_1$, where ρ is the density.

Otto cycle. A four-stroke cycle, two strokes being charging and exhausting processes. After an explosive mixture of air and petrol has been drawn in, it is compressed adiabatically, A B, and fired at B after which the pressure and temperature are increased rapidly at

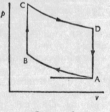

Otto cycle

constant volume, BC. The piston then moves out causing adiabatic expansion, CD, after which the exhaust valve opens reducing the pressure to atmospheric, DA. The next inward motion of the

piston sweeps out the exhaust gases to complete the cycle.

out of phase. *See* phase.

output. (1) The power, voltage, or current delivered by any circuit, device, or plant. (2) The terminals or other place where the signal is delivered.

output impedance. The *impedance presented to the *load by a circuit or device.

output transformer. A transformer used to couple an output circuit (usually of an *amplifier) to a load.

overcurrent release. *Syn.* overload release. A tripping device that operates when the current exceeds a predetermined value (usually adjustable).

overdamped. *See* damped.

overshoot. *See* pulse.

overtone. A constituent of a musical note other than the fundamental or lowest tone. The first overtone is the second *harmonic. Overtone and upper partial are synonymous terms. *See* partial.

overvoltage release. A *tripping device that operates when the voltage exceeds a predetermined value.

Owen bridge. A four arm a.c. bridge used to measure the self inductance, L, of an element in terms of the capacitance, C, and resistance, R, of other elements in the arms. The current in each arm is balanced by varying R_2 and then R_4 such that there is no potential difference between points A and B; then

$$\frac{R_1}{1/ifC_3} = \frac{ifL_2 + R_2}{R_4 + 1/ifC_4},$$

where f is the frequency and $i = \sqrt{-1}$.

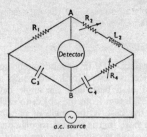

Owen bridge circuit

Equating real parts and imaginary parts of this equation gives: $R_1 R_4 C_3 = L_2$; $R_1 C_3 = R_2 C_4$. These relationships are thus independent of frequency.

oxygen point. The temperature of equilibrium between liquid and gaseous oxygen at a pressure of one standard atmosphere, taken as a fixed point in the *international temperature scale at 90·188 kelvin.

ozone layer. *Syn.* ozonosphere. *See* atmospheric layers.

P

pachimeter. An instrument for measuring the elastic shear limit of a solid material.

packing fraction. The fraction $f = (M - A)/A$ where M is the atomic mass of a nucleus and A its mass number. The curve of $f \times 10^4$ against A, in which $f = 0$ for ^{16}O, shows a minimum at about $A = 50$, the packing fraction being negative for mass numbers between 16 and 180. Positive values indicate a tendency to instability, and isotopes with these mass numbers ($16 > A > 180$) can be used in *nuclear fusion and *fission processes.

pad. *See* attenuator.

pair production. The simultaneous formation of a *positron and an *electron from a *photon. It occurs when a high energy gamma-ray photon (> 1.02 MeV) passes close to an atomic nucleus. *See also* annihilation.

palaeomagnetism. The study of the residual magnetization of certain rocks in order to determine the direction of polarization of the earth's magnetic field at the time of the rock's formation. The age of the rock can be found by radioactive *dating. A graph of polarity versus time shows that the earth's field has reversed many times during its history (i.e. north and south poles have interchanged) and that there is a variable period of time, a *magnetic interval*, between reversals.

panchromatic film. A photographic film that is sensitive to all colours of the visible spectrum.

paper tape. *Syn.* punched tape. A strip of paper upon which information is coded in the form of holes punched across it, each combination of holes representing a specific character, number, or symbol.

parallax. (1) If a moderately remote object is viewed from two points at the end of a base line, the angle between lines drawn from the object to each end of the base is the angle of parallax. If the base line is the interocular distance the angle is called *binocular parallax*. If two objects are in line with the eye and the eye is moved to the right, the further object demonstrates parallax by appearing to move to the right of the nearer object. Objects further away show the same parallactic displacement as that of the eye. An optical object and its image show an absence of parallax. (2) The *annual parallax* of a star is the maximum angle subtended at the star by the mean radius of the earth's orbit round the sun. (Mean in this connection is the average of the greatest and least values.) *See also* parsec.

parallel. Circuit elements connected so that the current divides between them and later re-unites are *in parallel*. For resistors of resistances $r_1, r_2, r_3, \ldots r_n$ in parallel (Fig. *a*), the total resistance R is given by

$$\frac{1}{R} = \frac{1}{r_1} + \frac{1}{r_2} + \frac{1}{r_3} + \ldots \frac{1}{r_n}.$$

The current in any branch is: $i_n = i(R/r_n)$ where i is the total current. For capacitors of capacitances $c_1, c_2, c_3, \ldots c_n$ in parallel (Fig. *b*), the total capacitance C is given by:

$$C = c_1 + c_2 + c_3 + \ldots c_n.$$

They behave as a large capacitor of the total plate area.

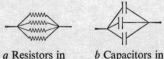

a Resistors in parallel   *b* Capacitors in parallel

paramagnetism. The property of substances that have a positive magnetic *susceptibility. It is caused by the *spins of electrons, paramagnetic substances having molecules or atoms in which there are unpaired electrons and thus a resulting magnetic *dipole moment. There is also a contribution to the magnetic properties from the orbital motion of the electron. The relative *permeability of a paramagnetic substance is thus greater than that of a vacuum, i.e. it is slightly greater than unity.

A paramagnetic substance is regarded as an assembly of magnetic dipoles that have random orientation. In the presence of a field the magnetization is determined by competition between the effect of the field, in tending to align the magnetic dipoles, and the random thermal agitation. For small fields and high temperatures the magnetization produced is proportional to the field strength. (At low temperatures or high field strengths a state of saturation is approached.) As the temperature rises the susceptibility falls according to *Curie's law or the *Curie–Weiss law.

Solids, liquids, and gases can exhibit paramagnetism. Some paramagnetic substances are ferromagnetic below their Curie point. (*See* ferromagnetism; diamagnetism; antiferromagnetism; ferrimagnetism.)

Certain metals, such as sodium and potassium, also exhibit a type of paramagnetism resulting from the magnetic moments of free, or nearly free, electrons in their conduction bands. This is characterized by a very small positive susceptibility and a very slight temperature dependence. It is known as *free electron paramagnetism* or *Pauli paramagnetism*.

parametric amplifier. A low noise microwave amplifier in which gain is achieved by periodically varying a circuit parameter, e.g. capacitance.

parasitic capture. *Capture of a neutron by an atomic nucleus without any consequent nuclear *fission occurring.

parasitic oscillations. Unwanted oscillations which may occur in the circuit of an amplifier or oscillator. Such oscillations usually have a frequency which is very much higher than the frequencies for which the circuit has been designed since the frequency is mainly determined by the stray inductances and capacitances of connecting leads and by interelectrode capacitances.

paraxial rays. Rays of light close to the optical axis of a system.

parent. *See* daughter product.

parity. *Syn.* space reflection symmetry. Symbol: P. The principle of parity invariance states that no fundamental distinction can be made between left and right; that the laws of physics are the same in a right-handed system of coordinates as they are in a left-handed system. This is true for all the phenomena described by classical physics. A *wave function, $\psi(x, y, z)$, describing a quantum mechanical system is said to have parity $+1$ if it remains unchanged on reflection through the origin, i.e. $\psi(x, y, z) = \psi(-x, -y, -z)$. If $\psi(x, y, z) = -\psi(-x, -y, -z)$ the wave function is said to have parity -1. In general wave functions do not have a definite parity since $\psi(-x, -y, -z)$ will not usually be proportional to $\psi(x, y, z)$. It is found that the wave functions describing individual elementary particles have a definite symmetry under reflection. This means that an intrinsic parity can be associated with elementary particles. The parity of the total wave function describing a system of elementary particles is conserved in *strong and *electromagnetic interactions but not in *weak interactions. Parity invariance requires that, if in some interaction a particle is produced with left-polarization (i.e. the particle spins in an opposite sense to the direction of motion) then it must also be possible for a right-polarized particle to be produced in a similar interaction and that, on average, equal numbers of each will occur. In *beta decay the electron is always left-polarized.

parsec. Symbol: pc. A unit of length, used in astronomy, equal to the distance at which a base line of one *astronomical unit subtends an angle of one second of arc. 1 parsec $= 3 \cdot 085\ 72 \times 10^{16}$ metres or about $3 \cdot 26$ light-years.

partial. A musical note consists generally of the simultaneous sounding of a group of tones, the frequency of each tone usually being related to the generating tone (viz. the fundamental) by the equation $A = nF$, where n is an integer, and A and F are frequencies of a tone of the series and of the fundamental respectively. Tones above the fundamental are known as overtones or upper partials, these two terms being synonymous. Harmonics are partials, but, since partials may be inharmonic, the converse may not be true.

partial pressure. The partial pressure of a gas in a mixture of gases occupying a fixed volume is the pressure that the gas would exert if it alone occupied the total volume. *See also* Dalton's law of partial pressures.

particle velocity. Symbol: u. The alternating component of the velocity of a medium that is transmitting sound. It is thus the total velocity of the medium minus the velocity that is not due to sound propagation. As the velocity is changing regularly with time the *root-mean-square value is usually taken.

partition function. *See* statistical mechanics.

parton model. A theory postulating that protons and neutrons have a substruc-ture made up of basic 'particles' called partons, which in the simplest form of the model can be identified with quarks. Experiments in which high-energy electrons were scattered by protons and neutrons have provided evidence for point-like substructures of hadrons, identified with partons. *See also* quark model.

pascal. Symbol: Pa. The *SI unit of *pressure, defined as the pressure that results from a force of one newton acting uniformly over an area of one square metre.

Pascal's principle. Pressure applied at any point of a fluid at rest is transmitted without loss to all other parts of the fluid. *See* hydraulic press.

Paschen–Back effect. An effect similar to the *Zeeman effect, but applicable to magnetic fields so strong that the vectors due to orbital and spin angular momentum of electrons each separately take up their possible orientations relative to the field direction. The hyperfine structure of spectral lines produced is quite different from that of the Zeeman effect, the lines being due to transitions between the energy levels of the electron orbits.

Paschen series. *See* hydrogen spectrum.

Paschen's law. The *breakdown voltage for a discharge between electrodes in gases is a function of the product of pressure and distance.

passive aerial. *See* directive aerial.

passive component. An electronic component that is not capable of amplifying or control function, e.g. resistors, capacitors, and inductors.

patching. A technique used in analog *computers enabling circuits to be connected together temporarily.

Pauli exclusion principle. The principle that no two *fermions can exist in identical quantum states. Thus no two electrons in an atom can be identical in all their *quantum numbers. An electron in an atom is characterized by four quantum numbers, n, l, m, and s. A particular *atomic orbital, which has fixed values of n, l, and m, can thus contain a maximum of two electrons since the *spin quantum number s can only be $+\frac{1}{2}$ or $-\frac{1}{2}$. Two electrons with opposing spins in an atomic orbital are said to be spin-paired.

Pauli paramagnetism. *See* paramagnetism.

p.d. Abbreviation for potential difference.

peak factor. The ratio of the *peak value of an alternating or pulsating quantity to its *root-mean-square value. For a sinusoidal quantity, the peak factor is $\sqrt{2}$.

peak inverse voltage. The maximum instantaneous voltage applied to a device in the reverse direction, i.e. the direction of maximum *resistance of the device. In a rectifying device it must be less than the *breakdown voltage of the device to prevent avalanche breakdown in a semiconductor or arc formation in a valve.

peak value. *Syn.* amplitude. The maximum positive or negative value of an alternating quantity or the maximum value of an *impulse voltage.

pelletron. *See* Van de Graaff generator.

Peltier constants. Constants that measure the heat developed (or absorbed) at the junction of a crystal bar and an isotropic metal, when the bar is cut with different crystallographic directions normal to the junction plane, and an electric current is then sent across the junction. *See* thermoelectric effects.

Peltier effect. *See* thermoelectric effects.

pencil (of rays). A slender cone or cylinder of rays that traverses an optical system, the pencil being limited by the *aperture stop. The central ray is the *chief ray.

pendulum. A device consisting of a mass, suspended from a fixed point, that oscillates with a known period, T. The various types include:

(1) *Simple pendulum.* A small weight suspended from a point by a light thread. The period of oscillation for small amplitudes of swing is determined by the formula $T = 2\pi\sqrt{l/g}$ where l is the length of the thread and g is the acceleration of *free fall.

(2) *Compound pendulum.* A rigid body of any convenient shape, e.g. a bar, swinging about an axis (usually a knife edge) through any point other than its centre of mass. The period, for small amplitudes of swing, is given by the formula for the simple pendulum in which l is replaced by

$$\frac{\sqrt{k^2 + h^2}}{h}$$

where k is the *radius of gyration about a parallel axis through the centre of mass, and h is the distance of the centre of mass from the axis of swing.

(3) *Horizontal pendulum.* A compound pendulum whose axis of rotation is nearly vertical. Used for finding the alteration in the direction of the force of gravity with time. A massive horizontal pendulum is the basis of a seismograph (known as the *Galitzin pendulum*).

(4) *Conical pendulum.* A simple pendulum in which the bob swings in a horizontal circle. The period, for a very small radius of swing only, is the same as for the simple pendulum.

penetrating shower. *See* cosmic rays.

Penning gauge. *Syn.* Philips's gauge. A high-vacuum gauge consisting of a wire ring electrode between two plates. 1000–2000 volts is applied between the ring and the plates. Electrons emitted from the plates move to the ring, but are compelled to do so in long spiral paths by an applied magnetic field. Ions are formed by collisions with remaining gas molecules and add to the normal current between the electrodes.

Penning ionization. The ionization of gas atoms or molecules by collision with *metastable atoms. The energy of the excited state is transferred to the gas particle, the metastable atom reverting to the ground state.

pentatonic scale. *See* musical scale.

pentode. A screen grid tetrode with an additional electrode between the screen grid and anode which is given a negative potential with respect to both anode and screen so that it can prevent low velocity secondary electrons from the anode returning to the screen. It must be of open mesh design so as not to impede free flow of the normal electron stream. *See* thermionic valve.

penumbra. *See* shadows.

perfect fluid. *See* fluid.

perfect gas. *See* ideal gas.

pericynthion. The time or the point at which a satellite launched from earth into lunar orbit is nearest to the surface of the moon. *Compare* apocynthion.

perihelion. When the earth is nearest to the sun (Jan. 3rd) it is said to be in perihelion with respect to the sun. Conversely, the sun is in *perigee* with respect to the earth. When the earth–sun distance is at its greatest value (July 4th), the corresponding terms are *aphelion* and *apogee*.

perilune. The time or the point at which a satellite launched from the moon into

lunar orbit is nearest to the surface of the moon. *Compare* apolune.

period. *Syn.* periodic time. Symbol: T. The time occupied in one complete to and fro movement of a given vibration or oscillation. The period is related to the frequency f and the angular frequency ω by the formula $T = 1/f = 2\pi/\omega$.

periodic table. The classification of chemical elements in the order of their *atomic numbers. The elements show a periodicity of properties, chemically similar elements recurring in a definite order. The sequence of elements is thus broken up into seven horizontal periods and eight vertical groups, the elements in each group showing close chemical analogies, e.g. in valency, chemical properties, etc. *See* Table 9, page 425.

peripheral devices. *Syn.* peripherals. Equipment associated with a *computer for handling input and output of information, storage, communication, etc.

periscope. An optical instrument to provide a view over or around an obstacle or from a submarine. In its simplest form it consists of two parallel mirrors at 45° to the direction of view; the top mirror receives light from the object and directs it down to the lower mirror close to the eye of the observer.

permalloy. An alloy with a high magnetic *permeability at low magnetic flux density and a low *hysteresis loss.

permanent gas. A gas whose *critical constants are such that it remains gaseous under very high pressure at normal temperatures. A gas that cannot be liquefied by pressure alone.

permanent magnet. A magnetized mass of steel or other ferromagnetic substance, of high retentivity and stable against reasonable handling. It requires a definite demagnetizing field to destroy the residual magnetism. *See* ferromagnetism.

permanent set. The strain remaining in a material after the stresses have been removed.

permeability. Symbol: μ. The ratio of the *magnetic flux density in a body or medium to the external *magnetic field strength inducing it, i.e. $\mu = B/H$. It has the units *henry per metre. The permeability of free space, μ_0, is called the *magnetic constant. The *relative permeability*, μ_r, is the ratio μ/μ_0. For most substances μ_r has a constant value. If it is less than unity the material is diamagnetic; if μ_r exceeds unity it is paramagnetic. Ferromagnetic substances have high permeabilities, which are not constant but vary with the field strength.

permeance. Symbol: Λ. The reciprocal of *reluctance. It is measured in henries.

permittivity. (1) *Absolute permittivity*. Symbol: ε. A measure of the degree to which a medium can resist the flow of charge, defined as the ratio of the *electric displacement to the intensity of *electric field that produces it. It is measured in farads per metre and has a value greater than unity. The absolute permittivity of free space, ε_0, is called the *electric constant. (2) *Relative permittivity*. Symbol: ε_r. The ratio of the absolute permittivity of a medium to the electric constant. The value varies from unity (for a vacuum) to over 4000 (for *ferroelectrics) but for most materials does not exceed 10. The quantity is also called the *dielectric constant* when referring to a property of the dielectric medium of a capacitor. It is better defined under these conditions as the ratio of the capacitance of the capacitor to the capacitance it would possess if the dielectric were removed.

persistence. *Syn*. afterglow. (1) The interval of time following excitation during which light is emitted from the screen of a *cathode-ray tube. (2) The faint luminosity observable in certain gases for a considerable period after the passage of an electric discharge.

personal equation. A systematic error of measurement made by an experienced observer.

perspex dosimetry. *See* dosimetry.

perturbation theory. An approximate method of solving a difficult problem if the equations to be solved depart only slightly from those of a problem already solved. For instance, the orbit of a single planet round the sun is an ellipse; the perturbing effect of the other planets modifies the orbit slightly in a way calculable by this method. The technique finds considerable application in *quantum mechanics.

perveance. The space-charge characteristic between electrodes in an electronic tube. It is equal to $j/V_a^{\frac{3}{2}}$, where j is the current density, and V_a the electrical potential of the collector.

Petzval surface. *See* curvature of field.

pH. A logarithmic measure of the hydrogen ion (or hydroxonium ion, H_3O^+) concentration of a solution. It equals the logarithm of the reciprocal of the hydrogen (or hydroxonium) ion concentration in moles per dm^3. Thus, if there are 10^{-8} mol dm^{-3} of hydrogen ions present, the solution has a pH of 8. If the pH is greater than 7 the solution is alkaline, and if it is less the solution is acid.

phase. (1) Of a periodic operation, quantity. The fraction of the *period that has elapsed, measured from a fixed datum. A sinusoidal quantity may be represented by a rotating vector, O B, whose length is proportional to the *peak value of the quantity and whose angular velocity, ω, is related to the frequency n by the relationship $n = \omega/2\pi$. The phase of the quantity with reference to another such quantity OA is given by the angle α between them. Alternatively, it may be stated that the phase difference between OA and OB is α.

Particles in periodic motion due to the passage of a wave are said to be in the same phase of vibration if they are moving in the same direction with the same relative displacement. Particles in a wavefront are in the same phase of vibration and the distance between two wavefronts in which the phases are the same is the wavelength. For the simple harmonic wave,

$$y = a \sin 2\pi(t/T - x/\lambda),$$

the *phase difference of the two particles at x_1 and x_2 is $2\pi(x_2 - x_1)/\lambda$. When light is reflected at the surface of a denser medium there is a change of phase of π. Periodic quantities having the same *frequency and *waveform are said to be *in phase* if they reach corresponding values simultaneously; otherwise they are said to be *out of phase*.

(2) One of the separate circuits or windings of a *polyphase system, machine, or other apparatus.

(3) *See* phase rule.

phase angle. The angle between the two vectors that represent two sinusoidal alternating quantities having the same frequency.

phase constant. *See* propagation coefficient.

phase-contrast microscope. *See* microscope.

phase delay. The ratio of the phase shift of a periodic quantity to its frequency.

phase diagram. A graph combining two conditional parameters (e.g. temperature, pressure, entropy, volume) of a substance drawn so that a particular curve

represents the boundary between two phases of the substance.

phase difference. (1) Symbol: φ. The difference of *phase between two sinusoidal quantities that have the same frequency. It may be expressed as a time or as an angle. (2) In an instrument transformer. The angle between the reversed secondary vector (current or voltage) and the corresponding primary vector. The phase difference is positive or negative according to whether the reversed secondary vector leads or lags the primary vector respectively.

phase discriminator. A *detector circuit in which the amplitude of the output wave varies in response to phase variations in the input wave.

phase modulation. A type of *modulation in which the phase of the *carrier wave is varied about its unmodulated value by an amount proportional to the amplitude of the modulating signal and at a frequency f, equal to that of the modulating signal, the amplitude, E_M, of the carrier wave remaining constant. A phase-modulated wave in which the modulating signal is sinusoidal may be represented by: $e = E_M \sin[2\pi Ft + \beta \sin 2\pi ft]$, where F is the frequency of the unmodulated carrier wave and β the peak variation in the phase of the carrier wave, caused by modulation.

phase rule. Substances are capable of existing in very different states of aggregation, called *phases*. Thus, water at ordinary temperatures and pressures can exist in a solid, liquid, or vapour phase. The term *component* is applied to the least number of chemically identifiable substances required to define completely the existing phases. Thus, in the three phases described above, there is only one component, namely water. The phase rule is defined by the equation $F = C - P + 2$, where C is the number of components in the system, P the number of phases present, and F the number of *degrees of freedom* of the system (the least number of independent variables defining the state of the system). Thus, if two phases and one component are present, the number of degrees of freedom is one; that is to say, to each pressure there corresponds a fixed temperature and on the pressure-temperature diagram (*see* phase diagram) there is a definite line separating the liquid from the vapour phases. Similar lines exist separating the solid–liquid phases and the solid–vapour phases. These three curves meet at the *triple point and this represents the only pressure and temperature at which the three phases can exist in equilibrium.

phase shift. Of a periodic quantity. Any change that occurs in the *phase of one quantity or in the *phase difference between two or more quantities.

phase space. A multidimensional space in which the coordinates represent the variables required to specify the state of the system, in particular a six-dimensional space incorporating three dimensions of position and three of momentum.

phase splitter. A circuit in which a single input waveform produces two output waves with a given *phase difference, e.g. the driving circuit (*see* driver) for a *push-pull amplifier.

phase velocity. The velocity with which wave crests and troughs travel through a medium; in fact the velocity with which the phase in a homogeneous train of waves is propagated. It is expressed by λ/T, λ being the wavelength and T the period of vibration. This is equivalent to v/σ, v being the frequency of vibration and σ the number of wavelengths per unit distance (wave number). *Compare* group velocity.

phase waves. *See* de Broglie waves.

Philips's gauge. *See* Penning gauge.

phlogiston theory. A theory of combustion, refuted by Lavoisier in the 18th century, that all combustible materials were supposed to contain phlogiston, which was released during combustion to leave calx (ash).

phon. The unit of equivalent loudness of a sound; it is a measure of the intensity level relative to a reference tone of defined intensity and frequency. The accepted reference tone has a *root-mean-square sound pressure of 2×10^{-5} pascal and a frequency of 1000 hertz (this being the threshold intensity at this frequency). A normal observer listens with both ears to the standard tone and the sound being measured alternately. The standard tone is varied in intensity until the observer judges it to be as loud as the sound under test. If then the standard tone is n decibels above the reference intensity, the equivalent loudness of the sound being measured is defined as n phons. With the decibel scale of intensity levels the intensity of a note is referred to its threshold intensity at the same frequency. The decibel and phon scales are not the same since the latter is subjective and the sensitivity of the ear to changes of intensity varies with frequency. The two scales are nearly the same between 500 and 10 000 hertz.

phonon. In the lattice vibrations of a crystal, the phonon is a *quantum of thermal energy. It is given by hf, where h is the Planck constant and f the vibrational frequency.

phosphor. A substance that emits light at temperatures below the temperature at which they would exhibit *incandescence. Fluorescent substances in particular are used on the screens of cathode-ray tubes or in fluorescent lamps. *See* luminescence.

phosphorescence. *See* luminescence.

phot. A unity of intensity of illumination viz. 1 lumen per sq. cm. 1 phot = 10^4 *lux.

photocathode. A *cathode from which electrons are emitted as a result of the *photoelectric effect.

photocell. *Syn.* photoelectric cell. Any light-electric *transducer. Originally it was a vacuum *diode with a *photocathode and *anode in which a current flowed when the photocathode was illuminated. The word is now commonly used with reference to photoconductors (*see* photoconductivity) consisting simply of a slab of *semiconductor either in the form of a bar or a thin polycrystalline film, with ohmic contacts fixed at opposite ends. When illuminated with light of a suitable wavelength an increase in conductivity occurs due to the generation of charge *carriers, either by band-to-band transitions (intrinsic) or by transitions involving forbidden-gap *energy levels (extrinsic). The gain is $\Delta I/eG_{pair}$ where ΔI = photocurrent in amperes, G_{pair} = total number of electron–hole pairs created per second per photon absorbed, e = electron charge.

photochromic substance. *Syn.* phototrophic substance. A substance that changes colour when light falls on it.

photoconductivity. Enhanced conductivity of certain *semiconductors, such as selenium, as a result of exposure to *electromagnetic radiation. The absorption of a photon in the material increases the energy of an electron in the valence band (*see* energy bands) of the solid. If the photon energy is insufficient to liberate the electron by the *photoelectric effect it may be enough to excite the electron into the conduction band. The presence of extra electrons in this band causes the photoconductivity. *See also* photocell.

photodetachment. The removal of an electron from a negative ion by a *photon of electromagnetic radiation to give a neutral atom or molecule. The *ionization potential of the negative ion is equal to the *electron affinity of the atom or molecule.

photodiode. A *semiconductor diode, operated with *reverse bias below the *breakdown voltage, whose conductivity is modulated by the absorption of light in or near the *depletion layer which exists at the *p–n junction. *Carriers generated outside the depletion region recombine without crossing the junction and therefore do not cause any current in the external circuit. Only these carriers which cross the junction contribute to the photocurrent, which is superimposed on the normally very small reverse saturation current. A common type of photodiode has a layer of intrinsic semiconductor between the p and n regions (p–i–n photodiode), which wholly contains the depletion layer allowing devices to be manufactured with a depletion width suitable for optimum sensitivity and frequency response.

photodisintegration. *See* photonuclear reaction.

photoelasticity. The study of the effects of stress upon light traversing transparent materials. A homogeneous isotropic medium may become doubly refracting under stress so that marked effects are produced with polarized light.

photoelectric cell. *See* photocell.

photoelectric constant. The ratio of the *Planck constant to the charge of the electron.

photoelectric effect. The *emission of electrons from matter by electromagnetic radiation of certain energies. For solids, electrons are only liberated when the wavelength of the illumination is shorter than a certain value (the *photoelectric threshold*). Most solids emit electrons when this value is in the *vacuum-ultraviolet region of the spectrum although some metals (e.g. Na, K, Cs, and Rb) emit for visible and *near-ultraviolet radiation.

The energy of the incident radiation is transferred in discrete amounts (*photons), each of magnitude $h\nu$. Each photon absorbed will eject an electron provided that the photon energy ($h\nu$) exceeds a certain value Φ – the *work function. The maximum kinetic energy of the electrons E is then given by $E = h\nu - \Phi$. This is known as *Einstein's photoelectric equation*. The electrons with this energy are the least strongly bound electrons in the solid. More strongly bound electrons will also be ejected with energies lower than E.

Gases and liquids can also emit electrons under the effect of light. For gases each electron is removed from a single atom or molecule and the work function in Einstein's equation is replaced by the *ionization potential. (*See* photoionization.)

photoelectron spectroscopy. *See* electron spectroscopy.

photoemission. Emission of electrons as a result of bombardment by photons, as in *photoionization or the *photoelectric effect.

photofission. *See* photonuclear reaction.

photography. When light falls on a sensitized emulsion, photoelectric action converts silver ions of the silver salts to silver atoms, forming a *latent image* in the emulsion. Following development of the film opaque specks of metallic silver form round each silver atom of the latent image. Subsequent fixing produces a permanent image on the film, a photographic *negative*, which is darkest where the original subject was lightest. A *positive* is produced from the negative by exposing another emulsion, e.g. one on photographic paper, to light that has passed through the negative.

Colour photography is based on a *subtractive process. The film consists of three layers of emulsion, each of which is sensitive to one of three *primary colours red, green, and blue. Following exposure the blue components of the subject will be recorded as a latent image in the blue-sensitive emulsion and likewise for the red and green components. The final image in the print or transparency is formed from the correct proportions of cyan, magenta, and yellow, the *complementary colours of red, green, and blue. *See also* reciprocity law.

photoionization. Ionization of an atom or molecule by electromagnetic radiation. A photon can only remove an electron if its energy exceeds the first *ionization potential (I_1) of the atom. The excess energy ($h\nu - I_1$) is taken up by the positive ion and the electron and distributed between their kinetic energies. Since the mass of the ion is always much greater than that of the electron its extra energy is negligible and thus $E = h\nu - I_1$, where E is the kinetic energy of the electron. This is simply Einstein's photoelectric equation (*see* photoelectric effect) applied to a single atom or molecule. The radiation capable of photoionizing molecules and atoms has energy greater than the *photoelectric threshold* which lies in the ultraviolet region of the spectrum. If the energy of the radiation is high enough, more strongly bound electrons may be removed from the neutral species. For example electrons may be ejected with energy E_2 ($< E_1$), where $E_2 = h\nu - I_2$ and I_2 is the second *ionization potential. The atom is then left in an electronically *excited state.

photolithography. A technique used in the manufacture of *semiconductor devices, *thin film circuits, and *printed circuits. A pattern is transferred from a photographic *mask onto the substrate. The substrate is then covered with a *photoresist and is exposed to light through the mask. The depolymerized portions are washed away leaving a pattern of polymerized material, which acts as a barrier to an etching substance or a mask in deposition processes before being stripped.

photolysis. The chemical decomposition or dissociation of molecules as a result of the absorption of light or other electromagnetic radiation.

photomagnetism. Paramagnetism produced in a substance when it is in a phosphorescent state.

photometer. *See* photometry.

photometry. Photometry is concerned with measurements of light intensity and amounts of illumination. Two types of measurement are possible. In one, the radiation is evaluated according to its visual effects, i.e. according to judgment by observers (*see* luminosity and spectral luminous efficiency). The physical quantities measured in this way are preceded by the adjective *luminous*. This distinguishes them from physical quantities measured in units of energy, for which the adjective *radiant* is used. *Visual photometry* is the branch of photometry in which the eye is used to make comparisons. In *physical photometry* the measurements are made by physical receptors, such as the *photocell, *thermopile, and *bolometer. An instrument for evaluating radiation in energy or power units is called a *radiometer.

Measurements of *luminous intensity are made with *photometers* in which the intensity of the lamp under test is compared with that of a standard lamp. The general method is to adjust the position of a screen with respect to the two lamps until the intensities of illumination of the screen due to the two lamps are equal. The luminous intensities of the two sources are then proportional to the squares of their respective distances

from the screen. In the *Lummer–Brodhun photometer*, when the intensities of illumination of the two sides of the screen are equal, the field of view seen through the eyepiece will be evenly illuminated. In practice a rather more complicated prism is used at P, and a match is looked for between the two evenly contrasted fields. Other photometers include the *grease-spot and *shadow photometers. If the sources of

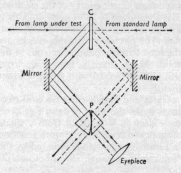

Lummer–Brodhun photometer

light are of different colours, a *flicker photometer is used. A photometer for measuring the directional characteristics of a source is called a *goniophotometer*. *See also* integrating photometer.

photomicrography. The recording of microscope images onto photographic media. The recorded image forms a *photomicrograph*.

photomultiplier. An *electron multiplier in which the primary electrons causing the cascade are produced by the *photoelectric effect. The cathode of such a tube is a *photocathode which is illuminated by some means. Photomultiplier tubes are frequently used in *scintillation counters.

photon. The *quantum of electromagnetic radiation. It has an energy of $h\nu$ where h is the *Planck constant and ν

the frequency of the radiation. For some purposes photons can be considered as *elementary particles travelling at the *velocity of light (*c*) and having a momentum of $h\nu/c$ or h/λ (where λ is the wavelength). Photons can cause excitation of atoms and molecules and more energetic ones can cause ionization (*see* photoionization). *See also* Compton effect; photonuclear reaction; Table 8, page 425.

photonuclear reaction. *Syn.* photodisintegration. A reaction occurring when a high-energy *photon, such as a gamma-ray or X-ray photon, collides with an atomic nucleus. As a result the nucleus disintegrates. In certain cases the photon appears to knock out a neutron (*photoneutron*) or proton (*photoproton*). In other cases the nucleus appears to absorb the photon and then break up as a result of its higher energy – in some cases fission occurs (*photofission*).

photoresist. An organic photosensitive material used in *photolithography. Negative photoresists are materials that polymerize due to the action of light: positive photoresists are polymeric materials that are depolymerized by the action of light. The polymerized material acts as a barrier to etching substances.

phototransistor. A bipolar junction *transistor in which the *base electrode is left floating and the base signal is supplied by excess *carriers generated by illumination of the base. The *emitter current depends on the illumination until equilibrium is established between carrier generation and base recombination current when the emitter current saturates.

phototrophic substances. *See* photochromic substance.

photovoltaic effect. If cuprous oxide is formed on a copper surface and contact is made to the copper and to the front surface of the cuprous oxide (as for example by a wire mesh) a current is produced in an external circuit between these two contacts when light falls on to the oxide. The effect is explained by

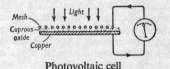

Photovoltaic cell

assuming the presence of an extremely thin barrier layer between the oxide and the copper. Electrons liberated in the oxide by light can readily pass across to the copper, but are blocked from returning. The e.m.f. tending to return the electrons creates the current in the external circuit. Other combinations, such as selenium on iron, also show the effect. *See* rectifier photocell.

physical optics. *See* optics.

pick up. A *transducer that converts intelligence (usually recorded) into electric signals. *Crystal pick ups* consist of a piezoelectric crystal that is stressed by the mechanical vibrations in the grooves of a record producing a piezoelectric e.m.f. in the crystal. *Ceramic pick ups* are similar to crystal pick ups in that their output is also due to the piezoelectric effect. They are more reliable and stable under ambient conditions. *Magnetic pick ups* have a small inductance coil in the field of a magnet. Mechanical vibrations in the grooves of the record cause the coil to move and hence the magnetic flux through the coil changes. The induced current in the coil depends on the magnitude of the vibrations and provides the signal for the audio-system.

pico-. Symbol: p. The prefix meaning 10^{-12}, e.g. $1pF = 10^{-12}$ farad. The use of $\mu\mu$ as a symbol for this prefix is now deprecated.

piezoelectric effect. In some asymmetrical crystals, *piezoelectric crystals*, the surfaces become oppositely electrically charged when subject to pressure, quartz and Rochelle salt showing this effect to a marked degree. These electric charges are proportional to the tension applied; the sign of the charges changes when a tension of the crystal is changed into a compression. The converse effect, in which the crystal expands along one axis and contracts along the other when subjected to an electrical field, also occurs. *See* piezoelectric oscillator.

piezoelectric oscillator. An oscillator formed from a piezoelectric crystal cut in a particular crystal direction and suitably mounted between two metal electrodes The crystals are usually trigonal, with three major axes (X, Y, Z). The crystal slice used in the oscillator is cut with its major surface either perpendicular or parallel to the X-axis (electric axis).

The effectiveness of power and stability of oscillations depend to a large extent on the mounting used. The air gap between the top plate and the crystal may have some effect on the frequency. Piezoelectric crystals are most conveniently set in vibration by the aid of undamped electric oscillations which may be generated electronically at any desired frequency and intensity. The connections between the crystal and the electric oscillator may be made in various ways. In general the circuits used can be divided into two main types:

(*a*) The crystal can replace the *tuned circuit in the oscillator, providing the resonant frequency of the oscillator.
(*b*) It can be coupled to the oscillator circuit, which is tuned almost to the crystal frequency, and can control the oscillator frequency by *pulling the frequency to its own natural frequency, so preventing drift of the oscillator frequency. Crystal oscillators are very stable.

pi-meson (π-meson). *Syn.* pion. *See* meson.

pinch effect. *See* fusion reactor.

pinch-off. *See* field-effect transistor.

pincushion distortion. *See* distortion (light).

p–i–n diode. A semiconductor *diode with a region of almost *intrinsic semiconductor between the p-type and n-type regions.

pion. *Syn.* pi-meson. *See* meson.

Pirani gauge. A low-pressure gauge in which electrically heated wire loses heat by conduction through the gas. A constant potential difference is maintained across the wire and its resistance variation with pressure observed. Alternatively, the resistance is kept constant by varying the applied p.d. which is measured. Its range is 10^{-2} to 10^{-5} mmHg.

piston gauge. *See* free-piston gauge.

pitch. (1) (sound). A subjective quality of a sound that determines its position in a musical scale. It may be measured as the frequency of the pure tone of specified intensity that is judged by the average normal ear to occupy the same place in the musical scale. Although pitch is measured in terms of frequency it is also dependent on the loudness and quality of the note. As the intensity is increased the pitch of a low frequency note is lowered while that of a high note is raised. (2) Of a screw thread, etc. The distance apart of successive threads (or of successive teeth of a gear wheel).

Pitot tube. An instrument used for measuring the total (static and dynamic) pressure of a fluid stream. It consists essentially of a tube of small bore connected at one end to a *manometer, the other end being open and pointing upstream. Fluid cannot flow through the tube; the pressure registered at the manometer is the stagnation pressure at the nose of the tube which, by *Bernoulli's theorem, will be $p_0 + \frac{1}{2}\rho V^2$ where p_0 is the static pressure, ρ the density, and V the velocity of the undisturbed stream.

The term Pitot tube is commonly used for the true *Pitot static tube*. The tube A represents the Pitot tube connected to

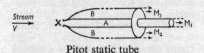

Pitot static tube

the manometer M_1 (which registers the total pressure), the point X being the stagnation point. The tube B is the static tube connected to manometer M_2 registering the static pressure. The difference pressure is the quantity $\frac{1}{2}\rho V^2$. The Pitot static tube is used to measure the stream velocity and is used on aircraft to measure the relative wind speed.

planar process. The most commonly used method of producing junctions in the manufacture of *semiconductor devices. A silicon substrate has an oxide layer grown onto the surface. Holes are etched in the oxide layer, using *photolithography, and impurities are diffused into the substrate through these holes forming *diffused junctions in the substrate. The impurity profile is such that the junction meets the surface of the substrate below the oxide, which provides a stable surface for the silicon and keeps surface leakage currents to a minimum.

planck. The unit of *action. It is equal to one joule second.

Planck constant. Symbol: h. A universal constant having the value $6 \cdot 626\ 196 \times 10^{-34}$ J s. *See* Planck's law.

Planck function. Symbol: Y. The negative of the *Gibbs function divided by the thermodynamic temperature.

Planck's formula. *See* black body radiation; radiation formula.

Planck's law. The law that forms the basis of *quantum theory. The energy of *electromagnetic radiation is confined to small indivisible packets or *photons, each of which has an energy $h\nu$, where ν is the frequency of the radiation and h is the *Planck constant.

plane of flotation. *See* buoyancy.

plane of symmetry. The plane across which reflection of each point in a lattice or other system of points will bring the system to self-coincidence.

plane polarized light. Light in which the vibrations are rectilinear, parallel to a plane, and transverse to the direction of travel (linearly polarized). Light reflected from a surface of polished glass at an angle of incidence $\tan^{-1}(n)$ is plane polarized with vibrations parallel to the surface (*Brewster's law*). It is said to be polarized in the plane of incidence, the plane of vibration (electric vector) being perpendicular to the plane of polarization. Plane polarized light may be produced by reflection or transmission through a pile of plates, by *double refraction in dichroic substances, e.g. tourmaline and Polaroid, in Nicol prisms, etc. Optically active substances rotate the plane of polarization. *See* polarizing angle.

planetary electron. An electron orbiting around the nucleus of an *atom.

plan position indicator (PPI). *See* radar.

Planté cell. The first primitive accumulator, consisting of rolled lead sheets (Planté plates) dipping into dilute sulphuric acid.

plasma. (1) A region of ionized gas in a *gas-discharge tube, containing approximately equal numbers of electrons and positive ions. (2) A highly ionized substance at very high temperature, such as the material in the sun, in which *thermonuclear reactions can occur. The atoms present are nearly all fully ionized and the substance consists of electrons and atomic nuclei. This has been described as a fourth state of matter. *See* fusion reactors.

plasma oscillations. Under certain conditions oscillations of the ions and electrons (independent of the conditions of an external circuit) may be set up in the *plasma of a *gas-discharge tube, and they can cause a scattering of a stream of electrons greater than that explainable by ordinary gas collisions.

plasmatron. A gas-discharge tube in which a plasma acts as the conducting path between a hot cathode and the anode. An input signal modulates the anode current by varying the cross section or conductivity of the plasma.

plastic deformation or flow. A permanent deformation of a solid subjected to a stress. It is sometimes produced in single crystals of metals even by vanishingly small forces.

plate. (1) The anode in a thermionic valve. (2) An electrode in an *accumulator.

platinum resistance thermometer. *See* resistance thermometer.

Plumbicon. *See* camera tube.

pneumatics. The branch of physics dealing with the dynamic properties of gases.

p–n junction. The region at which two dissimilar types of *semiconductor meet. A p–n junction can perform various functions depending on the geometry,

the bias conditions, and the doping level in each semiconductor region. Most semiconductor *diodes, *transistors, etc. utilize the properties of one or more p–n junctions. If the materials are dissimilar, e.g. silicon and germanium, the junction is a *heterojunction.* Normally the same material but of opposite type is used to produce a simple p–n junction. Under reverse bias conditions (i.e. negative bias applied to the p-type semiconductor) a depletion layer is produced at the junction as the *holes in the p-type material and the *electrons in the n-type region are attracted to the electrodes. Very little current flows until *breakdown occurs. (*See diagram* at diode.) Under forward bias conditions, carriers are attracted across the junction into the region of opposite type (where they become *minority carriers) and a current flows in the external circuit. The forward current increases exponentially with the voltage, i.e. $I = I_0(e^{eV/kt} - 1)$ where I_0 is the reverse saturation current, e the electronic charge, V the applied voltage, k the Boltzmann constant, and T the thermodynamic temperature.

p–n–p transistor. *See* transistor.

Pockel's effect. The *Kerr effect as observed in a piezoelectric substance.

Poinsot motion. (1) The motion of a rigid body with one fixed point, O, acted upon by no forces. (2) The motion of a rigid body relative to the centre of mass, O, provided that all the forces acting are equivalent to a single force through the centre of mass. In such motion, the direction and magnitude of the angular momentum vector drawn through O are constant at all times.

point contact transistor. *See* transistor.

point defect. *See* defect.

point function. A quantity whose value depends on the position of a point in space, e.g. magnetic field, temperature, density.

point group. A set of symmetry operations (rotation about an axis, reflection across a plane, or combinations of these), not including translation, which when carried out on a periodic arrangement of points in space brings that system of points to self-coincidence. *See* crystal systems.

poise. Symbol: **P.** The CGS unit of dynamic *viscosity. It is the tangential force per unit area required to maintain unit difference in velocity between two parallel planes in a liquid that are separated by unit distance; 1 poise = 0·1 pascal second.

poiseuille. Symbol: **Pl.** A unit of dynamic *viscosity defined as the viscosity of a liquid that sets up a tangential stress of one pascal across two planes separated by one metre when the velocity of streamlined flow is one metre per second. The unit is identical with the *SI unit of dynamic viscosity (the pascal second), but the name has not received international recognition.

Poiseuille flow. The steady laminar flow of a viscous fluid through a pipe of circular cross section such that the velocity distribution has the form of a paraboloid of revolution, the velocity being a maximum at the centre of the pipe, zero at the boundary walls, and the velocity being constant along any line parallel to the axis of the pipe. Assuming *Newton's laws of fluid friction for a viscous fluid, the quantity of fluid flowing per second is given by $Q = \pi(p_1 - p_2)r^4/8\mu l$ where p_1, p_2 are the initial and final pressures on a cylinder of fluid, length l and coefficient of viscosity μ, the radius of the pipe being r. This is known as *Poiseuille's law.*

Poisson distribution. A frequency distribution often applicable in practice to discontinuous variables. It can be applied to a radioactive decay process to predict the probability that a specific event (decay) will occur in a given period. It is the limit of the *binomial distribution. As the number of trials, n, increases, the probability, p, decreases and $np = m$ where m is the average number of times an event occurs in n trials. The probability of r successes in n trials is then: $m^r e^{-m}/r!$.

Poisson's equation.

$$\frac{\partial^2 V}{\partial x^2} + \frac{\partial^2 V}{\partial y^2} + \frac{\partial^2 V}{\partial z^2} = \nabla^2 V = -4\pi\rho,$$

where V is the electric potential at any point and ρ is the charge density.

Poisson's ratio. Symbol: μ or ν. The ratio of lateral contracting strain to the elongation strain when a rod is stretched by in-line forces applied to its ends, the sides being free to contract. If the volume does not change appreciably under stretching this ratio is 0·5 but the value is often less in practice.

polar axis. A crystal axis of rotation which is not normal to a reflection plane and which does not contain a centre of symmetry. Certain crystal properties will be dissimilar at opposite ends of such an axis.

polarimeter. An accurate instrument for measurement of rotation of the plane of polarization (*see* plane polarized light) by optically active liquids and solids. *See* saccharimeter.

polariscope. An instrument for studying polarization phenomena consisting of a polarizer from which polarized light passes to a transparent substance under investigation and then to a rotatable analyser. The simple (Biot) polariscope, which depends on polarization by reflection, consists of two inclined glass plates, one to polarize the light and the other (rotatable) to analyse it. Sometimes the analyser is a *Nicol prism or *Polaroid; sometimes both analyser and polarizer are Nicol prisms.

polarity. (1) The condition of a body or system in which there are opposing physical properties at different points. (2) The distinction between the north and south poles of a magnet or the positive and negative parameters (e.g. voltage, charge, current, etc.) in an electrical circuit or device.

polarizability. *See* molar polarization.

polarization. (1) (electrical) In a simple cell consisting of two dissimilar plates in an electrolyte, such as Zn and Cu in dilute H_2SO_4, the current obtained soon falls considerably. This is due to a layer of hydrogen bubbles that collects on the copper plate and not only partially covers the plate and increases the internal resistance of the cell, but also sets up an e.m.f. of opposite direction to that of the cell. This phenomenon is known as polarization. To make cells effective for longer period, some means must be adopted to prevent gas deposition. In the *Daniell cell, for example, it is changed, by using two solutions, into a copper coating on a copper anode which has no back e.m.f., and in the *Leclanché cell a chemical depolarizer is used which reacts with the hydrogen produced.
(2) (optics) The restriction in the direction and characteristics of the transverse vibrations of a light wave, as in *plane polarized light. Sometimes the vibration is an *elliptical* or *circular* path due to the rectangular composition of vibrations of equal period with an appropriate phase difference. *See* quarter-wave plate.
(3) *See* dielectric polarization.

polarizer. A crystal or conglomerate of crystals used to produce *plane polarized light (pile of plates, *Polaroid, *Nicol prism, etc.).

polarizing angle. *Syn.* Brewster angle. When light strikes a glass surface at an angle of incidence given by $\tan^{-1}(n)$, where n is the refractive index, the reflected light is *plane polarized. At this angle of incidence, the refracted ray makes an angle of 90° with the reflected ray (*Brewster's law*).

polarizing pyrometer. An instrument in which monochromatic light from a hot source is polarized and its intensity compared with that from a fixed lamp, also polarized, whose filament is maintained at a fixed but unknown temperature. The *Wanner optical pyrometer* is used for measuring the temperature of a hot source. Two beams, polarized at right angles, pass through a *Nicol prism to produce two adjacent semicircles of light. In one position of the Nicol the light from the lamp is completely extinguished and for a rotation of the Nicol through an angle φ both patches are made equally bright, whence $E_\lambda/L_\lambda = \tan^2\varphi$, where E_λ and L_λ are the intensities of light of wavelength λ emitted by the source and lamp respectively. If E_λ' is the intensity of the source when the temperature is changed from T to T' then

$$\frac{E_\lambda}{E_\lambda'} = \frac{\tan^2\varphi}{\tan^2\varphi'}$$

and since

$$\log_e \frac{E_\lambda}{E_\lambda'} = K\left\{\frac{1}{T'} - \frac{1}{T}\right\}$$

by the Wien displacement law,

$$2(\log_e \tan\varphi - \log_e \tan\varphi')$$
$$= K\left\{\frac{1}{T'} - \frac{1}{T}\right\}.$$

The scale may be calibrated using a source at a standard temperature T'.

Polaroid. A proprietary thin transparent film containing ultra microscopic polarizing crystals with their optic axes lined up parallel. One component of polarization is absorbed and the other is transmitted with little loss. By placing the axis of the Polaroid in an appropriate direction, stray plane polarized light (produced for example by reflection) causing glare can be removed.

Polaroid (Land) camera. A proprietary camera that yields finished positive prints or transparencies within about 60 seconds (colour) or 10 seconds (black and white) of the exposure, the developing and processing of the film taking place inside the camera.

pole. (1) The place towards which lines of magnetic flux converge, or from which they diverge. It usually exists near a surface of magnetic discontinuity and in the material of higher permeability. A north pole of a magnet is that which, if free, tends to move towards the north (magnetic) pole of the earth. (2) The midpoint of a convex or concave mirror. The line joining the centre of *curvature and the pole is the *principal axis* of the mirror. (3) *See* pole piece.

pole face. The end surface of the *core of a magnet through which surface the useful magnetic flux passes. In particular, in an electrical machine it is that surface of the core or pole piece of a *field magnet which directly faces the armature.

pole piece. *Syn.* pole; magnet pole. In an electrical machine, the portion of the magnetic circuit situated between the *yoke and the air gap. The term is also applied to either of the pieces of ferromagnetic material attached to the ends of an electromagnet or permanent magnet in various electrical devices.

polychromatic radiation. Electromagnetic radiation of more than one wavelength.

polyphase system. An electrical system or apparatus in which there are two or more alternating voltages having the same frequency and being displaced in

*phase relative to each other. A symmetrical polyphase (*n*-phase) system has *n* sinusoidal voltages of equal magnitude and frequency, with mutual phase differences of $2\pi/n$ rad (or $360/n$). An exception to this is the two-phase system (quarter-phase) in which the two voltages have a phase difference of 90°.

population inversion. *See* laser.

Porro prism. A total reflection prism used in the construction of prismatic telescopes and binoculars. The simplest form is a 45°, 90° prism receiving light through the hypotenuse face, and reflecting it back parallel to the original

Porro Prism

direction after successive internal reflection at the other two faces. This prism inverts in one direction only. The second prism of a binocular completes the inversion at right angles by placing its roof edge at right angles to the first.

positive electron. *See* positron.

positive feedback. *See* feedback.

positive glow. *Syn.* positive column. *See* gas-discharge tube.

positive logic. *See* logic circuit.

positron. *Syn.* positive electron. An *elementary particle with electron mass and positive charge equal to that of the electron; the antiparticle of the electron.

positronium. A short-lived association between a *positron and an *electron. There are two types: *orthopositronium* in

289

which the *spins of the particles are parallel and *parapositronium* in which the spins are antiparallel. The ortho-positronium decays with a mean life of about 10^{-7} s to give three photons. The parapositronium has a smaller mean life and produces two photons (*see* annihilation).

post office box. A form of *Wheatstone bridge that consists of a number of resistance coils arranged in a special box. Each coil is connected to two massive brass blocks in such a manner that it can be cut out of circuit by inserting a brass shorting plug into a hole drilled between the blocks.

potassium–argon dating. *See* dating.

potential. Electrostatic, magnetostatic, and gravitational potentials, at a point in the field: the work done in bringing unit positive charge, unit positive pole, or unit mass respectively from infinity (i.e. a place infinitely distant from the causes of the field) to the point. Gravitational potential is always negative but the electrostatic and magnetostatic potentials may be +ve or −ve. Since these fields are *conservative the potential is a function only of the position of the point. The difference in potential between two points is the work done in taking the unit object from one point to the other. Potential is a scalar quantity. *See also* kinetic and velocity potentials; magnetomotive force.

potential barrier. The region in a field of force in which the potential is such that a particle, which is subject to the field, encounters opposition to its passage.

potential difference. Symbol: V, U. The line integral of the electric field strength between two points. The work done when a charge moves from one to the other of two points (by any path) is equal to the product of the potential difference and the charge. *See* electromotive force.

potential divider. A chain of resistors, inductors, or capacitors connected in series and tapped to allow a definite fraction of the voltage across the chain to be obtained across one or more of the individual components. *See* potentiometer.

potential energy. *See* energy.

potential flow. *See* laminar flow.

potential function. From the theory of functions of a complex variable it is shown that a relation of the form $w = \varphi + \mathrm{i}\psi = \mathrm{f}(z)$ represents a two-dimensional irrotational motion of a fluid in the xy-plane where z is the complex variable $(x + \mathrm{i}y)$, φ the velocity potential, ψ the *stream function. The complex function $w = (\varphi + \mathrm{i}\psi)$ is called the potential function; equating the real and imaginary parts of the relation gives the lines of equivelocity potential and the stream lines of the irrotational motion.

potential gradient. The rate of change of potential, V, at a point with respect to distance x, measured in the direction in which the variation is a maximum. It is measured in volts per metre. The electric field strength, E, is numerically equal to the potential gradient but in the opposite sense:

$$E = -\mathrm{d}V/\mathrm{d}x.$$

potential scattering. *See* scattering.

potential transformer. *See* voltage transformer.

potential well. A region in a field of force in which the potential decreases abruptly, and on either side of which the potential is increased.

potentiometer. A form of *potential divider in which the fall of potential along a uniform wire is used to tap off any potential difference less than that between the ends of the wire. A typical use is in measuring the e.m.f. of a cell. If $XS = l_1$ when there is no deflection on the galvanometer G for the cell C and $XS = l_2$ for a similar condition with a

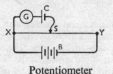

Potentiometer

standard cell of e.m.f. E_2, then $E_1/E_2 = l_1/l_2$. The true e.m.f. is given, as no current flows through the cell. In electronic circuits a potentiometer is any variable resistor with a third movable contact.

pound. A unit of mass formerly based on a platinum cylinder called the Imperial Standard Pound. The pound is now defined as 0·453 592 37 kilogrammes.

poundal. The f.p.s. unit of force, equal to the force required to give a mass of one pound an acceleration of 1 foot per second per second. 1 poundal = 0·138 255 newton.

powder photography. A crystal diffraction method in which the specimen is a randomly orientated crystalline powder (which is usually rotated) in a parallel beam of monochromatic X-rays (or electrons, neutrons, etc.). *See* X-ray analysis.

power. (1) Symbol: P. The rate at which energy is expended or work is done. It is measured in *watts.

The power W developed in a direct current electric circuit is given in watts by the expression $W = VI$, where V is the potential difference in volts and I is the current in amperes. In an alternating current circuit, $W = VI \cos \varphi$, where V and I are the r.m.s. values of the voltage and current and φ is the *phase angle between the current and the voltage. The apparent power is measured in volt-amperes. Cos φ is called the *power factor*. $IV \sin \varphi$ is called the *reactive power*. (*See* var.)

(2) (optics) Of a lens or mirror. The reciprocal of the focal length in metres, generally positive if converging and most commonly applied to the *dioptric power* of a lens. For mirrors, the term *catoptric power* is sometimes used to distinguish it from *reflecting power*. The latter is the ratio of the flux of light reflected to the incident flux for any surface reflecting light: it is usually expressed as a percentage. *Transmitting* and *absorbing powers* are similarly defined for transmission and absorption. The *effective* power of a lens at a certain point is the reciprocal focal distance measured from that point.

power amplification. The ratio of the power level at the output terminals of an amplifier to that at the input. In a magnetic amplifier it is the product of voltage amplification and current amplification using a specified circuit. In a transducer it is the ratio of the power delivered to the load to that absorbed by the input circuit, under specified operating conditions.

power amplifier. An *amplifier giving a power gain. It is usually used so that the output is not applied to the input of a further amplifying stage but to an output *transducer, such as an *aerial or *loudspeaker.

power component. *See* active current.

power factor. The ratio of the total power, in watts, dissipated in an electric circuit to the volt-amperes applied to the circuit or an equivalent circuit. *See* power.

power reactor. A *nuclear reactor designed to produce useful quantities of electric power.

power transistor. A *transistor with a dissipation rating higher than about 1 watt. Power transistors are used for switching or amplification and because of the relatively high power dissipation, which may be up to 100 watt, they usually require some form of temperature control.

Poynting's theorem. The rate of energy transfer from *electromagnetic radiation is proportional to the product of the electric and magnetic field strengths, i.e. to the surface integral of the *Poynting vector formed by the components of the field in the plane of the surface.

Poynting vector. A vector giving the direction and magnitude of energy flow in an electromagnetic field. It is equal to the vector product of the electric and magnetic field strengths at any point.

Prandtl number. The dimensionless group $(C\eta/\lambda\rho)$ occurring in the dimensional analysis of *convection in a fluid due to the presence of a hot body, where C is the heat capacity per unit volume of the fluid, η is its viscosity, λ is its thermal conductivity, and ρ its density.

preamplifier. An *amplifier used as an earlier stage to the main amplifier. It is frequently placed near the signal source (aerial, pick up, etc.), being connected by cable to the main amplifier. This improves the *signal-to-noise ratio as amplification of the initial signal occurs before it traverses the path to the main amplifier.

precession. If a body is spinning about an axis of symmetry OC (where O is a fixed point) and C is rotating round an axis OZ fixed outside the body, the body is said to be precessing round OZ. OZ is the precession axis. A gyroscope precesses due to an applied torque (called the *precessional torque*).

If the moment of inertia of the body

about OC is I and its angular velocity is ω, a torque K whose axis is perpendicular to the axis of rotation will produce an angular velocity of precession Ω about an axis perpendicular to both ω and the torque axis where $\Omega = K/I\omega$. *See* Euler's angles.

pre-emphasis (and de-emphasis). In a radiocommunication system employing *frequency modulation or *phase modulation, an improvement in the *signal-to-noise ratio can be effected by using pre-emphasis at the transmitter, i.e. by artificially increasing the *modulation factor for the higher modulation frequencies as compared with the lower modulation frequencies, and by using de-emphasis at the receiver, i.e. by reducing the relative strength of the higher audio frequencies to compensate for the effect of the pre-emphasis.

pressure. Symbol: p. At a point in a fluid, the force exerted per unit area on an infinitesimal plane situated at the point. In a fluid at rest the pressure at any point is the same in all directions. In a liquid it increases uniformly with depth, h, according to the formula

$$p = \rho g h.$$

ρ is the density of the fluid, and g is the acceleration of *free fall. In a gas under isothermal conditions it decreases exponentially with height h, according to the formula

$$p_h = p_0 e^{-(\mu g/RT)h}.$$

μ is the relative molecular mass, R is the *universal gas constant, and T is the thermodynamic temperature.

The S I unit of pressure is the *pascal. Pressure can also be measured in *atmospheres, millimetres of mercury (*mmHg), and millibars (*see* bar).

pressure gauges. (1) Primary gauges include the liquid column *manometers and the *free-piston gauge. (2) Secondary gauges include the *Bourdon gauge, *resistance gauge, etc. (3) *See* micro-manometers. (4) Vacuum gauges include the *McLeod and *Knudsen gauges which are primary gauges (although the Knudsen gauge is often made as a secondary gauge) and the *Pirani, *ionization, and *molecular gauges.

pressure head. Pressures are often measured in terms of the height of a column of liquid (often called the head of liquid or pressure head) capable of exerting that pressure, e.g. the head h of liquid, corresponding to a pressure p, is $h\rho g$ where ρ is the density of the liquid and g the acceleration of *free fall. *See* pressure.

pressurized-water reactor (P.W.R.). A type of thermal *nuclear reactor in which water under pressure (to prevent boiling) is used as both coolant and moderator.

Prévost's theory of exchanges. A body emits precisely the same radiant energy as it absorbs when it is in temperature equilibrium with its surroundings, conduction and convection having ceased.

primary. *See* primary winding.

primary cell. *See* cell.

primary colours. A set of three coloured lights (or pigments) that when mixed in equal proportions produce white light (or black pigment). One group consists of red, green, and blue; cyan (greenish-blue), magenta (reddish-blue), and yellow form another set. Red and cyan, green and magenta, and blue and yellow are pairs of *complementary colours. Three lights of primary colours can be mixed in suitable proportions to produce any other colour, excluding black, by an *additive process. Three pigments, paints, dyes, etc., of primary colours can be mixed to produce any colour, excluding white, by a *subtractive process. *See also* chromaticity.

primary electrons. Electrons incident on a surface distinguished from the secondary electrons that they release. *See* secondary emission.

primary radiation. *See* cosmic rays.

primary standard. A standard used nationally or internationally as the basis for a unit, e.g. the international prototype *kilogramme. *Compare* secondary standard.

primary winding. The winding on the supply (i.e. input) side of a *transformer, irrespective of whether the transformer is of the step-up or step-down type.

principal axis. *See* pole.

principal directions. The directions about which there is symmetry of crystal properties, such as refractive indexes, coefficients of thermal expansion, magnetic susceptibility, thermal conductivity, etc.

principal focus, planes (and points). *See* centred optical systems.

principal quantum number. *See* atom; atomic orbital.

principal ray. *See* apertures and stops in optical systems.

principle of equivalence. *See* relativity.

principle of indeterminancy. *See* uncertainty principle.

principle of least (or stationary) time. *See* Fermat's principle.

printed circuit. An electronic circuit, or part of a circuit, in which the conducting interconnections and certain components are formed on a board. The process starts with a thin board of insulating material that is coated with a conducting film, usually copper. A photographic

prism

mask is then used to coat part of the film
with protective material. The unprotec-
ted metal is then removed by etching,
leaving the desired pattern of interconnections and components. Other
components may then be added to the
circuit if required.

Double-sided printed circuits are
commonly produced in which both sides
of the board have a circuit formed on
them, with contacts to connect the two
sides as required. Printed circuits have
been produced with several alternating
layers of metal film and thin insulating
film mounted on a single board.

prism. A refracting medium bounded by
intersecting plane surfaces that both de-
viates a beam of light and disperses it
into its component colours (*see* dispersion). Prism combinations can be produced to deviate light without dispersion
(*see* achromatic prism) or to disperse a
beam without producing any mean deviation (*see* direct vision prism). The
main uses of prisms are (*a*) for deflection
or small angle deviation – *narrow angle*
prisms; (*b*) for large angle deviation and
dispersion – in *spectrometers, *refractometers; (*c*) for changing direction or
inverting or erecting images using total
internal reflection.

The prismatic effect of *narrow angle*
prisms is given by $P = (n - 1)A$, where
n is the refractive index, A the angle of
the prism, i.e. the angle made by the
refracting faces in a principal section
perpendicular to the refracting edge. P
is the angle of deviation (usually expressed in degrees) or the power of the
prism (expressed in *prism dioptres). The
*chromatic aberration C of a single
prism is ωP, where ω is the dispersive
power (*see* dispersion). For two prisms
the chromatic aberration C is ($\omega_1 P_1 +
\omega_2 P_2$) and total power $P = P_1 + P_2$.

For large angle deviation and dispersion, the angle of the prism, A, must
be large. Such prisms have a minimum
deviation (*see* deviation (angle of)), a
property used for the determination of

refractive index and of dispersion using
spectrometers.

prismatic binoculars. Binoculars in which
each half consists of a Kepler telescope,
the prisms serving the two-fold purpose
of reducing the length of the instrument
and also erecting the image. The prisms
are two *Porro prisms; one prism inverts
in one direction only, the second prism
completes the inversion, since its roof
edge is crossed at right angles to the roof
edge of the former.

prism dioptre. A unit of deviating power
of a prism based on a tangent measure
in centimetres on a scale placed one
metre away or a similar proportion. If θ
is the angle of deviation and P is in
prism dioptres, then $P = 100 \tan \theta$. The
unit is used mainly for narrow angle
prisms. *See* centrad.

probability. The numerical value of the
chance of occurrence of one or more
possible results of an unpredictable
event.

Independent events. If n is the total
number of ways in which an event can
occur, and m is the number of ways in
which an event can occur in a specified
way, then the ratio m/n is the *mathematical* (or *a priori*) *probability*. When a
dice is tossed the mathematical probability of obtaining the number 4 is 1/6.
In a random sequence of n trials of an
event with m favourable outcomes, as n
increases indefinitely the ratio m/n has
the limit P where P is the probability.

If in a number of trials an event has
occurred n times and failed m times the
probability of success in the next trial
is given by $n/(n + m)$. This is the
empirical (or *a posteriori*) *probability*.
The probability of a man not dying at a
certain age, based upon past observations (recorded, say, in a mortality
table), is an empirical probability.

The probability of a given number of
successes in a certain number of trials,
when the probability of success in a

single trial does not vary, is given by the *binomial distribution.

Dependent events. If two or more events are so related that the outcome of one affects the outcome of the other or others, the individual probability of each event is calculated in sequence and the product of these gives the *conditional probability.*

If a variable X can take on a set of discrete random values x_i, each of which has a probability p_i, the relative frequency of occurrence of any one of these values is $x_i p_i$; the cumulative frequency F, up to the value x_n is given by $F(x_n) = \sum_{i=1}^{n} x_i p_i$. If X varies continuously, then the cumulative frequency up to a value x_n is given by $F(x)_n = \int_{-\infty}^{x} f(x) \, dx$, where $f(x)$ represents the relative frequency of any specific value of x. The function $f(x)$ is called the *frequency function* or *probability density function.* The graph of the function $F(x)$ is a normal *frequency distribution.

probable error. That error such that the chances of the absolute magnitude of the *deviation being greater than or less than it are even. The arithmetic mean of n observations has a probable error which, according to the Gaussian theory of errors, is $n^{-\frac{1}{2}}$ times the probable error of a single observation. (*See* frequency distribution.)

Experimental results are often quoted in scientific literature as $(x \pm \delta)$, δ being a small quantity which may be (*a*) the probable error, (*b*) the standard deviation, (*c*) the error intelligently guessed (*see* errors of measurement).

probe. (1) A lead that contains or connects to a measuring or monitoring circuit and is used for testing purposes. (2) A resonant conductor inserted into a *waveguide or *cavity resonator for the purpose of injecting or extracting energy.

product of inertia. If Cartesian axes $OXYZ$ are fixed relative to a rigid body, the product of inertia of the body with respect to the axes OY, OZ is $\sum myz = F$, the summation being carried out for every particle of the body. (x, y, and z are the coordinates of a particle of mass m.) There are three such products of inertia: F, $G = \sum mzx$, and $H = \sum mxy$ and also three moments of inertia A, B, C about the axes OX, OY, OZ respectively given by

$$A = \sum m(y^2 + z^2), \ B = \sum m(z^2 + x^2)$$

and

$$C = \sum m(x^2 + y^2).$$

The moment of inertia, I, of the body about any axis L through the origin of coordinates is expressible in terms of A, B, C and F, G, H, and the direction cosines α, β, γ of the axis L with respect to the coordinate axes OX, OY, OZ:

$$I = A\alpha^2 + B\beta^2 + C\gamma^2 - 2F\beta\gamma - 2G\gamma\alpha \\ - 2H\alpha\beta.$$

program. A set of instructions to a *computer written in a *programming language*, which is designed to be mutually comprehensible to computers and programmers.

progressive wave. A wave propagated through an infinite homogeneous medium. For any type of wave motion a plane progressive wave may be represented by the equation of wave motion,

$$\frac{\partial^2 \xi}{\partial t^2} = \frac{c^2 \partial^2 \xi}{\partial x^2},$$

where ξ is the particle displacement at distance x from a fixed point along the direction of propagation, c is the wave velocity, and t is time measured from a fixed instant. For a plane progressive harmonic wave the solution is:

$$\xi = a \sin (2\pi/\lambda)(ct - x),$$

where a is the maximum particle displacement or amplitude and λ is the wavelength. For a given value of x the displacement ξ varies through a complete cycle when $(2\pi/\lambda)(ct - x)$ changes by 2π radians; the corresponding change in t is T, the *period. Thus, $(2\pi/\lambda)cT = 2\pi$ and $T = \lambda/c$.

prompt neutron. A neutron produced in a reactor by primary fission rather than by decay of a fission product.

propagation coefficient or constant. Symbol: P, γ. Of a transmission line used for telecommunication purposes. Consider a uniform line of infinite length supplied at its sending end with sinusoidal current having a specified frequency. At two points along the line separated by unit length (e.g. 1 km) let the currents under steady-state conditions be I_1 and I_2, where I_1 is nearer the source. Then the propagation coefficient per unit length of line at the specified frequency is the natural logarithm of the vector ratio of I_1 to I_2. P is a complex quantity and may be expressed as: $P = \alpha + i\beta$, so that: $e^{\alpha} \times e^{\beta i} = I_1/I_2$. The real part of P, (α), is called the *attenuation constant: $\alpha = \log_e|I_1/I_2|$nepers. The imaginary part of P, (β), is called the *phase constant* or *wavelength constant* and is measured in radians per unit length of line. It is the *phase difference between I_1 and I_2.

propagation loss. The energy loss from a beam of *electromagnetic radiation as a result of absorption, scattering, and the spreading out of the beam.

proper function and value. *Syn.* eigenfunction and -value. *See* wave function.

proportional counter. *See* proportional region.

proportional region. The operation voltage range for a radiation counter in which the *gas multiplication exceeds 1, its value being independent of primary ionization. A counter operating in this region is called a *proportional counter*.

The pulse size in the counter is proportional to the number of ions produced as a result of the initial ionizing

event. *See* Geiger counter; ionization chamber.

protective relay. A *relay that protects electrical apparatus against the damaging effects of abnormal conditions (e.g. overloads and internal faults). When such abnormal conditions occur, the relay causes the opening of a *circuit-breaker so that the faulty apparatus is automatically disconnected from the supply.

proton. A positively charged *elementary particle that forms the nucleus of the hydrogen atom and is a constituent particle of all nuclei. It is about 1836 times heavier than the electron. It is a stable *baryon of mass 938·26 MeV/c² ($1\cdot672\ 62 \times 10^{-27}$ kg) having charge $Q = 1$. It has *spin $J = \frac{1}{2}$, *isospin $I = \frac{1}{2}$ and positive *parity. It also has an intrinsic *magnetic moment of 2·793 nuclear *magnetons. Although there are many elementary particles having a lower mass, the proton cannot decay into these as it is the lowest mass particle with baryon number $B = 1$; baryon number is conserved in all interactions. *See also* Table 8, page 425.

proton microscope. A microscope similar to the *electron microscope but using a beam of protons rather than electrons. This allows a better resolving power and contrast.

proton number. *See* atomic number.

proton resonance. *Nuclear magnetic resonance of hydrogen nuclei.

proton synchrotron. A cyclic *accelerator of very large radius that can accelerate protons to extremely high energies: 28 GeV at CERN, Geneva; 70 GeV at Serpukhov, USSR; 500 GeV at Batavia, USA. It is basically similar to a *synchrotron. In a synchrotron a fixed orbit is maintained by increasing the magnetic field strength in proportion to the relativistic increase in mass. This leads to a constant angular frequency. This is possible because the electrons are travelling at close to the speed of light at an energy of a few MeV. The equivalent stable orbit at constant angular frequency is not achieved by protons until they have an energy of about 3 GeV. To maintain a fixed orbit up to this energy, the frequency of the accelerating electric field must be varied (it is constant in the synchrotron). The frequency of the field and the particle beam must remain in synchrony and also satisfy the relation $v = \omega r$ where v is the proton velocity, r is the radius of the orbit and ω is the angular frequency of the protons; $\omega = 2\pi f$, where f is the electric field frequency. The protons are accelerated by radio-frequency fields between the magnets, and can make several million revolutions in one second. The beam is both focused and maintained in a circular orbit by means of magnets. Strong *focusing is used. *See also* intersecting storage ring.

psi (ψ) particle. *Syn.* J particle. Either of two, or possibly more, massive unstable elementary particles (3·095 GeV and 3·684 GeV) first detected, in 1974, as resonances in electron-positron interactions. The lighter one has also been detected in e^+e^- pair production resulting from hadron collisions. The width of the resonance peak of $\psi(3095)$ implies a lifetime of about 10^{-20} second. This is considerably longer than the 10^{-23} second decay time characteristic of the *strong interaction by which all other heavy resonances decay.

Several theories have been used to explain the existence of such particles. Two of these hypotheses are modifications to the *quark model. In one theory, four rather than three quarks are postulated. The fourth quark possesses a real value (+1) of a new quantum number, called *charm*; it has a charge of 2/3. The other three quarks have zero charm. It is suggested that the ψ particles

are mesons consisting of a charmed quark and an anticharmed quark, the heavier particle being an excited state of the lighter one. The particles themselves would have zero charm.

In the other theory, it is proposed that a quark can take on one of three values of a quantum number known as *colour*. The original group of three quarks is thus expanded to nine. It is postulated that the three colours occur in equal proportions in all known baryons and mesons, so that these particles exhibit no net colour. The psi particles, however, are states of coloured matter in which the proportions of colour are unequal. Both these theories explain the long lifetime of the psi particles as being a result of decay inhibition due to the conservation of charm or colour.

psychrometer. A *hygrometer in which a strong draught is obtained past the wet and dry bulbs either by whirling on a sling or by a fan. The best known type is the *Assmann psychrometer* in which the necessary ventilation is provided by a clockwork driven fan.

p-type conductivity. Conductivity in a *semiconductor caused by a flow of *holes.

p-type semiconductor. An *extrinsic semiconductor in which the density of mobile *holes exceeds that of conduction *electrons. *See also* semiconductor.

Pulfrich refractometer. A *critical-angle refractometer for the accurate measurement of refractive index and dispersion. A glass block of high refractive index, n_G, is used, with its top face horizontal and polished with the specimen on this face (as a drop, if a liquid, or in a small cell on the top face; as a block if solid, with air film excluded by a film of liquid of high refractive index). Light at grazing incidence is refracted at the critical angle in the block and is further refracted at the exit face. A special angled observing telescope moving round a vertical graduated circle helps the location of the limiting ray emerging through the vertical side face. If the angle of emergence below the horizontal is α, the unknown refractive index, *n*, is given by $n = \sqrt{(n_G^2 - \sin^2\alpha)}$.

pulling. When an electronic oscillator is coupled to a circuit in which there is another independent oscillation, the oscillator frequency tends to change towards that of the independent oscillation. The tendency, known as pulling, is particularly strong if the two frequencies differ by only a small percentage.

pulsar. A member of a class of astronomical objects thought to be examples of *neutron stars. They have very small dimensions and are so compressed that inverse *beta decay has occurred, i.e. the electrons and protons have been forced to combine to form neutrons.

The pulsars are rapidly spinning bodies emitting energy in the radio regions of the spectrum. The energy is detected as rapid highly directional pulses from which the rotation rates (0·03–4 seconds) can be determined; these rates are generally lengthening due to loss of rotational energy. Surface magnetic flux densities are of the order of 10^8 teslas, and these cause both the radio and any optical radiation to be polarized (*see* polarization). Pulsars are believed to have been formed during the explosions of *supernovas.

pulsating current. An electric current that varies in magnitude in a regularly recurring manner. The term implies that the current is unidirectional.

pulsating star. *See* variable star.

pulse. A single transient disturbance manifest either as an isolated wave or applied mechanically to a body capable of being deflected; one of a series of

transient disturbances recurring at regular intervals. The term is also applied to a short train of high-frequency waves, as used in echo-sounding (*see* echo) and *radar. Thus a pulse may consist of a voltage or a current which increases from zero to a maximum value and then decreases to zero in a comparatively short time.

In practice a perfect geometrical shape is never achieved and a practical rectangular pulse is shown in the diagram. The magnitude of the pulse normally has a constant value, ignoring any spikes or ripples, and is called the *pulse height*. A practical pulse has a finite *rise time*,

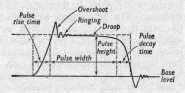

Practical rectangular pulse

usually occurring between 10 % and 90 % of the pulse height, and a finite *decay time*, occurring between the same limits. The *pulse width* is the time between the rise and decay time. A practical pulse frequently rises to a value above the pulse height and falls to the pulse height with damped oscillations. This is called *overshoot* and *ringing*. A similar phenomenon occurs as the pulse decays to the base level. *Droop* can occur in a rectangular pulse when the pulse height falls slightly below the nominal value. This is particularly associated with inductively coupled circuits (*see* inductive coupling). A group of regularly recurring pulses of similar characteristics is called a *pulse train*, and is usually identified by the type of pulses in the train, e.g. square wave, saw tooth wave, etc.

pulse code modulation. *See* pulse modulation.

pulse height analyser. *See* multichannel analyser.

pulse height discriminator. An electronic circuit that selects and passes *pulses whose amplitude lies between specified limits.

pulse modulation. A form of *modulation in which pulses are used to modulate the *carrier wave or, more commonly, in which a pulse train is used as the carrier. Information is conveyed by modulating some parameter of the pulses with a set of discrete instantaneous samples of the message signal.

In *pulse-amplitude modulation*, the amplitude of the pulses is modulated by the corresponding samples of the modulating wave. In *pulse-time modulation*, the samples are used to vary the time of occurrence of some parameter of the pulses, such as pulse width or frequency.

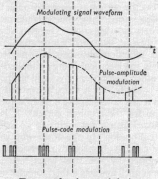

Forms of pulse modulation

All these types of pulse modulation are examples of uncoded modulation. In *pulse code modulation* only certain discrete values are allowed for the modulating signals. The modulating signal is sampled, as in other forms of pulse modulation, and any sample falling within a specified range of values is assigned a discrete value. Each value is assigned a pattern of pulses and the signal trans-

mitted by means of this code. Morse code is an example of a pulse code. Pulse modulation is commonly used for *time division multiplexing.

pulse regeneration. In any form of pulse operation the pulses can get distorted by the circuits or circuit elements. Pulse regeneration is the process of restoring the original form, timing, and magnitude to a *pulse or pulse train.

pulse shaper. Any circuit or device that is used to change any of the characteristics of a *pulse.

pumps, vacuum. Modern kinetic vacuum systems usually use two pumps in tandem. The backing or fore-pump which works directly to the atmosphere is one of the many forms of rotary oil pump. These pumps reduce the pressure to between 100 and 0·1 Pa according to the type. The second pump is usually a *diffusion* or *condensation pump*, which is rather similar in principle to the *filter pump but uses a jet of mercury vapour instead of water. There may be several such jets acting in tandem.

Molecular pumps work on the principle that a gas molecule striking a rapidly moving surface may be given a high velocity in the direction of the exit pipe. These pumps need a backing-pump. *See also* air pump; ion pump; sorption pump.

punched card. A card on which data is coded in the form of holes, often for use in a *computer. A character, number, or special symbol is represented by a pattern of holes punched in one column.

punched tape. *See* paper tape.

punch-through voltage. A type of *breakdown occurring in both bipolar and unipolar *transistors. In *bipolar transistors this occurs at a base–collector voltage at which the collector junction *depletion layer spreads through the entire base region. This has the effect of making the emitter junction reverse biased: eventually this junction breaks down and a collecting path from emitter to collector is established. The breakdown profile is very similar to the *avalanche breakdown of a simple p–n junction.

In unipolar (*field-effect) transistors as the *drain voltage increases the effective channel length decreases slowly. When it has been reduced to zero carriers from the source punch through to the drain, and the drain current rises catastrophically. The punch-through voltage is related to the doping levels and channel length and in many devices with high doping levels and relatively long channels, avalanche breakdown occurs first.

push–pull operation. The use in a circuit of matched devices operating with an 180° phase relation to each other. The

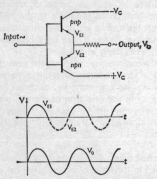

Complementary transistor push–pull operation

outputs are combined to produce an output signal which is a replica of the input waveform. Push–pull operation is frequently used for *class A and *class B amplification. Several means of input are used: one common input arrangement involves the use of complementary transistors; no phase change is required in the inputs.

pycnometer. A form of relative density (specific gravity) bottle consisting of a bulb between two capillary tubes, on one of which is a reference mark. The density of a liquid is measured by finding the weight of the known volume filling the vessel up to the mark.

pyranometer. *See* solarimeter.

pyrheliometer. An instrument for measuring the intensity of direct solar radiation at normal incidence, diffuse radiation being excluded. It can also measure radiation from a selected part of the sky. In the *Ångstrom pyrheliometer* two identical strips of blackened platinum are mounted so that one is exposed to the radiation at normal incidence, while the other is shielded. A difference in temperature between the two strips is determined by using a *thermocouple attached to the back of each strip and connected in series with a galvanometer. An electric current is passed through the shaded strip until the galvanometer registers no deflection. The two strips are then at the same temperature and solar radiation absorbed by one strip equals the electrical energy supplied to the other. The current gives a measure of the intensity. Each strip is exposed in turn to the radiation and a mean value is found for the required current. It is a standard instrument requiring no external calibration. In the *silver disc pyrheliometer* a blackened silver disc is supported by fine steel wires inside a copper shell and has a thermometer embedded in it. It is exposed to a narrow angle of solar radiation at normal incidence. The rate of temperature increase determines the radiation intensity. *See also* solarimeter; net radiometer.

pyroelectricity. The development of opposite electric charges at the ends of polar axes in crystals, such as tourmaline and lithium sulphate which do not possess a centre of symmetry, when there is a change of temperature.

pyrometer. An instrument for measuring high temperatures. There are several types: (1) The *optical pyrometer, which depends for its action on the Wien displacement law, $E_\lambda = (C_1/\lambda^5)\,[e^{-c_2/\lambda T}]$. Instruments of this type are used for the measurement of high temperatures on the *international temperature scale. (2) The *total radiation pyrometer*, which depends for its action on *Stefan's law $E = \sigma T^4$. The most convenient form is the *Féry total radiation pyrometer. (3) *See* resistance thermometer.

Q

Q-factor. A measure of the efficiency of a reactive electric circuit or component in an electric circuit; it is used particularly in connection with oscillating circuits. (1) For a simple oscillating circuit consisting of inductance and capacitance connected in series, the Q-factor is the ratio of the total series reactance of one kind (i.e. total inductive reactance or total capacitive reactance) to the total effective series resistance. Thus: $Q = \omega L/R$ or $Q = 1/\omega CR$, where $\omega = 2\pi \times$ resonant frequency. Since at resonance, $\omega L = 1/\omega C$, $Q = (1/R)\sqrt{L/C}$. (2) The Q-factor of an inductance coil or of a capacitor is the ratio of its reactance to its effective series resistance. Thus for a coil, $Q = \omega L/R$; for a capacitor, $Q = 1/\omega CR$. For coils used at radio frequencies Q values between about 100 and 300 are common. The *power factor of the coil or capacitor is given by $1/\sqrt{Q^2 + 1}$.

quadrant electrometer. In this *electrometer, a light foil-covered vane, supported by a quartz fibre, moves within hollow quadrantal segments of a metal box. Opposite quadrants are connected together, but insulated from the case of the instrument. A mirror is carried to reflect a spot of light and measure deflections of the vane. If the vane hangs symmetrically within the quadrants when the needle and both pairs of quadrants are at zero potential, then the deflection θ of the needle is

$$\theta = k(V_A - V_B)\left(V_C - \frac{V_A + V_B}{2}\right),$$

where V_A and V_B are the potentials of the pairs of quadrants, V_C is the potential of the vane, and k is a constant. V_C is usually made large with respect to V_A and V_B so that $\theta = k_1(V_A - V_B)$ or, if one pair of quadrants is earthed, $\theta = k_2 V_A$.

quadrature. Periodic quantities having the same *frequency and *waveform are said to be in quadrature when they differ in phase by 90°, i.e. one wave reaches its maximum value when the other passes through zero.

quadrature component. *See* reactive current.

quadripole. An electrical *network that has four terminals only, i.e. a pair of input terminals and a pair of output terminals. If its electrical properties remain unaffected when the input and output terminals are interchanged, it is described as a *symmetrical quadripole*.

quadrupole. A set of four electric charges or of two magnetic dipoles associated together as a unity. The potential V_r at a distance r from their centre of mass is given by

$$V_r = \frac{a_1}{r} + \frac{a_2}{r^2} + \frac{a_3}{r^3} + \ldots,$$

the terms on the right-hand side of the equation being known as the coulomb potential, the dipole potential, the quadrupole potential, etc. The quadrupole movement p is given by

$$p = \Sigma Q_i r_i s_i,$$

where the charges Q_i (or magnetic half dipoles) have positional coordinates (x_i, y_i, z_i) and r_i, s_i are any two co-ordinates.

quality (in sound). (1) The fidelity of reproduction of a sound. (2) *See* timbre.

quality factor. *See* dose.

quantum. *See* quantum theory.

quantum discontinuity. The discontinuous emission or absorption of energy accompanying a quantum jump.

quantum electrodynamics. A relativistic theory of quantum mechanics concerned with the motions and interactions of electrons, muons, and photons, i.e. with *electromagnetic interactions. Its predictions have been proved highly accurate. In the *Feynman propagator* approach, the scattering of electrons and photons is described by a matrix which is written as an infinite sum of terms corresponding to all the possible ways the particles can interact by the exchange of virtual electrons and photons (*see* virtual particle). Each term may be represented by a diagram (called a *Feynman diagram*). These diagrams are built up from vertices representing the emission of a (virtual) photon by an electron and propagators which represent the exchange of virtual photons or electrons, as in Fig. *a*. Fig. *b* shows the first few diagrams for electron–electron scattering.

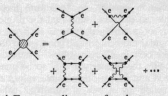

b Feynman diagrams for electron–electron scattering

Vertex   Photon propagator   Electron propagator

a Feynman diagrams

In these diagrams all lines joining two vertices are propagators. The lines having a vertex at only one of their ends and the other end free represent the physical particles before and after the interaction. A set of simple rules enables one to calculate the contribution to the scattering matrix from each of these diagrams.

quantum electronics. An application of the principles of *quantum mechanics to the study of the production and amplification of power at frequencies from 10^9 to 10^{11} hertz in solid crystals.

quantum mechanics. A mathematical physical theory that grew out of Planck's *quantum theory and deals with the mechanics of atomic and related systems in terms of quantities that can be measured. The subject developed in several mathematical forms, including *wave mechanics and *matrix mechanics, all of which are equivalent.

Relativistic quantum mechanics. Dirac extended the principles of quantum mechanics so that they also satisfied the principle of *relativity. This allowed the properties of electron spin to be obtained, in a natural way, from the relativistic *Schrödinger equation.

Table of Conserved Quantum Numbers

Quantum Number / Interaction	Angular Momentum J, J_3	Charge Q	Baryon Number B	Isospin I	Isospin Q.N. I_3	Strangeness S	Parity P	C-Parity C	G-Parity G	Lepton Numbers l_e, l_μ
Strong	√	√	√	√	√	√	√	√	√	—
Electromagnetic	√	√	√	×	√	√	√	√	×	—
Weak	√	√	√	×	×	×	×	×	×	√

quantum number. In *quantum mechanics, it is often found that the properties of a physical system, such as its angular momentum and energy, can only take certain discrete values. Where this occurs the property is said to be quantized and its various possible values are labelled by a set of numbers called quantum numbers. For example, regions in an atom in which the electron may move are characterized by quantum numbers n, l, and m (*see* atomic orbital). Properties of *elementary particles are also described by quantum numbers. For example an electron has the property known as *spin, the two states of which are conveniently characterized by quantum numbers $+\frac{1}{2}$ and $-\frac{1}{2}$. Similarly properties such as *isospin, *charge, and *hypercharge are characterized by quantum numbers. *See also* energy level.

quantum statistics. Statistics concerned with the distribution of elementary particles of a particular type amongst the various quantized energy levels. It is assumed that these particles are indistinguishable.

In *Fermi–Dirac statistics*, the *Pauli exclusion principle is obeyed so that no two identical *fermions can be in the same quantum mechanical state. The exchange of two identical fermions does not affect the probability of distribution but it does involve a change in the sign of the *wave function. The *Fermi–Dirac distribution law* gives the number of fermions (such as electrons), n_1, in a particular energy state, E_1: $n_1 = 1/[e^{E_1/kT} + 1]$, where k is the *Boltzmann constant and T is the *thermodynamic (absolute) temperature.

In *Bose–Einstein statistics* the Pauli exclusion principle is not obeyed so that any number of identical *bosons can be in the same state. The exchange of two bosons of the same type affects neither the probability of distribution nor the sign of the wave function.

The *Bose–Einstein distribution law* gives the number of bosons (such as mesons or photons), n_1, in a particular energy state, E_1: $n_1 = 1/[e^{E_1/kT} - 1]$. Planck's formula for the energy of a *black body at a particular wavelength can be derived from this distribution law.

quantum theory. A departure from the classical mechanics of Newton involving the principle that certain physical quantities can only assume discrete values. Several problems could not be solved by using Newtonian mechanics, in particular the characteristic maximum found in the spectral distribution curves of a *black body. These attempts were based on the idea that the energy of an oscillator is kT, where k is the *Boltzmann constant and T the thermodynamic temperature. This inability to explain the phenomenon has been called the *ultraviolet catastrophe.*

In 1900, Planck resolved the problem by discarding the idea that an oscillator can gain or lose energy continuously. He suggested that it could only change by some discrete amount which he called a *quantum*. This unit of energy is given by $h\nu$, where ν is the frequency and h is the *Planck constant. h has dimensions of energy $\times$ time, or *action. According to Planck an oscillator could only change its energy by an integral number of quanta, i.e. by $h\nu$, $2h\nu$, $3h\nu$, etc. This meant that the radiation in an enclosure had certain discrete energies.

In 1905 Einstein explained features of the *photoelectric effect by assuming that light was radiated in quanta (*photons). In 1907 he used the idea to interpret the behaviour of the heat capacities of solids at low temperatures (*see* Einstein's theory of specific heat capacities; Debye's theory of specific heat capacities).

A further advance was made by Bohr (1913) in his theory of atomic spectra (*see* atom; hydrogen spectrum). A refinement of Bohr's theory was introduced by Sommerfeld to account for fine structure in spectra. Other successes of quantum theory was its explanation of the *Compton effect and *Stark effect. Later developments involved the formulation of a new system of mechanics known as *quantum mechanics.

quark model. A theory postulating that all *hadrons are built out of three basic 'particles' called quarks. The three quarks are denoted p', n', and λ'. Their properties are given in the following table:

	Baryon Number B	Isospin I	Isospin quantum number I_3	Strange-ness S	Charge Q
p'	$\frac{1}{3}$	$\frac{1}{2}$	$\frac{1}{2}$	0	$\frac{2}{3}$
n'	$\frac{1}{3}$	$\frac{1}{2}$	$-\frac{1}{2}$	0	$-\frac{1}{3}$
λ'	$\frac{1}{3}$	0	0	-1	$-\frac{1}{3}$

Recent experiments indicate that four or more quarks might exist (*see* psi particle). All known *baryons are found to correspond to a combination of three quarks (e.g. the proton corresponds to a combination of two p' and a n', the Σ^0 to a p', n', and λ' combination). *Mesons are found to correspond to a combination of a quark and antiquark (e.g. the π^+ corresponds to a p', $\bar{n}'$ combination and the K^+ to a p' and $\bar{\lambda}'$). Antiparticles are obtained from their corresponding particles by changing quarks into antiquarks and vice versa. Mathematically the three quarks correspond to the basic multiplet of the group *SU(3). The singlet, octet, and decuplet of *unitary symmetry theory are obtained by either combining three quark multiplets (for baryon multiplets) or a quark and antiquark multiplet (for meson multiplets).

quarter phase. *Syn.* two-phase. *See* polyphase system.

quarter-wavelength line or transformer. A transmission line one quarter of a wavelength long, used as an *impedance matching device (i.e. impedance trans-former). It is used extensively in systems operating at the higher radio frequencies.

quarter-wave plate. A sheet of muscovite mica cleaved so that its interference colour in white light is pale neutral gray, and of such thickness that for sodium light incident normal to the cleavage surface a quarter wavelength path difference is produced between the ordinary and extraordinary rays. If *plane polarized light vibrating at 45° to the vibration planes strikes it, the light emerges circularly polarized; if vibrating in any other direction it yields elliptically polarized light.

quartz. A double refracting crystal, optically uniaxial and positive and rotating the plane of polarization to the left or right according to the variety, and to different extents for different colours. It transmits wavelengths between 180–4000 nm.

quartz-crystal clock. *See* clocks.

quartz-fibre manometer. *See* molecular gauges.

quartz-iodine lamp. A tungsten-filament electric lamp with a quartz envelope, filled with iodine vapour. It is much smaller than a conventional lamp of equivalent light output, and has a high working temperature (500–600° C). A very intense luminous flux is obtained at low operating voltage.

quasars. Members of a class of astronomical bodies known as quasi-stellar objects (QSOs) that also includes radio-quiet sources with similar properties. A number of quasars have exceptionally large *red shifts. They are not observed in galaxies, which is consistent with the normal interpretation of the large red shifts: if this large red shift is interpreted as being due to the *Doppler effect, then the objects must be at enormous distances, and would have intrinsic luminosities at least equivalent to most luminous galaxies. The greater part of the energy output is generally in the infrared region of the spectrum, and being polarized this suggests that *synchrotron radiation is the source, rather than thermal radiation.

Current theories suggest that a quasar may be some kind of galaxy with a massive central region to act as the source of energy, a less dense synchrotron shell of relativistic electrons, and a huge and low-density envelope through which filaments of hot gas move rapidly and give rise to the optical spectrum emission lines.

quench. A capacitor, resistor, or combination of the two placed across a con-tact to inhibit sparking when the current is cut off in an inductive circuit. Typically, a quench is employed across the make-and-break contacts of an induction coil.

quenching. *See* Geiger counter.

quiescent current. In any circuit, the current flowing in the circuit under conditions of zero applied signal.

Quincke's tube. *See* Herschel–Quincke tube.

Q-value. *Syn.* nuclear energy change; nuclear heat of reaction. The amount of energy produced in a *nuclear reaction, often expressed in millions of *electronvolts (MeV).

R

rad. A unit of absorbed *dose of radiation, equal to 0·01 joule per kilogramme (100 ergs per gramme) of material.

radar (RAdio Direction And Ranging). A system for locating distant objects by reflected radio waves. Pulse radar systems transmit pulses of high-frequency radio waves, the reflections being received between the transmitted pulses. Continuous wave systems transmit energy continuously, a small proportion being reflected by the target and returned to the transmitter. *Doppler radar* utilizes the *Doppler effect to distinguish between stationary and moving targets and to measure the velocity of moving targets by measuring the frequency change between transmitted and reflected waves.

In any of the above systems the direction and distance of the target is given by the direction of the receiving aerial, and the time between transmission and reception of the echo. The transmitting and receiving aerials can be made to rotate to scan an area, the return pulses being recorded by a cathode-ray tube circularly scanned in synchronization to produce an echo map of the scanned area. Such a tube is called a *plan position indicator* (PPI).

radian. A unit of angle. One radian encloses an arc equal to the radius of a concentric circle. 2π radians = 360°; 1 radian = 57·296° = 57° 17′ 45″. The radian is a supplementary *SI unit.

radiance. Symbol: L_e, L. For a point source of radiant energy it is the *radiant intensity, in a specified direction, per unit projected area, $L_e = dI_e/dA \cos \theta$, where A is the area and θ is the angle between the specified direction and the surface. For a point on a surface that is receiving radiant energy it is defined as the *irradiance (E_e) per unit solid angle (Ω), $L_e = dE_e/d\Omega$. The irradiance is taken over an area perpendicular to the direction of incident radiation.

The general equation of luminous intensity applying to both a point source and a point receptor, is

$$L_e = \frac{d^2\Phi_e}{d\Omega . dA \cos \theta},$$

where Φ_e is the *radiant flux. Radiance is measured in watts per steradian per square metre. *Compare* luminance.

radiant efficiency. Symbol: η_e, η. The ratio of the *radiant flux emitted by a source of radiation to the power consumed. *Compare* luminous efficacy.

radiant exitance. Symbol: M_e, M. The *radiant flux leaving a surface per unit area. It was formerly called the *radiant emittance*. It is measured in watts per square metre. *Compare* luminous exitance.

radiant exposure. Symbol: H_e, H. (1) The surface density of the total radiant energy received by a material. (2) A measure of the total energy of the radiation incident on a surface per unit area, expressed by the product of the *irradiance, E_e and the irradiation time: $H_e = \int E_e \, dt$. It is measured in joules per square metre. *Compare* light exposure.

radiant flux. *Syn.* radiant power. Symbol: Φ_e, Φ. The total power emitted or received by a body in the form of *radiation. The term is usually applied to the transfer of energy in the form of *electromagnetic radiation as opposed to particles, but it is not usually applied to radiowaves. It is measured in watts. *Compare* luminous flux.

radiant heat. *See* heat.

radiant intensity. Symbol: I_e, I. The *radiant flux (Φ_e) emitted per unit solid angle (Ω) by a point source in a given direction: $I_e = d\Phi_e/d\Omega$. It is measured in watts per steradian. *Compare* luminous intensity.

radiant quantities. Pure physical quantities used in *photometry in which *electromagnetic radiation is evaluated in energy units. They are distinguished from their corresponding *luminous quantities by adding a subscript e (for energy) to their symbols.

radiation. Any form of energy propagated as rays, waves, or a stream of particles but especially light and other electromagnetic waves, sound waves, and the emissions from radioactive substances.

radiation belts. *See* Van Allen belts.

radiation formula. The formula, devised by Planck, to express the distribution of energy in the normal spectrum (spectrum of *black body radiation). Its usual form is

$$8\pi ch d\lambda/\lambda^5(\exp[ch/k\lambda T] - 1)$$

which represents the amount of energy per unit volume in the range of wavelengths between λ and $\lambda + d\lambda$, where h is the *Planck constant and k the *Boltzmann constant.

radiation impedance. *See* radiation resistance.

radiation physics. The study of radiation, particularly *ionizing radiation, and the physical effects it can have on matter.

radiation pressure. (1) The pressure exerted upon a surface exposed to electromagnetic radiation, the value of which is proportional to the radiant energy density in the space to which the surface is exposed. For diffuse radiation it may be shown that the total normal pressure exerted is $U/3$, where U is the total energy density of the incident radiation.

(2) The steady pressure exerted on a surface by sound waves, the mean value of which, $\overline{P}$, is given by $\frac{1}{2}(\gamma + 1)E$, where E is the energy density and γ the ratio of the *specific heat capacities, assuming an adiabatic process to occur. The sound pressure has also been ascribed to the energy arriving at the surface per second, i.e. as $P = I/c$ or $2I/c$ if the waves are reflected, where I is the intensity or strength of sound and c is the velocity of sound.

radiation pyrometer. A *pyrometer that depends for its action upon the effect of thermal radiation from a hot body. In one form, heat rays from the hot body are focused upon a sensitive *thermocouple. The e.m.f. produced in the latter is a function of the temperature of the hot body and is either measured by means of a potentiometer or is utilized to produce a deflection of a galvanometer or a millivoltmeter.

radiation resistance or impedance. At a surface vibrating in a medium. The portion of the total *resistance (unit area, acoustical, or mechanical) due to the radiation of sound energy into the medium.

The mean power radiated per unit area of plane wave front is

$$\tfrac{1}{2}\rho c \xi^2_{max} = \tfrac{1}{2}\rho c f^2 a^2$$

where ρ is the density of the medium, c the velocity of sound in it, ξ_{max} is the maximum sound particle velocity which is equal to fa (f being the frequency and a the amplitude of the vibration).

In the analogous electrical case, this equation represents the power of dissipation in a circuit of resistance ρc. The quantity ρc is usually known as the radiation resistance or impedance of a medium which is transmitting *plane* waves. The characteristic impedance for a spherical wave of radius r is expressed as

$$z = \rho c(X' + iY'),$$

where

$$X' = \frac{k^2 r^2}{k^2 r^2 + 1}, \quad Y' = \frac{kr}{k^2 r^2 + 1}$$

and

$$k = \frac{2\pi}{\lambda} = \frac{2\pi f}{c}$$

(λ being the wavelength).

The first term $\rho c X'$ is a resistance term and the second term is a reactance. If r is very large z will reduce to ρc as for plane waves. If kr is small the radiation impedance or resistance is approximately $\rho c k^2 r^2 = 4\pi^2 f^2 \rho r^2 / c$. We may include this impedance whenever there is a change from plane to spherical waves.

radiation sickness. Illness resulting from exposure of body tissue to a large dose of *ionizing radiation or from the effects of a nuclear explosion.

radiative capture. *See* capture.

radiative collision. A collision that takes place between two charged particles and from which *electromagnetic radiation is emitted due to the conversion of part of the kinetic energy. *See* bremsstrahlung.

radio. The use of *electromagnetic radiation to transmit or receive impulses or signals without connecting wires. Also the process of transmitting or receiving such signals. The term is usually confined to the communications system transmitting audio information (wireless).

radioactive age. The age of a geological or archeological specimen, determined by radioactive *dating.

radioactive collision. A particular type of *nuclear reaction in which a neutron enters a nucleus and a γ-photon is emitted. The new nucleus formed has the same atomic number but its mass number is increased by unity. This type of reaction is used extensively for producing radioactive isotopes.

radioactive series. Most of the *radioisotopes of natural elements have *atomic numbers (Z) in the range $Z = 81$ to $Z = 92$. These radioisotopes can be grouped into three radioactive series: the *uranium series, thorium series,* and *actinium series.* The *mass numbers of these radioisotopes can be represented by a set of numbers: $4n$ (thorium series), $4n + 2$ (uranium series), and $4n + 3$ (actinium series), where n is an integer between 52 and 59. The three *parent isotopes at the head of each series are long-lived radioisotopes with *half-lives in the region 10^9–10^{10} years. They are uranium-238 (uranium series), thorium-232 (thorium series), and uranium-235 (actinium series). The final isotopes are all stable isotopes of lead.

There is a fourth radioactive series, the *neptunium series* ($4n + 1$) in which the half-life of the three isotopes at the top of the series, plutonium-241, americium-241, and neptunium-237 are much shorter than the parents of the other three series. These radioisotopes have therefore either disappeared from the earth's surface or are present in negligible quantities.

radioactive tracer. A definite quantity of *radioisotope introduced into a biological or mechanical system so that its path through the system and its concentration in particular areas can be determined by measuring the radioactivity with a *Geiger counter, *gamma camera, or a similar device.

radioactivity. The spontaneous disintegration of the nuclei of some of the isotopes (*radioisotopes) of certain elements with the emission of *alpha particles or *beta particles, sometimes accompanied by a *gamma ray. The processes involved in *alpha decay and *beta decay alter the chemical nature of the atom involved, because of the change

309

in *atomic number, and usually result in a more stable nucleus. Specific energy changes take place in the nucleus during a disintegration and any excess energy possessed by the nucleus after the expulsion of an α- or β-particle is emitted in the form of a γ-ray *photon. Another particle that can be emitted by the nucleus is the *positron (an antielectron), the disintegration process being analogous to β-decay. It is possible for a γ-ray alone to be emitted, when a *metastable state of a radioisotope decays to a lower energy state of the same isotope. A radioisotope can disintegrate into two different energy states of the same nucleus, forming a pair of nuclear *isomers. *Electron capture is another disintegration process.

Natural radioactivity is the disintegration of naturally occurring radioisotopes. The bombardment of nuclei by high-energy α-particles, protons, neutrons, deuterons, carbon atoms, etc., produces *artificial radioisotopes*, which decay by the same processes as natural isotopes. It has been possible to create many isotopes having an atomic number greater than that of uranium (92). These are the *transuranic elements*, produced by bombarding heavy stable atoms. They are all radioactive.

The activity of both natural and artificial radioisotopes decreases exponentially with time. The time taken for half a given number of atoms of a particular radioisotope to be transformed is called the *half-life. It can vary from $1 \cdot 5 \times 10^{-8}$ seconds up to $1 \cdot 4 \times 10^{10}$ years. The fraction of atoms decaying in a certain time is not truly constant. Radioactive decay is a statistical phenomenon and the half-life is an average value of very many disintegrations.

radio astronomy. The study of astronomy through the radio signals emitted by some celestial bodies. The signals originate from sources of nonthermal radiation and are associated with bodies both within and outside the solar system. A *radio telescope is used for observing, and amongst the objects discovered by radio techniques are *quasars and *pulsars. Radio astronomy also includes the use of radar for measuring planetary distances, etc.

radiobalance. An instrument in which the heating due to the absorption of radiation is neutralized by the cooling due to the Peltier effect at one junction of a thermocouple, thus enabling the amount of incident radiation to be measured absolutely.

radiocarbon dating. *See* dating.

radio frequency (r.f.). Electromagnetic radiation in the *frequency band 3 kilohertz to 300 gigahertz. Also alternating currents in this frequency range.

radio-frequency heating. *Dielectric heating or *induction heating when the alternating field has a frequency greater than about 25 kHz.

radiogenic. Resulting from radioactive *decay.

radiogoniometer. An apparatus by means of which the bearing of radio waves incident upon a fixed (i.e. non-rotating) aerial system to which it is connected may be determined. It consists fundamentally of two fixed coils mounted with their axes at right angles and a third coil that can be rotated inside the other two.

radiography. The production of shadow photographs (*radiographs*) of the internal structure of bodies, opaque to visible light, by the radiation from X-rays or by gamma rays from radioactive substances.

radio interferometer. *See* radio telescope.

radioisotope. An *isotope of an element that undergoes *disintegration.

radiology. The study and application of X-rays, gamma rays, and other penetrating *ionizing radiation.

radiolucent. *See* radiopaque.

radioluminescence. The emission of visible *electromagnetic radiation from a radioactive substance.

radiolysis. The chemical decomposition of materials into ions, excited atoms, and molecules, etc., by *ionizing radiation.

radiometer. An instrument for measuring radiation in energy or power units, i.e. one used in physical *photometry and meteorology. The term is especially used for instruments that detect and measure infrared radiation.

radiomicrometer. An extremely sensitive detector of radiation. A thermocouple of antimony and bismuth is joined in series with a single copper loop suspended by a quartz fibre between the two poles of a magnet. Radiation falling on one Sb–Bi junction causes a current to flow in the copper loop which is therefore deflected, the deflection being obtained from the movement of a spot of light reflected from a mirror carried by the loop.

radionuclide. Any radioactive *nuclide.

radiopaque. Opaque to radiation, especially X- and gamma rays. Radiopaque substances, such as bones, are visible on a radiograph (*see* radiography). *Radiotransparent* is the converse of radiopaque, i.e. transparent to radiation. Radiotransparent substances, such as skin, are not visible on a radiograph. If a medium is almost entirely transparent to radiation it is *radiolucent*.

radio receiver. A device that converts radio waves into audible signals. A simple receiver consists of a receiving aerial, a tuner that can be adjusted to the desired carrier frequency, preamplifier,

detector, audio-frequency amplification circuit, and a loudspeaker. *See also* superheterodyne receiver.

radiosonde system. A compact apparatus comprising a meteorograph and radio transmitter that is carried into the earth's atmosphere by a balloon and transmits radio signals indicative of the temperature, pressure, and humidity.

radio source. An extra-terrestrial source detected with a *radio telescope. Many sources are extended, the radio energy emanating from interstellar material. Discrete sources are often called *radio stars*.

radiospectroscope. An apparatus for displaying (usually on a cathode-ray tube) an analysis of the radio-frequency energy arriving at an aerial. The wavelengths in actual use for transmission at any particular time are shown, and by the height and spread of the trace on the tube face some indication of the field strength and modulation is given.

radio star. *See* radio source.

radio telescope. A transmitter-aerial arrangement, used in *radio astronomy, that is suitable for sending out and, more especially, receiving radio signals from beyond the earth. One of the two basic forms is the steerable parabolic reflector, or dish, consisting of a wire mesh approximately shaped and mounted so that it can be directed to any part of the sky without serious distortion. A pencil beam of radiation is received from a small but not highly defined area of sky.

The second basic form is the *radio interferometer* consisting of two or more fixed or steerable radio aerials separated by a known distance and connected to the same radio receiver. *Interference occurs between waves from a *radio source that are received by the aerials. The position of the source can thus be determined. If large numbers of aerials are used, they are generally arranged in parallel rows or in two rows at right angles to each other. Alternatively the method of *aperture synthesis may be employed. The interferometer is more sensitive than the parabolic dish as it can detect radiation from sources of small angular diameter.

radiotherapy. The use of beams of *ionizing radiation, such as X-rays, energetic electrons, and the stream of gamma rays from the radioisotope cobalt-60, in the treatment of cancer. A sufficient amount of radiation must be given to kill the cancer cells without harming intervening tissue. This is achieved by irradiating from several different directions with a narrow beam so that the tumour receives the maximum dose.

radiotransparent. *See* radiopaque.

radio waves. Electromagnetic radiation of *radio frequency, used in *radio and *television broadcasting and other communications systems and also in *radio astronomy. *See* ionosphere; modulation; aerial.

radio window. *See* atmospheric window.

radius of curvature. *See* curvature.

radius of gyration. A length representing the distance, in a rotating system, between the point about which rotation occurs and the point to which (or from which) a transfer of energy has the maximum effect. In a system of moment of inertia I and mass m the radius of gyration k is given by $k = (I/m)^{\frac{1}{2}}$.

rainbow. The continuous spectrum derived from the sun as source and observed as one or more arcs in the sky with the observer at their centre. Water droplets act as the dispersing system. The primary bow is due to one total internal reflection in the droplets, and has an

angular dispersion of 56′ at a mean altitude of 42°; the violet is on the inside. The secondary bow, due to two internal reflections, has angular dispersion of 1°32′ at a mean altitude of 51°; it is much fainter than the primary bow and has the red on the inside.

Raman effect. A scattering effect in which the scattered light differs in wavelength from the incident light (generally longer as with Stokes's law but may be shorter). The effect is distinguished from *fluorescence in that it is not a resonance effect – the incident light differs in wavelength from that of the absorption band of the substance. In addition, the scattered light has a much smaller intensity than most fluorescent light. *See* scattering.

Ramsden eyepiece. In its most elementary form, two planoconvex lenses of equal focal length, equal to the separation of the curved surfaces facing one another.

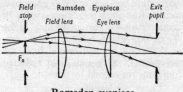

Ramsden eyepiece

Commonly the separation is reduced to $\frac{2}{3}$ of the lens focal length. It is better than the *Huygens eyepiece for spherical aberration, distortion, and longitudinal chromatic aberration, but suffers from lateral chromatism. The achromatized Ramsden is called the *Kellner eyepiece.

random access. *See* direct access.

random noise. *See* noise.

Rankine cycle. An ideal steam engine cycle since it is theoretically reversible. It differs from the *Carnot cycle in that a separate boiler and condenser are used. Beginning at A with the working substance as water in the boiler, AB represents isothermal expansion at con-

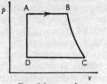

Rankine cycle

stant pressure (*see* diagram); BC the adiabatic expansion of the steam in the cylinder during which it cools to the temperature of the condenser; and CD the isothermal compression at constant pressure. DA represents the transfer of the cold water to the boiler and at A the water is heated to the temperature of the boiler. The first three stages are identical with those of the Carnot cycle.

Rankine temperature. Symbol: °R. An obsolete thermodynamic temperature scale linked to the Fahrenheit degree. Absolute zero on this scale is −459·67°F, therefore °R = °F + 459·67. The ice point is 491·7°R, often taken as 492°R. 1K = 1·8°R.

rarefaction. The converse of *compression.

raster. *See* television.

ratio. Of a *transformer. For a single-phase power transformer, the ratio of the e.m.f.s induced in the primary and secondary windings. (1) *Voltage ratio of a power transformer*. The ratio of the voltage between terminals on the higher-voltage side to the voltage between terminals on the lower-voltage side at *no-load. (2) *Turns ratio of a transformer* (general). The ratio of the number of turns in the phase winding associated with the higher-voltage side to the number of turns in the corresponding phase winding associated with the lower-voltage side. For a single-phase transformer, the voltage ratio is substantially

equal to the turns ratio but this is not generally the case for a polyphase transformer. It is possible for the latter type to have a turns ratio which is less than unity while the voltage ratio is greater than unity. (3) *Of an *instrument transformer*. The ratio of the primary current (or terminal voltage) to the secondary current (or terminal voltage) under specified load conditions.

rational intercepts, law of. If the edges formed by the intersections of three faces on a crystal are chosen as axes of reference OX, OY, OZ and a fourth face intersects these axes in A, B, and C, then any other face on the crystal will intercept the axes in A', B', C' such that $OA/OA' = h$, $OB/OB' = k$, $OC/OC' = l$ where h, k, and l are rational whole numbers rarely exceeding 6, and where (h, k, l) are said to be the *Miller* or *rational indices* of the face, relative to the axes OA, OB, OC.

rationalization of electric and magnetic quantities. A technique that has been used to modify electrical and magnetic equations so as to provide a more rational 'common sense' approach. The technique is best explained by reference to three examples. The magnitude of the *magnetic flux density B at a point distance r from an infinitely long straight wire carrying a current I and situated in a vacuum can be derived from Ampere's theorem as

$$B = 2\mu_k I/r$$

where μ_k is the *permeability of free space. In the CGS system μ_k has unit value. In another set of units μ_k may be given the value K, so that

$$B = 2\mu_k I/Kr. \qquad (1)$$

A similar discussion to determine the magnetic flux density at the centre of a flat circular coil of radius r and N turns yields

$$B = 2\pi\mu_k NI/Kr. \qquad (2)$$

313

A completely different kind of analysis gives the capacitance C of an isolated evacuated sphere of radius r as

$$C = K\varepsilon_k r \qquad (3)$$

where ε_k is the *permittivity of free space.

On further consideration, each of these three formulae has an irrational appearance. The magnetic field around a point on a straight wire is well known to be circular, and yet the quantity 2π that characterizes the concept of circularity does not occur in equation (1). The magnetic field at the centre of a flat circular coil is quite uniform and parallel, and yet equation (2) contains the 2π that was expected in equation (1). The electric field emanating from a sphere is, of course, three dimensionally symmetrical yet no 4π appears in equation (3). Each of the equations can be put into a rational form by making $K = 4\pi$. Thus

for a straight wire $B = \mu_k I / 2\pi r$

for a circular coil $B = \mu_k NI / 2r$

for a spherical
condenser $C = 4\pi\varepsilon_k r$.

0π implies linearity, 2π implies circular symmetry, and 4π implies spherical symmetry. The permeability and permittivity of free space have magnitudes changed by a factor of 4π, and are termed the *magnetic and *electric constants. In SI units μ_k is taken as $4\pi \times 10^{-7}$.

ray. A mathematical concept to give a first order representation of the rectilinear propagation of light energy and basic to geometrical optical theory. In an isotropic medium, the rays are normal to the wavefront; in double refraction, the ordinary rays are normal to the wavefront, while it is only in unique cases that the extraordinary rays are so. In general, rays are the shortest optical paths between wavefronts.

Rayleigh disc. A device based upon the principle that a light disc tends to set itself at right angles to the direction of an air stream whether the stream is alternating or direct. A small mica disc is suspended by a quartz or glass thread so as to lie at an angle to the opening of a cylindrical resonator when it is unexcited. When it is excited, the alternating air flow round the disc causes it to rotate. For small angles of deflection the rotation is proportional to the sound intensity in the resonator tube and consequently to the intensity in the undisturbed field.

Rayleigh–Jeans formula. *See* black body radiation.

Rayleigh limit. To prevent detectable deterioration in the quality of an image, the optical path differences should not exceed $\lambda/4$.

Rayleigh refractometer. *See* refractive index.

Rayleigh scattering. The scattering of light by particles of dimensions small compared with the wavelength of light. For linearly polarized incident light of wavelength λ, the scattered intensity bears to the incident intensity the ratio

$$\frac{I}{I_0} = \frac{\pi^2 \sin^2 \theta}{r^2} (\varepsilon_r - 1)^2 \frac{V^2}{\lambda^4},$$

where θ is the angle between the electric vector of the incident beam and the direction of viewing, r is the distance from the particle at which observations are made, and the particle has volume V and is of material of dielectric constant ε_r relative to the surroundings. For unpolarized light, $\sin^2 \theta$ is replaced in the formula by

$$\tfrac{1}{2}(1 + \cos^2 \varphi),$$

where φ is the angle between the incident light and the direction of observation.

The fourth power dependence on wavelength means that blue light is much more strongly scattered than red light from a medium containing very fine particles. This is called the *Tyndall effect*. It accounts for the bluish appearance of smoke and of clear sky when the observation is not along the direction of illumination. The setting sun, seen through a considerable thickness of atmosphere, appears reddish because the light has been robbed of much of the blue end of the spectrum.

Rayleigh's criterion. *See* resolving power.

Rayleigh's law. In magnetic materials subjected to magnetic forces low in comparison with the maximum coercive force, the *hysteresis loss in a cycle varies directly as the cube of the induction. The law ceases to be valid at the force value at which the *Barkhausen effect takes place.

reactance. (1) (electrical). Symbol: X. If an alternating e.m.f. is applied to a circuit the total opposition to the flow of an alternating current is called the *impedance. The part of the impedance that is not due to pure *resistance is called the reactance and is caused by the presence of *capacitance or *inductance. If the alternating e.m.f. is given by $E = E_0 \cos 2\pi ft$, the peak value of the current in a circuit with resistance R and inductance L is I_0 where

$$I_0 = \frac{E_0}{\sqrt{R^2 + (2\pi f L)^2}}.$$

$\sqrt{R^2 + (2\pi f L)^2}$ is the impedance and $2\pi f L$ is the reactance, in this case the *inductive reactance*. Similarly for a circuit with resistance R and capacitance C,

$$I_0 = \frac{E_0}{\sqrt{R^2 + [1/(2\pi f C)^2]}}$$

Here $1/2\pi f C$ is the *capacitive reactance*. The reactance is the imaginary part of the complex impedance Z, i.e. $Z = R + iX$. It is measured in ohms.

(2) (acoustic). Symbol: X_a. The magni-

tude of the imaginary part of the acoustic *impedance. The *specific acoustic reactance* (symbol: X_s) is the imaginary part of the specific acoustic impedance. If the reactance is caused solely by inertia it is called the *acoustic mass reactance*. If it is due to stiffness it is called the *acoustic stiffness reactance*. The product of acoustic mass reactance and angular frequency is called the *acoustic mass* (symbol: m_a). The product of acoustic stiffness reactance and angular frequency is called the *acoustic stiffness* (symbol: S_a). For an enclosure of volume V with dimensions that are small compared with the wavelength of sound the acoustic stiffness is given by $\rho C^2/V$, where ρ is the density and C the velocity of sound in the medium.

(3) (mechanical). *See* impedance (mechanical).

reactance coil. *See* inductor.

reactance drop. *See* voltage drop.

reaction. (1) The force with equal magnitude but opposite direction that arises when any force acts on a body or system. *See* Newton's laws of motion, III. (2) A condition that arises in electronic valve circuits when part of the amplified current is fed back positively to the control grid. It can give additional *gain or can cause oscillation.

reactive current (or voltage). *Syn.* quadrature component; wattless component. The component of an alternating current (or voltage) that is in quadrature with the voltage (or current), the current and voltage being regarded as vector quantities.

reactive load. The *load in which the current and the voltage at the terminals are out of phase with each other. *Compare* non-reactive load.

reactive power. *See* power.

reactivity. An indication of the departure of a *nuclear reactor from the condition in which the reaction can just take place (the *critical* condition). The reactivity is defined by the expression $(1 - 1/k)$, where k is the ratio of the average number of neutrons produced in a given length of time to the total number absorbed or lost in the same length of time; it is called the effective *multiplication constant. $k > 1$ implies a supercritical condition for the reactor. $k < 1$ implies a subcritical condition.

reactor. (1) An electrical apparatus possessing *reactance and selected for use because of that property. (2) *See* nuclear reactor.

real-is-positive convention. *See* optics sign conventions.

real object, image. *See* object; image.

Réaumur's scale of temperature. A temperature scale in which the ice point is taken as 0° r. and the steam point as 80° r.

receiver. *See* radio receiver; aerial.

reciprocal lattice. A theoretical lattice associated with a crystal lattice. If a, b, and c are the sides of a unit cell of the real lattice then a', b', and c' define the reciprocal lattice, where

$$a' = \frac{b \times c}{a \cdot (b \times c)}, \quad b' = \frac{c \times a}{a \cdot (b \times c)},$$

and

$$c' = \frac{a \times b}{a \cdot (b \times c)}.$$

reciprocal theorem (Of Maxwell). If a force F applied to one point in an elastic system produces a deflection d at another point, the same force F applied at the second point in the direction of the original deflection produces a deflection d at the first point in the direction in which F was first applied.

reciprocity law. The *density of processed photographic material is a function of exposure (= light intensity × time) only, for a standard procedure of processing. (More accurately, density depends on It^p where p varies from 0·8 to 1·1 according to the emulsion.) When the intensity varies greatly from that to which a given emulsion is most sensitive, the reciprocity law no longer holds (*reciprocity failure*).

reciprocity relations (Onsager). If two flows (of heat, electricity, matter, etc.) J_1, J_2, produced by gradients or forces X_1, X_2, so interact that

$$J_1 = L_{11}X_1 + L_{12}X_2$$
$$J_2 = L_{21}X_1 + L_{22}X_2,$$

then, subject to a condition restricting magnitudes, $L_{12} = L_{21}$; and similarly for three or more interacting flows. These relations can be used to establish relations between thermoelectric coefficients or justify the use of a single mutual inductance between two circuits.

recombination rate. The rate at which *electrons and *holes in a *semiconductor recombine.

rectifier. An electrical device that permits current to flow in only one direction and can thus make alternating into direct current. It operates either by suppressing or attenuating alternate half cycles of the current waveform or by reversing them. The most common rectifiers are semiconductor *diodes.

rectifier instrument. A d.c. instrument (usually a *moving-coil instrument) pro-

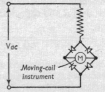

Circuit of rectifier instrument for use as an a.c. voltmeter

vided with a *rectifier so as to be suitable for making a.c. measurements. The rectifier usually consists of four *metal or semiconductor *diode rectifiers connected to form a bridge circuit (*see* diagram). Instruments of this type are usually calibrated to read *root-mean-square values on a.c. supplies of sinusoidal waveform.

rectifier photocell. *Syn.* barrier layer or blocking layer photocell. A light-sensitive cell that operates by the *photovoltaic effect. The cells are of two types: (1) *back layer*, in which the light has to pass through the emissive semiconducting layer and thus is usually red-sensitive since other components of the light are absorbed, and (2) *front layer*, in which the semiconductor is coated with a transparent metal film and light passes through this film to the barrier-layer immediately beneath it. These cells are more blue-sensitive and have a higher output as little light is lost. For low external resistances, under which conditions the leakage resistance of the cell can be ignored, the output is directly proportional to the light intensity – sensitivities of up to 0·5 mA per lumen being possible.

rectilinear propagation. The progress of light in straight lines in an isotropic medium; the *ray is the geometrical representation of it. On account of the wave character of light it is only approximately true (*see* diffraction). According to the general theory of *relativity, light rays travelling through free space are deflected towards any massive bodies they may pass.

red giant. A type of cool *giant star emitting light in the red region of the spectrum. A star expands to a red giant as it exhausts its nuclear fuel. *See* stellar spectra; Hertzsprung–Russell diagram.

red shift. A shift in the spectral lines of many extragalactic *stellar spectra towards the red end of the visible spectrum

relative to the wavelength of these lines in the terrestrial spectrum. It is thought to be due to the *Doppler effect caused by the recession of stars (*see* expanding universe). If λ and λ' are the wavelengths of a spectral line from a terrestrial and stellar source respectively, $\lambda/\lambda' = (c - v)$ $/c$, where v is the velocity of recession and c is the velocity of light. The term red shift is often used quantitatively for the ratio $(\lambda' - \lambda)\lambda'$, i.e. v/c. An immense red shift of 0·65 has recently been determined for a radio galaxy, implying a very great recessional velocity. At velocities approaching that of light the equation has to be modified:

$$\frac{\lambda - \lambda'}{\lambda'} = \sqrt{[(c + v)(c - v)]} - 1.$$

See also Hubble constant; quasar.

reduced distance. A distance in a medium divided by the refractive index of the medium. It may be regarded as an air-equivalent distance, and conjugate focus relations of refraction from one medium to another, using reduced distances, are the same as for a thin lens in air.

reduced equation of state. An *equation of state in which the variables p, v, and T are expressed as fractions of the *critical pressure, *critical volume, and *critical temperature respectively, these fractions being known as the *reduced pressure* (α), *volume* (β), and *temperature* (γ). The reduced form of (1) the Van der Waals equation is

$$\left(\alpha + \frac{3}{\beta^2}\right)(3\beta - 1) = 8\gamma,$$

(2) the Dieterici equation is

$$\alpha(2\beta - 1) = \gamma \exp[2(1 - 1/\beta\gamma)],$$

(3) the Berthelot equation is

$$\left(p + \frac{3p_c}{\beta^2\gamma}\right)\left(v - \frac{v_c}{3}\right) = RT$$

which on modification and neglecting small terms gives

317

$$pv = RT \left(1 - \frac{16}{3}\frac{1}{\alpha\gamma\beta^2} + \frac{1}{4\beta}\right).$$

reduced mass. Let a small particle of mass m be attracted by, and describe a closed orbit about, a heavier one of mass M. Then the equations describing the motion, assuming M to be fixed, may be transformed into those holding if M is not fixed (in which case both particles revolve around their common centre of gravity) by replacing m by μ, the reduced mass, where

$$\frac{1}{\mu} = \frac{1}{m} + \frac{1}{M}.$$

reduced pressure, temperature, volume. *See* reduced equation of state.

reference tone. An accepted standard pure tone of known intensity and frequency. Some such tone is necessary as the basis of any scale of sound intensity or loudness.

reflectance. *Syn.* reflection factor. Symbol: ρ. The ratio of the *radiant or *luminous flux reflected by a body to the incident flux. The term may be qualified by the adjectives *specular, diffuse,* and *total* according to the nature of the reflecting surface. *See also* reflectivity.

reflected current. *See* reflection coefficient.

reflected wave. *See* travelling wave.

reflecting microscope. *See* microscope.

reflecting power. *See* power.

reflecting telescope. *Syn.* reflector. An optical *telescope with a large-aperture concave mirror, usually paraboloid, of long focal length for gathering and focusing light from astronomical bodies. There is no *chromatic aberration and very little *spherical aberration and *coma, all of which occur in the *re-

fracting telescope. The mirror is also much easier to mount (by a back support) than the objective in a refractor. There are several types of reflecting telescope, including the *Newtonian, Herschelian* (now little used), and *Cassegrainian telescopes* (*see* diagram). They differ from each other in the additional optical system used to bring the image to a convenient point where it can be viewed by an *eyepiece.

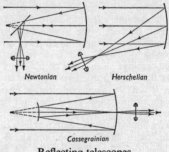

Newtonian   Herschelian

Cassegrainian

Reflecting telescopes

The intensity of the image depends on the amount of light collected (i.e. on the area of the mirror) and the time for which the image is viewed. The intensity of faint light emitted by astronomical bodies can therefore be considerably increased by focusing the image onto a photographic plate and exposing the plate for a long period. A spectrograph can be used in conjunction with the telescope to obtain *stellar spectra. *See also* Schmidt corrector; Maksutov telescope.

reflection. (1) When light strikes a surface of separation of two different media, some is thrown back into the original medium. If the surface is smooth, reflection is regular, otherwise it is diffuse. The two *laws of reflection,* viz. that incident ray, normal and reflected ray lie in the same plane, and the angle of incidence (with the normal) is equal to the *angle of reflection* (with the normal), suffice to determine the position and attributes of the image, whether at plane, curved, or multiple mirrors, etc. *Selective reflection* is said to occur when certain wavelengths are reflected more strongly than others. When reflection occurs at a denser medium there is a change of phase of π; when it occurs at a less dense medium there is no change of phase. *See also* total internal reflection.

(2) When a wave of sound is incident on the boundary surface between two media, it is partly reflected and the wave travels in the negative direction through the incident medium with the same velocity as it approached the boundary. The average wavelength of sound being 100 000 times the average wavelength of light radiation, it requires the reflecting surface to be 100 000 times the corresponding one in light to produce diffuse reflection or scattering. A mirror or lens to produce concentration of sound must be enormous compared with mirrors and lenses used in optical work. The same remark applies to gratings in sound diffraction (*see* acoustic grating). Plane waves when reflected may produce *standing waves. If the wavelength of the sound is small compared with the dimensions of the reflector, the ordinary geometrical laws of optics are applicable. The reflection of sound waves on a large scale produces *echoes. The surface of water forms a good reflector for sound waves in air, since the specific acoustic *impedances or resistances are widely different from each other.

reflection coefficient. In telecommunication engineering a uniform *transmission line is said to be correctly terminated (or matched) when the terminating impedance is equal to the *characteristic impedance of the line (symbol Z_0). If the terminating impedance (Z_R) differs from Z_0, the actual current in the line at the termination under steady-state conditions may be regarded as the vector sum of two currents, one being the current which would flow if Z_R were made equal to Z_0 (called the incident

current), the other being a current which is reflected from Z_R (called the reflected current). The vector ratio of the reflection current to the incident current is the reflection coefficient. In terms of the impedances Z_0 and Z_R: reflection coefficient $= (Z_0 - Z_R)/(Z_0 + Z_R)$.

reflection density. Symbol: D. The logarithm to base ten of the reciprocal of the *reflectance, i.e. $D = -\log_{10} \rho$.

reflection factor. *See* reflectance.

reflectivity. Symbol: ρ_∞. The *reflectance of a layer of material sufficiently thick that no change of reflectance would occur with increase in thickness.

reflector. (1) *See* reflecting telescope. (2) A layer of material surrounding the *core of a *nuclear reactor, whose purpose is to reflect some of the escaping *neutrons back into the core. (3) *See* directive aerial.

refracting angle (and edge). The angle formed by the two refracting surfaces of a prism in the principal section, i.e. a section perpendicular to the *refracting edge*, which is the edge formed by the intersection of the two refracting surfaces. This region is also called the apex of the prism.

refracting telescope. *Syn.* refractor. An optical telescope consisting essentially of two lens systems. The *objective is a convex lens of long focal length, f_1; the *eyepiece is a lens of short focal length, f_2.

In the *astronomical* or *Kepler telescope* (Fig. *a*), the eyepiece is convex and in normal adjustment the lenses are separated by the sum of the focal lengths producing a real but inverted image at infinity. The magnification is the ratio (f_1/f_2) of the focal length of the lenses. This is equivalent to the ratio of the angles ω/ω_0. The telescope can be used for terrestrial purposes only if an additional erecting system, such as in a

319

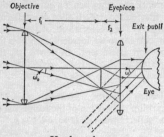

a Kepler telescope

*Fraunhofer eyepiece, is used (*see also* prism binoculars).

The *Galilean telescope* (Fig. *b*) produces an erect image, but the *exit port is virtual and lies inside the instrument. As the eye cannot be placed here, the exit port's best position is as near the eyepiece as possible thus restricting the field of view. The eye pupil acts as the *exit pupil. Under faint illumination the pupil of the eye expands and the resulting increased exit pupil renders the telescope more efficient at night than the Kepler telescope and is therefore employed in *night glasses*. The magnification is the ratio (f_1/f_2) of the focal lengths and is rarely greater than six.

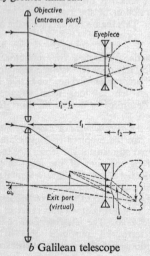

b Galilean telescope

The intensity of the image depends on how much light can be collected by the objective, i.e. on its area, and also on the time for which the image is viewed. Large objective lenses are very difficult to grind and to mount. In addition, *chromatic and *spherical *aberration, *coma, etc., have to be reduced to a minimum. Most of these problems are removed in *reflecting telescopes. *See also* telescope.

refraction. (1) Of light. The change of direction that a ray undergoes when it enters another transparent medium. The *laws of refraction* are (1) the incident ray, normal, and refracted ray all lie in the same plane and (2) *Snell's law, $\sin i / \sin i' = n'/n = \mu$ (a constant); n and n' are the *refractive indexes of the two media. According to wave theory, the direction of the wave front is altered because of the change of velocity. The action of prisms, lenses, etc., is explained by refraction.

The refractive defects of the eye include *myopia* (short sight), in which light is focused in front of the retina, and *hypermetropia* (long sight), in which light is focused behind the retina. Myopia is corrected by using suitable concave lenses and hypermetropia by using convex lenses.

(2) Of sound. A phenomenon, similar to that of light, in which a change of direction of the wave occurs when it reaches a point at which the wave velocity changes. If θ_1 and θ_2 are the angles of incidence and refraction of a plane wave and C_1 and C_2 the velocities in the two media, then

$$\frac{C_1}{C_2} = \frac{\sin \theta_1}{\sin \theta_2}.$$

Refraction occurs not only by a complete change of medium, but also by the gradual change of the properties of the same medium, for example by wind or temperature gradients. Such temperature or wind refraction in the atmosphere is analogous to the optical phenomena of mirage and has a very important influence on the range of transmission of sound in the atmosphere.

(3) Of lines of force. Electrical lines of force are refracted on passing at an angle from one dielectric medium to another. The tangents of the angles of incidence and refraction are in the ratio of the relative *permittivities.

refractive index. Symbol: *n*. The ratio of the sine of the angle of incidence to the sine of the angle of refraction. If the first medium is a vacuum, the value is the *absolute refractive index*. The absolute refractive index is thus the ratio of the velocity of light in a vacuum to the velocity of light in the medium, i.e. $n = c_0/c$. The value of the ratio for two media is the *relative refractive index*. If n_{12} is the relative index from medium 1 to medium 2, and n_{23} from medium 2 to medium 3, etc., then $n_{12} \cdot n_{21} = 1$; $n_{12} \cdot n_{23} \cdot n_{31} = 1$. In general, $n_{12} \cdot n_{23} \cdot n_{34} \ldots n_{k1} = 1$.

The relative refractive index is the ratio of the velocities of light in the two media, i.e. $n_{12} = c_1/c_2$. Commonly, the term refractive index refers to the value for sodium yellow ($\lambda = 589 \cdot 3$ nm) relative to air whose absolute index is $1 \cdot 000\ 29$. *Dispersion of light arises on account of differences of refractive index for different colours.

Refractive index can be measured by finding the angle of minimum *deviation of a solid in the form of a *prism. (A hollow glass prism may be used for a liquid.) Alternatively the *critical angle of incidence on an interface between two media can be found.

Interference methods can also be used. Light of wavelength λ_0 in a vacuum will have wavelength $\lambda = \lambda_0/n$ when in a medium of refractive index *n*. A length *l* in this medium contains $l/\lambda = ln/\lambda_0$ wavelengths. If therefore light from a given source is divided into two channels of equal length, one in a vacuum and the other in the given medium, there is an effective path difference of $(n - 1)l/\lambda_0$

and on reuniting the two beams, interference results. The *Jamin refractometer* divides the light by using reflections at the front and back surfaces of oblique thick glass blocks and uses two parallel tubes, one evacuated and the other slowly filled with gas while fringes are counted passing across the eyepiece.

The *Rayleigh refractometer* uses a pair of parallel slits across a collimating lens to give two beams through the gas tubes. The interference fringes are compared with a fixed fringe system and a compensating device of inclined glass plates enables the effective path difference to be compensated and the achromatic (uncoloured) fringes of the two systems to be brought to coincidence.

refractivity. An optical quantity equal to $n - 1$ where *n* is the refractive index. The *specific refractivity* is the ratio of the absolute refractivity to the density.

refractometer. An instrument for more or less direct measurement of *refractive index.

refractor. *See* refracting telescope.

refrigerator. A device for maintaining a chamber at a lower temperature than its surroundings. The ideal refrigerator is a *heat engine working backwards, work being done in taking heat from a condenser and transferring it to a source at a higher temperature.

regenerative braking. *See* electric braking.

regenerative cooling. A process used, e.g. in the *Linde process for liquefying air, in which compressed gas is cooled by expansion through a nozzle and the cool expanded gas is used to cool the oncoming compressed gas in a heat exchanger before it is cooled by expansion.

Regge pole model. A theoretical model used to describe the scattering of *elementary particles at high energies. In general, it is found that the *strong interactions involved in such processes cannot be described in terms of the exchange of a single elementary particle. Although the contribution from the exchange of low mass particles is usually the most important contribution to the *scattering amplitude, the contributions from the exchange of the higher mass *resonances cannot be neglected. Mathematically it is possible to describe the collective effect of exchanging all these particles in terms of the exchange of a few objects called Regge poles whose *spins increase with their effective masses. The

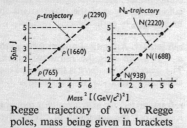

Regge trajectory of two Regge poles, mass being given in brackets

path traced out by the spin of a Regge pole as 'mass' varies is called a *Regge trajectory*. On a graph of spin against the square of the mass (*see* diagram), Regge trajectories are found to be approximately straight lines. The individual particles represented by a Regge pole have all quantum numbers the same except for their spins which differ by $\Delta J = 2n$ where n is an integer.

Regnault's hygrometer. A *hygrometer of the dew-point type consisting of two silver vessels A and G (*see* diagram), mounted side by side. Air may be blown from D through a tube C dipping into ether contained in A. This causes the ether to evaporate through E thus cooling the tube A until eventually, at the dew point, moisture condenses on the outside of A giving it a dull appearance compared with the surface of G. This temperature, and that at which the dullness disappears on allowing the appar-

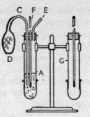

Regnault's hygrometer

atus to stand, are noted on the thermometer F, the mean giving the dew point, which, in conjunction with the room temperature, enables the relative humidity of the air to be calculated.

regulation. Of electrical generators, transformers, and power transmission lines. The changes that take place in the available voltage due to internal resistance (for direct current) or to internal impedance (for alternating current) when the load is changed under specified conditions.

rejector. The *impedance of a circuit comprising inductance and capacitance in parallel has a maximum value at one particular frequency. Such a circuit is a rejector for that frequency and its maximum impedance is called the *rejector impedance* or *dynamic impedance*. Compare acceptor.

relative aperture. *See* f-number.

relative atomic mass. *See* atomic weight.

relative density. *See* density.

relative-density bottle. *Syn.* specific-gravity bottle. A small flask with a perforated glass stopper which may be completely filled with a liquid. In order to determine the relative density of the liquid, the bottle is weighed empty (m_1), full of liquid (m_2), and finally, full of water (m_3). The relative density of the liquid is then

$$\frac{m_2 - m_1}{m_3 - m_1}.$$

Ingenious modifications of the procedure enable the relative density of powders, and of quantities of liquid insufficient to fill the bottle, to be found. *Compare* pycnometer.

relative humidity. *See* humidity.

relative permeability. *See* permeability.

relative permittivity. *See* permittivity.

relative velocity. The velocity of A relative to B is that velocity which B, supposing himself at rest, assigns to A. If A and B are moving in the same direction the relative velocity of A to B is $v_A - v_B$; if moving in opposite directions it is $v_A + v_B$. This only applies when v_A and v_B are very small compared to the velocity of light. *See* relativity.

relativistic state. A state in which a body is not subject to the laws of classical physics. For example, a body has a relativistic mass m (if m is recognizably in excess of the value m_0 when the body is at rest) resulting from the motion of the body: if its velocity is v,

$$m = m_0(1 - v^2/c^2)^{-\frac{1}{2}},$$

where c is the velocity of light.

relativity. A theory developed by Einstein in two parts. The first part, published in 1905 and now known as the *special theory of relativity*, was originally postulated to explain the results of the *Michelson–Morley experiment. This experiment showed that there was no measurable difference between the velocity of light when measured in the direction of the earth's rotation and when measured at right angles to this rotation. This observation conflicted with the classical law for relating velocities, i.e. $v_{AB} = v_A - v_B$, where v_A and v_B are the velocities of A and B as measured by one observer and v_{AB} is the velocity of A as measured by an observer travelling along with B. Einstein assumed that the laws of nature are the same

for all *frames of reference in uniform motion relative to each other and that the velocity of light (c) is the same in all such frames. He suggested that velocities should be related by the equation:

$$v_{AB} = \frac{v_A - v_B}{1 - (v_A v_B/c^2)}$$

(where v_A and v_B are in the same direction).

This is a general law applying to all bodies travelling at constant velocity. When v_A and v_B are small compared to c, the equation reduces to the simple classical law. However, at velocities approaching c the result is quite different. When $v_A = c$, $v_{AB} = c$. Thus the velocity of light is absolute and is not relative to the velocity of the observer.

This theory has several important consequences. First, it follows from Einstein's law of relative velocities that the length of an object at rest (l_0) in one frame of reference (A), will appear to an observer in another frame of reference (B) to have a length l_{AB} where,

$$l_{AB} = l_0 \sqrt{1 - (v_{AB}^2/c^2)}$$

and v_{AB} is the velocity of the two frames of reference relative to each other. If $v_{AB} = 0 \cdot 8c$, then $l_{AB} = 0 \cdot 6l_0$. This effect, called the *Lorentz–Fitzgerald contraction*, is negligible at low velocities.

A further consequence is the increase of mass with velocity, i.e.

$$m_v = \frac{m_0}{\sqrt{1 - (v^2/c^2)}}$$

where m_v is the mass of a body travelling at a velocity v, and m_0 is its *rest mass*. This increase of mass with velocity, which is negligible at normal velocities, has a profound effect at velocities of the order of c. For example, the average velocity of the electron around the nucleus of a hydrogen atom is about $0 \cdot 1c$; the consequent increase in mass of the electron causes the orbit to precess (*see* precession) around the nucleus.

This increase of mass with velocity

leads directly to the equation $E = mc^2$, where E is the energy associated with a mass m. Thus, mass is shown to be a form of energy and when it is destroyed (as in a *nuclear reaction) energy is evolved.

Time dilation is another consequence of special relativity; according to this phenomenon, if two observers are moving at constant velocity relative to each other, it will appear to each that the other's clocks have been slowed down. This affects the concept of *simultaneity.

A mathematical formulation of the special theory of relativity was given by Minkowski. It is based on the idea that an event is specified by four coordinates, three spatial coordinates and one time coordinate. These coordinates define a four-dimensional space and the motion of a particle can be described by a curve in this space, which is called *Minkowski space–time*. The coordinate axes of different observers are related by the *Lorentz transformation equations.

The special theory of relativity is concerned with relative motion between non-accelerated frames of reference. The second part of the theory, published in 1915 and known as the *general theory of relativity*, deals with general relative motion between accelerated frames of reference. In accelerated systems of reference certain fictitious forces are observed, such as the centrifugal and Coriolis forces found in rotating systems. These are known as fictitious forces because they disappear when the observer transforms to a non-accelerated system. For example, to an observer in a car rounding a bend at constant velocity objects in the car appear to suffer a force acting outwards. To an observer outside the car this is simply their tendency to continue moving in a straight line. The inertia of the objects is seen as a fictitious force and the observer can distinguish between non-inertial (accelerated) and inertial (non-accelerated) frames of reference.

A further point is that, to the observer in the car, all the objects are given the same acceleration irrespective of their mass. This implies a connection between the fictitious forces arising from accelerated systems and forces due to gravity, where the acceleration produced is independent of the mass (*see* free fall). For example, if an observer were placed in a sealed rotating spacecraft in space away from strong gravitational effects he would be unable to ascertain whether the force holding him on the 'floor' was gravitational or centrifugal. This leads to the *principle of equivalence* from which it follows that the inertial mass is the same as the gravitational mass.

A further principle used in the general theory is that the laws of mechanics are the same in inertial and non-inertial frames of reference.

The equivalence between a gravitational field and the fictitious forces in non-inertial systems can be expressed by using *Riemannian space–time*, which differs from the space-time of the special theory (*Minkowski space–time*). In special relativity the motion of a particle that is not acted on by any forces is represented by a straight line in Minkowski space-time. In general relativity, using Riemannian space–time, the motion is represented by a line that is no longer straight (in the Euclidean sense) but is the line giving the shortest distance. Such a line is called a *geodesic*. Thus space-time is said to be curved. The fact that gravitational effects occur near masses is introduced by the postulate that the presence of matter produces this curvature of space-time.

The predictions of general relativity only differ from Newton's theory by small amounts and most tests of the theory have been carried out through observations in astronomy. For example, it explains the shift in the perihelion of Mercury, the bending of light rays in the presence of large bodies, and the *Einstein shift. In Newton's theory of gravitation the fact that two bodies travel in curved paths in each other's presence is interpreted as being due to an inter-action between them. The general theory of relativity replaces this interpretation by the idea that it is due to the geometric properties of space itself. Many attempts have been made to formulate a *unified field theory in which the nuclear and electromagnetic interactions also result from the geometric properties of space–time. So far such attempts have been unsuccessful.

relaxation oscillations. (1) Oscillations characterized by a *sawtooth waveform, the vibrating system apparently relaxing at each peak and returning quickly to the zero position from which the build-up recommences. Such oscillations can only be maintained by the existence of an effectively steady applied unidirectional force.

(2) Oscillations of a system to which an impulse is applied intermittently. In this sense the waveform of a system in relaxation starts a succession of short trains of damped oscillations, for which the amplitude is renewed from time to time.

relaxation oscillator. An oscillator in which one or more voltages or currents change suddenly at least once during each cycle. The circuit is arranged so that during each cycle energy is stored in and then discharged from a reactive element (e.g. capacitance or inductance), the two processes occupying very different time intervals. An oscillator of this type has

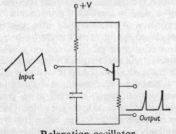

Relaxation oscillator

an output waveform that is far from being sinusoidal: square, triangular, and sawtooth waveforms can easily be pro-duced. Common types include the *multivibrator and *unijunction tran-sistor (*see* diagram).

relaxation time. Symbol: τ. (1) The time required for the *electric polarization of any point of a suitably charged dielectric to fall from its original value to $1/e$ of that value, due to the electric conduct-ivity of the dielectric. (2) Generally, the time required for an exponential vari-able to decrease to $1/e$ of its initial value. (3) The time required for a gas, in which the Maxwellian *distribution of velo-cities has been temporarily disturbed, to recover that state.

relay. An electrical device in which one electrical phenomenon controls the the switching on or off of an independent electrical phenomenon. There are many types of relay, most of which are either electromagnetic or solid-state relays.

Several types of electromagnetic relay exist. They usually depend on the action of a current through a coil, which attracts a pivoted armature, reed, or diaphragm, which in turn operates con-tacts or tilts a mercury switch.

In solid-state relays the switching action is achieved using a *thyristor or more commonly two thyristors (a *Triac). True solid-state relays have all components made from solid-state de-vices, with isolation between input and output terminals provided by a *light-emitting diode in conjunction with a photodetector.

Other types of relay include thermi-onically operated relays using the heating effect of a current and gas-filled relays such as the *thyratron.

reluctance. *Syn.* magnetic resistance. Symbol: R. The ratio of the *magneto-motive force, u, to the magnetic flux, Φ, i.e. $R = u/\Phi$. It has the units henry^{-1}.

reluctivity. The reciprocal of magnetic *permeability.

rem. *See* dose.

remanence. *Syn.* retentivity; residual magnetism. The residual *magnetic flux density in a substance when the magnetizing field strength is returned to zero. It is represented by OA or OB in the hysteresis curve shown. *See* hysteresis.

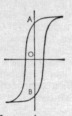

Hysteresis curve

repeater. A device used in telegraphic and telephonic circuits to repeat automatically in one or more circuits the signal currents in another circuit. A repeater usually introduces a degree of amplification (e.g. it incorporates an amplifier). When transmission takes place over great distances, repeaters are inserted at intervals along the line to compensate for the power loss in the latter.

residual. *See* deviation.

residual magnetism. *See* remanence.

resilience. The amount of potential energy stored in an elastic substance by means of elastic deformation. It is usually defined as the work required to deform an elastic body to the elastic limit divided by the volume of the body. It has the units J m^{-3}.

resistance. (1) (electrical). Symbol: R. The ratio of the potential difference across a conductor to the current flowing through it. (*See* Ohm's law.) If the current is alternating the resistance is the real part of the electrical *impedance Z,

i.e. $Z = R + iX$, where X is the *reactance. Resistance is measured in ohms. *See also* temperature coefficient of resistance. (2) (acoustic). Symbol: R_a. The real part of the acoustic *impedance. The *specific acoustic resistance* (Symbol: R_s) is the real part of the specific acoustic impedance. (3) (mechanical). *See* impedance (mechanical). (4) (thermal). Symbol: R. (i) The reciprocal of the *thermal conductance. The units are m^{2}K W^{-1}. (ii) The ratio of the temperature difference (θ) between two points and the mean rate of flow of entropy (S) between them, i.e.

$$R = \theta \frac{dS}{dt}.$$

The units are K^{2}W^{-1}.

resistance drop. *See* voltage drop.

resistance gauge. A gauge used for measuring high fluid pressures by means of the change in electrical resistance produced in manganin or mercury by those pressures. These gauges are calibrated with reference to the *free-piston gauge.

resistance pyrometers. *See* resistance thermometers.

resistance strain gauges. An instrument for measuring structural strains by the increase in electrical resistance of a wire or grid of wires attached to or supported by the structure.

resistance thermometers. Pyrometers in which the change in electrical resistance of a wire is used as the thermometric property. A small coil of wire, usually platinum but of other metals for use at low temperatures, is wound on a mica former and enclosed in a silica or porcelain sheath. It is placed in one arm of a *Wheatstone bridge and, as the measuring galvanometer is often at a great distance, duplicate leads are added which are placed in the other balancing arm and serve to compensate for temperature variations in the pyrometer leads. The instrument is useful over a very wide range from $-200°$ to over $1200°$ C.

resistivity. (1) Formerly called specific resistance. Symbol: ρ. The resistance of unit length of the substance with uniform unit cross-section. It is measured in Ω m. The product of the resistivity and the density is sometimes called the *mass resistivity*. (2) Thermal resistivity. Symbol: φ. The reciprocal of the *thermal conductivity. It is measured in m K W^{-1}.

resistor. ⌇⌇⌇ *Syn.* resistance. A piece of electrical apparatus possessing *resistance and selected for use because of that property. Carbon resistors are widely used in electronic circuits. They consist of finely ground carbon particles mixed with a ceramic material, encapsulated into insulated tubes. The casing has a set of coloured stripes denoting the value of the resistance. Other types are wirewound coils, usually of manganin and *film resistors*, in which a thin layer of resistive material is deposited on an insulating core.

resistor–transistor logic. A family of integrated *logic circuits in which the input is via a resistor into the *base of an inverting *transistor. They are susceptible to noise, but the power dissipated is relatively low.

resolving power. A measure of the ability of a *telescope or *microscope to produce detectably separate images of objects that are close together. A spectroscopic instrument is required to separate two wavelengths that are very nearly equal.

The resolving power of a telescope is measured by the angular separation of two point sources that are just detectably separated by the instrument. The smaller this angle, the greater is the resolving power. The image of a point source formed by the objective of the telescope

will consist of a diffraction pattern which has a central bright spot surrounded by alternate dark and light rings. Two point sources close together will give rise to two overlapping diffraction patterns. A cross section of the variation in intensity of the light in such a diffraction pattern is illustrated in Fig. *a*, while Figs. *b* and *c* show the resulting intensity produced by two patterns overlapping to different extents.

a Two patterns overlapping completely

b Two patterns very close together

c Two patterns sufficiently far apart to be separately distinguished

Rayleigh proposed that a reasonable criterion for resolution of two point sources was that the inner dark ring of one diffraction pattern should coincide with the centre of the second diffraction pattern, a condition which is known as *Rayleigh's criterion*. This leads to the condition that two point sources are resolved by a telescope objective of diameter D provided their angular separation is not less than $1 \cdot 22\lambda/D$, λ being the wavelength. The Rayleigh criterion, which is quite arbitrary,

327

corresponds in the combined diffraction pattern to an intensity ratio saddle to peak (AB/CD) of 0·81. The *Abbe criterion* for resolution is that the angular separation should not be less than λ/D.

The resolving power of a microscope is measured by the actual distance between two object points that can be detectably separated by the instrument. The greater the resolving power the smaller will this distance be. Application of the Rayleigh criterion yields the result that the least separation for resolution is $0·61\ \lambda/n \sin i$, where λ is the wavelength of the light used, n the refractive index of the medium between object and objective, and i the semi-angle subtended at the object by the edges of the objective. Abbe called the quantity ($n \sin i$) the *numerical aperture of the objective. Abbe stated that a separation of $0·5\lambda/n \sin i$ gave a more practical figure.

For good resolution the expression shows that the need is for higher numerical aperture and shorter wavelength. The numerical aperture may be increased by filling the space between object and objective with a medium of higher refractive index than air. This process is called *oil-immersion*, the medium usually chosen being cedar-wood oil. A good modern high-power microscope objective will have a numerical aperture of perhaps 1·6, corresponding to about 200 nm as the least separation for resolution. The resolving power may also be decreased by decreasing the wavelength of the radiation used, as in *ultraviolet microscopy* (*see also* electron microscope).

In a spectroscopic instrument, the requirement for resolution is for a detectable separation of wavelengths that are very nearly equal. In such cases, the *chromatic resolving power* is measured as the ratio of the wavelength studied to the difference in wavelengths which can just be separated.

If a prism spectrometer is used then, assuming the Rayleigh criterion, the resolving power is given by the expression ($t\ \mathrm{d}n/\mathrm{d}\lambda$) where t is the maximum thickness of prism traversed by the beam and $\mathrm{d}n/\mathrm{d}\lambda$ is the ratio of change in refractive index to change in wavelength for the material of the prism. In a simple spectrometer a value of about 10^3 is possible.

If a *diffraction grating is used, the resolving power is the product of the total number of lines illuminated and the order number of the spectrum being used. For a 7·6 cm concave grating used in the second order a resolving power of about 100 000 is theoretically possible. In some instruments, such as the *echelon grating and *etalon, resolving powers of one million or more are possible.

resonance. (1) A condition in which a vibrating system responds with maximum amplitude to an alternating driving force. The condition exists when the frequency of the driving force coincides with the natural undamped oscillatory frequency of the system. (*See* forced vibrations.)

(2) The *impedance in an alternating-current circuit with inductance and capacitance in series is: $Z = \sqrt{R^2 + [(\omega L) - (1/\omega C)]^2}$ where R is the ohmic resistance, $\omega = 2\pi \times$ the frequency, L is the inductance and C the capacitance. When $\omega L = 1/\omega C$ a condition is achieved where the impedance depends on the resistance alone, and as the resistance may be quite low for high values of L and C the current flowing will be high. This is the condition for resonance, and the circuit is said to be *tuned to the *resonant frequency*, $1/2\pi\sqrt{LC}$. The *voltage drops across either inductance or capacitance are usually great, but are out of phase with each other so that the total voltage drop in the circuit is small. Similar resonance can also be obtained when the capacitance and inductance are in parallel. In this case the currents in each branch are quite large, but out of phase so that they combine to give a small main circuit

current. In series resonance the combined impedance is low; in parallel resonance it is high.

resonance cross section. *See* cross section.

resonances. Extremely short-lived *elementary particles that decay by *strong interaction in about 10^{-23} second. A resonance may be regarded as a greatly increased probability of interaction between colliding particles at the resonance energy. If the energy of colliding particles is slowly increased a sudden peak in particle production is observed, at the resonance energy; production drops off as the energy is further increased. This indicates that a particle exists with a mass equal to the combined relativistic masses of the colliding particles. Over one hundred *meson and *baryon resonances are known; some of the more important of these are given in the following tables:

Baryon Resonances

	Mass (MeV/c^2)	Isospin, I	Spin, J	Parity, P
N(1470)	1470	$\frac{1}{2}$	$\frac{1}{2}$	$+1$
N(1520)	1520	$\frac{1}{2}$	$\frac{3}{2}$	-1
N(1535)	1535	$\frac{1}{2}$	$\frac{1}{2}$	-1
Δ(1236)	1236	$\frac{3}{2}$	$\frac{3}{2}$	$+1$
Λ(1405)	1405	0	$\frac{1}{2}$	-1
Λ(1520)	1520	0	$\frac{3}{2}$	-1
Σ(1385)	1385	1	$\frac{3}{2}$	$+1$
Ξ(1530)	1530	$\frac{1}{2}$	$\frac{3}{2}$	$+1$

resonance scattering. *See* scattering.

resonance theory of hearing. A sound wave reaching the ear passes down the auditory canal and causes vibrations of the drum behind which is a mechanical coupling of three bones leading to a window in the cochlea. The latter is a spiral tube of bone gradually diminishing in size, its cross section being divided into two by the basilar membrane. This membrane has about 24 000 fibres, arranged in groups from which a separate nerve leads to the brain. The resonance theory of hearing considers the fibres stretched radially throughout the basilar membrane to act as resonators. These fibres vary in length, tension, and loading throughout the membrane so that their natural frequencies cover the audible range. The incoming sound excites a small group of fibres having resonant frequencies near the frequency of the sound. The vibrations thus set up are communicated to the hair cells and the corresponding nerve transmits the sensation to the brain.

resonant cavity. *See* cavity resonator.

resonant frequency. *See* resonance.

rest energy. The energy equivalent of the *rest mass of a body or particle, usually given in electronvolts.

restitution. *See* coefficient of restitution.

Meson Resonances

	Mass (MeV/c^2)	Isospin, I	Spin, J	Parity, P	G-parity, G	Charge conj. parity, C
ρ	765	1	1	-1	$+1$	-1
ω	784	0	1	-1	-1	-1
K*	892	$\frac{1}{2}$	1	-1		
$\eta(X^0)$	958	0	0 or 2	-1	$+1$	$+1$
φ	1019	0	1	-1	-1	-1
f	1260	0	2	$+1$	$+1$	$+1$
A$_2$	1310	1	2	$+1$	-1	$+1$
K**	1420	$\frac{1}{2}$	2	$+1$		

rest mass. The *mass that a body or particle has when it is at rest. *See* relativity; relativistic state.

resultant tones. *See* combination tones.

retentivity. *See* remanence.

retina. The inner coat of the eye, consisting of nerve fibres and endings sensitive to light (rods and cones).

reverberation. The persistence of audible sound after the source has been cut off. If the time difference between reception of direct sound and its echo is less than about 1/15th of a second, true reverberation occurs and a number of echoes gives the sensation of a continuous sound of diminishing intensity. In the acoustics of large halls the *time of reverberation* is of considerable importance. It is defined as the time for the energy density to fall to the threshold of audibility from a value 10^6 times as great, i.e. a fall of 60 decibels. Optimum periods generally lie between 1 and 2·5 seconds. The value should be low for speech and light music but high for orchestral music. In general the optimum period is proportional to the linear dimensions of the room.

reverberation chamber. *Syn.* echo chamber. A room having a very long time of *reverberation and which is carefully designed to allow a uniform energy distribution of sound to be produced. For a room to have a long reverberation time there must be very little absorption by the exposed surfaces. Thus the walls and ceiling are usually plastered and then painted to ensure uniformity of surface throughout the room. However, these highly reflecting surfaces tend to produce *standing waves which prevent a uniform energy distribution. Standing waves may be avoided by using a room in which no two walls are parallel or by having a large steel reflector rotating silently in the room. It is also customary to use a revolving source which produces

a *warble tone. All sound from outside the chamber must be excluded and elaborate sound proofing is necessary.

reversal. (1) (photographic) The transformation of a photographic negative into a positive. *See* photography. (2) (spectroscopic) Bright emission lines in the spectrum of a discharge tube or flame may be *reversed*, i.e. apparently transformed into dark lines (absorption spectrum), when intense white light traverses the source and enters the spectroscope, due to selective absorption by the gas or vapour at the same frequencies as it emits. *See also* sodium-line reversal.

reverse bias. *See* reverse direction.

reverse direction. *Syn.* inverse direction. The direction in which an electrical or electronic device has the larger resistance. Voltage applied in the reverse direction is the *reverse voltage* or *reverse bias* and the current flowing is the *reverse current*.

reversibility principle (optics). If a reflected or refracted ray is reversed in direction it will retrace its original path.

reversible change. A change that is carried out so that the system is in *equilibrium at any instant and so that a slight decrease in the factor effecting the change causes every feature of the forward process to be completely reversed. This often means that the change must be carried out infinitely slowly since any kinetic energy could not change sign, and there must be no friction since this would always result in the evolution of heat. Such a process is never realizable in practice but close approximations to it can be attained. All practical processes involve *irreversible changes*, i.e. changes in which the system is not in equilibrium at all instants during the change.

reversible engine. A *heat engine that operates reversibly, in the sense described under reversible change. *See* Carnot cycle; Carnot's theorem.

Reynolds's law. The pressure head h required to maintain a liquid flow at constant velocity v through a pipe of length l and radius r is given by the equation:

$$h = klv^p/r^q.$$

The constants k, p, and q are known as the *Unwin coefficients*. k is generally very small; $p \approx 1$; $q \approx 2$.

Reynolds number. Symbol: (Re). A dimensionless quantity equal to $\rho vl/\eta$, where ρ is the density of a fluid of viscosity η, in motion with velocity v relative to some solid characterized by the linear dimension, l. For steady flow through a system with a given geometry, the flowlines take the same form at a given value of the Reynolds number. Thus flow of air through an orifice will be geometrically similar to that of water through a similar orifice if the dimensions and velocity are chosen to give identical values of the Reynolds number. *See* convection (of heat); dynamic similarity.

rheology. The study of the deformation and flow of matter.

rheometer. An instrument designed to measure the flow properties of solid materials by investigating the relationship between stress, strain, and time.

rheostat. A variable resistance connected into a circuit, in series, to vary the current flowing in the circuit. It often consists of a coil of high resistance wire with sliding contacts (arranged either along a straight tube, or in a circular arc), or it may have a number of resistance coils brought into the circuit by a rotary switch. The word is usually applied to physically large devices. Small rheostats, as used in electronic circuits, are usually called *potentiometers.

rheostat braking. *See* electric braking.

rhombic and rhombohedral system. *See* crystal systems.

rhumbatron. *See* cavity resonator.

ribbon microphone. A type of *microphone based on the principle that when a conductor moves perpendicular to a magnetic field, an e.m.f. is induced in it. The conductor is a very thin strip of aluminium alloy a few millimetres wide, loosely fixed in a strong magnetic field parallel to the plane of the strip. The resulting force on the ribbon due to a sound wave is proportional to the difference in pressure between the front and back of the ribbon. The e.m.f. can be made independent of frequency. The microphone has strong directional characteristics which can be used to reduce noise.

Richardson's equation. *Syn.* Dushman's equation; Richardson–Dushman equation. The basic equation of *thermionic emission relating the temperature of a body to the number of electrons it emits. It has the form:

$$j = AT^2 e^{-b/T},$$

where j is the electric current density, A and b are constants, and T the thermodynamic temperature. A depends on the nature of the metal surface and b can be put equal to φ/k, where φ is the *work function and k the *Boltzmann constant.

Riemannian space-time. *See* relativity.

Righi effect. *See* Leduc effect.

right ascension. *See* celestial sphere.

right-hand rule. For a dynamo. *See* Fleming's rules.

rigid body. A body in which the distance between every pair of particles remains constant under the action of any forces. An abstract concept in mechanics.

rigidity modulus. *See* modulus of elasticity.

ring current. A strong electric current flowing from east to west at a height of 5×10^7 m above the earth's surface and causing variations in the normal pattern of the earth's magnetic field. *See* geomagnetism.

ringing. *See* pulse.

ring main. (1) An electric main that is closed upon itself to form a ring. If the ring is supplied by a power station at one point only, then between that point and any other point in the ring to which a consumer may be connected there are two independent electrical paths. Hence, in the event of a fault in the ring, the latter can be broken and the faulty section disconnected without interrupting the supply to the consumer. (2) A domestic wiring system in which individual outlets have their own fuses, a number of such outlets being connected in parallel to a ring circuit.

ring winding. *Syn.* toroidal winding; Gramme winding. A winding in an electrical machine in which the coils are wound on an annular magnetic core, one side of each turn being threaded through the magnetic ring.

ripple (electrical). In general, a unidirectional current or voltage has a d.c. component and an a.c. component. The latter is called a ripple. The term is used particularly in connection with power supplies in which direct current is obtained from alternating current by means of a *rectifier. The ratio of the *root-mean-square value of the ripple (i.e. a.c. component) to the mean value (i.e. d.c. component) is called the *ripple factor*. A circuit (usually a type of *filter) designed to reduce the magnitude of a ripple is called a *smoothing circuit.

ripples. On a fluid surface. Waves of small amplitude on the surface of a fluid for which the wavelength is small and the effects of the *surface tension of the fluid are important. The velocity of ripples of length λ on a fluid of density ρ and surface tension σ is given by $\sqrt{(\lambda g/2\pi + 2\pi\sigma/\lambda\rho)}$, g being the acceleration of *free fall.

ripple tank. The similarity between a plane section of a three dimensional sound wave and *ripples on a water surface has been used to study the reflection, refraction, interference, and diffraction of sound waves. Ripples are produced in a rectangular tank by rods that can be dipped just under the surface. The depth of the liquid must be more than half the ripple wavelength.

rise time. *See* pulse.

r.m.s. value. *See* root-mean-square value.

Rochon prism. A double image prism consisting of two quartz prisms, the first to receive the light, cut parallel to the axis, the second with optic axis at right angles; their deviations are in opposition. The ordinary ray passes through undeviated and is achromatic; the extraordinary ray is deflected (doubling is produced).

rocket. A missile or space vehicle powered by reaction propulsion that carries both its own fuel and oxidant (if required). Rockets are therefore independent of the earth's atmosphere and are the power systems used in space flights. Most space flights have been powered by *chemical rockets* in which the thrust is obtained by the expansion occurring when a solid or liquid fuel (e.g. alcohol) reacts chemically with the oxidant (e.g. liquid oxygen). *Nuclear rockets* have also been used in unmanned space flights; in this case the thrust is obtained from a *nuclear reactor. Nuclear rockets present problems of *shielding for manned flights. Most rockets are multistage devices the first, or booster stage, being jettisoned in the less dense region of the upper atmosphere. This mass loss aids the vehicle's acceleration to its *escape velocity.

rods and cones. *See* colour vision.

roentgen (or röntgen). Symbol: R. The unit of exposure *dose of X- or gamma rays such that one roentgen produces in air a charge of $2 \cdot 58 \times 10^{-4}$ C on all the ions of one sign, when all the electrons released in a volume of air of mass 1 kg are completely stopped. $1R = 2 \cdot 58 \times 10^{-4}$ C kg^{-1}; $1C$ $kg^{-1} = 3880$ R. It is used for X-rays below 4 MeV.

roentgen-equivalent man (r.e.m.). *See* dose.

Roentgen rays. *See* X-rays.

rolling friction. *See* friction.

roof prism. *Syn.* Amici prism. *See* direct vision prism.

root-mean-square (r.m.s.) value. *Syn.* effective value; virtual value. The square root of the mean value of the squares of the instantaneous values of a current, voltage, or other periodic quantity during one complete cycle; it is the effective value of current or voltage in an alternating current. The r.m.s. value of a sine wave is the peak value divided by the square root of 2.

root-mean-square (r.m.s.) velocity. The square root of the *mean square velocity.

rotameter. An instrument that measures the rate of flow of fluids. It consists of a small float that, due to the motion of the fluid, moves vertically in a transparent calibrated tube. The height of the float gives a measure of the velocity of the fluid.

rotating sector. A device used in conjunction with a *pyrometer when measuring very high temperatures in order to cut by a known fraction the amount of radiation incident on the pyrometer. The true temperature T of a source is related to the temperature T_1 recorded by a total radiation pyrometer used with a sector subtending an angle θ at the centre, by the equation $T_1^4 = [(2\pi - \theta)/2\pi]T^4$. The speed of rotation of the sector is immaterial provided it is not too low.

rotational motion. *See* irrotational motion.

rotational quantum number. *See* energy level.

rotation and rotational field. *See* curl.

rotation of plane of polarization. *See* optical activity.

rotation photography. A crystal diffraction method in which a single crystal is allowed to rotate about an axis normal to an incident beam of monochromatic X-rays (or electrons, neutrons, etc.) the photographic film (plane or cylindrical) being stationary.

rotation spectrum. *See* spectrum.

rotatory dispersion. Dispersion resulting from the rotation of the plane of polarization being different for different wavelengths. *See* optical activity.

rotor. The rotating part of an electrical machine. The term is usually applied only to an a.c. (as distinct from a d.c.) machine. *Compare* stator. *See also* induction motor.

Routh's rule. The moment of inertia of a solid body about an axis of symmetry is

$$\frac{\text{mass} \times \text{sum of squares of the other semi-axes}}{3, 4, 5},$$

the denominator being 3, 4, or 5

333

according to whether the body is rectangular, elliptical, or ellipsoidal.

The circle is a special case of the ellipse. The rule works for a circular or elliptical cylinder about the central axis only, but for circular or elliptical discs it works for all three axes of symmetry. E.g. for a circular disc of radius a and mass M, the moment of inertia about an axis through the centre of the disc and lying (a) perpendicular to the disc, (b) in the plane of the disc is

$$(a)\ \frac{M(a^2 + a^2)}{4} = \frac{Ma^2}{2},\ (b)\ \frac{Ma^2}{4}.$$

See Lee's rule.

Rowland circle. A circle having a diameter equal to the radius of a particular concave *diffraction grating. If the slit, grating, and receiving screen lie on the circumference of this circle, the resulting spectrum will be in focus. Successively higher orders can be brought into focus by decreasing the distance between the slit and the grating. The Rowland circle is used in the mounting of a concave grating.

rubidium–strontium dating. *See* dating.

Russell–Saunders coupling. *See* coupling.

rutherford. Symbol: rd. A unit of *activity. It is the quantity of a nuclide required to produce 10^6 disintegrations per second. 1 rutherford = 2.7027×10^{-5} *curie.

rydberg. *See* atomic unit of energy.

Rydberg constant. *See* hydrogen spectrum.

Rydberg spectrum. An *absorption spectrum of a gas taken with ultraviolet radiation and used for determining *ionization potential. The spectrum contains a large number of lines, each corresponding to excitation of an electron from its *ground state to an *excited state. The lines form a series (*see* hydrogen spectrum) and become closer together as the energy increases. At one particular energy they merge into a continuum. This is the energy required to ionize the atom or molecule.

S

saccharimeter. An instrument for measuring the rotation of the plane of polarization of optically active solutions, especially sugars.

sagittal coma. *See* coma.

sampling. A technique of measuring only some portions of a signal, the resultant set of discrete values being taken as representative of the whole. The rate of sampling of a periodic quantity must be at least twice the frequency.

satellite. A natural or artificial body orbiting another body so large that the centre of mass of the system is well within the larger body. Many artificial satellites have been projected from the earth, either to orbit the earth itself or to orbit other bodies of the solar system.

Information satellites are designed to provide information concerning other bodies, outer space, or the earth and to relay it back by radio.

Communications satellites have a highly directional aerial that picks up radio signals from the earth and returns them by simple reflection (*passive satellite*) or relays them after amplification (*active satellite*). Synchronous satellites have a revolution period equal to the rotation period of the earth. (*See* synchronous orbit).

The period of revolution T of a satellite can be deduced by equating its centrifugal force to the force of gravity between it and the primary:

$$T^2 = 4\pi^2 r^3/Gm$$

(r = distance from centre of mass of primary; G = gravitational constant; m = mass of primary).

saturable reactor. *See* transductor.

saturated (and non-saturated) mode. The operation of a *field-effect transistor in

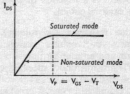

Saturated and non-saturated modes of an FET

a particular portion of its characteristic. Saturated mode is operation of the device in the portion of the characteristic beyond pinch-off, i.e. $V_{DS} \geqslant V_P$, where V_P is the pinch-off voltage (*see* diagram). The *drain current is independent of the drain voltage V_{DS}, in this region.

Non-saturated mode is operation of the device in the portion of its characteristic below pinch-off, i.e. $V_{DS} \leqslant V_P$.

saturated vapour. A vapour in dynamic equilibrium with its liquid at a given temperature; it can thus hold no more substance in the gaseous phase unless the temperature is raised. The pressure exerted by a saturated vapour depends only on the temperature. (*See* vapour pressure.) For certain saturated vapours the specific heat capacity can be negative. *See* negative specific heat capacities; supersaturated vapour.

saturated vapour pressure (SVP). The pressure exerted by a *saturated vapour.

saturation. (1) (magnetic). The degree of magnetization of a substance that cannot be exceeded however strong the applied magnetizing field. In this state all the domains (*see* ferromagnetism) are assumed to be fully orientated along the lines of force of the magnetizing field. (2) (light). *See* colour.

saturation current. The portion of the static *characteristic of an electronic device in which further increases in the voltage do not lead to a corresponding increase in the current, until *breakdown is reached. The actual value of the saturation current is a function of the device and the external circuit.

saturation resistance (or voltage). The resistance (or voltage) between the collector and emitter terminals of a bipolar *transistor, under specified conditions of base current, when the collector current is limited by the external circuit.

sawtooth waveform. A waveform whose amplitude varies linearly between two values, the time taken in one direction being very much longer than the time taken in the other (*see* figure). Sawtooth waveforms are usually produced by *relaxation oscillators.

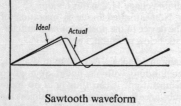

Ideal Actual

Sawtooth waveform

scalar. A quantity defined by a single magnitude (as distinct from a *vector which has magnitude and direction). Examples are mass, time, and wavelength.

scalar product. *See* vector.

scaler. A device that produces an output *pulse when a specified number of input pulses have been received. It is frequently used for counting purposes, particularly in conjunction with *scintillation counters for measuring *radioactivity.

scanning. The process of exploring an area in a methodical manner, in order to produce an electrical output which varies in time in a manner proportional to the magnitude of the information scanned. The technique is widely used in *tele-

vision and *radar. In *nuclear medicine part or all of the body may be scanned in order to determine the distribution of a particular radioisotope.

scanning electron microscope. *See* electron microscope.

scanning-transmission electron microscope (STEM). *See* electron microscope.

scattering. (1) The deflection of light energy by fine particles of solid, liquid, or gaseous matter from the main direction of a beam. If the particles are relatively large, reflection as well as diffraction plays a part; if the particles are small (smaller than a wavelength or as small as a molecule) the effect is diffractive. In *Rayleigh scattering the scattered intensity for small particles varies as $(1/\lambda^4)$ so that the scattered light from very small particles is bluish (Tyndall effect). Chalk dust particles are whitish – they are larger and reflection effects are more noticeable. The blue of the sky is due to scattering by air molecules, and the red sun is due to the removal of the blue by scattering from the direct beam.

(2) The deflection of sound waves by a reflecting surface whose dimensions are greater than the wavelength of the wave. The ratio of the intensities of the scattered to the incident waves is given by $I_s/I_i \propto V^2/\lambda^4 r^2$, where V is the volume of the scattering element and r is the distance from the element to the observation point. The *harmonics of the note will thus be reflected in increasing proportion towards the higher frequencies, the octave of a note reflected from a surface being sixteen times more intense than in the incident wave.

(3) The deflection of radiation resulting from the interaction of individual particles with the nuclei or electrons in the material through which the radiation is passing or with the photons of another radiation field. *Inelastic scattering* occurs as a result of an inelastic *collision in which net changes occur in the internal

energies of the participating systems and in the sum of their kinetic energies before and after the collision; there is no such energy change in *elastic scattering*, which occurs as a result of an elastic collision.

Thomson scattering is the scattering of electromagnetic radiation by free (or loosely bound) electrons, which can be explained in terms of the forced vibrations of the electrons of an atom which is absorbing radiation. These oscillating electric charges become the source of electromagnetic radiation of lower energy than the incident radiation and it is emitted in all directions. If I_0 is the intensity per unit area of the incident radiation, the total intensity, I, of the scattered radiation is given by $(8\pi/3) (e^2/mc^2)^2 I_0$, where e and m are the electronic charge and mass and c is the velocity of light. The quotient I/I_0 has the dimensions of an area and is the scattering *cross section of the electron. The elastic scattering of photons by electrons known as the *Compton effect, produces a reduction of energy of the photons. The *Raman effect involves scattering of photons by molecules.

Resonance scattering occurs at high energies when the incident wave can penetrate the nucleus and interact with its interior. If the wave is reflected at the nuclear surface, *potential scattering* takes place. (*See also* Coulomb scattering; scattering amplitude.) *Shadow scattering* results from the interference of the incident wave and scattered waves. *See also* Mie scattering.

scattering amplitude. One of the most important ways in which the interactions between *elementary particles can be investigated experimentally is by allowing a beam of high-velocity particles to collide with other particles. As a result of the collisions that occur some of the particles are deflected and in some cases the final particles may have different *quantum numbers from the initial ones (*see* strong interaction). Details of the scattering, such as the angular distribu-

tion of the final particles, will depend on the nature of the forces that act during the collision. The mathematical functions used to describe these scattering processes are called scattering amplitudes. From these amplitudes the angular distribution of the final particles can be calculated. Scattering amplitudes are usually written in terms of relativistically invariant quantities.

scattering coefficient. *See* linear attenuation coefficient.

schlieren photography. A method of photographing inhomogeneities, due to differences of density and refractive index, in a transparent medium using spark photography. The technique is useful for studying shock waves, convection currents, sound waves, flaws in glass, etc. When light from a spark is passed through the transparent medium, differences in refractive index within the medium cause refraction of the beam of light. These differences can be made to show up as streaks (German *Schlieren*) on a photographic plate.

Schmidt corrector. A transparent plate shaped like a convex lens at the centre and a concave lens around the periphery, placed at the centre of curvature of a concave spherical mirror. The divergence of peripheral rays and convergence of central rays removes *spherical aberration from the system. It is used especially in *reflecting telescopes, the system being called a *Schmidt telescope*.

Schmitt trigger. A type of *bistable circuit that gives a constant output when the input waveform exceeds a specific voltage. A flat-topped pulse is obtained from the output, irrespective of the input waveform. It is frequently used as a *trigger circuit.

Schottky barrier. *See* Schottky effect; Schottky diode.

Schottky defect. *See* defect.

Schottky diode. A *diode consisting of a metal–semiconductor contact (*Schottky barrier*), which has rectifying characteristics similar to a *p–n junction. It differs from a p–n junction diode in that the *diode forward voltage is different (lower for commonly used materials) and there is no charge stored when the diode is forward biased. The device can therefore be turned off very rapidly by the application of reverse bias, as the storage time is negligible. *See also* surface-barrier transistor.

Schottky effect. A reduction of the *work function of a solid due to the application of an external electric field leading to a consequent increase in its electron *emission. The presence of an accelerating field lowers the potential energy of electrons outside the solid. This leads to a distortion of the potential barrier and consequent lowering of the work function. In the case of a metal there is also a contribution from *image potentials. The lowering of the work function increases the electron current due to thermionic emission. In the Schottky effect the electrons leaving the solid pass over the potential barrier, as opposed to tunnelling through it. (*See* tunnel effect; field emission.)

The slow rise in saturation current of a thermionic valve with increasing anode voltage is due to the Schottky effect. *See also* Schottky diode.

Schottky noise. *Syn.* shot noise. In an electronic device, the emission of *electrons or *holes from an electrode (e.g. the collector of a *transistor or cathode of a *thermionic valve) occurs in a random manner. This results in variations in the current output from the device, producing noise.

Schrödinger wave equation. The basic equation of *wave mechanics expressing the behaviour of a particle moving in a field of force. It is based on the *de Broglie equation indicating that, in addition to its corpuscular properties, a particle behaves as a wave with wavelength λ given by $\lambda = h/p$, where p is the momentum. Any wave motion in one dimension follows an equation of the form:

$$\frac{d^2\varphi}{dx^2} + \frac{4\pi^2 f^2}{v^2}\,\varphi = 0$$

where φ is the displacement of the wave, v its velocity, and f its frequency. The equation can be applied to a de Broglie wave and Schrödinger's equation in one dimension is obtained:

$$\frac{d^2\psi}{dx^2} + \frac{8\pi^2 m}{h^2}(E - U)\psi = 0,$$

where E is the total energy, U the potential energy, and m the mass of the particle. In three dimensions the equation is

$$\nabla^2\psi + \frac{8\pi^2 m}{h^2}(E - U)\psi = 0,$$

where ∇^2 is the *Laplace operator. The equation can be applied to a system such as an atom (*see* atomic orbital) and a solution for ψ obtained. ψ is a mathematical function of the coordinates $(x, y,$ and $z)$ of the particle and is called the *wave function.

Schwarzschild radius. The critical radius to which matter in space must be compressed in order to form a *black hole. It is given by $2GM/c^2$, where M is the mass, G the gravitational constant, and c the velocity of light. It is true for a nonrotating black hole. The surface having such a radius is the *event horizon* of the black hole and defines the boundary from inside which neither mass nor radiation can escape. The enormous gravitational tidal forces inside the black hole draw matter towards the centre where it is destroyed in a region of infinite curvature, a space–time *singularity*, where the known laws of physics break down.

scintillation. The production of small flashes of light from certain materials (*scintillators*) as a result of the impact of radiation. Each incident particle produces one flash.

scintillation counter. A counter designed to measure the *activity of a radioactive source. The counter consists of a *scintillation crystal*, *photomultiplier tube, and amplifying and scaling circuits (*see* scaler). Gamma rays given off by the source into the crystal cause scintillations, which provide the input for the photomultiplier tube. The number of pulses out of the photomultiplier tube in a given time are counted and thus the activity of the source may be calculated. Scintillation counters are widely used as they are energy dependent, unlike *Geiger counters, since the frequency of the light emitted in the crystal, and hence the energy of the electrons emitted from the *photocathode, is dependent on the energy of the incident radiation.

scrambler. A circuit or device used in communication systems to make the transmitted signal unintelligible unless the appropriate circuit is used to unscramble it after reception.

screen grid. *See* thermionic valve.

screw dislocation. *See* defect.

search coil. *See* exploring coil.

second. (1) Symbol: s. The *SI unit of time defined as the duration of 9 192 631 770 periods of the radiation corresponding to the transition between two hyperfine levels of the *ground state of the caesium-133 atom. It was formerly defined as 1/86 400 of the mean solar day (*see* time) unless the context indicated that the sidereal day was intended. (2) Symbol: ″. A unit of angle equal to $\frac{1}{3600}$ degree.

secondary. *See* secondary winding.

secondary cell. *See* cell.

secondary electron. An electron emitted from a material as a result of *secondary emission.

secondary emission. If an electron moving at sufficiently high velocity strikes a metal surface the impact may cause other electrons to escape from the surface. The total energy of one incident electron is often sufficient to eject several secondary electrons. The principle is used in the *dynatron, in the *electron multiplier, and in *storage tubes. Secondary emission is also produced by the impact of positive ions on surfaces.

secondary extinction. An increase in absorption or decrease in diffraction that occurs as a result of previous reflection of an incident X-ray beam from suitably placed crystal planes, which causes the incident beam to become progressively weaker on passing through a large partially mosaic crystal.

secondary radiation. *See* cosmic rays.

secondary spectrum. *See* achromatic lens.

secondary standard. (1) A copy of a *primary standard for which the difference between the copy and the primary standard is known. (2) A quantity accurately known in terms of the primary standard and used as a unit.

secondary waves. *See* Huygens's principle.

secondary winding. The winding on the load (i.e. output) side of a *transformer irrespective of whether the transformer is of the step-up or step-down type.

sedimentation. The fall of particles in suspension in a liquid as a result of gravity, centrifugal force (*see* ultracentrifuge), etc. If, in free fall, the particles are spherical they attain terminal velocities dependent on the relative density of solid and liquid, the viscosity of the latter, and the size of the particles (*see*

Stokes's law). This result is used to separate particles of different sizes.

Seebeck effect. *See* thermoelectric effects.

seed crystal. A small crystal on which crystallization can begin, e.g. in a supersaturated solution or a supercooled liquid. It is used in the manufacture of *semiconductor devices.

Segrè chart. A graph in which the number of protons in nuclides is plotted against the number of neutrons. Stable examples will be found on, or in the vicinity of, a line with a gradient of 1: the gradient diminishes somewhat for nuclides of high atomic number.

Seidel sums or terms. *See* aberration.

seismograph. An instrument used to register the movement of the ground due to distant earthquakes, underground nuclear explosions, etc., consisting in principle of a massive pendulum set into motion by the force developed at its point of suspension.

seismology. The study of the structure of the earth by means of the waves (seismic waves) produced by earthquakes and nuclear explosions. *Seismographs at various points on the earth's surface record the arrival of the different kinds of waves that travel through the earth and along its surface. The waves can be deviated or reflected, speeded up or slowed down, as they come to the different interfaces of the layers (core, mantle, and crust) of the earth's interior. The velocity depends on the density and elastic properties of the medium. The source of the earthquake is called its *focus* and the nearest point on the earth's surface to the focus is the *epicentre*.

selection rules. Rules derived by *quantum mechanics specifying the transitions that may occur between different *energy levels of a system. For example, in a

change between two energy levels of vibration of a molecule the selection rule is that the vibrational *quantum number can only change by one unit, i.e. $\Delta V = 1$. Transitions that follow the selection rules are *allowed transitions. Forbidden transitions* are ones in which the rules are not followed and they are very unlikely, but not impossible.

selective absorption. The absorption of radiation of certain wavelengths in preference to others, as in coloured glasses and pigments. The colour is determined by the remaining light transmitted or reflected after absorption. All substances exhibit selective absorption, the wavelength often lying outside the visible region. *See also* absorption spectrum.

selective fading. *See* fading.

selective radiation. Radiation from a body with a relative spectral energy distribution differing from that of a *black body, or of a *grey body in which the radiation for all wavelengths is a constant fraction of that given by a black body. Although all substances show selective temperature radiation over the visible portion, many give an approximately grey radiation (*see* colour temperature). Incandescent gases and vapours show more or less extreme selectivity.

selective reflection. *See* reflection.

selectivity. The ability of a radio receiver to discriminate against signals having frequencies which are different from that to which the receiver is tuned.

selenium cell. A type of *rectifier photocell consisting of a thin layer of selenium coated onto a metal disc and covered with a film of gold or platinum which is sufficiently thin to allow light to pass through. It is used in *exposure meters and cameras.

self-capacitance. An inductance coil or a resistor has a certain amount of distributed capacitance (self-capacitance) which, to a first approximation, may be represented as a single capacitance connected in parallel with the coil or resistor.

self-excited. (1) Of an electrical machine (generator). Having the *field magnets wholly or substantially excited by a magnetizing current generated in the machine itself. (2) Of an *oscillator. Being in a state in which the oscillations build up to a steady output value, following application of power to the circuit, without any separate input of the required output frequency.

self-inductance. *See* electromagnetic induction.

Sellmeier's equation. A mathematically deduced formula to give the variation of refractive index, n, with wavelength in the neighbourhood of an absorption band (λ_0): $n^2 = 1 + A_0\lambda^2/(\lambda^2 - \lambda_0^2)$, A_0 being a constant for a given material. It fails within the region of the absorption band, agreeing better in the regions of wavelength for which the substance is transparent.

semiconductor. A material having a *resistivity between that of conductors and insulators and having a negative *temperature coefficient of resistance.

Intrinsic semiconductors are those materials having an energy gap between the conduction and valence bands (*see* energy bands) comparable to thermal energies and therefore the pure crystal has semiconductor properties. Electrons are thermally excited into the conduction band leaving an equal number of vacancies in the valence band. The action of an applied field causes conduction in both bands. The vacancies in the valence band are called *holes and are treated as positive charge carriers.

Extrinsic semiconductors are those materials whose properties depend on the presence of impurities in the crystal

lattice. The properties of the material depend on the type of impurity present.

Donor impurities are atoms with more valence electrons than are required to complete the bonds with neighbouring atoms. Extra energy levels are produced in the forbidden band close to the conduction band. These *donor levels* give up their electrons to the conduction band very easily at room temperature; the resulting positive charges are bound to the atom site. The number of conduction electrons is greater than the number of mobile holes and the semiconductor is *n-type*.

Acceptor impurities are atoms with fewer valence electrons than are required to complete the bonds and they accept electrons from any available source to complete the bonds. Their presence results in energy levels just above the valence band. These *acceptor levels* are readily occupied by electrons from the valence band, the electrons remaining bound to the atom site. A preponderance of mobile holes is left in the valence band producing a *p-type* semiconductor.

The conductivity of an extrinsic semiconductor depends on the amount and type of impurity present and this may be controlled by adding impurities. This is called *doping* and the amount of impurity is the *doping level*.

The predominant charge carriers in a semiconductor are called *majority carriers (e.g. electrons in n-type) and the others are *minority carriers (e.g. holes in n-type). Properties of an extrinsic semiconductor are described in terms of the minority carriers. The *bulk lifetime* is the average time interval between generation and recombination of minority carriers in the bulk of the material. Recombination can also take place near the surface: the *surface recombination velocity* is the ratio of the component, normal to the surface, of the electron (or hole) current density and the excess electron (or hole) volume charge density close to the surface. The *drift mobility* is the average drift velocity of excess minority carriers per unit electric field and the *diffusion length* is the average distance travelled by a minority carrier during its lifetime.

Junctions between semiconductors of different types form a fundamental part of modern electronic components and circuits. If two semiconductors are brought into contact with no external applied field, thermal equilibrium will be established between the two, and the condition of zero net current requires the Fermi level to be constant throughout the sample. Fig. *a* shows the situation before equilibrium is established between samples of p- and n-type semiconductor. Electrons and holes will cross the junction until an equilibrium is set up by the establishment of two *space charge regions preventing further flow of carriers. The space charge regions are due to ionized impurities on either side of the junction, and a voltage drop is formed across the junction, while maintaining the overall neutrality of the sample. The diffusion potential or built-in potential V_{bi} is given by

$$eV_{bi} = E_g - e(V_n + V_p) = E_{Fn} - E_{Fp}$$

(Fig. *a* and *b*), where *e* is the charge of an electron.

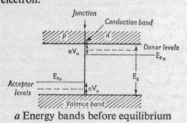

a Energy bands before equilibrium

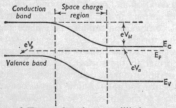

b Energy bands at equilibrium

The space charge region around the junction forms a *depletion layer, the width of which depends on the electric field in the interface and the numbers of acceptor and donor ions on either side of the junction.

If a voltage *V* is applied across the junction the electrostatic potential is given by $(V_{bi} + V)$ for reverse bias (positive voltage on the n-region) and $(V_{bi} - V)$ for forward bias (positive voltage on the p-region). The depletion width increases with reverse bias as the holes in the p-region are attracted to the negative electrode and vice versa in the n-region. The small reverse bias current flowing is due to minority holes in the n-region and electrons in the p-region crossing the junction.

Under conditions of forward bias the depletion width decreases as the built-in potential is reduced by the applied field, and the current through the sample increases exponentially with voltage.

Common semiconductor materials are elements falling into group 4 of the periodic table, such as silicon or germanium. Certain compounds, such as gallium arsenide, also make excellent semiconductors. These are classified as 3–5 or 2–6 depending on their positions in the periodic table. Commonly used impurities are those differing by a valency of one from the substrate material, i.e. groups 3 and 5 are used with group 4 material.

semiconductor counter. A *photodiode used as a radiation *counter.

semiconductor diode. Symbol: ▷| A *diode manufactured from semiconducting material.

semiconductor diode laser. A *laser, of semiconducting material, that is very much smaller, more robust, cheaper, and simpler to operate than other types of gas and solid-state lasers. The operating voltage is only 1·5–2 volts. The diode laser is a refinement of the *light-emitting diode. In a semiconductor such as gallium arsenide, when the p–n junction is sufficiently forward biased, electrons flow across the junction from the n-conduction band to the p-conduction band; this process is called electron *injection. These electrons, having a greater energy than normal, will combine with a *hole in that region and a photon is emitted having an energy approximately equal to the band gap energy. As the injection current is increased, stimulated emission (*see* laser) can occur above a threshold current: an injected excited electron can be stimulated to emit a photon by a photon from a previous recombination event. As the injection current increases, the stimulated emission increases. The diode can be constructed to have two flat ends of the crystal perpendicular to a flat p̄–n junction. These ends act as partially reflecting mirrors and the light can be reflected back into the p–n region, causing further amplification. An intense laser beam emerges from the mirror ends of the crystal. A very high current density is required and to prevent overheating, at room temperature, the beam has to be pulsed.

A continuous laser beam can be achieved by using a modified crystal. A region of pure GaAs is made adjacent to a region of aluminium gallium arsenide. The junction between these two regions of similar crystal structure (a *heterojunction*) can be used to reduce the threshold current required to achieve laser action, and a continuous laser beam is possible. The output power is tens of milliwatts at wavelengths between 700–900 nm and the efficiency can be as high as 10 %.

semipermeable membrane. A membrane used in dialysis and *osmosis that allows certain molecules in a fluid to pass through while stopping others.

semitone. The smallest pitch interval between successive tones of the present western *musical scales. In the scale of equal *temperament this frequency interval is ideally $2^{1/12}$.

sensation level. A measure of the intensity I of a sound with reference to the minimum audible intensity I_0. If the sensation level L is measured in decibels, then $L = 10 \log (I/I_0)$. I_0 is usually taken as 2·5 picowatts per square metre.

sensitivity. The response of a physical device to a unit change in the input.

sensor. *See* transducer.

separately excited. Of an electrical machine (generator). Having the *field magnets wholly or substantially excited by a magnetizing current that is obtained from a source other than the machine itself so that the excitation current is entirely independent of the load current supplied by the machine.

separation energy. The energy needed to remove one proton or neutron from the nucleus of a particular element.

series. Pieces of electrical apparatus are in series when they are connected so that one current flows in turn through each

a Resistors in series

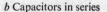

b Capacitors in series

of them. For conductors of resistances $r_1, r_2, r_3 \ldots r_n$ in series, the total resistance, R, is given by:

$$R = r_1 + r_2 + r_3 + \ldots + r_n$$

For capacitances $c_1, c_2, c_3 \ldots c_n$ in series the total capacitance, C, is given by:

$$\frac{1}{C} = \frac{1}{c_1} + \frac{1}{c_2} + \frac{1}{c_3} + \ldots + \frac{1}{c_n}.$$

Cells in series add their e.m.f.s.

series-characteristic motor. *Syn.* inverse-speed motor. Any electric motor the speed of which decreases substantially with increase of load, as with a series-wound or heavily compound-wound motor. *Compare* shunt-characteristic motor.

series-wound machine. A d.c. machine in which the *field magnets are wholly or substantially excited by a winding which is connected in *series with the armature winding, or alternatively which is connected so as to carry a current proportional to that in the armature winding. *Compare* compound-wound machine; shunt-wound machine.

servomechanism. A closed-sequence control system that is automatic and power-amplifying.

sextant. An instrument for measuring angles (up to 120°) between two objects, and particularly the angle between an astronomical body and the horizon (i.e. its altitude). The horizon is observed

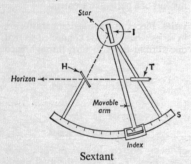

Sextant

through the upper clear half of a fixed horizon glass H by applying the eye to the eyepiece of the telescope T. The index glass I is rotated until the image of a star is reflected from I into the lower silvered half of H, and thence to T. The required angle is read from the graduated scale S at the point indicated by an arm attached to I.

shadow mask. A perforated metal sheet placed between the *electron guns and

the screen of some *colour television picture tubes to allow the correct selection of colours on the screen.

shadow photometer. A simple photometer that uses a rod in front of a screen; the two light sources to be compared are adjusted until the shadows thrown just touch and match in intensity. The *luminous intensities are then in the ratios of the squares of the distances of the sources from the shadows thrown by each.

shadows. The shape and relative density of shadows can be explained in terms of geometric optics. A point source delivers rays to an obstacle, the extremities of which limit light which may pass; the shadow throughout is complete (*umbra*). With an extended source the shadow shows variation of density – umbra and *penumbra*. When the edges of geometric shadows are examined more carefully, *diffraction phenomena are evident and these are more marked as the size of the obstacle is decreased.

shadow scattering. *See* scattering.

shear. *See* strain; stress.

shear modulus. *See* modulus of elasticity.

shear stress. *See* stress.

shell. *See* atom; electron shell; shell model.

shell model. *Syn.* quasi-atomic model. Any of the models of the nucleus in which the interactions between *nucleons are approximated by assuming the nucleons move in a single central potential. By solving the *Schrödinger equation corresponding to this potential a set of possible *energy levels are obtained. Each of these energy levels will, in general, contain a number of different quantum mechanical states. The sets of states corresponding to the same energy are called *shells*. Being *fermions, the nucleons must obey the *Pauli exclusion principle. Therefore no two nucleons can occupy the same quantum state. The nucleons will try to reach the lowest energy possible by filling the lowest energy states first. The more nucleons there are, the more of the shells which will be filled. This is exactly analogous to the filling of atomic shells by orbital electrons in heavy elements. The shell model is useful in explaining why nuclei with certain proton or neutron numbers (called *magic numbers) are more stable than others. These are thought to correspond to nuclei in which the number of nucleons is just sufficient to fill a given number of shells.

shell-type transformer. A *transformer in which the *core encloses the greater part of the windings. The core is made of

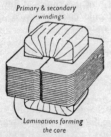

Primary & secondary windings

Laminations forming the core

Single-phase shell-type transformer

*laminations which are usually built up around the windings.

Shenstone effect. A considerable increase in photoelectric emission produced in some metals, such as bismuth, after an electric current has passed through.

shield. A mass of material (such as cement, etc.) surrounding a *nuclear reactor core, or other source of radiation, to absorb neutrons or other dangerous radiations. A *biological shield* is specially designed to protect laboratory workers and plant operators from harmful radiations.

shielding. Removal of the influence of an external energy field by surrounding a region with a wall of suitable material, such as one of high *permeability for removing stray magnetic fields.

shift register. A digital circuit used to displace a set of information in the form of pulses either to the right or left, which for a numerical expression may be the equivalent of multiplying by a power of the base. Shift registers are extensively used in *computers and calculating machines as storage elements or delay elements.

SHM. Abbreviation for simple harmonic motion.

shock waves. Waves of compression and rarefaction that originate in the neighbourhood of sharp points or roughness on obstacles exposed to the flow of a compressible fluid at high speeds. The local compressions and rarefactions set up in this way are not instantly reversible and are propagated out into the fluid as, in effect, sound waves. They transport momentum from the vicinity of the obstacle to a distance or convert kinetic energy into heat. *See also* sonic boom.

short circuit. An electrical connection of relatively very low resistance made intentionally or otherwise between two points in a circuit.

shot noise. *See* Schottky noise.

shower. A group of *elementary particles and *photons arising from the impact of a single particle of high energy. *See* cosmic rays.

shunt. (1) (general). If two electrical circuits are connected in *parallel either one is said to be in shunt with the other. (2) Of an instrument. A resistor, usually of low value, which is connected in parallel with an instrument such as an ammeter so that only a fraction of the main circuit current flows through the instrument, thereby increasing the range of the latter. (3) *See* magnetic shunt.

shunt-characteristic motor. An electric motor the speed of which remains substantially constant when the load is varied, as with a d.c. shunt-wound motor. *Compare* series-characteristic motor.

shunt-wound machine. A d.c. machine in which the *field magnets are wholly or substantially excited by a winding which is connected in *shunt with the armature winding. *Compare* compound-wound and series-wound machines.

sideband. In *modulation. A band of frequencies embracing either all the upper or all the lower *side frequencies.

side frequency. Any frequency produced as a result of *modulation. For example, in *amplitude modulation if a *carrier wave of frequency f_c is modulated by a sinusoidal signal of frequency $f_s (f_s \ll f_c)$, the resulting wave has three components, the frequencies of which are $f_c, f_c + f_s$ (the upper side frequency), and $f_c - f_s$ (the lower side frequency).

sidereal day, month, year, and time. *See* time.

siemens. Symbol: S. The *SI unit of electrical *conductance, defined as the conductance of an element that possesses a resistance of one ohm. The unit used to be called the mho or reciprocal ohm.

Siemens electrodynamometer. An *electrodynamic instrument in which the torque produced by the electromagnetic forces is balanced against the torque of a spiral spring by adjustment of a calibrated torsion head attached to the spring. It may be an ammeter, voltmeter, or wattmeter and can be used with direct or alternating current.

sigma particle. An *elementary particle classified as a *hyperon.

sigma pile. A neutron source plus *moderator but without any fissile material, used to analyse the properties of the moderator.

signal. In an electronic circuit or system. The variable parameter by means of which information is conveyed through the system.

signal generator. Any circuit or device that produces an electrical parameter which is adjustable and controllable. Most commonly, a voltage source with variable amplitude, frequency, and waveform is used. The term is usually applied to sine-wave generators; those generating pulse waveforms are called pulse generators.

signal-to-noise ratio. The ratio of one parameter of a wanted signal to the same parameter of the *noise at any point in an electronic circuit, device, or transmission system.

sign convections. *See* optics sign conventions.

Sikes's hydrometer. *See* hydrometer.

silent discharge. An inaudible electrical discharge that takes place at high voltage and involves a relatively high dissipation of energy. Such a discharge readily takes place from a conductor that has a sharp point.

silicon-controlled rectifier (SCR). *Syn.* thyristor. Symbol: ⊶ A *semiconductor *rectifier whose forward anode-cathode current is controlled by means of a signal applied to a third electrode, called the gate. The basic construction is shown in the diagram.

Current does not flow in the device until a positive current is applied to the gate. Once the device is conducting, current continues to flow even after the cessation of applied signal to the gate, and may only be cut off by reducing the

Silicon-controlled rectifier

anode voltage to near zero. The mini-mum anode–cathode current at which conduction can continue is the holding current. The SCR is the solid-state equivalent of the *thyratron valve.

The most important applications of SCRs are in a.c. control systems and solid-state *relays. Phase control is a type of a.c. operation when the device is switched on only during part or all of the positive half-cycle. A version of the SCR for switching a.c. is the *Triac*. It is almost equivalent to two anti-parallel SCRs made in a single chip but operates with a single gate connection.

similarity principle. *See* dynamic similarity.

simple harmonic motion (SHM). The motion of a body subjected to a restraining force directly proportional to the displacement from a fixed point in the line of motion. The force equation is

$$m\ddot{x} = kx,$$

where m is the inertia of the body, and k is the restraining force per unit displacement. Putting k/m equal to ω^2, the solution of the equation is: $x = A \cos(\omega t + \alpha)$, where A is the maximum displacement, ω is the *angular frequency ($\omega =$

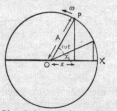

Simple harmonic motion

$2\pi f$), and α is the angle determining the displacement at $t = 0$ and is called the *epoch*. The period is given by $T = 2\pi/\omega$.

SHM may be represented graphically as the projection on to a straight line of the path of a particle travelling in a circle with uniform velocity. The amplitude A is the radius of the circle and the angle α is the angular displacement from the fixed line OX at $t = 0$.

simple microscope. *See* microscope.

simulator. A device that mimics the be-haviour of an actual system but is made from components that are easier, cheaper, or more convenient to manu-facture. Simulators are frequently used for solving complex problems.

simultaneity. To be truly simultaneous events must occur not only at the same time but also at the same place. For example an event on Jupiter might be observed to occur simultaneously with an event on earth. However, as the two events occur in different frames of reference, and as the information cannot travel from one frame of reference to the other faster than the speed of light, the two events would not, in fact, have occurred simultaneously.

sine condition. If n and n' are refractive indexes of media in front of and beyond a surface, y and y' the object and image sizes, α and α' the angles made between the conjugate rays and the axis passing through the axial feet of the object and image, then $ny \sin \alpha = n'y' \sin \alpha'$ is the sine condition. For paraxial rays, when α and α' are both small the condition reduces to $ny\alpha = n'y'\alpha'$. This is the *Lagrange law*. The condition is necessary

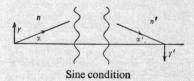

Sine condition

347

for freedom from *coma and is equivalent to the condition imposed by Seidel's second sum. *See* aberration.

sine galvanometer. An instrument similar to the *tangent galvanometer except that the coil and scale are rotated together, while current is flowing, to return the needle to zero. The current is proportional to the sine of the angle of rotation.

sine wave. *See* sinusoidal; equivalent sine wave.

singing. Unwanted self-oscillation in a telecommunication transmission system. The term is used particularly in connection with telephone lines in which *repeaters are incorporated.

singing arc. An oscillatory current can be set up by shunting an arc with an inductance and capacitance in series, and this oscillation is impressed on the arc itself so that it emits a musical note due to variation in the heating effect.

single crystal. A crystal in which the atomic planes of the same kind are sufficiently parallel to diffract a collimated beam of incident radiation cooperatively and thus to give single spots in the diffraction pattern.

single-phase. Of an electrical system or apparatus. Having only one alternating voltage.

single-shot. *See* monostable.

single-sideband transmission. The transmission of one only of the two *sidebands produced by the *amplitude modulation of a *carrier wave, the latter being suppressed at the transmitter so that it is not transmitted. At the receiver, it is necessary to reintroduce the carrier artificially by combining the sideband with a locally generated oscillation. The frequency of the latter should be as nearly as possible equal to that of the

original carrier. The main advantages of this method of transmission over that in which the carrier and the two sidebands are transmitted (*double-sideband transmission*) are the reduction in transmitter power (since the carrier and one sideband are not transmitted) and the reduction of the *bandwidth required for the transmission of signals within a specified *frequency band.

singularity. *See* Schwarzschild radius.

sink. *See* source.

sinusoidal. Of a periodic quantity. Having a *waveform that is the same as that of a sine function. It is only the shape of the graph which is significant. For example, two e.m.f.s represented by $e_1 = E_1 \sin \omega t$ and $e_2 = E_2 \cos \omega t$ would both be described as sinusoidal e.m.f.s and are both *sine waves*.

siphon. An inverted U-tube with one limb longer than the other, used for transferring liquid from one level to a lower level through a level higher than both. The shorter limb dips into the liquid and when the siphon is full liquid flows out of the lower end: if p is atmospheric pressure then the pressure at T is

Siphon

$p - p'$ and at R it is $p - p''$, where p' and p'' result from the weight of liquid in the limbs TS and RS respectively. Since $p'' > p'$ then the liquid will flow from T to R.

SI units (Système International d'Unités). The internationally agreed system of *coherent units that is now in use for all scientific and most technological purposes in many countries (including the UK). SI units are based on the *MKS system and replace the units used in the *CGS system and the *f.p.s. system (Imperial units). SI units are of three kinds: the *base*, *supplementary*, and *derived units*. There are seven base units for the seven dimensionally independent physical quantities shown in Table 2 on page 422. Table 3 gives the two supplementary units and Table 4 gives the fifteen derived units with special names and symbols. All these units are defined in this dictionary in their alphabetical place. The SI unit of any other quantity is derived by multiplication and/or division of the base units without introducing any numerical factors. SI units are used with a set of fourteen prefixes to form decimal multiples and submultiples of the units. Table 5 lists these prefixes and their symbols.

A number of conventions are observed in the printing or writing of SI units. Symbols for a prefix are written next to the symbol for the unit without a space, e.g. cm, but a space is left between symbols for units in derived units, e.g. N m for newton metre. The letter s is never added to a symbol to indicate a plural; 10 ms indicates ten milliseconds, not ten metres. Compound prefixes are never used, e.g. nm for 10^{-9} metre is correct, mμm is incorrect. A symbol for a unit with a prefix attached is regarded as a single symbol which can be raised to a power without using brackets, e.g. cm^2 means $(0.01$ m$)^2$ and not 0.01 m^2. The word gramme has a special place in SI units; although it is not an SI unit itself, prefixes are attached to the symbol g and not to kg, e.g. 10^3 kg is written Mg and not kkg. When writing numbers with SI units the digits are arranged in groups of three, but a space rather than a comma is placed between each group. E.g. 10^5 is written 100 000 not 100,000 and 10^{-5} is written 0.000 01. If a number consists of only 4 digits it is written without spaces, e.g. 1000 or 0.0001.

SI units make quite clear the relationship between a physical quantity (say length l) and the units in which it is expressed, i.e.

Physical quantity $=$ numerical value $\times$ unit

Or, in the case of length, $l = n$ m

where n is a numerical value and m is the agreed symbol for the SI unit of length, the metre. This equation should be treated algebraically, e.g. the axis of a graph or a column of a table giving numerical values in metres should be labelled l/m. If the axis or column gives the values of $1/l$, it should be labelled m/l.

Six's thermometer. *See* maximum and minimum thermometer.

skew distribution. *See* frequency distribution.

skiatron. A cathode-ray tube in which the usual coating of fluorescent substances is replaced by a screen of alkali halide crystals which become darkened under electron bombardment. It can be arranged so that the trace remains on the screen until erased.

skin effect. A nonuniform distribution of electric current over the cross section of a conductor when carrying an alternating current. The current density is greater at the surface of the conductor than at its centre. It is due to electromagnetic (inductive) effects and becomes more pronounced as the frequency of the current is increased. It results in a greater *I^2R loss in the conductor than that which occurs when the current is uniformly distributed and, in consequence, the *effective resistance of a conductor when carrying alternating current is greater than the true resistance, and the high frequency resistance is greater than its d.c. or low frequency resistance. With very high frequencies hollow or stranded conductors may be used.

skin friction. The resistance or drag experienced by a body in relative motion with a fluid, due to the *laminar motion of the fluid and the large rate of shear of the fluid close to the body boundaries.

sky wave. *See* ionosphere.

sliding friction. *See* friction.

slip. Of an *induction motor. The ratio of the difference between the *synchronous speed and the actual speed of the motor to the synchronous speed.

slip ring. *Syn.* collector ring. A ring, usually made of copper, which is connected to and rotates with a winding (as, for example, in certain types of electrical machines), so that the winding may be connected to an external circuit by means of a *brush or brushes resting on the surface of the ring.

slip-ring rotor. *See* induction motor.

slope resistance. *Syn.* electrode a.c. resistance; electrode differential resistance. Of a specified electrode in an electronic device. The ratio of a very small change in the voltage applied to the particular electrode to the corresponding change in the current in that electrode, the voltages of all other electrodes being maintained constant at specified values. For example, the collector slope resistance $r_c = \partial V_c / \partial I_c$, where V_c is the collector voltage and I_c is the collector current.

slowing-down density. Symbol: q. A measure of the rate at which *neutrons lose energy by collisions in a *nuclear reactor, expressed by the number of neutrons per unit volume falling below a certain energy per unit time. *See* Fermi age theory.

slow neutron. A neutron with a kinetic energy that does not exceed a few electronvolts. The term is sometimes loosely applied to a *thermal neutron.

slow vibration direction. The direction of the electric vector of the ray of light which travels with least velocity in the crystal and which therefore corresponds to the largest refractive index.

slug. (1) *Syn.* geepound. The unit of mass to which a force of one pound-force gives an acceleration of one ft. second^{-2}. Thus one slug is equivalent to g pounds. (2) The *metre slug* has an acceleration of one m s^{-2} when continuously acted on by a force of one kilogramme-force.

small-signal parameters. If the behaviour of an electronic device is represented by the instantaneous values of current and voltage appearing at the terminals of a four terminal *network, the small-signal parameters are the coefficients of the equations representing this behaviour for small values of input. *See also* transistor parameters.

smoothing circuit. A circuit used for the purpose of reducing the amplitude of a *ripple. It is commonly a form of low-pass *filter but may consist of a single inductance.

Snell's law. The law of refraction in which $\sin i / \sin i' = n'/n = $ constant, where i is the angle of incidence, i' is the angle of *refraction, and n and n' are the *refractive indexes of the first medium and the second (refracting) medium.

Soddy and Fajans's rule. The emission of an α-particle from a radioactive element causes a decrease of two in atomic number, and the emission of a β-particle increases the atomic number by unity, with consequent changes in the position of the element in the periodic table.

sodium-line reversal. If a gas (especially a flame) containing sodium vapour is placed in the path of radiation from a radiator of known temperature, the temperature of the gas can be determined spectroscopically. When the gas temperature, T_1, is less than that of the radiator,

T_2, the absorption D-line of sodium can be observed. If T_1 is increased, or T_2 decreased, then when T_1 becomes equal to T_2 *reversal occurs and the absorption line is replaced by an emission line that stands out against the continuous spectrum of the radiator.

soft radiation. *Ionizing radiation with a low degree of penetration: most commonly applied to X-rays of relatively long wavelength.

soft shower. *See* cosmic rays.

soft vacuum tube. A vacuum tube in which the degree of the vacuum is such that ionization of the residual gas influences the electrical characteristics of the tube.

software. The *programs associated with a *computer system.

solar cell. Any device that converts solar energy (light, heat, etc.) into electrical energy. Examples include semiconductor devices operating by the *photovoltaic effect and *thermopiles. A *solar battery* consists of several solar cells.

solar constant. The flux of solar energy passing normally through unit area at the earth's mean orbital distance. The value is 1390 W/m².

solar day, month, year, and time. *See* time.

solarimeter. *Syn.* pyranometer. An instrument for measuring the total solar radiation intensity received on a horizontal surface. In the *Moll-Gorczynski solarimeter* incoming radiation raises the temperature of one set of junctions of a *thermopile above the ambient temperature of the other junction set. The resulting e.m.f. is a measure of radiation intensity and is independent of ambient temperature, wind velocity, etc. In the *Eppley pyranometer*, a central white disc

is surrounded by a concentric black ring. Exposure to solar radiation causes the black ring to rise in temperature, the difference between the black and white surfaces being measured by thermocouples. The resulting signal is proportional to radiation intensity.

solar units. A set of units in which certain properties of the sun such as the mass, diameter, density, and luminosity are taken as unity; the same properties of other stars can then be compared to those of the sun.

solar wind. A stream of ionized particles, mainly protons and electrons, that flow from the sun in all directions. The average energy is much lower than that of *cosmic rays, the velocity being between 350–800 kilometres per second. The number of particles and their velocity increase following solar activity such as sunspots and flares. The solar wind causes the shape of the earth's magnetic field to be unsymmetrical (*see* magnetosphere), the lines of force being considerably extended in the direction of the wind, beyond the earth. Changes in the intensity of the wind produce fluctuations in the magnetic field causing magnetic storms and affecting radio communications. *See also* aurora; Van Allen belts.

solenoid. A coil of wire with a length that is large compared with its diameter. At a point inside the solenoid and on its axis, where the ends subtend semiangles θ_1, θ_2, the magnetic flux density B is given by:

$$B = \tfrac{1}{2}\mu_0 nI(\cos \theta_1 + \cos \theta_2).$$

n is the number of turns per unit length, I the current, and μ_0 the *magnetic constant. (The formula ignores end effects.)

solenoidal. A *vector field that has no divergence in a specific region of space, the lines of force (or of flow) either forming closed curves (e.g. the magnetic field

351

of a current) or terminating at infinity or on bounding surfaces (e.g. the electric field between capacitor plates).

solid angle. Symbol: ω or Ω. An area is said to subtend in three dimensions a solid angle at an outside point. The solid angle is measured by the area subtended (by projection) on a sphere of unit radius or by the ratio of the area (A) intercepted on a sphere of radius r to the square of the radius (A/r^2). The unit of solid angle is the *steradian. The solid angle completely surrounding a point is 4π steradians. If a small area (dA) is at a distance r from a point and its normal makes an angle θ with a line drawn to the point, the solid angle formed by the area and point is ($dA \cos \theta/r^2$).

solidification curve. *See* ice line.

solid-state memory. *See* memory.

solid-state physics. The branch of physics concerned with the structure and properties of solids and the phenomena associated with solids. These phenomena include electrical conductivity, especially in *semiconductors, *superconductivity, *photoconductivity, *photoelectric effect, and *field emission.

solid-state relay. *See* relay.

solstice. (1) One of the two points at which the ecliptic is furthest north or south of the celestial equator. (*See* celestial sphere.) (2) One of the two days of the year when the sun is at these points, being the day with the greatest number (*summer solstice*) or least number (*winter solstice*) of daylight hours.

solution pressure. The osmotic pressure of a solution in equilibrium with undissolved solid.

sonar. *Syn.* asdic. A contraction of *sound navigation ranging.* A method of locating underwater objects by transmitting an ultrasonic pulse and detecting the reflected pulse. The time taken for the pulse of sound to travel to the object and return gives an indication of the depth of the object.

sone. A unit of loudness. The loudness L in sones is defined by the formula $\log_2 L = 0 \cdot 1$ $(P - 40)$, where P is the equivalent loudness measured in *phons. The scale has been chosen so that a sound of x sones seems to the listener to be k times as loud as a sound of x/k sones. Experiment has shown this to be justified for loudness between $\frac{1}{4}$ and 250 sones.

sonic boom. The noise originating from the backward projected *shock waves set

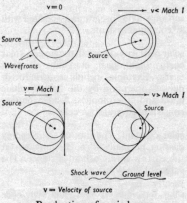

v = Velocity of source

Production of sonic boom

up by an aircraft travelling at supersonic speed. As the velocity increases, *wavefronts originating from the source of sound crowd closer together (*see* diagram). At speeds above Mach 1, two conical lines, tangential to the wavefronts, delineate the shock waves set up by atmospheric pressure discontinuities. In level flight, the intersection of the shock wave cone with the ground forms a hyperbola at all points on which the sonic boom is heard simultaneously.

sonometer. *See* monochord.

sorption pump. A type of vacuum pump that relies for its action on the adsorption of gas by a material, which is contained in a bulb connected to the system and cooled by liquid air.

sound. The branch of physics that deals with the origin, propagation, and reception of vibrations. As the human ear has a restricted range of perception of *pitch sound is strictly limited to those vibrations whose frequencies lie between about 20 and 20 000 hertz (audio frequencies). However it is convenient to include infrasonic and ultrasonic vibrations in the same study. The source of sound executes vibrations. In order to do so, it must possess elasticity, in the sense that when it is displaced from its position of rest and is released a force comes into play tending to restore it to that position, and inertia, in the sense that in returning it overshoots its equilibrium position and so oscillates to and fro.

The propagation of the sound through the surrounding medium involves portions of the medium in vibration (*see* compression), but because of a progressive lag in the taking up of these vibrations, the disturbance is propagated with a finite velocity known as the *velocity of sound. Sound travels through a medium as a longitudinal wave motion. Finally the waves are picked up by receivers which may be of a biological or physical nature.

sound absorption coefficient. The ratio of the sound energy absorbed by a surface or material at a given frequency to that incident upon it under the same conditions. The value varies with frequency.

sound energy reflection coefficient. The ratio of the sound energy reflected from a surface or material at a given frequency to that incident upon it under the same conditions. The value varies with frequency.

sound film. A cinematograph film with a sound track at one side of the picture frames to provide simultaneous reproduction of the sound associated with the vision projection. The sound track consists of variations in width or density of a silver image, ideally related in linear fashion in frequency and amplitude to the original sound. In reproduction, a beam of light projected through the sound track is amplitude-modulated by these variations. The modulation is converted into an audio-frequency signal by a photocell. The signals are amplified sufficiently to operate a loudspeaker system. In practice, the volume range of the recorded signal is compressed to a range of about 40 to 50 decibels, particularly to raise the lower sound levels above the inherent noise level of the system. The frequency range normally recorded is from 50 to 12 000 hertz.

sound flux. Symbol: P. The rate of flow of sound energy. For a plane or spherical progressive wave with a velocity c in a medium of density ρ, at any point

$$P = p^2 A/\rho c$$

where p is the *sound pressure at that point and A is the area through which the flux passes. Sound flux is measured in *watts.

sounding balloons. *Syn.* balloon sondes. Small balloons used for carrying recording instruments into the earth's atmosphere.

sound insulation. *See* reverberation chamber; dead room.

sound intensity. The *sound flux through unit area normal to the direction of flow. For a sinusoidal sound wave the intensity I is related to the *sound pressure p and the density ρ of the medium by

$$I = p^2/\rho c,$$

where c is the velocity of the sound. The SI unit is watt per square metre.

353

sound pressure. The instantaneous value of the periodic portion of the pressure at a particular point in a medium that is transmitting sound. It is that part of the pressure that is due to the propagation of sound in the medium and has an average value of zero over a period of time. It is measured in newtons per square metre.

sound pressure level. Twenty times the logarithm to base ten of the ratio of the r.m.s. *sound pressure to a reference sound pressure (stated or taken to be 2×10^{-5} N m^{-2} in air and 0.1 N m^{-2} in water). It is measured in decibels.

sound-wave photography. *See* schlieren photography.

source. (1) The point at which lines of flux originate in a *vector field, such as an electrostatic field. A *sink* is a point at which lines of flux terminate. (2) A point at which fluid is continually emitted and from which the flow is radial and uniform. A negative source is called a sink. The strength of a source (m) is the quantity of fluid emitted in unit time. The quantity emitted is sometimes expressed as $4\pi m'$; the symbol m' then defines the strength. (3) The electrode in a *field-effect transistor by means of which charge carriers (electrons or holes) enter the inter-electrode space. (4) Any energy-producing device.

source impedance. The impedance of any energy source presented to the input terminals of a circuit or device. An ideal voltage source will have zero source impedance whereas an ideal current source will have infinite source impedance.

space charge. In any device, a region in which the net charge density is significantly different from zero. In a *semiconductor space-charge regions can exist in equilibrium under zero applied bias condition forming potential barriers, which must be overcome by the applied bias before current flows.

space group. A set of operations (rotation about an axis, reflection across a plane, translation, or combinations of these) that when carried out on a periodic arrangement of points in space brings the system of points to self-coincidence. *See also* crystal structure.

space quantization. *See* spin.

space reflection symmetry. *See* parity.

space-time. *See* four-dimensional continuum.

spallation. A particularly vigorous nuclear decay caused by a bombardment of a target by high energy particles, resulting in the emission of a number of alpha- and beta-particles.

spark. A visible *disruptive discharge of electricity between two places at opposite high potential. It is preceded by ionization of the path. There is a rapid heating effect of the air through which the spark passes, which creates a sharp crackling noise. The distance a spark will travel is determined by the shape of the electrodes and the p.d. between them.

spark chamber. A particle detector with a very short recovery time, developed from the *spark counter. The simplest type has one or more pairs of thread-like electrodes, about 2 cm apart in a gaseous atmosphere. Charged particles are first detected by a *counter, which causes the voltage between the electrodes to be increased extremely rapidly. The passage of the particle produces a spark, whose position can be found by photographic or electronic means. Following a rapid decrease in electrode voltage, the chamber is scanned for subsequent events, such as collisions and disintegrations, before further use. The counter may be operated so that only a particular type or event triggers the chamber.

spark counter. A type of radiation detector used in the detection and measurement of charged particles, especially *alpha particles. The counter consists of a pair of electrodes in the form of a wire or mesh anode in close proximity to a metal plate cathode. A high potential difference is applied across the electrodes, its value being just less than that required to cause a discharge across the air gap. If a particle approaches the anode, the field between the electrodes is increased sufficiently to cause a spark discharge. At the moment of discharge the anode potential drops significantly. The number of particles may be measured by photography or counting circuits designed to respond to the change in voltage.

spark discharge. *See* conduction in gases.

spark gap. An arrangement of electrodes specially designed so that a disruptive discharge takes place between them when the applied voltage exceeds a predetermined value.

sparkover. *See* flashover.

spark photography. Any form of photography in which a spark provides the illumination, as in *schlieren photography.

specific. The use of the adjective *specific* to qualify the name of an extensive physical property is now restricted to the meaning 'per unit mass'. When the physical quantity is denoted by a capital letter (e.g. *L* for the latent heat), the specific quantity is denoted by the corresponding lower-case letter (*l* for the specific latent heat).

specific acoustic impedance, reactance, and resistance. *See* impedance, resistance, and reactance (acoustic).

specific activity. Symbol: *a* .The *activity per unit mass of a radioisotope.

specific charge. The ratio of the charge on an *elementary particle to the mass of that particle; the charge per unit mass of a particle. *See also* e/m.

specific gravity. *See* density.

specific-gravity bottle. *See* relative-density bottle.

specific heat capacity. Symbol: *c*. The *heat capacity per unit mass; the quantity of heat required to raise the temperature of unit mass of a substance by one degree. In S I units it is measured in joules per kilogramme kelvin. The temperature variation of the specific heat capacities of solids is given by the *Debye theory, and also *Einstein's theory, both derived from quantum theory. (*See also* Dulong and Petit's law.)

For a gas there are two principal specific heat capacities depending on the way in which the temperature is increased. If the pressure is kept constant the specific heat capacity at constant pressure c_p is obtained; if the volume is kept constant the specific heat capacity at constant volume c_v is obtained. The value c_p/c_v is the constant *gamma (γ). The difference $c_p - c_v$ is equal to the work done in expansion. For an ideal gas, in which the internal energy is independent of the volume, $c_p - c_v = R$, where R is the *universal gas constant. These equations are derived from the general thermodynamic equation

$$c_p - c_v = T\left\{\frac{\partial p}{\partial T}\right\}_v \left\{\frac{\partial V}{\partial T}\right\}_p$$

while $\left(\dfrac{\partial c_v}{\partial V}\right)_T = T\left(\dfrac{\partial^2 p}{\partial T^2}\right)_v$

and $\left(\dfrac{\partial c_p}{\partial p}\right)_T = -T\left(\dfrac{\partial^2 p}{\partial T^2}\right)_p$

give the variation of specific heat capacities with volume and pressure. On the kinetic theory the *molar heat capacity at constant volume of a gas is given by $F \times R/2$ assuming the equipartition of energy, where F is the number of degrees

355

of freedom. Although this result is by no means true for real gases, the specific heat capacity does increase greatly with the atomicity of the molecule. *See also* negative specific heat capacities.

specific humidity. *See* humidity.

specific inductive capacity. A former name for relative *permittivity.

specific latent heat of fusion. *Syn.* enthalpy of melting. Symbol: l_f or ΔH_s^1. The quantity of heat required to change the state of unit mass of a substance from the solid to the liquid state at the melting point. It is measured in joules per kilogramme. *See* Clausius–Clapeyron equation.

specific latent heat of sublimation. *Syn.* enthalpy of sublimation. Symbol: l_s or ΔH_s^g. The quantity of heat required to change unit mass of a substance from the solid to the vapour state without change of temperature. It is measured in joules per kilogramme. *See* Clausius–Clapeyron equation.

specific latent heat of vaporization. *Syn.* enthalpy of evaporation. Symbol: l_v or ΔH_f^g. The quantity of heat required to change unit mass of a substance from the liquid to the vapour state at the boiling point. It is measured in joules per kilogramme and is given by the *Clausius–Clapeyron equation.

The specific latent heat of vaporization decreases as the temperature increases, eventually becoming zero at the *critical temperature. For all substances the variation of specific latent heat with temperature is given by the thermodynamic formula

$$\frac{dl_v}{dT} - \frac{l_v}{T} = c_2 - c_1$$
$$- \frac{l_v}{v_2 - v_1}\left\{ \left(\frac{\partial v^2}{\partial T}\right)_p - \left(\frac{\partial v_1}{\partial T}\right)_p \right\},$$

where c_1 and c_2 are the specific heat capacities of the liquid and vapour respectively. An empirical formula gives

$l_v \propto (T_c - T)^{\frac{1}{3}}$ where T_c is the critical temperature.

specific optical rotary power. Symbol: α_D. A measure of the *optical activity of a substance in solution. It is given by the equation $\alpha_D = \alpha V/ml$, where α is the angle of rotation of the plane of polarization when light traverses a pathlength l of a solution containing a mass of substance m in a volume V. The units are $m^2\,kg^{-1}$.

specific reluctance. The former name for *reluctivity.

specific resistance. The former name for *resistivity.

specific volume. Symbol: v. The volume of unit mass of a substance; the reciprocal of density.

spectral. (1) Of or relating to a spectrum. (2) Of or relating to monochromatic radiation.

spectral class. *See* stellar spectra.

spectral lines. *See* spectrum; hyperfine structure of spectral lines.

spectral luminous efficacy. *See* luminous efficacy.

spectral luminous efficiency. A ratio expressing the ability of the eye to judge the power of *monochromatic radiation of a particular wavelength, λ. It is equal to the ratio of the *radiant flux at a wavelength λ_m to that producing an equal sensation of *luminosity at the wavelength of interest λ. The comparison is made under standard photometric conditions and λ_m is chosen so that the maximum value of the ratio is unity. The spectral luminous efficiency varies with wavelength and is a maximum at about 555 nm (green) for bright sources, shifting to 505 nm (greenish-blue) for faint sources.

spectral type. *See* stellar spectra.

spectrograph. *See* spectrometer.

spectrometer. (1) An instrument for producing, examining, or recording a *spectrum. When an emission spectrum is investigated the radiation from the source is passed through a *collimator which produces a parallel beam of radiation. This is dispersed by a prism or *diffraction grating, the angular deviation depending on the wavelengths present. In a simple spectrometer (Fig. *a*) light from the source S is collimated by C and dispersed by the prism. The telescope T is used to observe the resulting spectrum and can be rotated around the prism table so that the angular deviation and hence wavelength of the spectral lines, bands, etc., can be measured. The angles of prisms and *refractive indexes can also be determined.

a Simple spectrometer

Fig. *b* shows a spectrometer employing a concave diffraction grating. Radiation enters at the slit S_1, and is reflected by the grating G through S_2, onto a detector D, such as a *photomultiplier. In this instrument both slits are kept constant and the grating is rotated through a range of angles. At each particular angle of the grating, radiation of a particular wavelength is focused onto the exit slit. A graph of the angle of the grating (as abscissa) against the response of the photomultiplier can, with suitable calibration, give a curve of wavelength against intensity of radiation.

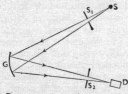

b Spectrometer using concave diffraction grating

When an absorption spectrum is investigated a continuous source of radiation is usually used. This may be passed through the sample and then into the spectrometer so that the distribution of intensity with wavelength is found. Alternatively the continuous spectrum can be passed into the spectrometer so that one particular wavelength of radiation is selected and passed through the sample onto the detector. The wavelength can be varied by changing the position of the grating or prism. In this way the spectrometer is used to isolate one wavelength of radiation, and is called a *monochromator*.

Spectrometers are often called *spectroscopes*. A *spectrophotometer* is an instrument for measuring the intensity of each wavelength in a spectrum, and the term is often used synonymously with spectrometer. If photographic recording is used in the instrument it is called a *spectrograph*.

(2) A similar instrument for determining the distribution of energies in a beam of particles, such as electrons (*see* electron spectroscopy) or ions (*see* mass spectrometer).

spectrophotometer. *See* spectrometer.

spectroscope. *See* spectrometer.

spectroscopy. The technique of producing *spectra, analysing their constituent wavelengths, and using them for chemical analysis or the determination of energy levels and molecular structure. A spectrum is formed by the emission or absorption of electromagnetic radiation accompanying changes between the energy levels of atoms and molecules. The frequency of the radiation depends on the type of energy levels involved and spectroscopic techniques are used over a very wide range of frequencies and yield a wide variety of information. *See also* spectrometer.

spectrum. (1) Any particular distribution of *electromagnetic radiation, such as

357

the display of colours produced when white light is dispersed by a prism or *diffraction grating. The term is also applied to a plot of the intensity of electromagnetic radiation against wavelength, frequency, or energy, or to a photographic record of dispersed electromagnetic radiation.

Spectra can be obtained with a *spectrometer. The spectrum is characteristic of the radiation itself in that it specifies the wavelengths that are present and their intensities. It is also characteristic of the substance that is emitting or absorbing the radiation (*see* emission spectrum; absorption spectrum). A spectrum in which there is a continuous region of radiation emitted or absorbed is a *continuous spectrum*. An example is the spectrum of visible and infrared radiation emitted by a *black body. The spectra of gaseous atoms often contain a number of sharp bright lines of emitted radiation or a number of dark lines on a continuous background due to absorption. Such spectra are called *line spectra* and occur when atoms make transitions between definite energy levels. *Band spectra* contain a series of regularly spaced lines that are very close together and may not be resolved by the apparatus used to disperse the radiation. They are characteristic of emission or absorption by molecules.

Spectra are also classified according to whether the radiation is in the X-ray, ultraviolet, visible, infrared, or microwave region of the spectrum and according to whether the process producing or absorbing the radiation involves a change in electronic, vibrational, or rotational energy levels. Thus in the visible and ultraviolet regions changes occur between electronic energy levels and an *electronic spectrum* is obtained. These are line spectra in the case of atoms and band spectra in the case of molecules. In the *near infrared region spectra result from changes from a rotational level in one vibrational level to a rotational level in another vibrational

level. A spectrum of this type is called a *vibration–rotation spectrum*. Changes between rotational energy levels in the same vibrational level lead to absorption or emission of radiation in the far infrared and *microwave regions and the formation of a *rotation spectrum*. At the other end of the scale, ultraviolet spectra are electronic spectra of ions. X-ray spectra involve changes of electronic energy levels of inner tightly bound electrons. (*See* X-rays.)

(2) Any distribution of energies, momenta, velocities, etc. in a system of particles, as in a mass spectrum (*see* mass spectrometer) or an electron spectrum (*see* electron spectroscopy).

spectrum analyser. *See* multichannel analyser.

speculum. A copper–tin alloy (Cu 67%, Sn 33%) used for metal mirrors and reflection diffraction gratings. It takes a high polish and does not tarnish readily.

speed. (1) The rate of increase of distance travelled with time. (*Compare* velocity.) (2) Of photographic material. A value specifying the sensitivity of photographic material to light. (3) A measure of the ability of a photographic lens to pass light, being proportional to the inverse *f-number of the lens.

sphere gap. A spark gap having spherical electrodes. A sphere gap can be used to measure extra high voltages with great reliability.

spherical aberration. When rays are traced after reflection or refraction at large aperture surfaces (commonly spherical), they do not unite accurately at a focus. When the outer zones focus within the focal point for paraxial rays the spherical aberration is said to be positive (mirror) or undercorrected (lens). The image of a point appears as a circular disc. The best focus is between the two extreme foci, at

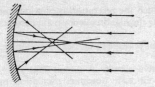

a Spherical aberration (mirror)

which point the image is the *circle of least confusion*. For a particular zone of the lens, the *longitudinal spherical aberration* is the axial separation of the images formed by rays passing through that zone and those through the centre of the lens.

First order theory of this aberration is based on the use of the first two Seidel sums (*see* aberration). In practice it may be eliminated from mirrors by using a paraboloidal or ellipsoidal surface. Alternatively a *Schmidt corrector can be

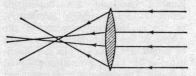

b Spherical aberration (lens)

used. With a lens, the aberration is reduced by using small angles of incidence on the lens surfaces and sharing the deviation equally between the surfaces. Thus a telescope objective is roughly planoconvex with the convex face towards the object.

The term spherical aberration is also used to embrace all the aberrations due to the sphericity (form) of surfaces, e.g. spherical aberration, coma, radial astigmatism, curvature of field, and distortion (Seidel aberrations).

spherical lens. A lens whose surfaces are portions of a sphere.

spherometer. An instrument for measuring the curvature of the surfaces of lenses and mirrors.

spike. A current or voltage transient of extremely short duration.

spin. The electron is assumed to have an intrinsic angular momentum in addition to any angular momentum due to its orbital motion. This intrinsic angular momentum is called spin. It is quantized in values of $\sqrt{s(s+1)}h/2\pi$, s being the *spin quantum number* and h the *Planck constant. For an electron s can have values of $+\frac{1}{2}$ and $-\frac{1}{2}$, leading to the two possible states in which an electron can exist. An electron with spin behaves like a small magnet with an intrinsic *magnetic moment (*see also* magneton). The two states of different energy result from interaction between the magnetic field due to the electron's spin and that caused by its orbital motion. There are two closely spaced energy levels resulting from the two possible spin directions and these lead to the two lines seen in a *doublet.

In an external magnetic field the angular momentum vector of the electron precesses (*see* precession) around the field direction. Not all orientations of the vector to the field direction are allowed; there is quantization so that the component of the angular momentum along the direction is restricted to certain values of $h/2\pi$. The angular momentum vector has allowed directions such that the component is $m_s(h/2\pi)$, where m_s is the *magnetic quantum number*. For a given value of s, m_s has the values s, $(s-1), \ldots -s$. This phenomenon is called *space quantization*.

The resultant spin of a number of particles is the vector sum of the spins (s) of the individual particles and is given the symbol S. For example, in an atom two electrons with spins of $\frac{1}{2}$ could combine to give a resultant spin of $S = \frac{1}{2} + \frac{1}{2} = 1$ or a resultant of $S = \frac{1}{2} - \frac{1}{2} = 0$.

Alternative symbols used for spin are J (for elementary particles) and I (for nuclei). Most elementary particles have a non-zero spin which may either be integral or half integral. (*See* boson;

359

fermion.) The spin of a nucleus is the resultant of the spins of its constituent nucleons.

spin quantum number. *See* spin.

spontaneous fission. Nuclear *fission that takes place independently of external circumstances and is not initiated by the impact of a neutron, an energetic particle, or a photon.

spreading coefficient. Imagine a drop of a liquid, A, instantaneously resting on the surface of another liquid, B, with which it is immiscible. The three forces acting on unit length are numerically equal to the surface tensions T_A and T_B of the liquids and their interfacial surface tension T_{AB}. The condition for equilibrium is that these three forces shall balance. The quantity $(T_B - T_A - T_{AB})$ is called the spreading coefficient and if this is positive the drop will spread.

spreading resistance. Of a *semiconductor device. The component of resistance due to the bulk of the semiconductor away from the junctions and contacts.

spring balance. A device with which a force is measured by the extension produced in a helical spring. It is used in weighing. The extension produced is directly proportional to the force (weight).

sputtering. The evaporation of particles of a cathode during the discharge of electricity through a gas. The method can be used to coat a nonconductor with a thin adhesive metallic film.

square wave. A pulse train consisting of rectangular pulses with *mark–space ratio equal to unity.

squegging oscillator. An *oscillator in which the oscillations build up in amplitude to a peak value then fall to zero. It is a type of *relaxation oscillator in

which the relaxation oscillations modulate the high frequency main oscillations.

squirrel-cage rotor. *See* induction motor.

stable circuit. A circuit that does not produce any unwanted oscillations under any operating conditions.

stable equilibrium. *See* equilibrium.

staggered aerial. *See* aerial array.

standard atmosphere. Symbol: atm. A unit of pressure equal to 101 325 newtons per square metre (pascals).

standard cell. An electric cell used as a voltage-reference standard. *See* Clark cell; Weston standard cell.

standard deviation. *See* deviation.

standard illuminant. An illuminating source set up for standard colorimetry, i.e. to enable measurements of the colours of non self-luminous samples to be determined. The samples are illuminated at 45° to the normal and viewed normally. Three standards are prescribed having *colour temperatures of 2848 K, 4800 K, and 6600 K.

standard temperature and pressure (STP). A standard condition for the reduction of gas temperatures and pressures. Standard temperature is 0° C (273·15 K); standard pressure is 101 325 newtons per square metre (very nearly equal to the former standard pressure of 760 mm Hg).

standing wave. *Syn.* stationary wave. A wave incident normally on a boundary of the transmitting medium is reflected either wholly or partially according to the boundary conditions, the reflected wave being superimposed on the incident wave and thereby creating an interference pattern of *nodes and antinodes. If the incident wave is represented by

$$\xi = a \sin (2\pi/\lambda)(ct - x),$$

then for total reflection from a rigid boundary the reflected wave would be

$$\xi = -a \sin (2\pi/\lambda)(ct + x),$$

and the combination would be

$$\xi = a \sin (2\pi/\lambda)(ct - x) \\ - a \sin (2\pi/\lambda)(ct + x),$$

i.e.

$$\xi = -2a \sin (2\pi/\lambda)x \cos (2\pi/\lambda)ct.$$

This is a wave which remains stationary, the displacement being always zero at $x = 0$, $\lambda/2$, λ, $3\lambda/2$, etc. (nodes), and vibrating with amplitude $2a$ at $x = \lambda/4$, $3\lambda/4$, $5\lambda/4$, etc. (antinodes).

In contrast, at a free boundary the phase of the reflected wave is the same as that of the incident wave, thus creating an antinode at the boundary. The stationary wave pattern has, however, the same spacings between nodes and antinodes as before.

In practice the reflection may be only partial, thus creating minimum deflections at the nodes instead of the zero deflections.

Stanhope lens. A thick biconvex lens magnifier, with front surface of radius two-thirds the thickness and a concentric back surface with radius one-third the thickness (glass assumed). The object to be viewed is put in contact with the front surface.

Stanton number. The reciprocal of the *Prandtl number. *See* convection (of heat).

star. A self-luminous celestial body. *See* stellar spectra; Hertzsprung–Russell diagram; celestial sphere; magnitude.

star connection. A method of connection used in *polyphase a.c. working in which the windings of a transformer, a.c. machine, etc., each have one end connected to a common junction the latter being called the *star point*. In three-phase working, the winding is also

known as the *Y connection. Compare* mesh connection.

Stark effect. The wavelength of light emitted by atoms is altered by the application of a strong transverse electric field to the source, the spectrum lines being split up into a number of sharply defined components. The displacements are symmetrical about the position of the undisplaced line, and are proportional to the field strength up to about 100 000 volts per cm.

Stark–Einstein equation. The formula for the energy per mole E absorbed in a photochemical reaction. If f is the frequency of the absorbed radiation $E = hLf$ where h is the *Planck constant and L the *Avogadro constant.

stat-. A prefix which, when attached to the name of a practical electrical unit, denotes the corresponding unit in the CGS-electrostatic system. This system of units is no longer employed.

static characteristic. *See* characteristic.

static friction. *See* friction.

statics. The branch of *mechanics dealing with bodies at rest relative to some given frame of reference, with the forces between them, and with the equilibrium of the system. *Hydrostatics* is a branch of statics dealing with the equilibrium of fluids and with their stationary interactions (e.g. pressure, flotation) with solid bodies.

static tube. *See* Pitot (static) tube.

stationary orbit. A *synchronous (24 hour) orbit lying in or approximately in the plane of the equator.

stationary state. In *quantum theory or *quantum mechanics. The state of an atom or other system which is fixed, or determined, by a given set of quantum

361

numbers. It is one of the various energy states that can be assumed by an atom.

stationary time principle. *See* Fermat's principle.

stationary wave. *See* standing wave.

statistical mechanics. The theory in which the properties of macroscopic systems are predicted by the statistical behaviour of their constituent particles. For example, if a large collection of molecules is considered its total energy is the sum of all the individual energies of the molecules. These in turn are energies of vibration, rotation, and translation, and electronic energy. According to *quantum theory a molecule can only have certain allowed energies; it can be thought of as occupying any of a number of *energy levels. Consequently the system as a whole can also have any number of possible energy levels, E_1, E_2, E_3, ... If a large collection of systems is considered, each containing the same amount of substance, there will be a distribution of systems over energy levels: N_1 will have energy E_1, N_2 energy E_2, etc. According to the Maxwell–Boltzmann distribution law (*see* distribution of velocities):

$$\frac{N_1}{N} = \frac{g_1 \, e^{-E_1/kT}}{\sum_1 g_1 \, e^{-E_1/kT}},$$

where N_1 systems have energy E_1, N is the total number of systems, and g_1 is the *statistical weight of this energy level. The expression $\sum_1 g_1 \, e^{-E_1/kT}$ is called the *partition function* and has the symbol Z. A collection of systems of this type is called a *canonical ensemble*. The average energy of a system, E, is $\sum N_1 E_1 / \sum N_1$ and consequently $E = kT^2 (\partial \log Z / \partial T)$.

In statistical mechanics it is assumed that this average instantaneous value of a property over a large number of systems is the same as the average value of this property for one system over a period of time. Thus the expression gives

the *internal energy of the system. The partition function of the canonical ensemble is related to the energy levels of the individual molecules by the equations:

$$Z = z^L \text{ and } z = \sum_j g_j \, e^{-\varepsilon_j/kT}.$$

Here z is the partition function of the assembly of molecules with energy ε_1, ε_2, ε_3, etc. Usually the partition function of 1 mole is considered and L is the *Avogadro constant. In principle, statistical mechanics can be used to obtain thermodynamic properties of a system from a knowledge of the energy levels of its components. However in many cases it is difficult to evaluate the partition functions because of interactions between the particles. *See also* quantum statistics.

statistical weight. *Syn.* degeneracy. Symbol: g. If a system has a number of possible quantized states and more than one distinct state has the same energy level this energy level is said to be *degenerate* and its statistical weight is the number of states having that energy level. *See also* statistical mechanics.

stator. The portion of an electrical machine that includes the non-rotating magnetic parts and the windings associated with them. The term is normally used only in connection with a.c. machines. *Compare* rotor.

steady-state theory. A theory in *cosmology postulating that the universe has always existed and will continue to exist in a steady state such that the average density of matter does not vary with distance or time. To offset the change in density of the *expanding universe, matter must be created in the space left by the receding stars and galaxies at a rate of about 10^{-43} kg m^{-3} s^{-1}. Evidence indicates that the density is not constant throughout the universe and thus has changed in periods of the universe's history. *Compare* *big-bang theory. *See also* cosmic background radiation.

steam calorimeter. A calorimeter in which the amount of heat supplied is calculated from the mass of steam condensed on the body under test. *See* Joly's steam calorimeter.

steam engine. A machine that takes heat from a steam boiler, performs external work, and rejects a smaller amount of heat to a condenser. *See* Rankine cycle.

steam line. The curve showing the variation of the boiling point of water with pressure, i.e. the variation of the saturation pressure of water vapour with pressure.

steam point. The temperature of equilibrium between the liquid and vapour phases of water at standard pressure. Its former importance was as the upper fixed point on the Celsius scale of temperature. Thermodynamic temperature is now based on the triple point of water, and its value (273·16 K) has been chosen to make the steam point equal to 100° C within the limits of experimental measurement. At a pressure p (in mm Hg) the steam point has a value of $100 + 0.0367 (p - 760) - 2.3 \times 10^{-5} (p - 760)^2$. This temperature is the boiling point of water at a given pressure.

steel. *See* alloy.

Stefan's law. *Syn.* Stefan–Boltzmann law. A formula relating the radiant flux per unit area emitted by a *black body (*radiant exitance) to the temperature. It has the form $M_e = \sigma T^4$, where M_e is the radiant exitance and σ is *Stefan's constant*. $\sigma = 2\pi^5 k^4/15h^3c^2$, where k is the Boltzmann constant, c the velocity of light in a vacuum, and h is the *Planck constant. σ has the value 5.6697×10^{-8} W m^{-2} K^{-4}.

stellar evolution. *See* Hertzsprung–Russell diagram.

stellar spectra. Stars emit radiation over a wide range of wavelengths, the maximum amount of energy being emitted at a particular wavelength. This wavelength will occur in the infrared or at the red end of the visible spectrum if the energy emitted is not very high (a cool star). An energetic star (a hot star) emits at the blue end of the spectrum.

Various groups of emission and absorption lines appear in a star's spectrum depending on temperature. Stars are usually classified according to their spectra and can be grouped into *spectral types*: O (blue, 40 kK), B (blue-white, 20 kK), A (white, 9 kK), F (white-yellow, 7 kK), G (yellow, 6 kK), hK (orange, 4·5 kK), and M (red, 3kK). The sun is a G-type. There are additional classes of extremely hot (80 kK) W stars and cool (2·5–3 kK) S, R, and N stars. At temperatures above 50 kK only ionized gases exist. At lower temperatures metals, such as calcium, appear and in even cooler stars elementary molecules can survive. Stellar spectra thus indicate chemical composition as well as temperature. *See also* Hertzsprung–Russell diagram.

St Elmo's fire. The brush discharge from the pointed parts of ships or aircraft when in a strong atmospheric electrical field.

step-down, step-up transformer. *See* transformer.

step wedge. A block or sheet of material having a series of layers successively more opaque to a given radiation in steps of definite value.

steradian. Symbol: sr. A unit of *solid angle. One steradian is subtended at the centre of a sphere of radius r by a portion of its surface of area r^2. 1 sphere $= 4\pi$ sr. The steradian is the supplementary *SI unit of solid angle.

stereographic projection. A projection obtained by assuming a crystal to be placed within a sphere from the centre C of which normals are drawn to the crystal faces; these normals intersect the sphere in points which are then joined to a pole P on the surface of the sphere. The straight lines thus obtained intersect a plane through C normal to CP to give the stereographic projection. The term has a wide mathematical significance which covers the projection of any points or figures on the surface of a sphere, from a pole P on the surface on to the plane through the centre C normal to PC.

stereophonic reproduction. Reproduction of sound by means of two or more separate channels so as to give an illusion of location and direction from which a sound has originated.

stereoscope. An instrument by which an image is given an impression of depth by presenting to the eye two slightly different viewpoints of it.

stereoscopic microscope. *See* microscope.

stiffness. *See* reactance (acoustic).

stilb. Symbol: sb. A unit of *luminance equal to 1 *candela per square centimetre. 1 stilb $= 10^4$ *nits.

stimulated emission. *See* laser.

stochastic process. A process resulting from the random behaviour of its generators.

stokes. Symbol: St. The *CGS unit of *kinematic viscosity. 1 St $= 10^{-4}$ metre squared per second.

Stokes–Kirchhoff equation. *See* absorption (of sound).

Stokes's law. Of fluid resistance. The drag D of a sphere of radius r moving with a velocity V through a fluid of infinite extent is $D = 6\pi\eta r V$, where η is the *viscosity. The law holds only for a restricted range of conditions.

stop. *See* apertures and stops in optical systems.

stop number. *See* f-number.

stopping power. A measure of the effect of a substance upon the kinetic energy E, of a charged particle passing through it. (1) The *linear stopping power*, S_1, is the energy loss per unit distance: $S_1 = dE/dx$, expressed in Me V/cm or ke V/m. (2) The *mass stopping power*, S_m, for a substance of density, ρ, is the energy loss per unit surface density: $S_m = S_1/\rho$. (3) The *atomic stopping power*, S_a, is the energy loss per atom per unit area of the substance normal to the motion of the charged particle: $S_a = S_1/n$, where n is the number of atoms per unit volume. Stopping power is often expressed relative to that of a standard substance, such as air or aluminium.

storage device. Equipment used for holding information in a *computer, usually in binary form. It may be a magnetic *disk, *tape, *drum, or *memory.

storage time. (1) In general, the time for which information may be stored in any device, without significant loss of information. (2) Of a p–n junction. The time interval observed between application of a reverse bias and cessation of forward current.

storage tube. An *electron tube in which information may be stored for a determined and controllable time, and extracted as required. Various operating principles are used in storage tubes and many different types exist.

The most common types of tube in general use are *charge storage tubes* in which the information is stored as a pattern of electrostatic charges. The information to be stored is used to modulate the intensity of an electron beam. This beam scans a target causing *secondary emission, so producing the charge pattern. In a storage cathode-ray tube the information is extracted by passing electrons through the target onto the screen. The electron density depends on the deposited positive charge and the resulting light image on the screen is equivalent to the original information. In another type, an electron beam scans the target and its intensity is modulated by the stored charge. This beam is then collected on an electrode to give an electronic signal.

Storage tubes also operate by *photoconductivity effects. The photoconductive target is exposed to a light image or modulated electron beam and the conductivity is increased in proportion to the radiation intensity. An unmodulated electron beam scans the target, discharging the target areas and so producing an output signal.

STP. *Syn.* NTP. Abbreviation for standard (normal) temperature and pressure.

strain. The change of volume and/or shape of a body, or part of a body, due to applied forces. The three simplest strains are: (1) *longitudinal*: change in length per unit length (e.g. when stretching a wire); (2) *volume*: change in volume per unit volume (e.g. when a hydrostatic pressure is applied to a body); (3) *shear*: angular deformation without change in volume (e.g. a rectangular block strained so that two opposite faces become parallelograms, the others not changing shape). The radian measure of the change in angle θ at one corner is a measure of the strain. θ is small in practice and is equal to the tangential displacement of two planes unit distance apart. *See* homogeneous strain; stress.

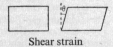

Shear strain

strain gauge. An instrument for measuring strain at the surface of a solid body in terms of the change in electrical

resistance, capacitance, or inductance or the piezoelectric and magnetostriction effects produced by the strain.

strangeness. Symbol: *S*. A *quantum number associated with *elementary particles that is conserved in *strong and *electromagnetic interactions but not in *weak interactions. Its existence was postulated in order to explain the fact that some elementary particles (e.g. kaons, Σ, and Λ) that were expected to decay very rapidly by strong interaction (since they could do so without violating any of the known conservation laws), had much longer lifetimes than expected. *See also* hypercharge.

stratosphere. *See* atmospheric layers.

stray capacitance. Any capacitance in a circuit or device due to interconnections or electrodes in the circuit.

stream function. In two-dimensional motion of a fluid the stream function (ψ) at any point *P* is defined as the flow across a curve *AP* where *A* is a fixed point in the two-dimensional plane. If the plane is the Cartesian plane *xy* then the component velocities at any point (x, y) are $V_x = -\partial\psi/\partial y$ and $V_y = \partial\psi/\partial x$. In axisymmetrical three-dimensional motion of a fluid – motion which is the same in every plane through a certain axis of symmetry – there is a similar function (ψ) whose value at a point *P* is defined as $1/2\pi$ of the flow out of a surface of revolution formed by rotating a curve *AP* about the axis, where *A* is any fixed point in the meridian plane of *P*. This function is called the *Stokes's stream function*. In both cases the curves: $\psi = $ constant, give the streamlines of the fluid motion.

streaming potential. A difference of potential set up between the two sides of a porous material such as clay when water is forced through. It is the potential set up between the ends of a capillary tube when an electrolyte is forced through it. *Compare* electro-osmosis.

streamlines. A line drawn in a fluid so that the tangent at any point is in the direction of the fluid velocity at that point. The aggregate of streamlines at any instant of time forms the flow pattern.

stress. A system of forces in equilibrium producing or tending to produce *strain in a body or part of a body. The simplest stresses are: (1) *tensional* or *compressive stress*, e.g. the force per unit area of cross section applied to each end of a rod to extend or compress it; (2) *hydrostatic pressure*, e.g. the force per unit area applied to a body by immersion in a fluid; (3) *shear stress*, e.g. the system of four tangential stresses producing shear (*see* strain). *See* stress components; modulus of elasticity.

Shear stress

stress components. Stress components are the internal forces arising between contiguous parts of a body due to applied surface and body forces. Consider an infinitesimal plane area within the body; the force exerted by the matter on one side to that on the other can be resolved into components normal and tangential to the area that are called the *tensional* (or *compressive*) *stress component* and the *shear stress component* respectively,

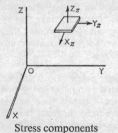

Stress components

at the area. Except in the special case of hydrostatic pressure, the stress at a point depends on the orientation of the area used in defining it.

The component stresses at three infinitesimal orthogonal areas at the point (x, y, z) are three tensional stresses X_x, Y_y, and Z_z (*see* diagram) and six shear stresses, pairs of which are equal, i.e. $X_y = Y_x$, $Z_x = X_z$, $Y_z = Z_y$. From these it is possible to calculate the stress across an infinitesimal area however orientated.

stretched string. If a long thin flexible wire, stretched between two rigid supports, is excited into vibration, *standing waves are set up due to the superposition of two transverse progressive waves travelling in opposite directions with velocity $V = \sqrt{T/m}$, where T is the tension and m the mass per unit length. In the fundamental mode there is a single loop with an antinode at the centre and nodes at the ends. In this case the wavelength is twice the length of the string l, and the fundamental frequency is $f = \sqrt{T/m}\,(2l)^{-1}$. The various* partials are produced when the string vibrates in several loops. All the partials are *harmonic, their frequencies being obtained by multiplying that of the fundamental by the number of loops on the string. A string may vibrate with several partials at the same time, their number and magnitude depending on the method of excitation.

string galvanometer. *See* Einthoven galvanometer.

stripping. A *nuclear reaction in which a *nucleon of the bombarding nucleus is captured by the struck nucleus without the nuclei merging to form a compound nucleus. The *Oppenheimer–Phillips (O–P) process* is a reaction in which a low-energy deuteron gives its neutron to a nucleus without entering it.

stroboscope. An instrument producing an intense flashing light whose frequency can be adjusted to synchronize with some multiple of the frequency of rotation or vibration of a moving object or part, making it appear stationary. It is used to study the motion and also to determine rotation or vibration speeds.

strong focusing. *See* focusing.

strong interactions. Interactions between *baryons and *mesons (*hadrons) involving the strong interaction force. This force is about one hundred times greater than the *electromagnetic force between charged elementary particles. However, it is a short range force – it is only important for particles separated by a distance of less than about 10^{-15} m. The *nuclear force is an example of a strong interaction force. Just as the electromagnetic interaction between charged particles may be described in terms of the exchange of virtual photons (*see* virtual particle), so strong interactions between hadrons may be described in terms of the exchange of virtual hadrons. In strong interactions any hadron can act as the exchanged particle providing certain *quantum numbers are conserved. These quantum numbers are the total angular momentum, charge, *baryon number, *isospin (both I and I_3), *strangeness, *parity, *charge conjugation parity, and *G-parity. Where all the necessary quantum numbers can be conserved, elementary particles can decay by a strong interaction. The characteristic decay time is 10^{-23} s. *See* bootstrap theory; exchange force; Regge pole model.

SU(3). *See* unitary symmetry.

subcarrier. A *carrier wave used to modulate another carrier wave.

subcritical. *See* chain reaction.

sublimation. The direct transition from solid to vapour, or vice versa, without any liquid phase being involved.

substandard. A standard measuring device not quite as accurate as the primary standard, used as the intermediate link between the primary standard and the device being calibrated or checked.

subtractive process. A process by which colours can be produced or reproduced by mixing absorbing media (or *filters) of three different dyes or pigments, called *subtractive primaries*. The colour of light reflected by (or passing through) the mixture is determined by the *absorption, or subtraction, of specific colours by each medium.

summation tone. *See* combination tones.

sunspots. Dark patches seen on the sun's surface that are regions of cool gas. Their presence is connected with local variations in the sun's magnetic field. They appear in cycles having a period of about 11 years.

superconductivity. A phenomenon occurring in many metals and alloys. If these substances are cooled below a *transition temperature*, T_c, close to absolute zero, the electrical resistance becomes vanishingly small. There is also a marked change in the variation with temperature of the *specific heat capacity. Superconductivity results from a change in the behaviour of the conduction electrons in the material. There is a dynamic pairing of electrons (a *Cooper pair*) such that if the energy state with *wave number σ and *spin $\frac{1}{2}$ is occupied by an electron, then so is the state with wave number $-\sigma$ and spin $-\frac{1}{2}$. These pairs are superimposed in phase. This pairing creates an energy gap in the electron energy spectrum. The *tunnel effect can occur in superconductors, even in the case of two superconductors separated by an insulating layer (*see* Josephson effect).

When a superconducting loop or hollow tube, in a weak magnetic field, is cooled down through T_c the magnetic flux is trapped in the loop. This is the

Meissner effect. The flux is constant, being unchanged by variations in the external field. It is sustained by super-currents circulating around the loop. Any field variation is countered by Lenz's law, by the induction of an appropriate supercurrent. The superconductivity however can be destroyed if the field becomes too large or if a current is passed through the loop. (*See also* cryotron.)

The current produced in a closed ring by the Meissner effect will continue to flow for a considerable time after the external field is removed, as long as the temperature is kept below T_c. This effect is used in *superconducting magnets*. In the 1960s superconducting alloys, such as niobium-titanium, niobium-zirconium, and niobium-tin, were developed. These can carry very high current densities of up to 2 kA/mm^2 while maintained at about 4·5 K, leading to magnetic flux densities of over 10 tesla. A parallel development in low-temperature techniques means that superconducting d.c. motors and generators and a.c. generators are now a practical proposition. The flux densities achieved are far in excess of the 2 tesla that is the limit for iron. The output of both a.c. and d.c. generators would also far exceed that of conventional machines, being well over 100 MW. The efficiency is higher and the size smaller. There is no power dissipation and thus no need for cooling systems. Superconducting magnets can, and in some cases are being used in high-energy *accelerators, *fusion reactors, power transmission, and transportation.

supercooling. The process by which liquids, by slow and continuous cooling, are reduced to a temperature below the normal freezing point. A supercooled liquid is a *metastable state and the introduction of the smallest quantity of the solid at once starts solidification. Small mechanical disturbance may also initiate solidification which, once started, will continue with the evolution of heat until the normal freezing point is reached.

supercritical. *See* chain reaction.

superdense theory. *See* big-bang theory.

superfluid. A fluid that flows through fine channels without friction and has very high *thermal conductivity at extremely low temperatures. Helium below 2·186 K is a superfluid. At this temperature, called the *lambda point*, the *specific heat capacity and the density are at a maximum. As the temperature is reduced the thermal conductivity of the liquid helium increases extremely rapidly reaching a value 10^6 times the value above the lambda point. In wider channels, above a critical velocity, there is a small but finite amount of friction.

supergiant. *See* Hertzsprung–Russell diagram.

superheating. The heating of a liquid above its normal boiling point without boiling occurring. *See also* supercooling.

superheterodyne receiver. The most widely used type of radio receiver, in which the incoming signal and a locally generated signal are fed into a mixer. The output consists of a signal of ultrasonic frequency equal to the difference between the locally generated signal and the carrier frequencies, but containing all the original modulation. This signal, the *intermediate frequency* (or i.f.) signal, is amplified and detected in an i.f. amplifier, and passed onto the audio-frequency amplifier. The high-gain amplification and great selectivity of this receiver result from the use of the inter-mediate frequency.

superhigh frequency (SHF). *See* frequency band.

supernova. A star that explodes as a result of instabilities following the exhaustion of its nuclear fuel. The explosion involves an enormous energy release. Matter is ejected at relativistic speeds, forming an expanding shell of debris called a *supernova remnant* and often leaving a *pulsar at the centre.

superposition. Two or more vibrations or waves may be superimposed upon each other to give a single complex vibration or wave, there being no mutual interaction. Thus the displacement at any instant is given by the sum of the instantaneous displacements of the individual components. The superposition of two waves, y_1 and y_2, both of frequency n produces a wave y of the same frequency, its amplitude and phase being functions of the component amplitudes and phases. Thus if

$$y_1 = a_1 \sin (2\pi nt + \delta_1)$$

and $\qquad y_2 = a_2 \sin (2\pi nt + \delta_2)$

then the resultant vibration, y, is given by

$$y = y_1 + y_2$$
$$= A \sin (2\pi nt + \Delta),$$

where

$$A = \sqrt{a_1{}^2 + a_2{}^2 + 2a_1 a_2 \cos (\delta_1 - \delta_2)}.$$

and $\tan \Delta = \dfrac{a_1 \sin \delta_1 + a_2 \sin \delta_2}{a_1 \cos \delta_1 + a_2 \cos \delta_2}$.

The superposition principle holds whenever linear phenomena occur. In elasticity each stress is accompanied by the same strains whether it acts alone or in conjunction with others; it is true so long as the total stress does not exceed the limit of proportionality.

super-regenerative reception. A method of reception of ultra-high frequencies by means of a radio receiver employing an oscillating *detector, the oscillations of which are periodically stopped (or quenched) at a frequency dependent on the input frequency. There is very great amplification but the selectivity is rather poor compared to a *superheterodyne receiver.

supersaturated vapour. A vapour, the pressure of which exceeds the saturation vapour pressure at that temperature. It is unstable and condensation occurs in the presence of suitable nuclei.

supersonic flow. The movement of a fluid at a speed exceeding the velocity of sound in the fluid. In such a case, changes of density in the flow can no longer be neglected. As the speed of an object moving through a fluid is increased through the velocity of sound and beyond, the resistance (drag) rises due to the formation of *shock waves. *See also* sonic boom.

surface-barrier transistor. A *transistor in which the usual p–n junctions are replaced by metal-semiconductor contacts called Schottky barriers (*see* Schottky diode). Hole storage under saturation conditions is zero with the Schottky barriers and the transistors are useful for very high-speed switching applications.

surface-charge transistor. *See* charge-transfer device.

surface colour. Coloured light reflected by a surface as distinct from the more common body colour that arises from reflection after some penetration into the medium. Transmitted light by bodies showing surface colour is complementary to the reflected colour.

surface energy. The energy per unit area of exposed surface. The (total) surface energy in general exceeds the *surface tension, which is the *free* surface energy, concerned in isothermal changes.

surface forces. *See* force.

surface recombination velocity. *See* semiconductor.

surface tension. Symbol: γ. Due to the mutual attractions between molecules in a liquid, a molecule in the interior is attracted in all directions, but one at the surface is only attracted inwards from the surface. The surface thus tends to contract to the smallest possible area, e.g. a free drop tends to a spherical shape. The work done in creating unit area of surface against these forces at constant temperature is called the *free surface energy*. If the liquid surface is assumed to be in tension in all directions, the force required to hold the straight edge of a plane liquid surface is γ, the surface tension (usually expressed in newtons per metre). If the surface is stretched isothermally so that the edge moves unit distance so creating unit area of new surface, the work done is γ (in joules). Thus the surface tension expressed in newtons per metre is numerically and dimensionally equal to the free surface energy in joules per square metre but it is not the total surface energy.

Due to the surface tension there is a pressure difference between the two sides of a liquid surface equal to $\gamma(1/R_1 + 1/R_2)$, where R_1 and R_2 are the radii of curvature of two perpendicular normal sections.

surge. An abnormal transient electrical disturbance in a conductor such as that produced in a *transmission line by lightning, sudden faults, switching operations, etc.

surge generator. *See* impulse generator.

susceptance. Symbol: B. The imaginary part of the *admittance, Y, i.e. $Y = G + iB$ where G is the *conductance. It is the reciprocal of the reactance and is measured in *siemens.

susceptibility. (1) (magnetic). Symbol: χ_m. The magnetic susceptibility is defined as $\mu_r - 1$, where μ_r is the relative *permeability. (2) (electric). Symbol: χ_e.

The electric susceptibility is defined as $\varepsilon_r - 1$, where ε_r is the relative *permittivity.

Sutherland's formula. One of several formulae proposed to show the variation of viscosity η of a gas with thermodynamic temperature T:

$$\eta = \eta_0(T/273)^{\frac{3}{2}}(273 + k)/(T + k).$$

k is constant for a given gas and η_0 is the viscosity at $0°$ C.

S V P. Abbreviation for saturated vapour pressure.

sweep. *See* time base.

switch. A device for opening or closing a circuit, or for changing its operating conditions between specified levels. Switches may consist of a mechanical device, such as a *circuit breaker, or a solid-state device, such as a *transistor, *Schottky diode, or *field-effect transistor.

synchrocyclotron. *Syn.* frequency-modulated cyclotron. A modification of the *cyclotron in which the magnetic field remains constant but the frequency of the accelerating electric field is slowly decreased. In the cyclotron as the velocity becomes relativistic an increase in mass occurs and as a result the particle gets out of phase with the alternating electric field. To counteract this, the alternating frequency in the synchrocyclotron is slowly decreased so that the particles remain in phase with the field. Energies in the region of 400–500 MeV can be obtained. *Compare* synchrotron.

synchronous alternating-current generator. *Syn.* alternator; synchronous generator. An electrical machine for generating alternating current. It has a number of *field magnets which are usually excited by means of field windings carrying direct current obtained from an independent source. The frequency of the generated e.m.f.s and currents is determined by the number of magnetic poles in the machine and the speed at which it is driven (*see* synchronous speed). This type of generator can operate and deliver its output independently of any other source of alternating current.

synchronous capacitor. A *synchronous motor designed to run unloaded and overexcited so as to take a *leading current at low *power factor from the supply system and thus to be electrically equivalent to a capacitor. In this form it is used extensively for power-factor improvement.

synchronous clock. A *clock in which a *synchronous motor drives the mechanism which advances the hands. The timekeeping is determined entirely by the frequency of the a.c. electricity supply to which the motor is connected and the user has no control over it.

synchronous induction motor. Basically, an *induction motor having a slip-ring rotor and a direct-coupled d.c. exciter. It is started as an induction motor, with consequent high starting torque. When it is running with small *slip, direct current from the exciter is injected into the rotor circuit. The motor then acts as a *synchronous motor, with consequent constant speed and high or leading *power factor.

synchronous motor. An a.c. electric motor, the mean running speed of which is independent of the load and which is determined by the number of its magnetic poles and the frequency of the electric supply. (*See* synchronous speed.) A typical industrial motor of this type consists of a stator carrying a winding, which, when connected to the a.c. supply, produces a magnetic field which rotates in space, and a rotor excited by direct current. The rotor is, fundamentally, an electromagnet which locks with the field produced by the stator and rotates at the

same speed as the field. By overexciting the rotor, the motor can be made to operate at a leading *power factor.

synchronous orbit. An orbit around the earth in which a satellite makes one complete revolution in the period (24 hours) in which the earth rotates once on its axis.

synchronous speed. The speed of rotation of the magnetic flux in an a.c. machine. It is given by: $n_s = f/p$ r.p.s., where n_s = synchronous speed, f = frequency in hertz of the a.c. supply, p = number of pairs of magnetic poles for which the a.c. winding has been designed.

synchrotron. *Syn.* betatron synchrotron; electron synchrotron. A cyclic *accelerator based on the *betatron but which uses a constant-frequency electric field in addition to a changing magnetic field.

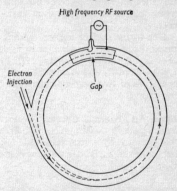

The vacuum tube of a synchrotron

As in the betatron, the increasing magnetic field strength H counteracts the relativistic increase in mass at high velocities. Then, while the magnetic field is increasing, a high-frequency electric field is applied across a gap in a metallic cavity inside the circular vacuum tube. The frequency is in synchronism with the constant angular frequency of the electrons, which are accelerated while in the cavity. At the required energy the electrons are deflected from the path. Very high energies in the GeV range have been achieved. *See also* proton synchrotron.

synchroton radiation. Polarized electromagnetic radiation generated by the motion of charged relativistic particles, usually electrons, in the magnetic field of a synchrotron. Because many regions in the universe are associated with very high magnetic fields, the radiation derived from these regions is also called synchrotron radiation.

synoptic chart. A map showing wind, barometric pressure, etc., at a particular time. It is used in weather forecasting.

systematic error. *See* errors of measurement.

Système International d'Unités. *See* SI units.

T

tachometer. An instrument for measuring angular speeds.

tachyon. A particle postulated to move with a velocity greater than that of electromagnetic radiation, such that as it accelerates it loses energy. Of the two properties rest mass and energy, one must be real and the other imaginary. If it exists it may be detected through the emission of *Cerenkov radiation or *cosmic ray collisions.

Talbot's law. The apparent intensity, I, of a light source, flashing at a frequency greater than 10 hertz, is given by $I = I_0(t/t_0)$, where I_0 is the actual intensity, t is the duration of the flash, and t_0 is the total time. The light appears steady due to the persistence of vision. *Compare* Blondel–Rey law.

tandem generator. A modification of the *Van de Graaff generator in which a doubling of the energy of the particles is achieved for the same accelerating potential. Negative ions are accelerated from earth potential, the electrons are stripped off and the resulting positive ions are accelerated back to earth potential. This is produced by connecting two generators in series.

tangent galvanometer. A *galvanometer in which a short magnetic needle is suspended at the centre of a narrow circular coil of wire of radius large compared with the length of the needle. The plane of the coil is placed along the magnetic meridian so that a current in the coil deflects the needle against the controlling force of the earth's magnetic field. The tangent law of the *magnetometer applies, i.e. the current through the coil is proportional to tan θ, where θ is the angle of deflection of the needle. The galvanometer can be used to com-

pare currents or to determine the earth's field if the current is known.

tangential coma. *See* coma.

tangent law. The law given by $ny \tan \alpha = n'y' \tan \alpha'$, where n is the refractive index of the object space, y the object size, and α the angle of inclination of a paraxial ray from an axial point on the object. The symbols with a dash refer to the image side.

tapping. A conductor (lead or wire) that is brought out from, and makes electrical connection with, any point between the ends of a winding or coil, as in a *transformer.

telecommunications. The study and practice of the transference of information by any kind of electromagnetic system, e.g. wire, radio, etc., as in telephony, *television, *radio, etc.

telemetry. A means of making measurements, in which the measured quantity is distant from the recording apparatus and the data is transmitted over a particular telecommunication system from the measuring position to the recording position.

telephoto lens. A photographic lens that can produce a large image of a distant object with normal camera extensions. It consists of a converging lens followed by a diverging lens after the manner of the Galilean telescope (*see* refracting telescope), but with a separation such that convergence to a real image occurs.

telescope. (1) An optical device for producing a magnified or intensified image of distant objects. It can be either a *reflecting or *refracting telescope or a combination of lens and mirror as in the

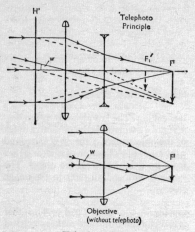

H'

Telephoto
Principle

W

F_1' F^1

γ

Objective
(*without telephoto*)

W

F^1

Telephoto lens

*Schmidt telescope (*see* Schmidt corrector) or *Maksutov telescope. *See also* resolving power; magnifying power.

Telescopes for astronomical purposes can be mounted in several ways. In an *equatorial mounting* the telescope rotates about a polar axis which points towards the celestial poles and is parallel to the earth's axis. The telescope turns at the same rate as the *diurnal motion of celestial bodies by means of a clock drive. It has two graduated circles reading right ascension and declination (*see* celestial sphere).

The *Coudé system* consists of a reflector or refractor having an equatorial mounting. The image is formed, after an additional reflection, at a point on the polar axis (the *Coudé focus*). As this point remains fixed with respect to the earth, and thus to the observer, light can be analysed with a permanently installed spectograph, etc.

In the *meridian circle*, the telescope is mounted on an east-west axis so that it turns in the meridian plane. It is used to give the altitude of a star at the moment it crosses the meridian and for deducing right ascension and declination.

(2) An electronic device for detecting

and amplifying electromagnetic radiation outside the visible region of the spectrum, including the *radio telescope and the *electron telescope.

television. A telecommunication system in which visual and audible information is transmitted. The basic elements of the system are a *television camera to convert the visual information into electrical signals, amplifying, control, and transmission circuits to transmit the information, and a television receiver which detects the signals and produces an image on the screen of a cathode-ray tube. Audio information is transmitted simultaneously and the final product is a sound and visual image of the original scene.

The information on the target in the television *camera tube is extracted by *scanning, and the spot on the screen of the receiver tube is scanned in synchronism with it to produce the image. A process of rectilinear scanning is used in which the electron beam traverses the target area in both the horizontal and vertical directions, the number of horizontal scans being much greater than the number of vertical scans so that as much of the target area is covered as possible. Each horizontal traverse is a *line* and the repetition rate is the *line frequency*. Each complete vertical scan is a *field* or *raster*. Sawtooth waveforms are used to deflect the beam at the end of a line and at the end of the raster. *See also* colour television.

television camera. The device used in a *television system to convert the optical images from a lens into electrical signals. It consists of an optical lens system, *camera tube, and preamplifier. The resulting output is further amplified and transmitted in the broadcasting network.

The camera used in *colour television consists of three camera tubes each of which receives information that has been selectively filtered to provide it with light from a different portion of the spectrum.

Light from the optical lens system is directed at an arrangement of dichroic mirrors each of which reflects one colour and allows other frequencies to pass through. The original multicoloured signal is split into red, green, and blue components, and the video output from the three camera tubes represents the red, green, and blue components of the image.

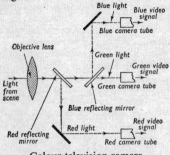

Colour-television camera

The scanning systems in the three tubes are driven simultaneously by a master oscillator to ensure that the output of each tube corresponds to the same image point.

temperament. The adjustment of tuning of the notes of a keyboard instrument to give a near diatonic scale (*see* musical scale) for all keys. In the diatonic scale the frequency of each note is a fixed multiple of that of the key note, i.e. $1\frac{1}{8}$, $1\frac{1}{4}$, $1\frac{1}{3}$, etc. If diatonic scales were built up on all keys, the number of finger keys to the octave would be very large. In order to keep to the traditional number of 13 finger keys with a minimum of mistuning, modern keyboard instruments are tuned to the scale of *equal temperament* in which the mistuning is evened out over the whole octave. The octave is divided into twelve intervals with a semitone ratio of $2^{1/12}$. Only the octaves are true, but the errors are not such that an ear accustomed to the system feels distress. Such a tuning permits the use of the same keys for different scales. The

following table gives a comparison between the scales of *just intonation* (diatonic) and equal temperament. A (440 hertz) has been taken as the standard in both scales quoted.

Just intonation

C	D	E	F	G	A	B	C
264	297	330	352	396	440	495	528

Equal temperament

C	D	E	F	G	A	B	C
261·6	293·7	329·6	349·2	392·0	440	493·9	523·3

temperature. Symbol: T. The temperature of an object is a property that determines the direction of heat flow when the object is brought into thermal contact with other objects: heat flows from regions of higher to those of lower temperatures. *See* thermodynamics (second law).

To assign numerical values, various scales of temperature have been established. The *international temperature scale is now used for scientific purposes, temperature being expressed in °C or *kelvin. Temperature is a measure of the kinetic energy of the molecules, atoms, or ions of which a body or substance is composed. The *thermodynamic temperature of a body is now treated as a physical quantity and is measured in kelvin.

The measurement of low and moderate temperatures (roughly up to 500° C) is usually classed as *thermometry* while *pyrometry* covers the high temperature ranges.

temperature coefficient of resistance. For any material the small change in the resistance of the material for changes in the thermodynamic temperature of the material. At a given temperature T, the resistance of a material is given by:

$$R_T = R_0 + \alpha T + \beta T^2$$

where $R_0 =$ resistance at absolute zero, and α and β are constants, dependent on the particular material. In general β is negligible, and α is the temperature coefficient of resistance.

Conductors usually have a positive

coefficient of resistance, semiconductors and insulators have a negative coefficient of resistance. This results from the energy distribution of electrons in the material (*see* energy bands). Conductors always have energy levels available for conduction, and increasing the temperature above absolute zero causes nuclei to vibrate about their lattice positions and scatter the conduction electrons more as they drift through the material. This has the effect of increasing the resistance.

In semiconductors and insulators, where a forbidden band exists between the valence and conduction bands, increasing the temperature increases the number of electrons which can cross the forbidden band and decreases the resistance.

temperature inversion. *See* inversion.

tensile strength. The *ultimate strength of a material as measured under tension.

tensimeter. A device for measuring differences in vapour pressure. In the diagram water may be put in one bulb and an organic liquid in the other. Air is removed and the bulbs sealed off. The apparatus is then placed in a thermostat and the differential manometer enables the vapour pressure difference to be determined at the temperature of the thermostat. Since the vapour pressure of water is accurately known, the vapour pressure of the other liquid may be determined.

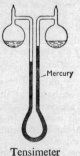

Mercury

Tensimeter

tensor. Vector notation is not always sufficiently general to express the relationships between physical quantities. For example, in an isotropic medium the vectors electric displacement *D* and field strength *E* have the same direction and are related by the scalar quantity *permittivity. In a non-isotropic medium the vectors are not in the same direction and have to be related by a tensor. Tensors are involved with transformations from one set of coordinates to another and are abstract mathematical entities, which cannot be visualized.

A point in *n*-dimensional space can be specified by a set of *n* coordinates, x_1, x_2, ... x_n, written in the form x_i. If a transformation of coordinates is made, the x_i become x_i' in the new coordinate system. A set of *n* magnitudes can be formed A_1, A_2, ... A_n, each one being a function of the original coordinates x_i. The set is denoted A_i. When the transformation occurs these change to A_i'. Such a set is a tensor if certain transformation laws hold. A tensor of rank *r* has *n* to the power *r* components. A tensor of rank zero is a *scalar and a tensor of rank 1 is a *vector. If there is a tensor equation for a physical system in one coordinate system it also holds on transformation to another coordinate system.

tera-. Symbol: T. The prefix meaning 10^{12}; e.g. 1 Tm = 10^{12} metres.

terminal velocity. The velocity with which a body moves relative to a fluid if the resultant force on the body is zero. From *Stokes's law the terminal velocity of a sphere falling in a fluid under gravity is

$$V = \frac{2}{9} \frac{(\sigma - \rho)}{\eta} r^2 g,$$

where σ is the body density, ρ is the fluid density, r is the radius of the sphere, and η is the coefficient of viscosity.

termination. A load impedance placed at the end of a transmission line to ensure *impedance matching and prevent reflection.

tesla. Symbol: T. The *SI unit of *magnetic flux density, defined as one weber of magnetic flux per metre squared.

Tesla coil. An apparatus for generating very high frequency currents at high potential. An induction coil or spark, discharging across a spark gap, feeds the primary of a transformer through two large capacitors. The transformer is wound on a large open frame, the primary having only a few turns.

tetragonal system. *See* crystal systems.

tetrode. Any electronic device with four electrodes, in particular a four-electrode *thermionic valve in which an auxiliary grid is used to decrease the anode–cathode resistance or to increase the anode–grid resistance to high frequency currents (screen–grid valve).

theodolite. A telescope fitted with spirit levels and angular scales for measuring altitude and azimuth; it is used in surveying, etc.

theorem of parallel axes. If the moment of inertia of a body of mass M about an axis through the centre of mass is I, the moment of inertia about a parallel axis distant h from the first axis is $I + Mh^2$. If the radius of gyration is k about the first axis, it is $\sqrt{k^2 + h^2}$ about the second.

therm. A unit of heat used in the gas industry, equal to 100 000 btu.

thermal agitation. The random movement of the molecules of a substance, the energy of which is, by the *kinetic theory, synonymous with the heat content of the substance.

thermal capacity. A former name for *heat capacity.

thermal conductance. *See* heat transfer coefficient.

thermal conductivity. Symbol: λ. The rate at which heat passes through a small area A inside a body is given by $dQ/dt = \lambda A \, dT/dx$, where dT/dx is the temperature gradient normal to the area A in the direction of heat flow, and λ is the thermal conductivity of the body at temperature T. The units are $J \, s^{-1} \, m^{-1} \, K^{-1}$.

On the *kinetic theory, the thermal conductivity of a gas is given by $\lambda = \frac{1}{3}\rho \bar{c} L C_v$, so that the conductivity is independent of the pressure. This is not true at very low pressures when the conductivity becomes proportional to the pressure. The thermal conductivity of a solid metal is related to the electrical conductivity by the *Wiedemann–Franz law.

thermal diffusivity. Symbol: α. The quantity defined by the expression $\lambda/\rho c$, where λ is the *thermal conductivity, ρ is the density, and c is the specific heat capacity. It has the units metre squared per second.

thermal effusion. *See* thermal transpiration.

thermal equilibrium. The condition of a system in which the net rate of exchange of heat between the components is zero.

thermal neutron. A neutron that is approximately in thermal equilibrium with its surroundings, i.e. one that has a kinetic energy of kT where T is the thermodynamic temperature and k is the Boltzmann constant. At 20° C a thermal neutron has an energy of about 0·0253 eV ($4·048 \times 10^{-21}$ joule). Thermal neutrons can be produced by passing *fast neutrons through a *moderator. This process is called *thermalizing*.

thermal noise. *See* noise.

thermal power station. A power station

377

in which electrical energy is produced by conversion from the heat of combustion of a fuel such as coal, coke, or oil.

thermal radiation. When bodies are heated they emit radiant energy whose quantity and quality depend on the thermodynamic temperature T of the body. For any given body that radiation which depends only on temperature is known as thermal radiation. It is excited by the thermal agitation of molecules or atoms, and its spectrum is continuous from the far infrared to the extreme ultraviolet. *See* black body radiation.

thermal radiator. A body emitting radiation as a result of thermal vibration of the atoms or molecules.

thermal reactor. *See* nuclear reactors.

thermal resistance. *See* resistance (thermal).

thermal transpiration. *Syn.* thermal effusion. A phenomenon occurring when a temperature gradient exists in a tube containing gas at such a pressure that the mean free path of the molecules is not negligible compared with the tube diameter. The pressure then is no longer uniform but is greatest at the high temperature end. The term also applies to the case of a gas contained in two vessels at different temperatures connected by a porous medium whose holes are small compared with the mean free path of the molecules. At equilibrium, the ratio of the pressures in the vessels equals the ratio of the square roots of the thermodynamic temperatures of the vessels.

thermionic cathode. A *cathode that provides a source of electrons due to *thermionic emission, which is caused either by passing a current through the cathode itself (*direct heating*) or by surrounding the cathode with a heater coil (*indirect heating*).

thermionic emission. The release of electrons from a solid as a result of its temperature. It is caused when electrons within the solid gain enough kinetic energy to overcome the potential barrier at the surface (*see* work function). The number of electrons emitted rises sharply with temperature (*see* Richardson's equation). *See also* Schottky effect.

thermionics. The study of the emission of electrons from heated bodies and their subsequent behaviour and control, especially in vacuo as in the *thermionic valve.

thermionic valve. A multi-electrode evacuated *electron tube, containing a *thermionic cathode as the source of electrons. It has rectifying properties since the current is unidirectional and flows only when a positive potential is applied to the anode. Under *reverse-bias conditions no current flows until *breakdown occurs. With three or more electrodes amplification is possible, the current flowing between anode and cathode being modulated by a voltage applied to one or more other electrodes.

The simplest valve is the *diode*, which is often used as a rectifier. With zero anode potential, electrons emitted from the cathode form a *space charge region round the cathode and exist in dynamic equilibrium with electrons being emitted. If a positive potential is applied to the anode, electrons are attracted to it and a current flows (Fig. *a*). In the *space-charge limited* region of the characteristic, the current is limited by the mutual

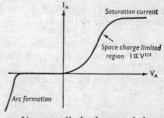

a Vacuum-diode characteristic

repulsion of electrons and obeys Child's law, where $I \propto V^{3/2}$.

The diode characteristic is modified by interposing additional *control electrodes, called grids, which are usually of wire mesh. The triode has one extra electrode, a control grid. The anode current at a given anode voltage depends on the grid voltage. A varying grid voltage causes relatively large changes in anode current, thus amplification can be achieved (Figs. *b*, *c*). Adding more electrodes tends to reduce a.c. transmission

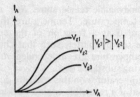

b Anode characteristics of a triode

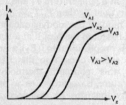

c Transfer characteristics of a triode

through the valve. These *screen-grid valves*, such as the pentode (Fig. *d*), are

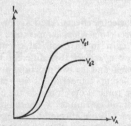

d Characteristics of a pentode

widely used in amplifying circuits. Valves with even more electrodes, such

as the hexode, have been designed to produce particular characteristics.

For most applications valves have been superseded by their solid-state equivalents: *p–n junction diodes, bipolar junction *transistors, *field-effect transistors, etc. Some special-purpose valves are still important.

thermistor. A composite *semiconductor made into a convenient rod-like or plate form. It has a very large negative *temperature coefficient of resistance, and can be used for temperature measurement, or as a controlling element in electronic control circuits. It can also be used to balance the positive temperature coefficient of resistance of metal leads.

thermoammeter. *See* ammeter.

thermocouple. An electrical circuit consisting of two dissimilar metals, in which an e.m.f. is produced when the two junctions are at different temperatures. This is due to the Seebeck effect (*see* thermoelectric effects). The thermocouple is often used as a temperature measuring device. For the measurement of temperatures up to about 500° C copper/constantan or iron/constantan couples are used; at temperatures up to 1500° C chromel/alumel or platinum/platinum–10% rhodium alloy are used; and at still higher temperatures iridium/iridium–rhodium. The sensitivity of a thermocouple instrument is increased by connecting a number of junctions, in series, forming a *thermopile.

thermodynamic potential. *See* Gibbs function.

thermodynamics. The study of the interrelation between heat and other forms of energy. It is concerned with systems of very large numbers of particles so that thermodynamic variables, such as pressure p, volume V, and temperature T, are statistical quantities. The *kinetic theory of heat is an attempt to relate the thermodynamic variables with the dynamic variables of the individual molecules. Thermodynamics is only concerned with changes of energy and not with the mechanism by which that change is brought about. It is based on three fundamental laws:

1st law of thermodynamics. This states simply that heat is a form of energy and that in a closed system the total amount of energy of all kinds is constant. It is therefore the application of the principle of conservation of energy to include heat energy. An alternative statement of the law is that it is impossible to construct a continuously operating machine that does work without obtaining energy from an external source. A mathematical interpretation of the law is that $\delta Q = dU + \delta W$, where δQ is the heat absorbed by the system, dU is the increase in internal energy, δW is the work done by the system.

2nd law of thermodynamics. This deals with the direction in which any chemical or physical process involving energy takes place: it is impossible to construct a continuously operating machine which does mechanical work and which cools a source of heat without producing any other effects. In nature, heat is never found to proceed up a temperature gradient of its own accord, this being one special case of the law, which may also be stated in the form: no self-acting machine can transfer heat continuously from a colder to a hotter body and produce no other external effect. *Carnot's theorem, based on the 2nd law, and consideration of the *Carnot cycle lead to the concept of *thermodynamic temperature. When a working substance is taken through a complete Carnot cycle its total change in *entropy is zero, and the entropy of a substance is a definite function of its condition, just as its pressure, volume, temperature, or its internal energy. This result is a direct deduction from the second law, and may be regarded as a statement of that law. Thus for a perfectly reversible process

$$\delta Q = T\,dS = dU + \delta W.$$

If, as is usually the case, the only external force is a uniform pressure p, then

$$T\,dS = dU + p\,dV,$$

this being a convenient mathematical statement of the first and second laws taken together.

3rd law of thermodynamics: *see* Nernst heat theorem. *See also* enthalpy; Gibbs function; Helmholtz function.

thermodynamic temperature. *Syn.* absolute temperature. Temperature that is measured as a function of the energy possessed by matter, such that changes of temperature are independent of the working substance used.

Temperatures on this scale are defined so that if a reversible engine working on a *Carnot cycle takes up a quantity of heat q_1 at a temperature T_1 and rejects a quantity q_2 at T_2, then $T_1/T_2 = q_1/q_2$.

The modern thermodynamic temperature is based on the idea that a temperature T is proportional to $f(E_T)$, a function of the energy chosen so that $f(0) = 0$. Using this concept, thermodynamic temperature is regarded as a physical quantity that can be expressed in the units called *kelvin, the triple point of water being defined as 273·16 kelvin. In practice thermodynamic temperature is measured on the *international temperature scale.

thermoelectric effects. A series of phenomena occurring when temperature differences exist in an electrical circuit: (1) *Seebeck effect*: If two different metals are joined and the two junctions are kept at different temperatures an electromotive force is developed in the circuit. The circuit constitutes a *thermocouple. The e.m.f. is not affected by the presence of other metal junctions in the circuit if they are all maintained at the same temperature. The e.m.f. is given by the equation: $E = \alpha + \beta\theta + \gamma\theta^2$, where θ is the temperature difference between the hot and cold junctions, and α, β, and γ are constants that depend on the metals comprising the circuit. γ is normally quite small so that for a small temperature difference the e.m.f. change is directly proportional to this difference.

(2) *Peltier effect*: If a current is passed round a circuit consisting of two different

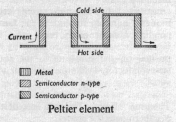

- ▥ Metal
- ▨ Semiconductor n-type
- ▧ Semiconductor p-type

Peltier element

metals or a metal and semiconductor, heat is liberated at one junction and absorbed at the other. This effect, the converse of the Seebeck effect, is reversible: reversing the current causes the hot and cold junctions to switch. To gain a significant temperature difference semiconductors must be used. A *Peltier element* contains several metal-semiconductor junctions in series, with n-type and p-type semiconductors alternating. It acts as a heating or cooling element.

(3) *Kelvin* (or *Thomson*) *effects*: A potential difference is developed between different parts of a single metal if there is a temperature difference between them. Also if a current passes through a wire in which a temperature gradient exists, this current causes a flow of heat from one part to the other – the direction of flow depending on the metal concerned. If two points in a metal differ in temperature by an amount dT, the electromotive force in this element of metal is σdT, where σ is the *Thomson coefficient*. The quantity σ is positive when directed from points of lower to points of higher temperature.

thermoelectric series. A series of metals arranged so that if a thermocouple is made from two of them, current flows at the hot junction from the metal occurring earlier in the series to the other metal.

thermogalvanometer. *See* galvanometer.

thermograph. A recording thermometer. *See* Bourdon tube.

thermoluminescence. *See* luminescence.

thermomagnetic effect. *See* magneto-caloric effect.

thermometer. A device for measuring the temperature of a body, from a measurement of some property of the working substance that depends on temperature. A fluid suitable for use in a thermometer should possess a marked degree of expansion for a small temperature rise, a uniform expansion rate, good thermal conductivity, chemical stability, a high boiling point (if liquid), and a low freezing point (if liquid) or liquefaction point (if gaseous).

thermometry. *See* temperature.

thermonuclear reaction. A reaction that involves the *nuclear fusion of particles and nuclei possessing enough kinetic energy to initiate and sustain the process. *Thermonuclear energy* is released during the reaction. The reaction rate increases rapidly with temperature, the required temperature being in the million degrees range. The energy in most stars is produced by such processes. *See also* fusion reactor.

thermophone. A source of sound waves, consisting of a thin metal strip of very small heat capacity that is mounted between two terminal blocks. Alternating current passing through this strip causes periodic variations in its temperature and expansions and contractions of the air surrounding it. The corresponding pressure variations are radiated in the form of sound waves. The sound output is low but may be amplified.

thermopile. A device consisting essentially of a large number of *thermocouples connected in series to give an easily measurable e.m.f. when heat radiation is allowed to fall on one set of junctions, the other set being shielded from the radiation.

thermosphere. *See* atmospheric layers.

thermostat. A device that responds to changes of temperature and automatically actuates a mechanical valve, electric switch, etc. Common types depend for their action upon the variation with temperature of the expansion of a metal rod, the shape of a spring, or the pressure (and/or volume) of a gas. Thermostats are usually employed to regulate the supply of heat in situations where a substantially constant temperature is to be maintained.

theta pinch. *See* fusion reactor.

thick-film circuit. A circuit consisting of interconnections and *passive components (usually resistors and inductors) deposited on a glass or ceramic substrate by techniques such as silk-screen printing. The deposited layers consists of glazes and cements (ceramic/metal alloys) whose thickness is usually in the range 2 to 20 μm. Active components and capacitors are often added on *chips with wire bonds to the thick-film circuit. The resulting circuit is then a form of hybrid *integrated circuit.

thick lens. A real lens, as distinct from a hypothetical infinitely thin lens. In a thick lens the separation between the two surfaces cannot be ignored.

thick mirror. *See* mirror.

thin-film circuit. A circuit consisting of interconnections and components deposited on glass or ceramic substrates usually by *vacuum evaporation or *sputtering. The deposited layers are up to a few micrometres thick. Components are usually passive, but active components such as the *thin-film transistor have been made.

thin-film transistor (TFT). A type of insulated gate *field-effect transistor constructed by thin-film circuit techniques. Cadmium sulphide is the *semiconductor most often used, and the layers forming the device may be deposited on the substrate in the order semiconductor, insulator, metal or vice versa.

Thomson effects, Thomson coefficient. *See* thermoelectric effects.

Thomson scattering. *See* scattering.

thorium series. *See* radioactive series.

three-body problem. The most important example of the *n*-body problem. The determination of the positions and motions of three bodies in a mutual gravitational field.

three-phase. Of an electrical system or device. Having three equal alternating voltages between which there are relative *phase differences of 120°.

threshold frequency. The minimum frequency giving rise to the *photoelectric effect. The value of the frequency depends on the metal exposed to the light beam.

threshold of hearing. That minimum intensity level of a sound wave that is audible. It occurs at a loudness of about 4 phons (equal to 4 decibels at 1 kHz).

threshold voltage. The voltage at which a particular characteristic of an electronic device first occurs.

thyratron. *Syn.* gas-filled relay. A gas-filled *triode in which the voltage on the grid controls the starting of the discharge in the tube. Under normal operating conditions, a positive potential is applied to the anode, the potential being greater than the *ionization potential of the gas. A negative potential is applied to the grid, and, if sufficiently large, this neutralizes the effect of the anode potential at the cathode and prevents any current flowing. If the grid voltage is reduced in magnitude (made less negative) the field at the cathode increases until the discharge starts. This is called *striking* of the tube. Once the discharge has started the grid has no further effect on the anode current even if the voltage is made very negative. This is because positive ions in the discharge cluster around the grid and shield the main discharge from the effects of the negative grid potential. At the instant of striking, the anode to cathode voltage falls to approximately the ionization potential of the gas, and the discharge may only be stopped by reducing the anode potential below this value (usually about 10–15 V). (*See* diagram.)

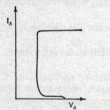

Thyratron, anode characteristic

Thyratrons are often used as relays and for counting radioactive particles. Application of a small positive potential from the trigger circuit or radiation detector superimposed on the fixed negative potential of the grid causes the tube to strike, a reduction in anode potential turning it off again.

thyristor. *See* silicon-controlled rectifier.

tight-coupled inductor. A very efficient inductor, in which the square of the mutual inductance is only slightly less than the product of the self inductances.

timbre. The distinguishing quality, other than pitch or intensity, of a note produced by a musical instrument, voice, etc. The quality is generally stated to be dependent upon the relative amplitude and number of the *partials, the resulting waveform being determined by the *superposition of the component partials.

time. Symbol: t. The practical measurement of time formerly depended on determining the period of rotation of the earth relative to the astronomical bodies. An atomic *clock and other types of clocks are now used for more precise measurements of time. Time is measured in *seconds in *SI units.

(1) *Solar time* is measured by successive intervals between transits of the sun across the meridian, and is shown on a sundial. *Mean solar time* averages out this interval over the course of one year, and is employed in day-to-day work. The solar day begins at midnight. The *mean sun* is a point that moves uniformly around the celestial equator (*see* celestial sphere) in the same total time as the real sun takes round the ecliptic. The difference between apparent and mean solar time, up to 16 minutes, is known as the *equation of time*. (2) *Sidereal time* is measured by successive transits of the first point of Aries, ♈ (*see* celestial sphere), across the meridian, and is indicated by the position of astronomical bodies relative to the horizon. *Mean sidereal time* averages out this interval over the course of one year and is employed by astronomers.

(3) The *solar year* (or *tropical year*) is the interval between successive arrivals of the sun at the first point of Aries. It is equal to 365·242 19 days of mean solar time (approximately 365 days 5 hours 49 minutes). The *solar month* is the period

383

of time taken by the moon to return to the same longitude after one complete revolution round the earth. It equals 27·321 58 days (approximately 27 days 7 hours 43 minutes 4·5 seconds). The mean *solar day* (about 24 hours 3 minutes 56·5 seconds) is the average period of time taken by the earth to make one complete revolution on its axis, measured between two successive transits of the sun across the meridian. The *sidereal year* is the time taken by the sun to move once around the celestial sphere. It equals 365·256 36 days (approximately 365 days 6 hours 9 minutes). It is slightly longer than the solar year because ♈ is moving on the celestial sphere due to *precession of the earth's orbital motion. The *sidereal month* is the time taken by the moon to complete one revolution around the earth, measured between two successive *conjunctions with a particular star. It equals 27·321 66 days (about 27 days 7 hours 43 minutes 11 seconds). The *sidereal day* is the time for the earth to make one complete revolution, measured between two successive transits of a particular star across the meridian. The mean day is 23 hours 56 minutes 4·091 seconds. The *calendar year* (or *civil year*) is adjusted so that its average length is that of the solar year.

time base. *Syn.* sweep. In many applications of *cathode-ray tubes, it is necessary for the luminous spot to be given a deflection that is a function (usually a linear function) of time. This particular deflection is known as a time base. In CROs a *sawtooth waveform is usually employed, i.e. at the end of each useful trace the luminous spot is returned rapidly to its starting point.

time constant. Physical quantities such as voltage, current, and temperature sometimes decrease with time in such a manner that, at any instant, the rate of decrease of the quantity v is given by

$$-\frac{\mathrm{d}v}{\mathrm{d}t} = \frac{v}{T} \qquad \text{(i)}$$

where T is the time constant. In this case, the time constant is the time taken for the quantity to decrease to 1/e (approximately 0·368) of its initial value. Alternatively, a quantity may increase with time in such a manner that, at any instant:

$$\frac{\mathrm{d}v}{\mathrm{d}t} = \frac{1}{T} (V - v) \qquad \text{(ii)}$$

where V is the ultimate value of the quantity (a constant). In this case, the time constant is the time taken for the quantity to increase from zero to $1 - 1/e$ (approximately 0·632) of its ultimate value. The time constant is particularly important in connection with electrical circuits. For example, in a circuit containing either (a) a resistance in series with a capacitance, or (b) a resistance in series with an inductance, which is connected suddenly to a constant-voltage d.c. supply, the component voltages, current, and charge (as appropriate) vary as in (i) or (ii) above. The time constant in seconds for circuit (a) may be calculated by multiplying the resistance in ohms by the capacitance in farads, and for circuit (b) by dividing the inductance in henries by the resistance in ohms.

time delay. *See* time lag.

time dilation. *See* relativity.

time division multiplexing. A method of *multiplex operation in which each of the input signals is sampled and transmitted sequentially. The time of switching from one to the next must be such that each signal is sampled many times in the course of a cycle. *Pulse modulation is frequently used for time division multiplexing.

time lag. *Syn.* time delay. The time that lapses between the closing of one circuit in a circuit-breaker, relay, or similar apparatus, and the closing of the main current circuit.

time-lapse photography. A means of obtaining a speeded-up version of a slow process, such as a flower opening, by recording single exposures, taken at regular intervals, on ciné film without moving the camera and then projecting the film at normal speed.

time switch. A switch that incorporates a type of clock mechanism for making and /or breaking an electric circuit at times which are predetermined by the setting of the mechanism.

tint. *See* colour.

tone. (1) An audible note containing no *partials. (2) The quality of a musical sound, e.g. loud tone, soft tone. (3) The interval of a major second, e.g. C to D, as opposed to a *semitone.

tone control. A means of adjusting the frequency response of an audio-frequency amplifier in order to compensate for deficiencies in the audible output and hence achieve a more pleasing result.

tonne. Symbol: t. A metric unit of mass. 1 t = 1000 kg. Often called a metric ton, it differs in size from an imperial ton (1016 kg) by about $1\frac{1}{2}\%$.

toric lens. A lens with a toroidal surface, i.e. a surface generated by a circular arc rotating about an axis that does not pass through the centre of the circle. The curvature in one plane is then different from that in an orthogonal plane. These lenses are used to correct *astigmatism in the eye.

toroidal winding. *See* ring winding.

torque. *See* moment.

torquemeter. *Syn.* dynamometer. An apparatus for measuring the torque exerted by the rotating part of a prime mover, electric motor, etc.

torr. A unit of pressure used in vacuum technology. It is equal to 1/760 standard atmosphere pressure (very closely, 1 mm Hg or 133·322 newtons per square metre).

Torricellian vacuum. *See* barometer.

Torricelli's law. The velocity of efflux of a fluid from an orifice in a reservoir is $\sqrt{2gH}$, where H is the depth of the orifice or more precisely of the *vena contracta below the free surface of the reservoir.

torsional hysteresis. *See* hysteresis.

torsional vibrations. Vibrations in a body, usually a cylindrical bar or tube, in which the displacement is in the form of a twist due to the application of an alternating torque to one end of the body, the other end being clamped.

torsional waves. Waves formed in a medium, usually a cylindrical bar or tube, as the result of the application of torsional vibrations to one or more parts of the medium. The velocity, c, is given by $c = \sqrt{G/\rho}$, where G is the modulus of rigidity (*see* modulus of elasticity), and ρ is the density.

torsion balance. A very sensitive balance consisting of an arm attached to a fibre; when a force is applied to the arm the fibre twists until the torque on the arm is balanced by that in the fibre. Since the latter is proportional to the angle of twist, this quantity is determined by the use of a light pointer. Torsion balances are employed in the measurement of small forces such as those associated with surface tension and static charges.

total emission. Of a *thermionic valve. The greatest value of the current which it is possible to obtain from the cathode by *thermionic emission when the cathode is heated under normal conditions and when the anode (together with all the other electrodes, which must be connected to it) is raised to a potential sufficiently high to ensure saturation.

total heat. *See* enthalpy.

total radiation pyrometer. *See* pyrometer.

total (internal) reflection. When light strikes the surface of an optically less dense medium at an angle of incidence greater than the *critical angle, instead of emerging into the less dense medium it is reflected back into the denser medium. Total reflection prisms have a wide application in instruments for changing direction of rays, for producing lateral inversion, or for completing inversion of the image. Although the reflection is total, the light actually penetrates a small distance into the rarer medium.

Total reflection also occurs with other waves: e.g. with sound, at moderately oblique incidence from air to water, and with X-rays, at almost grazing incidence from air to a solid or liquid.

tourmaline. A mineral crystal that exhibits dichroic properties, i.e. doubly refracting with selective absorption of the ordinary ray while transmitting the extraordinary ray.

track. An illuminated track of an ionizing particle created in a *cloud chamber, *bubble chamber, etc.

tracking. (1) Of any two electronic devices or circuits. An arrangement by which an electrical parameter of one device varies in sympathy with the same or another parameter of the second device, when both devices are subjected to a common stimulus. In particular, some applications of *ganged circuits require a constant difference in the resonant frequencies of two *tuned circuits. (2) The formation of electrically conducting paths (often by carbonization) on the surface of solid dielectrics

and insulators, when subjected to high electrical fields.

transconductance. *See* mutual conductance.

transducer. *Syn.* sensor. Any device for converting a non-electrical parameter (e.g. sound, pressure, light) into electrical signals, the variations in the electrical signal parameter being a function of the input parameter, and vice versa. Transducers are used in the electro-acoustic field, the term being applied to gramophone pick-ups, microphones, and loudspeakers, and are also used as measuring instruments.

The physical quantity measured by the transducer is the *measurand* and the portion of the transducer in which the output originates is the *transduction element*. The device in the transducer that responds directly to the measurand is the *sensing element*.

Several basic transduction elements can be used in transducers for different measurands. They include capacitive, electromagnetic, inductive, photoconductive, photovoltaic, and piezoelectric elements. Most transducers require external electrical excitation for their operation; exceptions are self-excited transducers such as piezoelectric crystals, photovoltaic, and electromagnetic types.

Most transducers provide linear (analog) output, i.e. the output is a continuous function of the measurand, but some provide digital output in the form of discrete values.

transductor. *Syn.* saturable reactor. A control device in which a number of windings on a magnetic core carry currents which react on each other. Usually a standing current in one winding is adjusted to bring the core to a magnetic state in which small changes in one circuit can control large powers in coupled circuits. Variations in the control circuit must be slow relative to the frequency of supply current, but it is possible to use up to 2000 hertz and thus to control signals in the lower audio-frequency range.

transfer impedance. The ratio of the voltage applied to one specified pair of terminals of an electrical network to the resulting current that flows between another specified pair of terminals under specified conditions. It is usually expressed in vector form.

transformation. *See* transition.

transformer. An apparatus without moving parts for transforming electrical energy at one alternating voltage into electrical energy at another (usually different) alternating voltage, without change of frequency. It depends for its action upon mutual induction (*see* electromagnetic induction) and consists essentially of two electric circuits coupled together magnetically. One of these circuits, called the primary, receives energy from an a.c. supply at one voltage, and the other circuit, called the secondary, delivers energy to the load at (usually) a different voltage. If core losses are ignored,

$$\frac{\text{Primary voltage}}{\text{Secondary voltage}} = \frac{\text{No. of turns in primary}}{\text{No. of turns in secondary}}.$$

The transformer is described as *step-up* or *step-down* according to whether the secondary voltage is respectively greater or less than the primary voltage. Apart from the property of voltage transformation, it has the property of current transformation. *See* autotransformer; voltage transformer; current transformer.

transients. Temporary disturbances in a system resulting from the sudden incidence of an impulse or the application or removal of a driving force. The form of any such transient is characteristic of the system, but its magnitude is a function of the magnitude of the impulse or driving

force. The persistence of the transient is controlled by the dissipative components of the system. An example of the production of transients is that of *forced vibrations.

transistor (*trans*fer re*sistor*). A multi-electrode *semiconductor device in which the current flowing between two specified electrodes is modulated by the voltage or current applied to one or more specified electrodes. The first transistors, invented in 1948, were *point contact transistors* which are now obsolete.

Modern transistors fall into two main classes: bipolar devices, which depend on the flow of both *minority and *majority carriers through the device, and unipolar transistors (*see* field-effect transistors) in which current is carried by majority carriers only.

Bipolar junction transistors. (Usually simply called *transistors*.) The electrodes are called *emitter, *base, and *collector. The basic device consists of two *p-n junctions in close proximity, with either the n or p regions common to both junctions (Figs. *a* and *b*) forming either *p-n-p* or *n-p-n transistors* respectively. If a suitable voltage is applied across the transistor, one junction becomes *for-

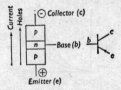
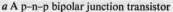

a A p–n–p bipolar junction transistor

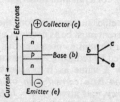
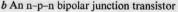

b An n–p–n bipolar junction transistor

ward biased and the other junction *reverse biased. Current flows across the forward-biased junction; majority carriers from the emitter cross into the collector and some minority carriers enter the emitter from the base. (In an n–p–n transistor the majority carriers are electrons and the minority carriers are holes; in a p–n–p transistor the opposite applies.) The total current flowing in the device is related by

$$I_e = I_b + I_c$$

where I_c is emitter current, I_b base current, and I_c collector current.

Voltage amplification is achieved using the emitter as the input terminal. This operation is called common base operation; the characteristics are shown in Figs. *c* and *d*.

c Common base output characteristics of a junction transistor

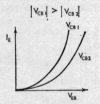

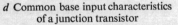

d Common base input characteristics of a junction transistor

For efficient amplification, the collector current must be as nearly equal to the emitter current as possible; this may be achieved by reducing the base current to as low a value as is practicable. The *common base current gain* or *collector efficiency*, α, is given by $\alpha = I_c/I_e$, and is a function of a particular device. The

base current $I_b = (1 - \alpha)I_e$. For any given transistor the ratio $I_c:I_b:I_c = 1:(1 - \alpha):\alpha$ is constant.

Current amplification is achieved by applying an input signal to the base (*common emitter operation). This causes a corresponding change in the collector current to maintain the ratio $\alpha : 1 - \alpha$. The *beta current gain factor is defined as $\beta = I_c/I_b = \alpha/(1 - \alpha)$, and can be very large if α approaches unity.

The maximum collector current is limited by the components in the external circuit and if β is large, small changes in base current can easily generate maximum collector currents causing saturation of the transistor. The collector-emitter voltage at saturation drops to a small value determined by the external circuit and the transistor may therefore be used as a *switch.

One of the most important differences between holes and electrons is the difference between their mobilities, electrons being about three times as mobile as holes. This makes devices depending mainly on electron flow much faster in operation than those depending on the flow of holes, and capable of being used at higher frequencies. This accounts for some of the small differences between n–p–n and p–n–p transistors. However, in principle they are the same.

Transistors have now replaced *thermionic valves as the general purpose active electronic device, except for some very specialized uses. They are small, robust, require small supply voltages, and are relatively easy to manufacture, cheap, and ideally suited for most applications: n–p–n transistors are most commonly used, and the semiconductor material is usually silicon.

transistor parameters. A transistor is a non-linear device whose behaviour is difficult to represent exactly by a set of mathematical equations. When designing transistor circuits the behaviour of the transistor is represented approximately by *equivalent circuits which act as models of the device. The particular equivalent circuit used will be the one that is most appropriate for the type of circuit being designed (i.e. for use with large signals, small signals, as switches, etc.).

Matrix parameters. The transistor is represented by an equivalent circuit with two input terminals and two output terminals. This is a two port network.

Two port network

Over a small portion of its operating characteristic the device is assumed to behave linearly. This is particularly true in small-signal operation, but is only an approximation for large-signal operation. The input and output voltages and currents are related by two simultaneous equations that have the general form $[A] = [p] [B]$ where A and B represent current or voltage and p the particular parameter used.

Other equivalent circuits are made up of components relating to the actual physical nature of the device rather than the more abstract linear networks involved in the matrix parameter treatment.

transistor-transistor logic (TTL). A family of integrated *logic circuits similar in operation to a *diode transistor logic circuit but with the cluster of *diodes at the input replaced by a multi-emitter *transistor; usually the output stage is *push-pull.

TTL is a widely used type of integrated logic circuit and is characterized by high speed of operation, medium power dissipation and *fan-out, and good immunity to *noise.

transit circle. *Syn.* meridian circle. *See* telescope.

transition. (1) Any change accompanied by a marked alteration of physical pro-

perties, especially a change of phase (*see* transition temperature). (2) A sudden change in the energy state of an atom or nucleus between two of its *energy levels. A nuclear transition in which an alpha or beta particle is emitted is called a *transformation.* *See also* selection rules.

transition temperature. The temperature at which a change of phase occurs, viz. the freezing point, boiling point, or sublimation point. The term is also used for the temperature at which a substance becomes superconducting.

transit time. In an electronic device, the time taken for an electron to pass directly from one specified point to another under given operating conditions.

translation. The movement of a body or system in such a way that all points are moved in parallel directions through equal distances.

transmission density. *Syn.* optical density. Symbol: D. The logarithm to base ten of the reciprocal of the *transmittance, i.e. $D = \log_{10} 1/\tau$.

transmission factor or coefficient. *See* transmittance.

transmission line. (1) An electric line for conveying electric energy from a power station, or a substation, to other stations or for transmitting from one point to another the currents used to convey messages or other signals. (2) The one or more conductors for connecting an aerial either to a source of energy (e.g. transmitter) or to a receiver, the conductor(s) being substantially non-radiating. This type of transmission line is usually called a *feeder.* A transmission line is described as being smooth or uniform if its series resistance, series inductance, shunt conductance, and shunt capacitance are all distributed uniformly along its length.

transmission loss. In any telecommunication system, the power at a point remote from the transmitter end is, in general, different from that at a nearer point. The ratio of the two powers, expressed in *decibels, is the transmission loss between the two points.

transmissivity. A measure of the ability of a material to transmit radiation as measured by the *internal transmittance of a layer of substance when the path of radiation is of unit length and the boundaries of the material have no influence.

transmittance. *Syn.* transmission factor or coefficient. Symbol: τ. A measure of the ability of a body or substance to transmit electromagnetic radiation, as expressed by the ratio of the transmitted flux to the incident flux.

Translucent bodies transmit light by diffuse transmission – the path of the light is independent, on the macroscopic scale, of the laws of *refraction. Transparent bodies on the other hand have regular transmission with no diffusion of light. In general, a body exhibits mixed transmission and the total transmittance can then be divided into a regular transmittance (τ_r) and a diffuse transmittance (τ_d) where $\tau = \tau_r + \tau_d$. *See also* internal transmittance; transmission density.

transmittancy. A measure of the ability of a solution to transmit radiation, as determined by the ratio of the *transmittance of the solution to the transmittance of the same path length of solvent. The solution can be a solid or liquid solution.

transmitter. In any telecommunication system, the device, apparatus, or circuits by means of which the signal is transmitted to the receiving parts of the system. *See also* aerial.

transmutation. The formation of one element from another, generally naturally as a result of radioactive decay or artificially as a result of particle bombardment.

transport number. *See* migration of ions.

transport phenomena. The class of phenomena due to the transfer of mass, momentum, or energy in a system as a result of molecular agitation, including such properties as thermal conduction and viscosity.

transuranic elements. *See* radioactivity.

transverse mass. The relativistic mass in a direction perpendicular to the motion of the particle relative to the observer, given by

$$m_t = \frac{m_0}{\sqrt{(1 - \beta^2)}},$$

for a particle of rest mass m_0 moving with relative velocity $\beta = v/c$, expressed as a fraction of the velocity of light. *Compare* longitudinal mass.

transverse vibrations. Vibrations in which the displacement is perpendicular to the main axis or direction of the vibrating body or system and so to the direction in which waves are travelling. Typical examples are the vibrations of a string or tuning fork.

transverse waves. Waves in which the displacement of the transmitting medium is perpendicular to the direction of propagation. Examples include *electromagnetic radiation and surface *water waves.

travelling microscope. A *microscope with a low magnifying power (normally about $\times 10$) and a graticule placed in the plane of the eyepiece. It is mounted on rails to enable it to travel in the horizontal or vertical, or both, and is used to make very accurate determinations of length, e.g. on a photographic plate. Measurements are correct to 0·01 mm or

better, over a distance of perhaps 0·2 m
or more.

travelling wave. Consider (hypothetically) a loss-free uniform *transmission
line of infinite length situated in a
medium of relative permittivity ε_r and
relative permeability μ_r. If this line is
connected to a sinusoidal a.c. supply at
its sending end, electrical energy is transmitted along the line and the instantaneous values of the current and voltage
at all points along the line are distributed
in space as sine waves, which travel in
the direction from the sending end to the
receiving end with a velocity given by
$c/\sqrt{\varepsilon_r \mu_r}$, where c is the velocity of light.
Either of these sine waves may be
regarded as a travelling wave (of current
or voltage respectively). More generally,
it is an electromagnetic wave that travels
along and is guided by a transmission
line: sinusoidal conditions are not
implicit (e.g. a surge propagated along a
conductor or transmission line is also a
travelling wave). Losses in the line cause
a reduction in the velocity given above
and also give rise to *attenuation. The
above also applies to a line of finite
length if it is terminated at its receiving
end with an impedance equal to its
*characteristic impedance. If an impedance discontinuity occurs at any point
in the line (i.e. if there is an abrupt
change in the characteristic impedance),
reflection takes place at that point and
the initial travelling wave (incident
wave) is divided into a transmitted wave
which travels towards the receiving end
and a reflected wave which travels from
the point towards the sending end.

travelling-wave tube. An *electron tube
that depends on the interaction of a
velocity-modulated electron beam with
several resonant cavities to produce
amplification at microwave frequencies.
The tube is a modification of the multicavity *klystron tube. Several resonant
cavities are placed along the length of the
tube and coupled together with a *trans-

Travelling-wave tube

mission line. The electron beam is velocity modulated by the radio-frequency
input signal at the first resonant cavity,
and induces radio-frequency voltages in
each subsequent cavity. If the spacing of
the cavities is correctly adjusted the voltages at each cavity induced by the modulated electron beam are in phase and
travel along the transmission line to the
output, with an additive effect, so that
the power output is much greater than
the power input. Some energy travels in
the other direction along the transmission line (the backward waves) but the
contributions are out of phase with each
other and cancel out.

In the *backward-wave oscillator* the
backward waves are in phase with each
other and provide positive *feedback to
the input cavity allowing the tube to
oscillate.

Triac. *See* silicon-controlled rectifier.

triboelectricity. *See* frictional electricity.

tribology. The study of *friction, lubrication, and wear of surfaces in relative
motion.

triboluminescence. *Luminescence resulting from *friction.

trichromatic theory of vision. *See* colour
vision.

triclinic system. *See* crystal systems.

trigger. Any stimulus that initiates a

particular response from an electronic circuit or device.

trimmer. *Syn.* trimming capacitor. An adjustable capacitor of relatively small maximum capacitance in parallel with a fixed capacitor to enable the capacitance of the combination to be finely adjusted.

Trinitron. *See* colour picture tube.

triode. Any electronic device with three electrodes, such as bipolar junction *transistors, *thyratrons, etc. The term is usually applied to a three electrode evacuated *thermionic valve.

triode–hexode. A multiple (or multi-electrode) *thermionic valve containing a triode and a hexode. The triode portion is normally used as an oscillator and the hexode as a *mixer or frequency-changer.

trip coil. *See* tripping device.

triple point. The point of intersection on a p/T diagram of the three lines expressing the equilibrium conditions for the three physical states of the substance. At the triple point the three phases can coexist. It is the point where the ice, steam, and hoarfrost (*sublimation) lines intersect. *See also* thermodynamic temperature.

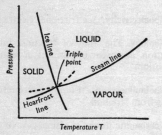

Triple point

tripping device. A device that when actuated, sets free the restraining mechanism of a *circuit-breaker, causing the latter to break the circuit. Some common types are hand operated; others are operated electromagnetically by means of, for example, a *trip coil*, which consists of a coil and a movable plunger or armature.

tristimulus values. *See* chromaticity.

triton. A nucleus of an atom of tritium, containing one proton and two neutrons.

tropical year. *See* time.

troposphere. *See* atmospheric layers.

tube. *Syn.* valve. Abbreviation of electron tube, especially in the US.

tube of flux. *Syn.* tube of force; field tube. The vector field of electrical force can be divided into tubes which are bundles of lines of electrical intensity. The lateral surface of the tube is made up of lines of

Tube of flux

force so that the intensity at any point of that surface is tangential to it and the *flux is the same through all cross sections. The field strength at any part of the tube is inversely proportional to the section at that place, taken normal to the lines, the tube narrowing as the field intensity increases. A unit tube is one through which unit flux flows.

tuned circuit. An oscillatory electrical circuit containing inductance and capacitance or their equivalent (such as a piezoelectric crystal), which has been adjusted so as to be resonant at the frequency of an applied signal. The process of adjusting the circuit to a condition of *resonance is known as *tuning* and may be carried out by adjusting the capacitance of the circuit (*capacitive tuning*) or by adjusting the inductance of the circuit (*inductive tuning*).

tuning fork. A suitably proportioned metal bar bent into the shape of a U and mounted upon a stem at the base of the U. If excited by bowing, striking, or pressing the prongs together, a note consisting almost entirely of fundamental is faintly heard, the prongs moving in together and out together. Overexcitation elicits a few very weak, mostly inharmonic, upper *partials. The tuning fork maintains a constant frequency for long periods and can therefore be used as a standard of pitch for musical instruments. The frequency varies very slightly with amplitude of vibrations and temperature. Forks, which have been made for frequencies as high as 90 k Hz, are generally made of steel, invar, or elinvar. The use of resonators coupled to the fork through the stem increases the sound output and also only reproduces the fundamental since the upper partials of the fork and resonator are not similar.

tunnel diode. *Syn.* Esaki diode. A highly doped *p–n junction *diode whose characteristic shows a large reverse current and a portion of the forward current having negative resistance (*see* diagram).

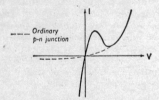

Characteristic of a tunnel diode

The shape of the characteristic is caused by the *tunnel effect, electrons tunnelling through the *forbidden band, from the valence to the conduction bands (*see* energy bands). At reverse voltages a large tunnelling current is observed. With increasing forward bias on the junction, the tunnel effect contributes less and less, producing the negative resistance portion, until finally the for-

ward voltage characteristic resembles that of an ordinary p–n junction.

tunnel effect. The movement of particles through barriers which, on classical theory, they would have insufficient energy to surmount. Classically, if a particle moves in one direction with

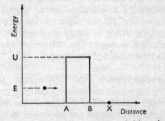

Particle approaching a potential barrier

kinetic energy E and approaches a potential energy barrier of height U it can get over it by converting some of its kinetic energy into potential energy. If $E < U$ the probability of finding the particle at a point X (*see* diagram) would be zero. However even when $E < U$ the particle can tunnel through the barrier. This is explained by wave mechanics. If the *wave function, ψ, of the particle is considered inside the region of the barrier, i.e. taking point A as $x = 0$, the Schrödinger equation has the form:

$$\frac{d^2\psi}{dx^2} + \frac{8\pi^2 m}{h^2}(E - U)\psi = 0,$$

and has a general solution

$$\psi = A \exp\left[\frac{2\pi i x}{h}\sqrt{2m(E - U)}\right]$$

where A is a constant, m the particle mass, h the Planck constant, x the distance into the barrier, and $i = \sqrt{-1}$. If $E < U$ the solution is $\psi = A \exp\left[-(2\pi x/h)\sqrt{2m(U - E)}\right]$. Thus, provided the barrier is not infinitely thick or wide there is a finite probability of the particle crossing this region and reaching X. The effect is too unlikely

393

to occur in macroscopic systems but is the basis of *alpha decay and *field emission.

turbine. An engine in which rotational energy is obtained from the motion of a fluid. In the *impulse turbine* the fluid emerges from sets of nozzles and plays on the blades of a rotating wheel (the rotor). In a *reaction turbine* a ring of stationary blades replaces the nozzles and the rotor is made to rotate by the reaction between the stationary blades and the blades of the rotor.

turbo-alternator. An alternator (e.g. *synchronous alternating-current generator) intended for steam-turbine drive. Turbo-alternators are employed in thermal power stations for generating alternating current.

turbulence. The state of a fluid possessing a non-regular motion such that the velocity at any point may vary in both direction and magnitude with time. Turbulent motion is accompanied by the formation of eddies and the rapid interchange of momentum in the fluid. The change from laminar to turbulent motion occurs at a critical value of *Reynolds number. The drag resistance to a body for turbulent flow is proportional to the square of the velocity as compared with the resistance for laminar flow which is proportional to the velocity.

turns ratio. *See* ratio.

tweeter. A loudspeaker of small dimensions designed to reproduce sounds of relatively high frequency. *Compare* woofer.

two-phase. Of an electrical system or device. Having two equal alternating voltages between which there is a relative *phase difference of 90°.

Tyndall effect. *See* Rayleigh scattering.

U

ultimate strength. The limiting stress (in terms of force per *original* unit area of cross section) at which a material completely breaks down (i.e. fractures or crushes).

ultracentrifuge. A centrifuge operating at a very high angular velocity, suitable for use with colloidal solutions. It is used to separate colloidal particles and also can be used to estimate their size and measure the molecular weights of very large molecules, such as proteins. Quantitative instruments have a transparent cell and the formation of sediment (*see* sedimentation) is photographically recorded.

ultra-high frequency (UHF). *See* frequency bands.

ultramicrobalance. A very sensitive balance for accurate weighing to 10^{-8} grammes.

ultramicroscopy. The rendering visible of particles which are smaller than those resolvable by ordinary methods, as in dark-field illumination (*see* microscope).

ultrasonics. The study and application of frequencies beyond the limits of hearing of the human ear, i.e. the frequencies about 20 kilohertz and upwards. There is no theoretical upper limit to the ultrasonic frequency, although with the existing means of production, experiments are limited within the range from 20 kHz to 5 MHz.

Ultrasonic frequencies can be generated by means of the *piezoelectric effect or *magnetostriction effect or mechanically by the *Galton whistle or *Hartmann generator. A piezoelectric oscillator can be used to generate, detect, and measure the waves.

An alternative method of detection is based on the *diffraction of light that occurs in a liquid traversed by ultrasonic waves. The series of compressions and rarefactions that constitute ultrasonic waves in a liquid act as a diffraction grating. For a narrow monochromatic beam of light, wavelength λ_l, passing through the liquid at right angles to the ultrasonic beam, wavelength λ_s, the angle of diffraction, α_k, for the kth order is given by:

$$\sin \alpha_k = \frac{k\lambda_l}{\lambda_s}.$$

It is a very accurate method for measuring the wavelength of sound and hence the velocity of sound at ultrasonic frequency in liquids.

ultraviolet catastrophe. *See* quantum theory.

ultraviolet microscopy. *See* resolving power; microscope.

ultraviolet (UV) radiation. Electromagnetic radiation lying between the visible and X-ray regions of the spectrum, i.e. between about 380 nm and 5 nm. For some purposes it is convenient to subdivide this range into *near and far ultraviolet (*see also* vacuum ultraviolet).

Substances which may be transparent to light absorb strongly as the wavelength is decreased in the ultraviolet, e.g. Crookes 'A' at 360 nm, ordinary crown 300 nm, quartz 180 nm, fluorspar 120 nm. In the extreme ultraviolet, most substances become opaque or show selective absorption, and even small paths in air or gas at low pressure may show considerable absorption. Atmospheric absorption by ozone in the stratosphere restricts the solar ultraviolet at 290 nm. Incandescent bodies even at high temperature yield a relatively small proportion of ultraviolet to total radiation.

Arc and spark discharges and vacuum-tube discharge, e.g. hydrogen at 5 mmHg pressure, mercury vapour, etc., with enclosures of transparent media (quartz), are the main sources. The radiation can be detected by its photographic action, fluorescence and photoelectric effects, etc.

umbra. *See* shadows.

Umklapp process. A collision process between *phonons, or between phonons and electrons. The crystal momentum is not conserved (no conservation principle applies). The process is responsible for thermal resistance in non-conducting materials.

uncertainty principle. *Syn.* Heisenberg uncertainty relation; indeterminacy principle. The principle that the product of the uncertainty in the measured value of a component of momentum (p) and the uncertainty in the value of position (x) is of the same order of magnitude as the *Planck constant. It is usually written in the form: $\Delta p \times \Delta x \sim h$. A more precise statement replaces h by $h/4\pi$. The uncertainty principle is a consequence of the fact that any measurement of a system must disturb the system under investigation, with a resulting lack of precision in measurement. A similar relationship applies to any pair of quantities with the dimensions of *action (J s), such as energy and time, thus $\Delta E \times \Delta t \sim h/4\pi$.

The effects of the uncertainty principle are not apparent with large systems because of the small size of h. However the principle is of fundamental importance in the behaviour of systems on the atomic scale. For example the principle explains the inherent width of spectral lines: if the lifetime of an atom in an *excited state is very short there is a large uncertainty in its *energy level and a line resulting from a transition is broad. It also explains the exchange of mesons in the nucleus (*see* virtual particle).

One consequence of the uncertainty principle is that it is impossible to predict the behaviour of a system and the principle of *causality cannot apply at the atomic level. *Quantum mechanics gives a statistical description of the behaviour of physical systems.

undercurrent (or undervoltage) release. A *tripping device that operates when the current (or voltage) falls below a predetermined value.

uniaxial crystals. Crystals belonging to the tetragonal, rhombohedral, and hexagonal systems; they are double refracting except for light travelling through them in the direction of the principal crystallographic axis. In this direction they are singly refracting. Iceland spar (calcite) and quartz are uniaxial; the former is an *optically negative crystal and the latter is a positive crystal.

unified atomic mass unit. *See* atomic mass unit.

unified field theory. A theory that seeks to unite the properties of gravitational, electromagnetic, and nuclear fields so that a single set of equations can be used to predict all their characteristics. At present it is not known whether such a theory can be developed, or whether the physical universe is amenable to a single analysis in terms of the current concepts of physics. *See also* neutral weak current.

unifilar suspension. A type of suspension used in electrical instruments in which the moving part is suspended on a single thread, wire, or strip. The controlling (or restoring) torque is produced by the twisting of the thread, etc.

uniform temperature enclosure. An enclosure whose walls are maintained at a constant temperature. The amount and kind of radiation within such an enclosure are independent of the nature of the walls and the contents of the enclosure, depending only on the temperature of the walls. Such radiation is called full or black-body radiation since the radiation inside the enclosure is identical with that emitted by a *black body at the same temperature.

unijunction transistor. *Syn.* double-base diode. A *transistor consisting of a bar of lightly doped *semiconductor (usually n-type) with a region of highly doped opposite polarity semiconductor located near the centre. Ohmic contacts are formed to each end of the bar (the *base) and the central region (the *emitter). If a voltage V_b is applied across the bar a potential

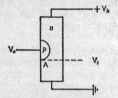

Unijunction transistor

drop will be present through the bar. Let the potential on the less positive side of the junction at point A be V_1. If a voltage V_e is applied to the emitter, for $V_e < V_1$, the junction will be *reverse biased and very little current will flow. If V_e is increased to $V_e = V_1$, the junction will become *forward biased at point A and the current will increase rapidly. V_e may now be reduced below V_1 and current will continue to flow. The voltage V_2 is the point at which the junction becomes reverse biased once again and the current is cut off if V_e is reduced below V_2. The most common use of the unijunction transistor is in *relaxation oscillator circuits.

unipolar transistor. A *transistor in which current flow is due to the movement of *majority carriers only. *See* field-effect transistors.

unitary symmetry. A generalization of *isospin theory. Isospin is concerned

with a mathematical group called $SU(2)$ (the special unitary group of 2×2 matrices). Unitary symmetry is concerned with a group called $SU(3)$. It predicts that as far as *strong interactions are concerned *elementary particles can be grouped into multiplets containing 1, 8, 10, or 27 particles and that the particles in each multiplet may be regarded as different states of the same particle. Unitary symmetry multiplets contain one or more isospin multiplets. All particles in a multiplet have the same spin (J), parity (P), and baryon number (B). The multiplets are most clearly illustrated by plotting the constituent particles on a graph of *hypercharge (Y) against isospin quantum number (I_3). Examples of a meson and baryon octet (multiplet of 8 particles)

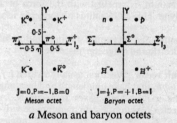

a Meson and baryon octets

(Fig. *a*) and a baryon decuplet (10 particle multiplet) (Fig. *b*) are illustrated. The predictions of $SU(3)$ theory do not agree with experiment as well as those of isospin. If it were an exact symmetry of

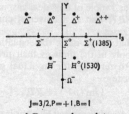

$J=3/2, P=+1, B=1$

b Baryon decuplet

elementary particles, all particles in a multiplet should have the same mass; this is far from true. However, $SU(3)$

theory was used to predict the existence of the omega-minus particle, Ω^- (needed to complete the decuplet). *See* quark model.

unit cell. The smallest crystal unit possessing the entire symmetry of the whole periodic structure. Defined in terms of six elements or parameters: a, b, c, the lengths of the cell edges (taken as axes), and α, β, γ, the angles between the axial directions.

unit planes (and points). Conjugate planes of a system for which the lateral magnification is unity. *See* centred optical systems.

unit pole. A magnetic pole that when placed 1 cm from an equal pole, in a vacuum, is repelled with the force of 1 dyne. This CGS unit is no longer in use.

units. *See* SI units; rationalization of electric and magnetic quantities.

unit vector. *Vectors, usually written i, j, and k, that have unit length and lie along the x-, y-, and z-axes respectively. A vector function, F, can therefore be written $F = xi + yj + zk$. As the angles between these unit vectors are 90°, the scalar and vector products are either zero or one.

universal gas constant. Symbol: R. The constant occurring in the *equation of state for 1 mole of an *ideal gas, namely $pV = RT$, that is a universal constant for all gases.

Actual gases obey this equation of state only in the limit as their pressure tends to zero, i.e. for an actual gas we may write

$$\operatorname*{Lim}_{p \to 0} (pV) = RT,$$

The pressure exerted by a gas is shown by kinetic theory to be

$$p = \tfrac{1}{3}mvC^2,$$

where m is the mass of the molecules, v

is the molecular density, C is the root-mean-square velocity of the molecules. Considering one mole of the gas, L being the number of molecules present, i.e. Avogadro's number, and V the *molar volume then

$$pV = \tfrac{1}{3}mLC^2,$$

and V is independent of the nature of the gas at given values of p and T. Thus

$$\tfrac{3}{2}RT = \tfrac{1}{2}mLC^2.$$

This expression shows that R is equal to two-thirds of the total translational energy of the molecules in 1 mole of a gas at a temperature of 1 kelvin.

The Boltzmann constant k is given by the ratio R/L and R has the value 8·314 35 J K^{-1} mole^{-1}.

universal motor. An electric motor which is suitable for use with direct current or alternating current. It incorporates a *commutator and is usually *series-wound.

universal shunt. A galvanometer shunt that is tapped so that it can pass $\frac{1}{10}$, $\frac{1}{100}$, $\frac{1}{1000}$, etc., of the main current through the galvanometer, thus providing various measurement ranges.

unsaturated vapour. A vapour at a certain temperature that does not contain the maximum amount of the substance in the gaseous phase. Such a vapour may undergo slight isothermal compression without condensation occurring, and obeys the *ideal gas laws approximately.

unstable equilibrium. *See* equilibrium.

Unwin coefficients. *See* Reynolds's law.

upper atmosphere. The outer layers of the gaseous envelope surrounding the earth above about 30 km. It includes part of the stratosphere. *See* atmospheric layers.

uranium series. *See* radioactive series.

V

vacancy. A position in a crystal lattice that is not occupied by an atomic nucleus. A vacancy should not be confused with a *hole. *See* defect.

vacuum evaporation. A technique used for producing a coating of one solid on another, usually a coating of metal or semiconductor, by evaporation at high temperature in a vacuum.

vacuum flask. *See* Dewar vessel.

vacuum gauge. *See* pressure gauges.

vacuum pump. *See* pumps, vacuum.

vacuum tube. An evacuated *electron tube.

vacuum ultraviolet. Part of the ultraviolet region of the spectrum, in which the radiation is absorbed by air and experiments have thus to be performed in vacuo. The wavelength is less than about 200 nm.

valence band. *See* energy band.

valence electrons. Electrons in the outermost shell of an atom that are involved in chemical changes. *See also* energy bands.

valve. *Syn.* electron tube. A device in which two or more electrodes are enclosed in an envelope usually of glass, one of the electrodes being a primary source of electrons. The electrons are most often provided by thermionic emission (*thermionic valve), and the device may be either evacuated (vacuum tube) or gas-filled (gas-filled tube). The name derives from the rectifying properties (*see* rectifier) of the devices, i.e. current flows in one direction only. *See also* multielectrode valve.

valve reactor. A circuit including a valve that is arranged to operate as a reactor. The value of the reactance is dependent upon the valve and circuit constants. It is employed in radio transmitters for *frequency modulation and in circuits for *automatic frequency control.

valve voltmeter. An *amplifier using *thermionic valves, with a measuring instrument in the output circuit. Such instruments are used to measure both d.c. and a.c. voltages. They are being superseded by *digital voltmeters.

Van Allen belts. *Syn.* radiation belts. Several belts of energetic charged particles, mainly electrons and protons, orbiting in an equatorial plane around the earth and confined there by its magnetic field. There are two belts of electrons, approximately 2000–5000 and 13 000–19 000 kilometres above the earth's surface. The protons appear to be distributed in many layers between the electron belts. The inner belts contain more energetic particles than the outer belts. The *solar wind is probably the principal source of particles in the outer belts, their energy and number fluctuating with solar activity. Particles in the inner shells could be low-energy *cosmic rays.

Van de Graaff accelerator. A type of *accelerator in which a *Van de Graaff generator is used to provide a high-voltage source.

Van de Graaff generator. A high voltage electrostatic generator that can produce potentials of millions of volts. It consists essentially of an endless insulated fabric belt moving vertically. A charge is applied to the belt by the needle points A from an external source of up to 100 kV. This charge is carried continuously up into a large hollow sphere C where collector points B remove it. The potential of the sphere continues to increase (no charge residing on the interior) and is limited only by the leakage rate of the supporting insulators. In the latest generators the fabric belt is replaced by a

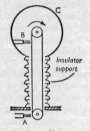

Van de Graaff generator

series of metal beads connected by insulating string. This system, called the *pelletron*, has been developed to enable a voltage of 30 M V to be produced by two generators in series. This device is called a *tandem generator.

Van der Waals equation of state. *See* equations of state.

Van der Waals forces. Weak intermolecular and interatomic forces that are electrostatic in origin. If two molecules have permanent *dipole moments and are in random thermal motion then some of their relative orientations cause repulsion and some attraction. On average there will be a net attraction. A molecule with a permanent dipole can also induce a dipole in a neighbouring molecule and cause mutual attraction.

These dipole–dipole and dipole–induced dipole interactions cannot occur between atoms. The Van der Waals forces between single atoms arise because of small instantaneous dipole moments in the atoms themselves, resulting from their fluctuating electronic distribution. This instantaneous dipole can polarize a neighbouring atom, producing the weak attraction. The potential energy, E_p, of each of these three interactions

takes the form $E_p = -A/r^6$, where A is a constant for a particular atom or molecule and r is the atomic or molecular separation. E_p is called the *Lenard–Jones potential*. Van der Waals forces are responsible for departures from *ideal gas behaviour in real gases.

Van't Hoff factor. Symbol: i. A factor introduced into the equation for osmotic pressure (*see* osmosis) to account for the fact that electrolyte solutions deviate from this equation and have a higher osmotic pressure than that expected, due to their dissociation into ions. The factor is the ratio of the actual number of entities present in the solution to the number that would be present if no dissociation occurred. The equation for the osmotic pressure (Π) of electrolytes is thus $\Pi V = iRT$.

vaporization coefficient. The rate of vaporization per unit surface area of solid or liquid at temperature T is given by

$$\frac{\mathrm{d}m}{\mathrm{d}t} = \alpha p \sqrt{\frac{M}{2\pi RT}}$$

where p is the vapour pressure of the vapour of molecular weight M and α is the vaporization coefficient which is necessarily less than unity.

vapour. A substance in gaseous form but below its *critical temperature so that it could be liquefied by pressure alone, without cooling to a lower temperature.

vapour density. *See* density.

vapour pressure. The pressure exerted by a *vapour. For a vapour in equilibrium with its liquid, the vapour pressure depends only on the temperature of the liquid and is known as the *saturated vapour pressure (S V P) at that temperature. The variation of vapour pressure with temperature over a small range is given by the *Kirchhoff formula, $\log p = A - B/T - C \log T$.

vapour-pressure thermometer. A thermometer that uses the fact that the (saturation) vapour pressure of a liquid is a function only of temperature. Thermometers of this type are the most reliable for the measurement of temperatures below the boiling point of helium ($-268°$ C). He, NH_3, SO_2, CO_2, CH_4, C_2H_4, O_2, and H_2 may be used as the working liquid in the thermometer. The range is very limited since very high or very low pressures cannot be conveniently measured.

var. A unit of *power identical to the *watt but used for the reactive power of an alternating current. One var is one volt times one ampere.

varactor diode. A semiconductor *diode, operated with reverse bias so that it acts as a voltage dependent capacitor. The *depletion layer at the junction acts as the dielectric, the n- and p-regions act as the plates. A diode used in this way is usually designed to have an unusually large capacitance. The depletion layer width and therefore the capacitance depend on the voltage across the junction. If the semiconductor type changes abruptly from n-type to p-type then $C \propto V^{-\frac{1}{2}}$. If the semiconductor type changes gradually (linearly graded junctions) then $C \propto V^{-\frac{1}{3}}$.

varactor tuning. A means of tuning employed in receivers (e.g. television receivers) in which *varactor diodes are used as the variable capacitance elements.

variable-focus condenser. *See* Abbe condenser.

variable star. A star, such as a *nova or *supernova, that varies in brightness. The variation in an *intrinsic variable* is caused by changes in internal conditions. A *pulsating star* is of this kind, the light variation being due to expansion and contraction of the star. The variation can also be due to external causes.

variance. The square of the standard *deviation.

variometer. A variable inductor that usually consists of a fixed coil connected in series with a movable coil so that by moving (rotating) the latter the coupling between the two coils, and hence also the self-inductance of the series combination, may be varied.

varistor. A resistor with characteristics that do not follow Ohm's law. Usually the resistance is made to decrease with voltage increase for both directions of current – no rectifying property being evident.

vector. A quantity that has direction as well as a magnitude, e.g. displacement, velocity, angular velocity, force, couple, electric field strength. A vector can be represented pictorially by a line whose length is proportional to the magnitude of the quantity and whose direction is that of the vector.

(1) *Vector addition.* If two vectors A and B are represented in magnitude and direction by the adjacent sides of a parallelogram, the diagonal represents the vector sum $(A + B)$ in magnitude and direction.

(2) *Vector multiplication.* There are two ways of multiplying vectors. (i) The *scalar product* of two vectors equals the product of their magnitudes and the cosine of the angle between them and is a scalar quantity. It is written $A \cdot B$. (ii) The *vector product* of two vectors A and B is defined as a vector of magnitude $A B \sin \theta$ having a direction perpendicular to the plane containing them. It is written $A \times B$.

In printing, vectors are distinguished from scalars by printing the symbols in bold italic letters.

vector field. A *field, such as a gravitational field or magnetic field, in which the magnitude and direction of the vector quantity are one-valued functions of position. They can be mapped by curved lines whose direction at any point is that of the vector and whose density (i.e. number per unit area crossing an infinitesimally small area perpendicular to the lines) is proportional to the magnitude of the vector at the point. These lines are called lines of flux (or force).

vector product. *See* vector.

velocity. (1) Symbol: v. Linear velocity is the rate of increase of distance traversed by a body in a particular direction. Speed is similarly defined with the omission of reference to direction. Thus, velocity is a *vector quantity and speed a *scalar one. *See also* relative velocity. (2) *See* angular velocity.

velocity modulation. If a beam of electrons or ions passes through a sharply defined region, such as a *cavity resonator, where it is subjected to a rapidly fluctuating alternating electric field, the individual electrons will be retarded or accelerated according to the half-cycle prevailing when they enter the region. If retarded, the electrons following will catch up (and the converse) so that the total effect will be a *bunching* of the electron beam into a series of pulses similar to the rarefactions and compressions of a sound wave. Such a beam is said to be velocity modulated. Velocity modulation is employed for the amplification and generation of microwave frequencies in *electron tubes such as the *klystron and *travelling-wave tube.

velocity of light. Symbol: c. The velocity of light in free space is $2 \cdot 997\ 925 \times 10^8$ m s^{-1}. According to the special theory of *relativity, this velocity is not only constant but also cannot be exceeded in free space (*compare* tachyon). It is independent of the velocity of the observer. Not only light but all *electromagnetic radiation travels at this velocity in a vacuum. For waves the frequency v and wave-

length λ are related by $c = v\lambda$. The velocity of light in a particular medium, such as air or water, depends on the *refractive index of the medium. Energy E and mass m are related by the velocity of light in Einstein's equation $E = mc^2$.

velocity of sound. Symbol: c. The velocity of sound in dry air at STP is $331 \cdot 4$ m s^{-1}. In sea water it is 1540 m s^{-1} and in fresh water 1410 m s^{-1}. The transmission of sound may involve either longitudinal, transversal, or torsional wave motion, according to the medium. The velocity with which the waves travel is dependent on elasticity and density. The velocity of sound of small amplitude elastic waves in any extended medium is given by the equation $c = \sqrt{K/\rho}$ where K is the appropriate *elastic constant and ρ is the normal density of the medium. For fluid media such as gases or liquids K is the bulk *modulus of elasticity while for solids the coefficient of rigidity must be introduced.

In general, there are two elasticities for any fluid medium, the adiabatic and the isothermal, and the ratio between them is equal to the ratio between the two specific heat capacities (γ). For gases, the compressions and rarefactions in sound waves take place so rapidly that the changes are adiabatic and therefore the velocity of sound $c = \sqrt{\gamma p/\rho}$, where p is the gas pressure.

The velocity of sound in a gas depends upon the temperature in accordance with the relation $c_\theta = c_0 \sqrt{1 + \alpha\theta}$ where c_0 and c_θ are the velocities of sound at 0 and $\theta°$ centigrade and α is the coefficient of expansion of the gas. The velocity is independent of both the pressure, except at very high pressures, and of frequency, except at high frequencies (*see* dispersion of sound). The velocity depends upon the nature of the gas since γ and p are involved in the equation. Hence, moisture and impurities affect the velocity.

In solids longitudinal as well as torsional and transverse waves are set up. The velocities of propagation consequently are different as determined by the elastic constants.

velocity potential. If the velocity of a point (x, y, z) of a fluid has components (Cartesian) u, v, w, and there exists a scalar function φ such that $u = -\partial\varphi/\partial x$, $v = -\partial\varphi/\partial y$, $w = -\partial\varphi/\partial z$ then the motion is irrotational and φ is called the velocity potential.

velocity ratio. *See* machine.

vena contracta. When a jet issues from an orifice in a reservoir tank the change in direction of the stream lines is not completed at the orifice but continues past the orifice causing the subsequent jet section to be smaller than that of the orifice. The point of the jet where the contraction is complete is called the vena contracta, and at this point the stream lines are all parallel and the pressure of the fluid is that of the surrounding medium.

venturi tube. A device used for measuring the quantity of fluid flowing through a pipe. The principal features are: the inlet sections, XY, (*see* diagram), which converges to the throat, YZ, which consists of a short straight portion of the pipe.

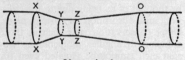

Venturi tube

From the throat the pipe diverges again. ZO, usually to the original size. The quantity of fluid flowing per second through the pipe is given by

$$Q = \frac{A_1 A_2}{\sqrt{A_1{}^2 - A}} \sqrt{\frac{2(p_1 - p_2)}{\rho}}$$

where A is the area of cross section, p the pressure (static) of the fluid, ρ the fluid density and the suffixes 1 and 2 refer to the inlet and throat respectively.

Verdet constant. *See* Faraday effect.

vergence. The convergence and divergence of rays. Reciprocal distances measure vergence. *Reduced vergence* is the reciprocal of a *reduced distance.

Vernier scale. A short scale sliding on the main scale of a length or angle measuring instrument. It is used for determining the fraction of the smallest interval into which the main scale is divided by the instrument pointer, which is the zero division of the Vernier scale. For example, in the diagram the Vernier scale has 10 intervals equal to 9 intervals on

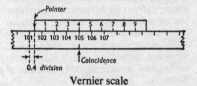

Vernier scale

the main scale. The zero division of the vernier (the pointer) is reading 101·4 divisions on the main scale.

vertex focal length (and power). The distance measured from the last surface of a thick lens or combination of lenses to the principal focus is the vertex focal length: its reciprocal is the vertex power.

very high frequency (VHF). *See* frequency bands.

very low frequency (VLF). *See* frequency bands.

vibration. The rapid to and fro motion characteristic of an elastic solid (e.g. a tuning fork) or a fluid medium influenced by such a solid. The time occupied in each to and fro motion is constant and is called the *period. The frequency is the number of vibrations per unit time and is, therefore, the inverse of the period. *See* column of air; stretched string; damped.

vibrational quantum number. *See* energy level.

vibration galvanometer. A moving coil galvanometer having the coil suspended on a wire, under tension. It can be tuned for frequencies between 40 Hz and 5000 Hz, by varying the tension of the wire. Small a.c. currents at the resonant frequency can produce a large response, so that the device can be used as a current detector in a.c. bridges, etc.

vibration–rotation spectrum. *See* spectrum.

vibrator. A device for producing an alternating current by periodically interrupting or reversing the current obtained from a direct-current source. It is operated electromagnetically and has a vibrating armature which alternately makes and breaks one or more pairs of contacts.

video frequency. The frequency of any component of the signal produced by a *television camera. Video frequencies lie between 10 hertz and 2 MHz. An amplifier designed to amplify video-frequency signals is called a *video amplifier*.

vidicon. *See* camera tube.

vignetting. The progressive reduction in the cross-sectional area of a beam of light passing through an optical system as the obliquity of the beam is increased. It is due to obstruction of the beam by mechanical apertures, lens mounts etc., of the system.

virgin neutrons. Neutrons from any source that have not been involved in any collisions.

virial expansion. The behaviour of a real gas may be expressed by the relation

$$pv = RT + Bp + Cp^2 + Dp^3 + \ldots$$

The empirical constants $B, C, D \ldots$ are

known as the 2nd, 3rd, 4th, $\ldots$ *virial coefficients*.

virial law (due to Clausius). The mean kinetic energy of a system is equal to its *virial which depends only on the forces acting on the atoms and not on their motions.

virtual cathode. In a *thermionic valve. The surface, situated in the region of a *space charge, at which the potential is a mathematical minimum and the potential gradient (or electric force) is zero. It acts as if it were a source of electrons.

virtual image, object. *See* image; object.

virtual particle. Because of the *uncertainty principle it is possible for the law of *conservation of mass and energy to be broken by an amount ΔE providing this only occurs for a time Δt such that $\Delta E \Delta t \leqslant h/4\pi$. This makes it possible for particles to be created for short periods of time where their creation would normally violate conservation of energy. These particles are called virtual particles. The electrostatic force between charged particles may be described in terms of the emission and absorption of virtual photons by the particles. Similarly the *nuclear force between *nucleons may be thought of as being due to the emission and absorption of virtual pions. Other conservation laws such as those applying to angular momentum, *isospin etc., cannot be violated even for short periods of time.

virtual work principle. A system with workless constraints is in equilibrium under applied forces if, and only if, zero (virtual) work is done by the applied forces in an arbitrary infinitesimal displacement satisfying the constraints. *See* constrain.

viscometer. A device for measuring the viscosity of a fluid (liquid or gas). The main types include those based on (a) the flow of fluids through capillary tubes (*see* Poiseuille flow); (b) the time of fall of a sphere through a liquid; (c) the torque needed to keep two concentric cylinders in rotation when the space between is filled with the liquid under test; (d) the rate of damping of a vibrating body by the fluid. *See also* Ostwald viscometer;

viscosity. The property of fluids by virtue of which they offer a resistance to flow. Newton's law of viscous flow for streamline, as opposed to turbulent, motion is $F = \eta A \, dv/dx$, where F is the tangential force between two parallel layers of liquid of area A, dx apart, moving with a relative velocity dv. The quantity η is called the *coefficient of viscosity* (or just the viscosity) of the liquid and is measured in N s m^{-2}. Viscosity of a liquid decreases with temperature but that of a gas increases.

A very large number of liquids obey Newton's law in that the viscosity is independent of the velocity gradient (dv/dx); these are called *Newtonian fluids. See also* anomalous viscosity; kinematic viscosity.

viscosity gauge or manometer. *See* molecular gauge.

viscosity of a gas. On the *kinetic theory, the viscosity of a gas is given by the equation

$$\eta = \tfrac{1}{3}\rho \bar{C} L$$

where ρ is the density, $\bar{C}$ the mean velocity, and L the mean free path. Since the product (ρL) is independent of the pressure, on this theory the viscosity of a gas should be independent of the pressure (Maxwell's law). At very low pressures the law breaks down, the effective viscosity becoming proportional to the pressure, a fact which is made use of in the design of low pressure manometers.

viscous damping. Damping in which the opposing force is proportional to velo-

city, such as the damping resulting from viscosity of a fluid or from *eddy currents.

viscous flow. *See* Newton's laws of fluid friction; viscosity.

visible spectrum. The continuous *spectrum of visible radiation, i.e. radiation lying in the wavelength range between 380 and 780 nm. It is seen in the *rainbow and in the display of colours produced when a beam of white light is dispersed by a prism or *diffraction grating. There is a continuous variation of wavelength but seven colours are usually distinguished: violet, indigo, blue, green, yellow, orange, and red; red is the component of longest wavelength. The value of the longest wavelength to which the eye is sensitive depends on the brightness, and can be extended to almost 900 nm if a very high power light source is used.

voice frequency. *See* audio frequency.

Voigt effect. The double refraction produced when light traverses a vapour acted on by a transverse magnetic field, the vapour acting as a uniaxial crystal with axis parallel to the field direction.

volt. Symbol: V. The *SI unit of electric *potential, *potential difference, and *electromotive force, defined as the potential difference between two points on a conductor carrying a current of one ampere when the power dissipated is one watt. In practice voltages are measured by comparison with the electromotive force of a *Weston standard cell using a *potentiometer.

voltage. Symbol: V. The potential difference between two specified points in a circuit or device. It is expressed in volts.

voltage amplifier. *See* amplifier.

voltage between lines. *Syn.* line voltage; voltage between phases. Of an electrical power system. The voltage between the two lines of a single-phase system, or between any two lines of a symmetrical three-phase system.

voltage doubler. An arrangement of two rectifiers to give double the voltage output of a single rectifier. The diagram

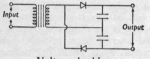

Voltage doubler

shows a typical circuit for *diode rectifiers.

voltage drop. (1) (general). The voltage between any two specified points of an electrical conductor is equal to the product of the current in amperes and the resistance in ohms between the two points (for direct current) or the product of the current in amperes and the impedance in ohms between the two points (for alternating current). In the case of alternating current, the product of the current and the resistance gives the *resistance drop* which is in phase with the current, whereas the product of the current and the reactance gives the *reactance drop* which is in *quadrature with the current. (2) In transformers. A *transformer may be considered as having a series internal impedance (Z) composed of a resistance (R) in series with an inductive reactance (X). When the transformer is supplying a load, this impedance causes the voltage (V_2) at the load terminals to be, in general, different from the internal voltage (V_1). The voltage drop (or *impedance drop*) is defined as the arithmetic difference between V_1 and V_2. For some conditions of loading, V_2 may be greater than V_1, in which case the voltage drop is negative and is described as a *voltage rise* (or *impedance rise*).

voltage ratio. *See* ratio.

voltage stabilizer. A device or circuit designed to maintain a voltage at its output terminals that is substantially constant and independent of either variations in the input voltage or in the load current. Circuits based on *gas-discharge tubes have largely been replaced by solid-state devices, such as a *Zener diode.

voltage transformer. *Syn.* potential transformer. An instrument transformer in which the primary winding is connected to the main circuit and the secondary winding is connected to an instrument (e.g. voltmeter). Voltage transformers are extensively used to extend the range of a.c. instruments and to isolate instruments from high-voltage circuits.

voltaic cell. *Syn.* galvanic cell. A primary *cell consisting of plates of dissimilar metals immersed in an electrolytic solution.

voltameter. *See* coulombmeter.

volt-amperes. Symbol: V A. The product of effective voltage and effective amperage (*root-mean-square values) in an alternating current circuit. *See* power.

voltmeter. A device for measuring *voltage. The most commonly used types of voltmeter are (i) d.c. instruments such as permanent-magnet moving coil instruments (ii) *digital voltmeters (iii) *cathode-ray oscilloscopes (iv) electrostatic voltmeters. Voltmeters require very high input impedances so that very little current is taken from the circuit to be measured. Digital voltmeters and cathode-ray oscilloscopes comply with this requirement, but a series impedance is used with d.c. instruments to increase their input impedances.

volume compressors (and expanders). A compressor is a device that automatically decreases the amplification when a signal has a large amplitude and increases the amplification when the signal amplitude is small so that the range of the amplitude variations in the transmission system is reduced. An expander is a device that operates so as to produce the opposite effect to a compressor, i.e. it increases the range of the amplitude variations in the transmission system. With suitable design, an expander included in one part of the system can be made to compensate for the effect of a compressor in another part of the system. The *signal-to-noise ratio of a transmission system can be improved by using a compressor at the transmitter and an expander at the receiver. A compressor and an expander used in this manner are together described as a *compandor*.

volume elasticity. *See* modulus of elasticity.

vortical field. *See* curl.

vorticity. In the three dimensional motion of a fluid the velocity of an element of fluid at the point (x, y, z) has Cartesian components u, v, w. The general motion of the element is three-part: (a) a general translation; (b) a pure strain motion; (c) a rotational motion of the whole element about an instantaneous axis. The component angular velocities in (c) are given by $\frac{1}{2}\xi$, $\frac{1}{2}\eta$, $\frac{1}{2}\zeta$, where

$$\xi = \frac{\partial w}{\partial y} - \frac{\partial v}{\partial z}, \eta = \frac{\partial u}{\partial z} - \frac{\partial w}{\partial x}, \zeta = \frac{\partial v}{\partial x} - \frac{\partial u}{\partial y}$$

The vector having the components ξ, η, ζ is called the vorticity at the point (x, y, z).

W

Wadsworth prism. An equilateral glass prism with a plane mirror at 45° with the base. A ray passing through the prism at minimum *deviation is reflected by the mirror to 90° deviation from the incident ray.

wall effect. Any significant effect of the inside wall of a container or reaction vessel on the behaviour of the enclosed system, such as the contribution to the current in an *ionization chamber made by electrons that are liberated from the inside walls rather than from the enclosed gas.

wall energy. The energy per unit area of the boundary between the domains in a ferromagnetic material (*see* ferromagnetism).

Wanner optical pyrometer. *See* polarizing pyrometer.

warble tone. A tone in which the frequency varies cyclically between two limits. The frequency variation is usually small compared with the actual frequency of the note and the warble occurs several times per second.

water equivalent. The mass of water that would have the same *heat capacity as a given body. It is numerically equal to the product of the body's mass and its specific heat capacity.

water waves. In the simplest form of surface wave which can be set up, the individual particles in the surface trace out circles of radius r with a frequency f. From the aspect of an observer travelling with the waves at their velocity c, the flow is steady and *Bernoulli's theorem can be applied to give

$$c = \frac{g}{2\pi f} = \sqrt{\frac{g\lambda}{2\pi}},$$

where g is the acceleration of *free fall. This treatment ignores surface tension, which is important for short waves and modifies their velocity. (*See* ripples.)

watt. Symbol: W. The *SI unit of *power (mechanical, thermal, and electrical), defined as the power resulting from the dissipation of one joule of energy in one second. In electrical circuits one watt is the product of one ampere and one volt.

watt-hour. A unit of work or energy, equal to one watt operating for one hour (equal to $3 \cdot 6 \times 10^3$ joules).

wattless component. *See* reactive current.

wattmeter. An instrument used for measuring electric power and having a scale graduated in watts, multiples of a watt, or submultiples of a watt.

wave. A curve of an alternating quantity plotted against time; a disturbance, either continuous (e.g. sinusoidal) or transient, travelling through a medium by virtue of the elastic and inertia factors of the medium, the resulting displacements of the medium being relatively small and returning to zero when the disturbance has passed. *See also* electromagnetic radiation.

wave analyser. An instrument for the resolution of a given waveshape into its fundamental and harmonic components. The analysis may be made manually or it may be made automatically according to the design of the instrument. The result is expressed in the form of frequencies and amplitudes of the various components. *See* spectrum analyser.

wave equation. The partial differential equation

$$\frac{\partial^2 U}{\partial x^2} + \frac{\partial^2 U}{\partial y^2} + \frac{\partial^2 U}{\partial z^2} = \frac{1}{c^2} \frac{\partial^2 U}{\partial t^2}$$

(or its counterpart in one or two dimensions or in other co-ordinates), the solution of which represents the propagation of displacements U as waves with velocity c. *See* wave mechanics.

waveform. Of a periodic quantity (*see* period). The shape of the graph obtained by plotting the instantaneous values of the quantity against time. The waveform is usually described as being distorted if it is not *sinusoidal. In acoustics the waveform determines the quality of the sound (*see* timbre).

wavefront. (1) The surface over which particles are vibrating in the same phase. The surface is normal to rays in isotropic media; in doubly refracting media a pair of wavefronts progress (forming the *wave surface*) and it is only for the ordinary wave that the wavefront is normal to the ordinary ray. The optical path between two successive positions of a wavefront, measured along rays, is constant. (2) *See* impulse voltage (or current).

wave function. Symbol: ψ. A mathematical function appearing in the *Schrödinger wave equation and describing the behaviour of a particle according to *wave mechanics. The particle is thought of as a wave (*see* de Broglie equation) and ψ is the displacement or amplitude of this wave with respect to position. An idea of the significance of the wave function can be obtained by considering light, which is also thought of in terms of waves and particles (*photons). The intensity of light at a point is proportional to the square of its amplitude at that point. It is also the number of photons at the point, i.e. the square of the amplitude of the light wave is proportional to the probability that a photon is present. Similarly, according to Born, the square of the amplitude of the matter wave,

$|\psi|^2$, is proportional to the probability of finding the particle in a specified position (*see also* atomic orbital). Thus the wave function expresses the lack of certainty in defining both the position and momentum of a particle (*see* uncertainty principle).

In general there is an infinite number of functions satisfying Schrödinger's equation, and certain boundary conditions have to be applied to make the solutions meaningful in physical terms. For example, ψ must always be finite; if it were infinite the particle would be localized at one point. The integral of $|\psi|^2$ over all space must be equal to 1, since this is the probability of finding the particle somewhere. Wave functions obtained when these conditions are applied are called *proper wave functions* and form a set of *characteristic functions of the Schrödinger wave equation. These are often called *eigenfunctions* and correspond to a set of fixed energy values in which the system may exist, called *eigenvalues* (proper values). Energy eigenfunctions describe *stationary states of the system.

waveguide. A hollow conducting tube containing a dielectric (or, alternatively, a cylindrical dielectric surrounded by another dielectric of different permittivity), used to guide within it an ultra-high frequency electromagnetic wave propagated along its length. The wave is reflected from the internal surfaces of the guide. *Cavity resonators may be introduced, and often an open bell-shaped end is added to radiate or collect the energy.

wavelength. Symbol: λ. The distance in a wave train between a vibrating particle and the nearest one vibrating in the same phase. If v is the velocity of a wave and f the frequency of vibration then $v = f\lambda$. When light travels in a medium, the wave velocity and wavelength both vary inversely as the refractive index. Wavelengths of *electromagnetic radiation are commonly used to describe particular regions of the spectrum and refer to the wavelengths in vacuum. (*See* electromagnetic spectrum.) For a moving source, the wavelength is reduced when the movement is in the same direction as the direction of travel of the wave. *See* Doppler effect; red shift.

wavelength constant. *See* propagation coefficient.

wave mechanics. One of the forms of *quantum mechanics that developed from de Broglie's theory that a particle can also be regarded as a wave (*see* de Broglie equation). This idea arose from the analogy between *Fermat's principle for light and the principle of *least action in mechanics. Wave mechanics is based on the *Schrödinger wave equation describing the wave properties of matter. It relates the energy of a system to a a *wave function, and in general it is found that a system (such as an atom or molecule) can only have certain allowed wave functions (eigenfunctions) and certain allowed energies (eigenvalues). In wave mechanics the quantum conditions arise in a natural way from the basic postulates as solutions of the wave equation.

wavemeter. An apparatus for measuring radio frequencies. It consists essentially of an oscillatory circuit tuned (*see* tuned circuit) to the frequency being measured, usually by means of a variable capacitor which is calibrated in terms of frequency. A device is incorporated which indicates when the circuit has been correctly tuned.

wave motion. The process of transmitting waves. Wave motion appears naturally in many different forms, the principal ones being surface waves (e.g. water waves), longitudinal waves (e.g. sound), transverse waves (e.g. electromagnetic radiation and waves in a vibrating string), and torsional waves (e.g. waves in a bar due to torsional vibrations at

one end). All types are governed by a single equation, the equation of wave motion (*see* progressive wave), and have the property of transmitting energy over considerable distances.

wave number. Symbol: σ. The reciprocal of the wavelength, i.e. the number of waves per unit path length. It is expressed in m^{-1}.

wave surface. *See* wavefront.

wavetail. *See* impulse voltage (or current).

wave theory of light. *See* corpuscular theory.

wave train. A succession of waves, especially a group of waves of limited duration.

wavetrap. A *tuned circuit, usually a *rejector, incorporated in a radio receiver to reduce interference at a particular radio frequency.

wave velocity. *See* phase velocity.

weak interaction. A kind of interaction between *elementary particles that is weaker than the *strong interaction force by a factor of about 10^{12}. When strong interactions can occur in reactions involving elementary particles the weak interactions are unimportant. However, sometimes strong and *electromagnetic interactions are prevented because they would violate the conservation of some *quantum number (e.g. *strangeness). When this happens weak interactions may still occur. The weak interaction force is thought to have an extremely short range. It has been suggested that it is associated with the exchange of a very heavy, and as yet undiscovered, particle called a *W-particle. If such a particle exists it would be expected to have a mass of several GeV/c^2. Most of the long-lived elementary particles decay as a result of weak interactions. For example, the kaon decay $K^+ \rightarrow \mu^+ + \nu\mu$ may be thought of as being a consequence of the K^+ breaking up into a virtual μ^+ and ν_μ (*see* virtual particle) which, due to a weak interaction between them, become separate physical particles. This decay process cannot take place by a strong or electromagnetic interaction because strangeness is not conserved. *Beta decay is another example of a weak interaction decay. Because it is so weak, particles which can only decay by weak interactions do so relatively slowly, i.e. they have long lifetimes. *See also* neutral weak current.

weber. Symbol: Wb. The *SI unit of *magnetic flux, defined as the flux that, linking a circuit of one turn, produces an electromotive force of one volt when the flux is reduced to zero at a uniform rate in one second. 1 Wb $= 10^8$ maxwell.

Weber–Fechner law. *See* loudness.

Wehnelt interrupter. An electrolytic interrupter consisting of a lead plate and a platinum wire sheathed by glass or porcelain so that only its tip is exposed, these being immersed in 30% sulphuric acid. This apparatus is put in series with the primary of an induction coil, the platinum point being the anode. By a combination of gas evolution and vaporization under the high current density the circuit is rapidly broken and remade at the point, very high frequencies of interruption being possible.

weight. (1) That force exerted on matter by the gravitational pull of the earth. In the case of a body of mass m the weight is mg where g is the acceleration of *free fall. If m is in kilogrammes, the weight is in newtons. (2) A standard mass. (3) Symbol: w. The weight of an observation (*see* weighted mean) is a measure of the reliability of the corresponding x, and can either be assigned intuitively or calculated from $w = (\text{probable error})^{-2}$.

weighted mean. Of a number of values $x_1, x_2, x_3 \ldots x_n$. The quantity given by:

$$\frac{w_1 x_1 + w_2 x_2 + \ldots w_n x_n}{w_1 + w_2 + \ldots w_n},$$

where w is the *weight.

Weiss constant. *See* Curie–Weiss law.

Weissenberg photography. A crystal diffraction method in which a single crystal is allowed to rotate about an axis normal to the incident beam of monochromatic radiation, while the cylindrical photographic film moves in a synchronized way, to and fro parallel to the rotation axis, screens being arranged so that only one layer line is recorded at a time. It is used for the measurement of intensities of diffracted spectra.

Weiss magneton. Weiss discovered that the susceptibilities of both iron and nickel, extrapolated to absolute zero, were multiples of 1123·5, and suggested that the molar susceptibility was always a multiple of this number. On this basis the magnetic moment of a single molecule, called the Weiss magneton, is $1·87 \times 10^{-21}$.

well. *See* potential well.

well-behaved. *See* characteristic function.

Wertheim effects. *See* Wiedemann effects.

Weston standard cell. *Syn.* cadmium cell. A cell constructed in an H-shaped glass

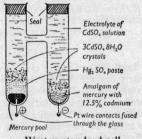

Weston standard cell

vessel, the constituents being shown in the diagram. The cell has a very low temperature coefficient of e.m.f. Its voltage at $t°$ C is given as:

$$E_t = 1·018\ 58 - 4·06 \times 10^{-5}(t - 20)$$
$$- 9·5 \times 10^{-7}(t - 20)^2 + 10^{-8}(t - 20)^3$$

See Clark cell.

wet and dry bulb hygrometer. A simple hygrometer consisting of an ordinary thermometer side by side with another thermometer whose bulb is surrounded by fibres dipping into water. Evaporation of water from the fibres cools the wet bulb. The rate of evaporation depends on the relative humidity of the air. Tables are used to calculate the relative humidity of the atmosphere from the difference in the thermometer readings. Two instruments of this type are *Mason's hygrometer and the Assmann *psychrometer. *See also* Apjohn's formula.

Wheatstone bridge. A network of resistances arranged as in the diagram. When the galvanometer shows no deflection the

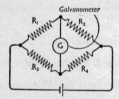

Wheatstone bridge circuit

currents in the four arms are balanced so that $R_1/R_2 = R_3/R_4$. Several forms of Wheatstone bridge exist: *see* post office box; Carey-Foster bridge; Kelvin double bridge.

white dwarf. Any of a large class of very faint stars that are thought to be in the last stage of stellar evolution. Its nuclear fuel is completely exhausted and it collapses, under its own gravitation, into a small but very dense body. *See also* Hertzsprung–Russell diagram.

white light. Light, such as daylight, containing all wavelengths of the visible spectrum at normal intensities so that no coloration is apparent.

white noise. *See* noise.

wholetone scale. *See* musical scale.

Wiedemann effects. *Syn.* Wertheim effects. Circular magnetic effects: (1) the twist produced in a rod due to interaction of longitudinal and circular fields; (2) the longitudinal magnetization produced by twisting a circular magnetized rod; and (3) the circular magnetic field produced by twisting a longitudinally magnetized rod.

Wiedemann–Franz law. The ratio of the thermal to electrical conductivity of all pure metals at a given temperature is approximately constant. Except at very low temperatures the law is fairly well obeyed. The ratio is also proportional to thermodynamic temperature though this does not hold at very low temperatures.

Wien effect. The increase in conductivity of an electrolyte under a high voltage gradient (of the order of $2\ MV\ m^{-1}$). The ion passes completely out of its ionic atmosphere during the *relaxation time and is thus free from the retarding effect normally encountered.

Wien's formula and Wien displacement law. *See* black body radiation.

Wigner effect. *Syn.* discomposition effect. A change in the physical or chemical properties of a solid as a result of radiation damage. The effect is caused by the displacement of atoms from their normal lattice positions as a result of the impact of nuclear particles.

Wigner force. A non-exchange force between the nucleons in an atom, acting over small distances.

Wigner nuclides. *See* mirror nuclides.

Wilson cloud chamber. *See* cloud chamber.

Wilson effect. When an insulating material is moved through a region of magnetic flux an induced potential difference is set up across the material. Because the creation of an electric current is inhibited by the nonconducting properties of the material, it becomes electrically polarized, a phenomenon known as the Wilson effect.

Wimshurst machine. An electrostatic generator consisting of two parallel plates rotating in opposite directions. Charges, induced on sections round the two perimeters, are collected by systems of pointed combs and are used to produce a spark.

windage loss. The power loss, usually expressed in watts, which occurs in an electrical machine as a result of the motion imparted to the gas or vapour (commonly air) surrounding the moving parts, by the latter. This loss is inherent in all electrical machines since ventilation is required for cooling purposes.

winding. Of an electrical machine, transformer, or other piece of apparatus. A complete group of insulated conductors designed to produce a magnetic field or to be acted upon by a magnetic field. A winding may consist of a number of separate conductors connected together electrically at their ends or may consist of a single conductor (wire or strip) which has been shaped or bent to form a number of loops or turns.

wind instruments. *See* column of air.

window. (1) When a medium, generally opaque to the passage of radiation, selectively transmits a particular small range of radiation it is said to operate as a window in that range. (*See* atmospheric windows.) (2) The thin sheet of material (often mica) covering the end of a *Geiger counter, through which the radiation is received.

wind tunnel. Essentially a hollow tube through which a uniform flow of air is passed. A model, constructed to scale, of all or part of an aircraft or missile is suspended in the air stream. From the observations made upon the model the behaviour of the aircraft in normal flight can be estimated. There is *dynamic similarity between the model and aircraft when *Reynolds number is the same in both cases.

wobbulator. A *signal generator whose output frequency is periodically varied through a definite range of values. It is used as a test instrument for the alignment of *tuned circuits and the measurement of the frequency response of electronic circuits and devices.

Wollaston prism. A double-image prism cut from a rhomb of calcite so as to separate the ordinary and extraordinary components of a ray of unpolarized light. Components tend to show colour effects.

Wollaston prism

For prism P the optic axis is parallel to AB; for prism Q it is normal to the plane of the paper.

Wood's glass. A glass having a high transmission factor in the ultraviolet range of the spectrum but relatively opaque to visible radiation.

woofer. A loudspeaker of large dimensions, used to reproduce sounds of relatively low frequency. *Compare* tweeter.

word. A string of *bits used to store an item of information in a *computer.

work. Symbol: *w, W*. Work is done when a *force moves its point of application. The amount of work is measured by the product of the force and the distance moved by the point of application in the direction of the force. Work is measured in joules, i.e. the work done when a force of 1 newton moves through a distance of 1 metre.

work function. Symbol: Φ. The difference in energy between the Fermi level (*see* energy level) of a solid and the energy of the free space outside the solid (the vacuum level). At the absolute zero of temperature the work function is the minimum energy required to remove an electron from a solid. In a metal there is a contribution to the work function from the *image potential that an electron would experience outside the metal. In a *semiconductor (*see* diagram) the *elec-*

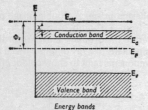

Energy bands

Work function and electron affinity of a semiconductor

tron affinity (Symbol: χ) is defined by the energy difference between the vacuum level and the bottom of the conduction band. Work function and electron affinity are usually defined as energies and measured in electronvolts, although volts are sometimes used.

wow. An undesirable form of *frequency modulation heard in the reproduction of high-fidelity sound and characterized by variations in pitch below about 10 Hz. In the case of a gramophone record it is often due to non-uniform rotation of the turntable. *See also* flutter.

W-particle. *Syn.* intermediate vector boson. A hypothetical particle thought to be exchanged between *elementary particles undergoing a *weak interaction. It thus plays the same role as the photon exchanged in an *electromagnetic interaction and the pion exchanged in a *strong interaction.

wrench. A force together with a couple whose axis is the line of action of the force. The quotient of the couple by the force is the pitch of the wrench and has the dimensions of a length. The magnitude of the force is the intensity and the line of action of the force is the axis of the wrench. In general, any system of forces can be reduced to a wrench.

X

xerography. A photographic copying process in which light is passed through the document to be copied and falls on an electrostatically charged plate, usually coated with selenium. This is discharged to an extent that depends on the intensity of the light. A powder with an opposite electric charge is then sprayed on the plate and sticks to the 'dark' areas where the plate has not been discharged. The powder, which is a mixture of graphite and a thermoplastic resin, is then transferred from the plate to a charged paper where it is fixed by heat treatment.

xi particle. An *elementary particle classified as a *hyperon.

X-ray analysis. X-rays are diffracted by crystals in a manner dependent on the wavelength of the rays and the space-lattice of the crystal. Thus X-ray diffraction provides a means for study of the structure of crystalline substances, or of substances which have crystalline phases. The method adopted depends on the form in which the substance is available. With large crystals *Laue diagrams can provide useful characterization, but more frequently the crystal is rotated when mounted at the centre of a cylindrical film, thus bringing successive sets of crystalline planes into position. The *Debye–Scherrer ring or powder method is used when the specimen consists of a number of small crystals. Because of the number of crystals, randomly distributed, some are usually available in each plane to diffract the X-ray beam. The plate may be set up as in Fig. *a* or *b*, or may be rotated in a cylindrical camera, which is

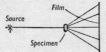

a Transmission method

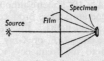

b Back reflection method

the most usual method. *See* Bragg's law; X-ray spectrum.

X-ray astronomy. The study of X-ray emission from stars. Since X-rays are absorbed by the earth's atmosphere instruments have to be mounted in space probes. The intensity and wavelengths of X-rays can be obtained with a *proportional counter.

X-ray crystallography. The study of crystal structure, texture, and behaviour, and the identification of crystals, by methods involving the use of X-rays. *See* X-ray analysis.

X-ray microscopy. *See* microscope.

X-rays. *Syn.* Roentgen rays. Electromagnetic radiation, lying between ultra-violet radiation and gamma rays in the spectrum, produced when electrons of sufficiently high energy bombard matter. They are generated most efficiently by accelerating a beam of electrons from a heated filament to a target of metal (usually tungsten) in vacuum. The spectrum of X-rays emitted by this *X-ray tube* consists of lines characteristic of the target material and a continuous waveband whose short-wave limit is determined by the voltage on the tube.

The characteristic X-rays are caused by the transitions of electrons between the various shells of the atom, while the continuous band of wavelengths is that of *bremsstrahlung caused by the deceleration of electrons in the vicinity of nuclei. *See also* absorption edge.

X-rays can be reflected, refracted, and polarized by suitable materials. They also show interference and diffraction effects. The wavelength varies between 10^{-7} and 4×10^{-10} metre although high-energy generators have produced much shorter wavelengths. In *quantum theory the energy, E, of X-ray photons is related to the frequency, v, by the expression: $E = hv$, where h is the *Planck constant.

X-rays ionize gases but the process is a secondary one caused by the electrons set free when X-rays interact with matter (*see* roentgen). They penetrate matter to a degree dependent on the wavelength of the rays. The intensity of radiation transmitted through a given material of thickness t is related to the initial intensity I_0, by the relation:

$$I = I_0\, e^{-\mu t}$$

where μ is the *absorption coefficient* of the material. The incident beam is weakened by (*a*) scattering caused by atoms, (*b*) the *photoelectric effect, and (*c*) the *Compton effect.

X-rays are widely used for investigating flaws in structures (radiography), diagnostic purposes (radiography), therapeutic purposes (destruction of diseased tissue), and investigating crystal structure (X-ray crystallography).

X-ray spectrum. When X-rays are scattered by atomic centres arranged at regular intervals, interference phenomena occur, crystals providing gratings of suitable small interval. The interference effects may be used to provide a spectrum of the beam of X-rays, since, according to *Bragg's law, the angle of reflection of X-rays from a crystal depends on the wavelength of the rays. For soft (lower energy) X-rays mechanically ruled gratings can be used. Each chemical element emits characteristic X-rays in sharply defined groups. They are known as the K, L, M, N, etc., series. There is a regular displacement of the lines of any series towards shorter wavelengths as the atomic number of the element concerned increases. *See* Moseley's law.

X-ray tube. *See* X-rays.

X-unit. *Syn.* X-ray unit. A small unit of length equal to $1 \cdot 002 \times 10^{-13}$ metre, formerly used to describe short ultraviolet and X-ray wavelengths.

Y

Yagi aerial. A sharply directional *aerial array used in *television and *radio astronomy that consists of one or two dipoles connected to the transmitting or receiving circuits, a parallel reflector, and a series of directors. The directors are parallel and spaced from 0·15 to 0·25 of a wavelength apart such that, in transmission, energy is absorbed from the field of the dipole and re-radiated so as to reinforce the field in a forward direction and oppose it in the reverse direction; in receiving, the signals are focused onto the dipole.

Y connection. *See* star connection.

year. *See* time.

yield point. A point on a graph of *stress versus *strain for a material at which the strain becomes dependent on time and the material begins to flow. *See* yield value.

yield stress. The minimum stress for *creep to take place. Below this value any deformation produced by an external force will be purely elastic.

yield value. The minimum value of stress that must be applied to a material in order that it shall flow.

ylem. A hypothetical substance consisting mainly of neutrons and having a density of about 10^{16} kg m^{-3}. It is supposed to be the material from which all matter has been formed.

yoke. A fixed piece of ferromagnetic material, which serves to complete a *magnetic circuit and which is not surrounded by a winding of any type. *See* core.

Young's fringes. *See* interference.

Young's modulus. *See* modulus of elasticity.

Yukawa potential. A potential used to explain *nuclear forces. Two particles of equal and opposite charge are attracted by an electromagnetic field and their mutual potential energy is $-e^2/r$, where e is their charge and r their distance apart. In the nucleus, short-range strong forces are acting (*see* strong interactions) and Yukawa assumed that their potential energy varied according to $e^{-\mu r}/r$ (the Yukawa potential) where μ is a constant, rather than by $1/r$.

Z

Zeeman effect. The splitting up of the spectral lines of a substance, such as sodium, when it is placed as an emitting source in a magnetic field. Each line is split into components: (*a*) two components circularly polarized when viewed parallel to the field; (*b*) three components plane polarized when viewed at right angles to the field (normal triplets); (*c*) multicomponent systems arising from multiplet components, e.g. D lines of sodium (*anomalous Zeeman effect*). If the field is applied along rather than across the beam of light, the undisplaced line is absent. The *inverse Zeeman effect* refers to the absorption of unpolarized light by vapours placed in a strong magnetic field.

The Zeeman effect is a quantum effect and results from the fact that the energy levels of individual electron orbits depend on their inclination to the applied field direction. The plane of each orbit can only assume specific angles, such that the projection of the total angular momentum on the field direction is an integral multiple of $h/2\pi$ (h = the *Planck constant). The Zeeman effect applies only to weak fields where the precession of the orbital angular momentum and the spin angular momentum (*see* spin) of the electrons about each other is much faster than the total precession around the field direction. For strong fields the *Paschen–Back effect predominates. The normal Zeeman effect is observed when the conditions are such that the *Landé factor is unity, otherwise the anomalous effect is found. This anomaly was one of the factors contributing to the discovery of electron spin.

Zener breakdown. A type of *breakdown, observed in reverse-biased p–n junctions, caused by electrons being excited directly from the valence band (*see* energy bands) to the conduction band by the electric field across the junction. It is observed in junctions in which very high *doping levels exist and the built-in potential across the junction is therefore high and the *depletion layer narrow. A very sharp increase in current is observed at the breakdown potential.

Zener diode. A semiconductor *diode with a well-defined reverse *breakdown voltage which is used as a voltage regulator. True Zener diodes have high levels of impurity concentration on both sides of the junction and low breakdown voltages (less than 6 V). The breakdown is true *Zener breakdown.

zenith. *See* celestial sphere.

zero error. *See* index error.

zero-point energy. The energy of an oscillator of frequency v at a temperature T is given by $kT[x/(e^x - 1)]$ where $x = hv/kT$, h being the *Planck constant and k the *Boltzmann constant. At high temperatures this energy converges to the value $(kT - hv/2)$ which does not equal the value (kT) predicted by classical mechanics. In order to make it converge to this value, the oscillator is assumed to have an energy $hv/2$ at absolute zero called the zero-point energy.

zeta pinch. *See* fusion reactor.

zeta potential. *Syn.* electrokinetic potential. According to Stern, the electrical layer at the boundary between solid and liquid is composed of two parts. In one, approximately one ion thick, there is a sharp potential fall, the other part showing a gradual rise or fall of potential and extending some way into the liquid. This part of the potential change is called the zeta potential, which is involved in electrosmosis and similar effects. The ζ potential in millivolts is given by $4\pi\eta v/\varepsilon_r E$, where E is the electric field, v the liquid velocity, η is the viscosity of the liquid medium, and ε_r its relative permittivity.

z-modulation. *See* intensity modulation.

zone. The faces of a crystal which intersect in parallel edges are said to belong to a zone, the direction that is common to all the faces being called the *zone-axis*. If $(h_1\ k_1\ l_1)\ (h_2\ k_2\ l_2)$ are the indices of two faces of a crystal, then a third face $(h_3\ k_3\ l_3)$ will lie in the zone of the other two if, and only if, $h_3 u + k_3 v + l_3 w = 0$ where $u = k_1 l_2 - k_2 l_1, v = l_1 h_2 - l_2 h_1, w = h_1 k_2 - h_2 k_1;\ (u\ v\ w)$ are then the *zone indices*.

zone of silence. A localized region in which sound and radio waves from a given source are not received. Waves travelling into the upper atmosphere are reflected by the *ionosphere (radio waves) or refracted as a result of changes in the temperature gradient in the different *atmospheric layers (sound). These waves are thus received in an area, beyond the zone of silence, at some distance from the source.

zone plate. *See* diffraction of light.

zone refining. A technique for producing very pure materials, used in the manufacture of *semiconductors. The sample is in the form of a bar and is slowly moved past a heater so that a molten zone passes along the length of the bar. Impurities in the material tend to concentrate in the melt and are thus segregated at one end of the sample.

zoom lens. A lens system consisting of converging and diverging elements one or more of which can be moved so that

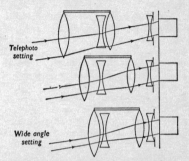

Optical compensation in a zoom lens

the focal length, which depends on the separation of the elements, can be continuously adjusted. The lens system is usually in two parts: the basic imaging system, for which the *f-number remains constant, and a variable-focus attachment.

419

Table 1. Conversion Factors

SI, CGS, and FPS units

Length	m	cm	in	ft	yd
1 metre	1	100	39·3701	3·280 84	1·093 61
1 centimetre	0·01	1	0·393 701	0·032 808 4	0·010 936 1
1 inch	0·0254	2·54	1	0·083 333 3	0·027 777 8
1 foot	0·3048	30·48	12	1	0·333 333
1 yard	0·9144	91·44	36	3	1

	km	mile	n. mile
1 kilometre	1	0·621 371	0·539 957
1 mile	1·609 34	1	0·868 976
1 nautical mile	1·852 00	1·150 78	1

1 light year = $9·460\ 70 \times 10^{15}$ metres = $5·878\ 48 \times 10^{12}$ miles.
1 astronomical unit = $1·496 \times 10^{11}$ metres.
1 parsec = $3·0857 \times 10^{16}$ metres = 3·2616 light years.

Velocity	m s^{-1}	km h^{-1}	mile h^{-1}	ft s^{-1}
1 metre per second	1	3·6	2·236 94	3·280 84
1 kilometre per hour	0·277 778	1	0·621 371	0·911 346
1 mile per hour	0·447 04	1·609 344	1	1·466 67
1 foot per second	0·3048	1·097 28	0·681 817	1

1 knot = 1 nautical mile per hour = 0·514 444 metre per second.

Mass	kg	g	lb	long ton
1 kilogramme	1	1000	2·204 62	$9·842\ 07 \times 10^{-4}$
1 gramme	10^{-3}	1	$2·204\ 62 \times 10^{-3}$	$9·842\ 07 \times 10^{-7}$
1 pound	0·453 592	453·592	1	$4·464\ 29 \times 10^{-4}$
1 long ton	1016·047	$1·016\ 047 \times 10^{6}$	2240	1

Force	N	kg	dyne	poundal	lb
1 newton	1	0·101 972	10^{5}	7·233 00	0·224 809
1 kilogramme force	9·806 65	1	$9·806\ 65 \times 10^{5}$	70·9316	2·204 62
1 dyne	10^{-5}	$1·019\ 72 \times 10^{-6}$	1	$7·233\ 00 \times 10^{-5}$	$2·248\ 09 \times 10^{-6}$
1 poundal	0·138 255	$1·409\ 81 \times 10^{-2}$	$1·382\ 55 \times 10^{4}$	1	0·031 081
1 pound force	4·448 22	0·453 592	$4·448\ 23 \times 10^{5}$	32·174	1

Pressure	N/m^2	kg/cm^2	lb/in^2	atm
1 newton per square metre	1	$1·019\ 72 \times 10^{-5}$	$1·450\ 38 \times 10^{-4}$	$9·869\ 23 \times 10^{-6}$
1 kilogramme per square centimetre	$980·665 \times 10^{2}$	1	14·2234	0·967 841
1 pound per square inch	$6·894\ 76 \times 10^{3}$	0·070 306 8	1	0·068 046
1 atmosphere	$1·013\ 25 \times 10^{5}$	1·033 23	14·6959	1

1 newton per square metre = 10 dynes per square centimetre.
1 bar = 10^{5} newtons per square metre = 0·986 923 atmosphere.
1 torr = 133·322 newtons per square metre = 1/760 atmosphere.
1 atmosphere = 760 mmHg = 29·92 in Hg = 33·90 ft water (all at 0° C).

Table 1. Conversion Factors (*continued*)

Work and Energy	J	cal$_{IT}$	kW hr	btu$_{IT}$
1 joule	1	0·238 846	2·777 78 × 10^{-7}	9·478 13 × 10^{-4}
1 calorie (IT)	4·1868	1	1·163 00 × 10^{-6}	3·968 31 × 10^{-3}
1 kilowatt hour	3·6 × 10^6	8·598 45 × 10^5	1	3412·14
1 British Thermal Unit (IT)	1055·06	251·997	2·930 71 × 10^{-4}	1

1 joule = 1 newton metre = 1 watt second = 10^7 erg = 0·737 561 ft lb.
1 electronvolt = 1·602 10 × 10^{-19} joule.

Table 2. Base SI Units

Physical quantity	Name	Symbol
length	metre	m
mass	kilogramme	kg
time	second	s
electric current	ampere	A
thermodynamic temperature	kelvin	K
amount of substance	mole	mol
luminous intensity	candela	cd

Table 3. Supplementary SI Units

Physical quantity	Name	Symbol
plane angle	radian	rad
solid angle	steradian	sr

Table 4. Derived SI Units with Special Names

Physical quantity	Name	Symbol
frequency	hertz	Hz
energy	joule	J
force	newton	N
power	watt	W
pressure	pascal	Pa
electric charge	coulomb	C
electric potential difference	volt	V
electric resistance	ohm	Ω
electric conductance	siemens	S
electric capacitance	farad	F
magnetic flux	weber	Wb
inductance	henry	H
magnetic flux density (magnetic induction)	tesla	T
luminous flux	lumen	lm
illumination	lux	lx

Table 5. Prefixes Used with SI Units

Factor	Name of Prefix	Symbol	Factor	Name of Prefix	Symbol
10	deca-	da	10^{-1}	deci-	d
10^2	hecto-	h	10^{-2}	centi-	c
10^3	kilo-	k	10^{-3}	milli-	m
10^6	mega-	M	10^{-6}	micro-	μ
10^9	giga-	G	10^{-9}	nano-	n
10^{12}	tera-	T	10^{-12}	pico-	p
			10^{-15}	femto-	f
			10^{-18}	atto-	a

Table 6. Fundamental Constants

Constant	*Symbol*	*Value (with estimated error)*
velocity of light	c	$2 \cdot 997\,925 \times 10^8$ m s^{-1}
magnetic constant (permeability of free space)	μ_0	$4\pi \times 10^{-7} = 1 \cdot 256\,64 \times 10^{-6}$ H m^{-1}
electric constant (permittivity of free space)	$\varepsilon_0 = \mu_0^{-1}c^{-2}$	$8 \cdot 854\,185\,3 \times 10^{-12}$ F m^{-1}
charge of electron or proton	e	$\pm\, 1 \cdot 602\,191\,7 \times 10^{-19}$ C
rest mass of electron	m_e	$9 \cdot 1095 \times 10^{-31}$ kg
rest mass of proton	m_p	$1 \cdot 672\,62 \times 10^{-27}$ kg
rest mass of neutron	m_n	$1 \cdot 674\,92 \times 10^{-27}$ kg
electronic radius	$r_e = \dfrac{e^2}{4\pi\varepsilon_0 m_e c^2}$	$2 \cdot 817\,939 \times 10^{-15}$ m
Planck constant	h	$6 \cdot 626\,196 \times 10^{-34}$ J s
Boltzmann constant	$k = \dfrac{R}{L}$	$1 \cdot 380\,622 \times 10^{-23}$ J K^{-1}
Avogadro constant	L, N_A	$6 \cdot 022\,169 \times 10^{23}$ mol^{-1}
Loschmidt's number	N_L	$2 \cdot 687\,19 \times 10^{25}$ m^{-3}
universal gas constant	$R = Lk$	$8 \cdot 314\,35$ J K^{-1} mol^{-1}
Faraday constant	$F = Le$	$9 \cdot 648\,670 \times 10^4$ C mol^{-1}
Stefan's constant	$\sigma = \dfrac{2\pi^5 k^4}{15 h^3 c^2}$	$5 \cdot 6697 \times 10^{-8}$ W m^{-2} K^{-4}
fine structure constant	$a = \dfrac{e^2}{2\varepsilon_0 hc}$	$7 \cdot 297\,351 \times 10^{-3}$
Rydberg constant	$R\infty = \dfrac{m_e e^4}{8\varepsilon_0^2 h^3 c}$	$1 \cdot 097\,373\,12 \times 10^7$ m^{-1}
gravitational constant	G	$6 \cdot 6732 \times 10^{-11}$ N m^2 kg^{-2}
acceleration of free fall (standard value)	g_n	$9 \cdot 806\,65$ m s^{-2}

Table 7. Spectrum of Electromagnetic Radiation

Wavelength/m		Frequency/kHz
10^{-13}		10^{19}
10^{-12}	gamma rays	10^{18}
10^{-11}		10^{17}
10^{-10}	X-rays	10^{16}
10^{-9}		10^{15}
10^{-8}	ultraviolet radiation	10^{14}
10^{-7}		10^{13}
10^{-6}	visible light	10^{12}
10^{-5}	infrared (heat) radiation	10^{11}
10^{-4}		10^{10}
10^{-3}		10^{9}
10^{-2}	E H F	10^{8}
10^{-1}	S H F — radio frequencies	10^{7}
1	U H F	10^{6}
10	V H F	10^{5}
10^{2}	H F	10^{4}
10^{3}	M F	10^{3}
10^{4}	L F	10^{2}
10^{5}	V L F	10
		1

Table 8. Long-Lived Elementary Particles

	Particle	Mass MeV/c^2	Isospin I	Spin J	Parity P	G-parity	Charge conj. parity	Mean Life/s
photon	γ	0		1	-1		-1	stable
leptons	ν	0		$\frac{1}{2}$				stable
	e	0·511		$\frac{1}{2}$				stable
	μ	105·7		$\frac{1}{2}$				$2 \cdot 2 \times 10^{-6}$
mesons	$\pi^{\pm}$	139·6	1	0	-1	-1		$2 \cdot 6 \times 10^{-8}$
	π^0	135·0	1	0	-1	-1	1	$8 \cdot 4 \times 10^{-15}$
	$K^{\pm}$	493·8	$\frac{1}{2}$	0	-1			$1 \cdot 2 \times 10^{-8}$
	K^0	497·7	$\frac{1}{2}$	0	-1			
	K^0_1	497·7	$\frac{1}{2}$	0	-1			$8 \cdot 6 \times 10^{-10}$
	K^0_2	497·7	$\frac{1}{2}$	0	-1			$5 \cdot 2 \times 10^{-8}$
	η	548·8	0	0	-1	1	1	
baryons	p	938·3	$\frac{1}{2}$	$\frac{1}{2}$	1			stable
	n	939·6	$\frac{1}{2}$	$\frac{1}{2}$	1			932
	Λ	1115·6	0	$\frac{1}{2}$	1			$2 \cdot 5 \times 10^{-10}$
	Σ^+	1189·4	1	$\frac{1}{2}$	1			$8 \cdot 0 \times 10^{-10}$
	Σ^0	1192·5	1	$\frac{1}{2}$	1			$1 \cdot 0 \times 10^{-14}$
	Σ^-	1197·4	1	$\frac{1}{2}$	1			$1 \cdot 5 \times 10^{-10}$
	Ξ^0	1314·7	$\frac{1}{2}$	$\frac{1}{2}$	1*			$3 \cdot 0 \times 10^{-10}$
	Ξ^-	1321·3	$\frac{1}{2}$	$\frac{1}{2}$	1*			$1 \cdot 7 \times 10^{-10}$
	Ω^-	1672·5	0	$\frac{3}{2}$*	1*			$1 \cdot 3 \times 10^{-10}$

* SU(3) predictions that have not been confirmed experimentally.

Table 9. Periodic Table of the Elements

1A	2A	3B	4B	5B	6B	7B		8		1B	2B	3A	4A	5A	6A	7A	0
1 H																	2 He
3 Li	4 Be											5 B	6 C	7 N	8 O	9 F	10 Ne
11 Na	12 Mg	←			transition elements						→	13 Al	14 Si	15 P	16 S	17 Cl	18 Ar
19 K	20 Ca	21 Sc	22 Ti	23 V	24 Cr	25 Mn	26 Fe	27 Co	28 Ni	29 Cu	30 Zn	31 Ga	32 Ge	33 As	34 Se	35 Br	36 Kr
37 Rb	38 Sr	39 Y	40 Zr	41 Nb	42 Mo	43 Tc	44 Ru	45 Rh	46 Pd	47 Ag	48 Cd	49 In	50 Sn	51 Sb	52 Te	53 I	54 Xe
55 Cs	56 Ba	57* La	72 Hf	73 Ta	74 W	75 Re	76 Os	77 Ir	78 Pt	79 Au	80 Hg	81 Tl	82 Pb	83 Bi	84 Po	85 At	86 Rn
87 Fr	88 Ra	89† Ac															

*lanthanides	57 La	58 Ce	59 Pr	60 Nd	61 Pm	62 Sm	63 Eu	64 Gd	65 Tb	66 Dy	67 Ho	68 Er	69 Tm	70 Yb	71 Lu
†actinides	89 Ac	90 Th	91 Pa	92 U	93 Np	94 Pu	95 Am	96 Cm	97 Bk	98 Cf	99 Es	100 Fm	101 Md	102 No	103 Lr

Table 10. Symbols for Physical Quantities

Name of quantity	Symbol	Name of quantity	Symbol
absorption factor	a	elementary charge, charge of proton	e
acceleration	a	emissivity	ε
activity, radioactivity	A	energy	E
admittance	Y	enthalpy	H
amount of substance	n	entropy	S
angle of optical rotation	α	equilibrium constant	K
angular frequency	ω		
angular momentum	L	Fermi energy	E_F, ε_F
angular velocity	ω	force	F
area	A, S	frequency	ν, f
atomic mass	m_a		
atomic number, proton number	Z	Gibbs function	G
		half life	$T_{\frac{1}{2}}, t_{\frac{1}{2}}$
Bohr magneton	μ_B	Hall coefficient	R_H
Bragg angle	θ	Hamiltonian function	H
bulk modulus	K	heat capacity: at constant pressure	C_p
capacitance	C	heat capacity: at constant volume	C_v
characteristic temperature	θ	heat flow rate	Ψ
charge density	ρ	height	h
coefficient of friction	μ	Helmholtz function	A, F
compressibility	κ, k		
concentration	c	illuminance, illumination	E_V, E
conductance	G	impedance	Z
conductivity	κ	internal energy	U, E
cross section	σ	irradiance	E_e, E
cubic expansion coefficient	γ		
Curie temperature	θ_C, T_C	Joule–Thomson coefficient	μ, μ_{JT}
Debye temperature	θ_D	kinematic viscosity	ν
decay constant	λ	kinetic energy	T, E_k, K
degeneracy (multiplicity) of an energy level	g	Lagrangian function	L
density	ρ	linear absorption coefficient	a
diameter	d	linear attenuation (extinction) coefficient	μ
diffusion coefficient	D		
Dirac constant	$\hbar$	linear expansion coefficient	a
efficiency	η	linear strain (relative elongation)	ε
electric charge	Q	loss angle	δ
electric current	I	luminance	L_V, L
electric current density	j	luminous emittance	M_V, M
electric dipole moment	p, p_c, u	luminous flux	Φ_V, Φ
electric displacement	D	luminous intensity	I_V, I
electric field strength	E		
electric flux	Ψ	magnetic field strength	H
electric polarization	P	magnetic flux	Ψ
electric potential	V	magnetic flux density, magnetic induction	B
electric potential difference	$U, \Delta V$		
electric susceptibility	χ_e	magnetic moment	m
electromotive force	E		
electron mass	m, m_e		

Table 10. Symbols for Physical Quantities (*continued*)

Name of quantity	Symbol	Name of quantity	Symbol
magnetic moment of particle	m, μ	quantity of heat	q, Q
magnetic quantum number	M, m_l	quantum number of	
magnetic susceptibility	χ, χ_m	electronic spin	S, s
magnetization	M	quantum number of nuclear	
magnetomotive force	F_m	spin	I
mass	m	quantum number of	
mass excess	Δ	vibrational mode	v
mass number, nucleon			
number	A	radiance	L_e, L
mean free path	λ, l	radiant exitance	M_e, M
mean life	τ	radiant flux, radiant power	Φ_e, Φ
molality	m_A	radiant intensity	I_e, I
molecular momentum	$p(p_x, p_y, p_z)$	radioactivity, activity	A
molecular position	$r(r_x, r_y, r_z)$	radius	r
molecular velocity	$u(u_x, u_y, u_z)$	radius vector, position vector	r
moment of force	M	ratio of heat capacities, C_p/C_v	γ, κ
moment of inertia	I	reactance	X
momentum	p	reduced mass	μ
most probable speed	$\hat{u}$	reflection factor	ρ
mutual inductance	M, L_{12}	refractive index	n
		relative atomic mass	A_r
Néel temperature	θ_N, T_N	relative density	d
neutron mass	m_n	relative permeability	μ_r
neutron number	N	relative permittivity (dielectric	
nuclear magneton	μ_N	constant)	ε_r
nuclear radius	r	relaxation time	τ
nuclear spin quantum		resistance	R, r
number	I, J	resistivity	ρ
nucleon number, mass		Reynolds number	(Re)
number	A	rotational quantum number	J, K
number of molecules	N		
number of turns	N	self inductance	L
		shear modulus	G
orbital angular momentum		solid angle	ω, Ω
quantum number	L, l_1	specific heat capacity: at	
osmotic pressure	Π	constant pressure	c_p
		specific heat capacity: at	
packing fraction	f	constant volume	c_v
period	T	specific optical rotatory power	a_m
permeability	μ	specific (radio) activity	a
permittivity	ε	specific volume	v
Planck function	Y	speed	u
plane angle	$a, \beta, \gamma, \theta, \varphi$	spin quantum number	S, s
polarizability	a, γ	surface charge density	σ
position vector, radius vector	r	surface tension	γ, σ
potential energy	E_p, V, Φ	susceptance	B
power	P		
pressure	p	temperature	T, t
principal quantum number	n, n_1	thermal conductivity	λ
propagation coefficient	γ	thermal diffusion coefficient	D_T
proton mass	m_p	thermal diffusion factor	a_T
proton number, atomic		thermal diffusion ratio	K_T
number	Z	thermal diffusivity	a

427

Table 10. **Symbols for Physical Quantities** (*continued*)

Name of quantity	Symbol	Name of quantity	Symbol
thermodynamic temperature	T	volume (bulk) strain	θ
time	t		
torque	T	wavelength	λ
transmission factor	τ	wavenumber	σ
		weight	G
velocity distribution function	$f(c)$	work	w, W
velocity of light in a vacuum	c, c_0	work function	Φ
velocity of sound	c		
vibrational quantum number	v	Young's modulus (modulus of elasticity)	E
viscosity	η		
volume	V, v		

Table 11. **The Greek Alphabet**

Letters		Name	Letters		Name
A	α	alpha	N	ν	nu
B	β	beta	Ξ	ξ	xi
Γ	γ	gamma	O	o	omicron
Δ	δ	delta	Π	π	pi
E	ε	epsilon	P	ρ	rho
Z	ζ	zeta	Σ	σ	sigma
H	η	eta	T	τ	tau
Θ	θ	theta	Y	υ	upsilon
I	ι	iota	Φ	φ	phi
K	κ	kappa	X	χ	chi
Λ	λ	lambda	Ψ	ψ	psi
M	μ	mu	Ω	ω	omega

Penguin Reference Books

THE PENGUIN DICTIONARY OF BIOLOGY

M. ABERCROMBIE

C. J. HICKMAN

M. L. JOHNSON

Fifth Revised Edition

In this dictionary the authors' aim is to explain biological terms which a layman may meet when reading scientific literature; to define the terms which a student of biology has to master at the beginning of his career – the thousand or so words which so grimly guard the approaches to the science; and to provide a reminder for the professional biologist reading outside his own narrow field. The entries are not restricted to a bare definition: some information about most of the things named is given, so as to convey something of their significance in biological discussion.

The authors have tried, as it were, to interpret a foreign language as it is actually used. It would be wrong to rely on etymology as a guide to correct usage. The meaning of a Greek root may be unequivocal, but biologists are not talking Greek: they are using a living language, and the proof of the meaning is in the speaking.

Penguin Reference Books

THE PENGUIN DICTIONARY OF SCIENCE

E. B. UVAROV

D. R. CHAPMAN

ALAN ISAACS

Fifth Edition: Completely revised and enlarged

This latest edition of the Penguin *Dictionary of Science* has been completely revised and now gives all numerical information in SI UNITS, which are fully defined.

Many new words, like fluidics, holography, mascons, polywater, pulsars, and the key words in computer terminology are explained simply and accurately. Some 600 additional chemical compounds have been added, together with many new tables.

Apart from this new material, the reader will find reliable definitions and clear explanations of the basic terms used in astronomy, chemistry, mathematics, and physics, with a smattering of the words used in biochemistry, biophysics and molecular biology. Notes are also included on all the chemical elements and most of their important compounds.

As a student's handbook and for the specialist outside his own field a *Dictionary Of Science* remains an indispensable aid, and for the general reader it provides an up-to-date guide to the numerous scientific and technical words which are increasingly coming into daily life.